New Drug Development:
A Regulatory Overview
Seventh Edition

MAXYGEN

New Drug Development:
A Regulatory Overview
Seventh Edition

by
Mark Mathieu

with contributions from
Christopher-Paul Milne

PAREXEL International Corporation
Waltham, MA
Publishers

New Drug Development:
A Regulatory Overview
Seventh Edition

by
Mark Mathieu
PAREXEL International Corporation

with contributions from
Christopher-Paul Milne

Cover Design: Art Directions

Acknowledgments

My sincerest thanks to those individuals who took time from their own demanding schedules to assist me in developing this text: Wayne Dankner, M.D.; Christopher-Paul Milne; Barbra Rosenberg; Anne Evans, D.V.M.; and Joanna White.

CONTENTS

CHAPTER 1

An Introduction to the U.S. New Drug Approval Process

As the regulatory gatekeeper to the world's most lucrative pharmaceutical market, the U.S. Food and Drug Administration (FDA) administers what generally is considered to be the world's most demanding drug regulation and approval process. Due to several factors, including the prescription drug user-fee program's (PDUFA) success in delivering a more efficient drug review process, the federal government's less-restrictive policies regarding drug pricing, and the drug industry's ever-intensifying efforts to focus its research and product-introduction efforts in this country, the United States is widely regarded as the world's "locus of innovation" for pharmaceutical research and development.

While the PDUFA III era (FY2003-FY2007) brought the increased user-fee funding the FDA needed to add review staff, to establish a $7 million "performance fund" to pursue initiatives for improving the drug review process, and to focus more intently on drug safety-related activities, it also brought a new FDA commissioner with a keen interest in improving the medical product review process and in having the agency play a more proactive role in addressing the dominant challenges in the product development process. During his brief, but active 17-month term as FDA commissioner (November 2002-March 2004), Center for Medicare and Medicaid Services Administrator Mark McClellan, M.D., Ph.D., spearheaded several high-profile agency initiatives, perhaps most notably an effort to address the so-called "pipeline problem": At the very time that the FDA had proven that it could review and clear greater numbers of new drugs more quickly and that the basic sciences seemed poised to lead to an explosion of new therapies, there was an abrupt and unmistakable slowdown in innovative medical therapies reaching patients. Following 1995, when industry submitted marketing applications for 48 new molecular entities (NME), NME submissions fell in seven of the next eight years—by 2003, industry submitted marketing dossiers for just 23 NMEs. With fewer new drugs to review, the FDA saw its NME approvals plummet from a record 53 in 1996 to just 21 in 2003.

In unveiling its so-called Critical Path Initiative in March 2004, the agency maintained that behind the pipeline problem was the reality that the "applied sciences" necessary for medical product development had failed to keep pace with the tremendous advances in the basic sciences. To supplement both basic research (fundamental understanding of biology/disease) and translational research (moving basic discoveries from concept into clinical evaluation), the agency argued that a new type of research called "critical path research" is necessary for providing new tools and concepts for the "three dimensions" along the "critical path" of medical product development—safety assessment, evaluation of medical utility, and product industrialization.

The centerpiece of the Critical Path Initiative will be a "product development toolkit" that will comprise "powerful new scientific and technical methods such as animal or computer-based predictive models, biomarkers for safety and effectiveness, and new clinical evaluation techniques...[and which will be used] to improve pre-dictability and efficiency along the critical path from laboratory concept to commercial product.... The product development problems we are seeing today can be addressed, in part, through an aggressive, collaborative effort to create a new generation of performance standards and predictive tools," the agency claimed. After conferring with outside experts and stakeholders, the FDA scheduled the first significant milestone for late 2004, when agency officials hoped to release the so-called National Critical Path Opportunities List, which will identify areas of product development that could most benefit from innovative approaches and emerging technologies.

Despite its high profile and lofty goals, the Critical Path Initiative is only one of perhaps an unprecedented number of current agency efforts specifically designed to improve the overall environment for medical product innovation and approval:

- As part of an agency-wide strategic plan first spearheaded by McClellan, the FDA introduced what it called the "Innovation Initiative," through which the agency is attempting to speed the development and approval of new drugs, biologics, and medical devices. Under the January 2003 Innovation Initiative, the FDA identified three key areas "for increased effort": (1) examining the root causes of multi-cycle NDA reviews and identifying and addressing "avoidable delays" and multiple review cycles; (2) instituting a continuous improvement/quality systems approach throughout the pre-market review process (e.g., enhanced reviewer training on good review management principles (see discussion below), further development of standards for the review process); and (3) expanding collaborative clinical and pre-clinical guidance development (e.g., working with external experts, disease-specific guidance). Many of the Innovation Initiative's provisions dovetailed with elements of PDUFA III and other programs. Under PDUFA III, for example, the FDA will retain an independent expert consultant to conduct a comprehensive study of the first-cycle review process (e.g., tracking all actions that take place during first-cycle reviews and identifying FDA and industry best practices that facilitated the review process).

- In late June 2003, FDA officials announced that they had established a non-PDUFA-related benchmark through which the agency would attempt to further reduce NDA review times: The agency would seek a 10% reduction in the median review time for the first 50% of NDAs (and BLAs for biologics) for new molecular entities that are approved in the FY2005 through FY2007 cohorts. In announcing the new goal, McClellan conceded that, "while improving review cycle performance [under the PDUFA goals] is important, that's not the bottom line. The bottom line is reducing the overall time for development and approval of safe and effective new medicines... Reducing cycle time alone is unlikely to achieve this goal... We will do more than ever to help avoid multiple cycles of review and to increase the likelihood that an application to FDA gets it right the first time."

- In July 2003, the FDA released a long-awaited draft guidance entitled, *Good Review Management Principles for PDUFA Products* to identify current best review practices and discuss "future review management improvements" regarding the first-cycle of NDA reviews. Overall, the draft GRMPs encouraged CDER review divisions to "identify and resolve minor deficiencies in an application that otherwise meets the statutory standards for approval during the first-cycle review," and to avoid "unnecessary multiple-cycle reviews." By year-end 2004, FDA officials hoped to release what they claimed would be a significantly reworked final version of the GRMP draft guidance.

- As the result of a comprehensive two-year assessment of its existing good manufacturing practice (cGMP) standards and programs, the FDA announced "a new framework for the regulatory oversight of manufacturing quality" in September 2004. Under this initiative, called *Pharmaceutical cGMPs for the 21st Century*, the FDA will implement a "quality systems management and a risk-based product quality regulatory system," which is in part designed to encourage industry's early adoption of new technological advances in its pharmaceutical manufacturing operations.

Several other developments are influencing the latest evolutionary phases of new drug development and approval in the United States, and illustrate how the FDA and other regulators are tilting, perhaps more than ever before, toward the future. International harmonization and the emergence of the common technical document (CTD) format, the accelerating shift from paper-based to electronic submissions, and the FDA's desire to establish standards for data submissions continued to reshape marketing dossier practices and requirements. As the FDA prepared to release a new guidance document on pharmacogenomics, the next wave of scientific advances was poised to assume an increasingly important role in drug development and the agency's decision-making processes. Further, the agency is establishing formal agreements with firms such as Gene Logic and Iconix Pharmaceuticals to gain access to commercial databases on gene expression and drug-related genomic effects and to leverage emerging scientific knowledge of the genetic basis of disease and drug effects. In addition, the FDA is reaching out and forming new partnerships in high-priority areas: A new FDA/NCI Interagency Oncology Task Force, for example, will focus on improving the efficiency of clinical research on and the scientific evaluation of new cancer therapies, while a newly formed multi-agency task force (FDA, NIH, NCI, among others) is assessing how the government can accelerate medical technology and innovation.

Given the number and nature of factors constantly acting upon it, the FDA's new drug approval process can never be characterized as a single, static process. Since new drugs present their own distinct risks and benefits, and because these risks and benefits are evaluated by different FDA reviewers and in the context of a constantly evolving medical and scientific knowledge base, the development and approval paths traveled by two new products are always different, sometimes considerably so. The nature of the drug development and approval process is, in large part, a function of the drug being developed and the condition being studied, and is tailored to ensure that the key questions regarding the compound's safety and effectiveness for this indication are addressed sufficiently before approval.

The FDA and the Food, Drug and Cosmetic Act

Despite the emerging trends outlined above, the foundations of the new drug approval process remain intact within the provisions of the Federal Food, Drug and Cosmetic Act (FD&C Act). Seen by many as the most complex law of its kind, the FD&C Act has at least three basic provisions that continue to shape the new drug development and review process:

1. The FD&C Act defines the term "drug," thereby identifying the universe of products subject to regulation as drugs. The statute defines drugs as "articles intended for use in the diagnosis, cure, mitigation, treatment, or prevention of disease in man..." and "articles (other than food) intended to affect the structure or any function of the body of man...."

2. The FD&C Act defines "new drug," thereby identifying which products are subject to the requirements of the new drug approval process. The law defines "new drug" as: "(1) Any drug (except a new animal drug or an animal feed bearing or containing a new animal drug) the composition of which is such that such drug is not generally recognized, among experts qualified by scientific training and experience to evaluate the safety and effectiveness of

drugs, as safe and effective for use under the conditions prescribed, recommended, or suggested in labeling thereof, except that such a drug not so recognized shall not be deemed to be a 'new drug' if at any time prior to the enactment of this Act it was subject to the Food and Drugs Act of June 30, 1906, as amended, and if at such time its labeling contained the same representations concerning the conditions of its use; or (2) Any drug (except a new animal drug or an animal feed bearing or containing a new animal drug) the composition of which is such that such drug, as a result of investigations to determine its safety and effectiveness for use under such conditions, has become so recognized, but which has not, otherwise than in such investigations, been used to a material extent or for a material time under such conditions."

3. The FD&C Act identifies, in the broadest possible terms, the criteria that all new drugs must meet to gain marketing approval. Before a new drug can be marketed in the United States, it must be the subject of an FDA-approved new drug application (NDA), which must contain adequate data and information on the drug's safety and "substantial evidence" of the product's effectiveness.

As similar laws do in other areas, the FD&C Act merely establishes the basic framework and essential principles of new drug approval. In other words, the statute must be interpreted, implemented, and enforced. Since the early 1900s, these responsibilities have fallen on the FDA.

It is the interpretive and discretionary powers granted to the FDA under the FD&C Act that give the agency such wide-ranging authority. Perhaps the most significant of these powers is the FDA's role in interpreting the legal requirement that a sponsor present substantial evidence of effectiveness prior to a drug's approval. While this is a statutory requirement, it is the FDA that decides what constitutes substantial evidence for each new drug. In deciding, on a case-by-case basis, what constitutes substantial evidence for each new drug, the agency determines the scientific testing and data submissions necessary to obtain marketing approval.

During the late 1990s, CDER made a greater effort to define the concept of substantial evidence and to communicate its expectations to industry. Through a May 1998 guidance entitled, *Providing Clinical Evidence of Effectiveness for Human Drug and Biological Products*, CDER offered what is likely its most detailed discussion on the efficacy data necessary to support new drug approval (see Chapter 5). The FDA Modernization Act of 1997 also offered a clarification of the substantial evidence concept by stating that the FDA can accept data from one adequate and well-controlled clinical trial supported by confirmatory evidence as sufficient to establish a drug's effectiveness.

New Drug Development and Approval: A Brief Overview of the Principal Steps

Despite the evolution and trends outlined above, new drugs face a reasonably well-defined development and approval process that has evolved over several decades. In fact, given CDER's continuing commitment to document and manage the drug review process through its GRMP initiative and its reinvigorated effort to assemble new and updated clinical development guidances for specific diseases, the drug development and approval process will likely remain one of the more transparent and better understood of the FDA's product approval processes.

The primary stages of the drug development and approval process fall within one of three classes of activities: (1) scientific testing designed to provide data on a product's safety and/or effectiveness; (2) the preparation and submission of these data and other information in regulatory applications; and (3) the FDA's review of regulatory submissions. While all drug development programs involve these core activities, it is important to note how fundamentally different each can be for any two products. Testing and submission requirements, for example, will be shaped by many factors, including the drug's proposed indication, the amount and nature of data already available on the drug and on compounds similar in molecular structure, and the availability of therapeutic alternatives for the target indication.

Preclinical Testing

Clearly, clinical trials represent the ultimate premarketing proving grounds for new pharmaceuticals. Because of the costs and risks inherent in using an untested drug in clinical testing, however, drug sponsors do not leap headlong into a clinical program once they have identified a promising compound. Prior to clinical studies, the sponsor seeks some evidence of the compound's biological activity, and both the sponsor and the FDA seek data indicating that the drug is reasonably safe for initial administration to humans.

Before initiating clinical studies, a drug sponsor must submit an application that provides information showing that the company can manufacture the drug, descriptions of the proposed clinical trials, and data establishing that the drug is reasonably safe for use in initial, small-scale clinical studies. Depending on whether the compound has been studied or marketed previously, the sponsor may have several options for fulfilling the last of these three requirements: (1) compiling existing nonclinical data derived from past *in vitro* laboratory or animal studies on the compound; (2) compiling data from previous clinical testing or marketing of the drug in the United States or another country whose population is relevant to the U.S. population; or (3) undertaking new preclinical studies designed to provide the evidence necessary to support the safety of administering the compound to humans.

For most NMEs and other drugs whose clinical safety and efficacy have not been established previously, preclinical *in vitro* and *in vivo* animal testing represents the first major step toward regulatory approval (see Chapter 2). During preclinical drug development, a sponsor evaluates the drug's toxic and pharmacologic effects. Genotoxicity screening is performed, as well as investigations on drug absorption and metabolism, the toxicity of the drug's metabolites, and the speed with which the drug and its metabolites are excreted from the body. At the preclinical stage, the FDA generally expects that sponsors will: (1) develop a pharmacological profile of the drug; (2) determine the acute toxicity of the drug in at least two species of animals; and (3) conduct short-term toxicity studies, the duration of which is based on the duration of the clinical studies that the sponsor will propose.

To leverage new scientific knowledge and better predict possible clinical drug effects, the FDA and other drug regulators continue to seek different and more relevant types of data and information from nonclinical testing programs. In September 2004, for example, the FDA released a revised draft ICH guidance to recommend a nonclinical testing strategy for assessing an investigational drug's potential for delaying ventricular repolarization, increasingly recognized as a significant human safety issue in recent years. In its continuing effort to obtain more relevant data and information on drug effects in pediatric patients, CDER released a February 2003 draft guidance entitled, *Nonclinical Safety Evaluation of Pediatric Drug Products*. Further, as part of an effort to create a tighter scientific linkage between nonclinical and clinical studies, the FDA is working to identify, evaluate, and establish relevant protein markers in the blood in both animal models and humans.

Once clinical trials begin, further *in vitro* and *in vivo* animal studies provide information essential to the continued clinical use and, ultimately, the approval of the drug. Long-term and specialized animal tests are needed to support the safety of testing a compound in larger patient populations and over longer periods. These tests also allow researchers to evaluate effects that are impractical or unethical to study in humans, such as drug effects over an entire life span, effects over several generations, and effects on pregnancy and reproduction.

Because preclinical drug development does not involve human exposure to an experimental compound, drug developers have considerable flexibility in manufacturing, shipping, and testing experimental drugs. Virtually the only regulatory limitations facing sponsors are the general animal welfare provisions contained in current federal and state animal protection statutes and regulations, and little more than a single FDA requirement detailed in federal regulations: "A person may ship a drug intended solely for tests in vitro or in animals used only for laboratory research purposes if it is labeled as follows: Caution: Contains a new drug for investigational use only in laboratory research animals, or for tests in vitro. Not for use in humans."

When a sponsor begins to compile safety data for submission to the FDA, a set of regulations called Good Laboratory Practice (GLP) apply. Because it will base important regulatory decisions on these data, the FDA uses GLP standards to ensure the quality of animal testing and the resultant data.

The Investigational New Drug Application

When a sponsor believes that it has sufficient data to show that a new drug is adequately safe for initial small-scale clinical studies, the company assembles and submits an investigational new drug application (IND). The IND is the vehicle through which a sponsor seeks an exemption from the statutory requirement that prohibits unapproved drugs from being shipped in interstate commerce. The sponsor seeks this exemption by alerting the FDA of its intent to conduct clinical studies with an investigational new drug.

In the IND, the sponsor submits information in three principal areas: (1) the results of all preclinical testing and an analysis of what implications these results have for human pharmacology and safety; (2) an analysis of the drug's chemical composition and the manufacturing and quality control procedures used in producing the compound; and (3) protocols describing the sponsor's plans for the initial-stage clinical studies proposed in the IND, and information describing the relevant qualifications of the investigators who will carry out these studies.

International harmonization, the transition to electronic submissions, an increasing regulatory focus on risk management, and advances in scientific knowledge are among the factors that are reshaping INDs and IND submission requirements. Recognizing the long-term benefits of having INDs submitted electronically, CDER is actively encouraging firms to submit INDs in the electronic common technical document (eCTD) format. In a November 2003 draft guidance, the agency took its first step to encourage—and in some cases, require—industry to submit pharmacogenomics information in INDs. As a result of the FDA's focus on risk management under PDUFA III, increasing numbers of INDs and NDAs are likely to feature what are called "risk minimization action plans" (RiskMAP), which are "strategic safety programs designed to meet specific goals and objectives in minimizing known risks of a product while preserving its benefits."

The FDA's Review of the IND

The IND review is unique among the FDA's application review processes. In many respects, this process and the FDA's treatment of INDs reflect the delicate balance between the federal government's responsibility to protect clinical trial subjects from unnecessary risks and its desire to avoid becoming an impediment to the medical research process. Given these dual goals, the FDA must perform a safety review of an IND prior to clinical trials, but has only 30 days in which to reach an initial determination on the filing.

The FDA's review of an IND focuses largely on several areas:

- *Pharmacology/Toxicology Review.* The reviewing pharmacologist examines the results of animal pharmacology and toxicology testing, and attempts to relate these results to human pharmacology.

- *Chemistry Review.* The reviewing chemist evaluates both the sponsor's manufacturing processes and control procedures to ensure that the compound is reproducible and is stable in its pure form. If a drug is either unstable or not reproducible, then the validity of any clinical testing would be undermined and, more importantly, the studies may pose significant risks. The chemistry reviewer also evaluates the drug's characterization and chemical structure, and compares the product's structure and impurity profile to those of other drugs (i.e., drugs known to be toxic).

- *Clinical Review.* The reviewing medical officer, who is generally a physician, evaluates the clinical protocols to ensure: (1) that subjects will not be exposed to unreasonable or unnecessary risks during clinical trials; and (2) that Phase 2 and Phase 3 trials (generally not submitted in the initial IND filing) are adequate in design to provide scientifically valid data.

- *Microbiology Review.* For INDs submitted for anti-infective and antiviral drug products, a microbiologist will evaluate data on a drug's *in vivo* and *in vitro* effects on the physiology of the target virus or other microorganism.

The FDA's principal goals during the IND review are: (1) to determine if the preclinical data show that the drug is reasonably safe for administration to humans; and (2) to determine if the protocol for the proposed clinical studies will expose clinical subjects to unnecessary risks (assuming the protocol proposes only Phase 1 studies).

If the FDA does not contact the applicant within 30 days of the IND submission, the sponsor may initiate clinical trials. In this way, the agency does not approve an IND, but allows the clinical studies proposed in the IND to proceed through its "administrative silence."

When the FDA decides that a certain clinical trial should be delayed, the agency contacts the sponsor within the 30-day period to initiate what is called a "clinical hold"—the delay of the clinical trial until potential problems or unanswered questions are addressed. Aside from the safety-related reasons mentioned above, the FDA may base a clinical hold on other grounds, including that the IND does not contain sufficient information to assess the risks of using the drug in clinical trials (see Chapter 4).

Clinical Trials

Clinical trials clearly represent the most critical and demanding phase in the drug development process. If a drug survives the rigors of clinical testing, the FDA's ultimate approval decision will be based primarily upon data derived from these studies—the agency has estimated that more than 80 percent of the average NDA for an NME comprises clinical data and analyses alone.

As they have in the past, emerging socio-political trends, regulatory initiatives, and advances in scientific knowledge are placing new demands on, and offering new opportunities to, companies undertaking clinical development programs for experimental drugs. Scientific advances in the understanding of specific drug effects continue to spotlight certain adverse drug effects—liver toxicities and QTc prolongation in particular—in the drug development and approval process, and have put growing pressure on drug sponsors to better characterize drug effects in these and other areas during the development process and, when necessary, to more fully explore such effects following approval. Given the push toward personalized medicine, the agency is now accepting and encouraging voluntary submissions of pharmacogenomic data so its reviewers can accelerate their understanding of the scientific issues in this emerging field. Under its Critical Path Initiative (see discussion above), the agency will be attempting to assemble a "product development toolkit" that will comprise powerful new scientific and technical methods such as computer-based predictive models (e.g., clinical trial simulation tools), biomarkers for safety and effectiveness, and new clinical evaluation techniques to improve the predictability and efficiency of the drug development process. To improve the efficiency of clinical research and NDA reviews, the FDA released a standard format called the Study Data Tabulation Model (SDTM), which sponsors can use to collect and submit clinical data. Further, the agency is creating working groups that will draw on experts from across the agency and from the broader scientific community to develop therapeutic area-specific guidances, initially for priority diseases such as oncology, diabetes, and obesity. In addition, the agency has announced plans to release a new guidance on proof-of-mechanism, screening, and microdose human studies to help researchers efficiently and safely identify the most promising drug candidates to pursue in more advanced clinical trials.

At the same time, the pharmaceutical industry itself is applying emerging technology and knowledge to clinical research challenges. After using its diagnostics expertise to develop a genotyping screen to identify likely responders to its investigational cancer therapy Zarnestra, for example, Johnson & Johnson saw the clinical trial subject response rate climb from 20% to 80%. Under an approach called "experimental medicine," other major companies are now undertaking ultra-small, limited human trials during a drug's development to obtain an earlier-than-ever assessment of the therapy's clinical potential and risks. Meanwhile, Pfizer and Lilly are funding university-based research designed to develop tools that will permit companies to identify likely "placebo responders," who can make experimental therapies seem less effective in the context of clinical trials, particularly studies for antidrepressants. Further, several major firms have disclosed that they are focusing more resources on early-stage clinical trials to select the optimum dose and to gain greater confidence in a drug's effects before investing in more costly Phase 3 trials.

Although clinical trials for different drugs can vary greatly in design, they are often similar in structure (see Chapter 5). Since researchers may know little about a new compound prior to its use in humans, testing the drug through serially conducted studies permits each phase of clinical development to be carefully designed to use and build upon the information obtained from the research phase preceding it. Clinical programs for most new drugs begin with the cautious use of an investigational compound in small, carefully selected population groups, and proceed into larger, more clinically relevant, and increasingly diverse patient pools.

While there is no statute or regulation that mandates a specific clinical trial structure or design, clinical development programs most often proceed in three primary stages, or phases:

- Phase 1: The cautious use of a drug in a few patients or normal human volunteers—20 to 80 subjects—to gain basic safety and pharmacological information. Specifically, these studies allow the sponsor to assess a drug's initial safety, tolerability and activity, safe dosage range, pharmacodynamics/pharmacokinetics, mechanism of action in humans, side effects (of various doses), and optimal route of administration.

- Phase 2: The use of the compound in a small number of subjects—100 to 200 patients—who suffer from the condition that the drug is intended to treat or diagnose. Phase 2 trials provide additional safety data and the first indication of a drug's clinical effectiveness in its proposed use. Results of Phase 2 studies can establish the foundation for key aspects of Phase 3 study design, including the dose, dosing regimen, and target population.

- Phase 3: Use of the drug in a significantly larger group of subjects (i.e., several hundred to several thousand) who suffer from the condition that the compound is proposed to treat or diagnose to gather additional effectiveness and safety information necessary for assessments of the drug's overall risk-benefit relationship. Because certain Phase 3 trials, called "pivotal" trials, will serve as the primary basis for the drug's approval, these studies must meet more rigorous standards (e.g., controls, blinding, randomization, size) in demonstrating, or confirming, the drug's therapeutic benefit.

The dire need for therapies for AIDS, cancer, and other life-threatening illnesses compelled the FDA to develop a variety of alternative models for clinical drug development. Some of these programs, which have been implemented by various regulations, were codified into law under the FDA Modernization Act of 1997 (see Chapter 15).

The New Drug Application

Since 1938, the new drug application (NDA) has been the vehicle through which drug sponsors formally propose that the FDA approve a new pharmaceutical for sale and marketing in the United States. To support a drug's approval, an NDA comprises thousands of pages of nonclinical and clinical test data and analyses, drug chemistry information, and descriptions of manufacturing procedures.

By August 2001, however, the ICH effort produced another option for companies seeking FDA approval to market a new drug in the United States—the common technical document, or CTD. At the conclusion of a "transition period" in July 2003, the FDA began to "highly recommend" that U.S. marketing dossiers be submitted in the CTD format. While the two other ICH parties (European Union and Japan) now require the use of the CTD format, the FDA continues to accept submissions in the traditional NDA format.

By mid-2004, however, it was obvious that the "recommended," but not mandatory, CTD format was gaining traction in the United States. By that time, industry had submitted 101 drug applications in the CTD format, and the rate at which CTD-formatted submissions were being filed continued to accelerate. Perhaps more significant was the reality that growing numbers of CTD submissions were being developed and filed for new molecular entities (NME), which showed that firms were increasingly willing to rely on the CTD format for their most important new product candidates.

It is important to note that the CTD differs from the NDA in format but not in content, and that the submission standards necessary to gain FDA approval have not been affected by the transition to the CTD format. While it is true that the CTD format may provide for more information in selected areas than a conventional NDA, the FDA's data and information requirements for drug approval are unaffected by the CTD.

Whether in the NDA or CTD format, the U.S. marketing dossier for a new drug is the largest and most complex premarketing application that the FDA reviews. The application must provide sufficient information, data, and analyses to permit agency reviewers to make several key determinations, including: (1) whether the drug is safe and effective in its proposed use(s), and whether the benefits of the drug outweigh its risks; (2)

whether the methods used in manufacturing the drug and the controls used to maintain the product's quality are adequate to preserve its identity, strength, and purity; and (3) whether the drug's proposed labeling is appropriate and, if not, what the drug's labeling should contain.

New international harmonization efforts, regulatory initiatives, and advances in scientific knowledge will shape the next evolutionary phase for the marketing dossier in the United States. CDER is now encouraging firms to consider submitting both INDs and NDAs in the electronic CTD (eCTD) format, for example. In addition, the FDA has taken its first steps to encourage—and in some cases require—the submission of pharmacogenomics data in marketing dossiers. As a result of the FDA's focus on risk management under PDUFA III, certain marketing applications are likely to feature what are called "risk minimization action plans," which are strategic safety programs designed to minimize the known risks of a product while preserving its benefits.

The NDA Review Process

No other aspect of the U.S. drug development and approval system has evolved as significantly since the early 1990s as the FDA's NDA review process. As the pendulum of public and political opinion has swung back and forth over this period, this closely watched process has been, at various times, buffeted by criticism from some who believe that it is too slow and, at other times, by those who maintain that the FDA's review process has been accelerated so much that Americans are now being exposed to potentially unsafe medications.

Upon its passage, PDFUA III seemed to offer something for industry, FDA critics concerned about drug safety in the era of faster agency review times, and the agency itself, which claimed that it would need new funding to hire the staff necessary to maintain existing performance levels. Specifically, PDUFA III (FY2003-FY2007) brought the FDA the increased funding it needed to hire additional staff, to establish a $7 million "performance fund" to pursue initiatives for further improving the NDA review process, and close to $80 million for risk-management and pharmacovigilance programs to help ensure drug safety.

PDUFA III's implementation largely coincided with the arrival of a new FDA commissioner intent on improving the NDA approval process. In a brief, but active 17-month tenure, then-FDA Commissioner Mark McClellan, M.D., Ph.D., led several initiatives that will drive the evolution of the NDA review process:

- As part of a new agency-wide strategic plan spearheaded by McClellan, the agency introduced what it called the "Innovation Initiative," though which the agency is attempting to speed the development and approval of new drugs, biologics, and medical devices (see discussion above).

- In late June 2003, FDA officials announced that they had established a non-PDUFA-related benchmark through which the agency would attempt to further reduce NDA review times: The agency would seek a 10% reduction in the median review time for the first 50% of NDAs (and BLAs for biologics) for new molecular entities that are approved in the FY2005 through FY2007 cohorts.

- In July 2003, the FDA released a long-awaited draft guidance entitled, *Good Review Management Principles for PDUFA Products* to identify current best review practices and discuss "future review management improvements" regarding the first-cycle of NDA reviews. Overall, the draft GRMPs encouraged CDER review divisions to "identify and resolve minor deficiencies in an application that otherwise meets the statutory standards for approval during the first-cycle review," and to avoid "unnecessary multiple-cycle reviews." Designed for both agency reviewers and industry, the draft GRMPs focus on each aspect of the all-important first-cycle review process for NDAs (e.g., presubmission, filing decision, review planning, review, communication, management of review timelines, advisory committee meetings, wrap-up labeling, and FDA action), and clarify the roles and responsibilities of FDA review staff at each stage of the process. The draft GRMPs represent CDER's latest move in a several-year effort to standardize the NDA review process, which the center has pursued in part through "review templates" for the NDA review disciplines. In April 2004, CDER released the *Clinical Pharmacology and Biopharmaceutics Review Template* to specify how agency reviewers should document clinical pharmacology and biopharmaceutics reviews. Then, in July 2004, CDER released a long-awaited *Clinical Review Template* in the form of MaPP 6010.3 to provide "a structured outline" for the clinical review and to "promote consistency in the documentation of [review] elements and provide for the ready retrieval of information."

The same forces affecting the nature of NDA submissions—the shift to the CTD and eCTD format, advances in scientific knowledge (e.g., pharmacogenomics), and the increasing focus on risk management—will influence NDA reviews as well.

Upon their submission, NDAs are forwarded to one of CDER's new drug review divisions—specifically, the division that handles the therapeutic area relevant to the submission. Following the NDA's submission, CDER reviewers—including the lead medical, chemistry, and pharmacology reviewers—will meet to determine if the application is sufficiently complete for a full review. NDAs that meet minimum submission criteria are "filed," or accepted for review, while those that do not trigger refuse-to-file (RTF) actions and are returned to their sponsors. In addition, to notify applicants as early as possible regarding potential "substantive deficiencies" that might derail filed NDAs as the review process proceeds, the FDA has agreed to communicate such deficiencies directly to applicants within 14 days after the 60-day application filing date through what are being called "74-day letters."

Once the review team decides that an NDA is fileable, it begins the "primary" review of the application. During this evaluation, each member of the review team sifts through volumes of research data and information applicable to his or her expertise:

- Clinical Reviewer: Evaluates the data from, and analyses of, clinical studies to determine if the drug is safe and effective in its proposed use(s) and if the product's benefits outweigh its risks.

- Pharmacology/Toxicology Reviewer: Evaluates the entire body of nonclinical data and analyses, with a particular focus on the newly submitted long-term test data, to identify relevant implications for the drug's clinical safety.

- Chemistry Reviewer: Evaluates commercial-stage manufacturing procedures (e.g., method of synthesis or isolation, purification process, and process controls) and the specifications and analytical methods used to assure the identity, strength, purity, and bioavailability of the drug product. It is important to note that, in September 2004, CDER announced that it would be adopting a "modern, risk-based pharmaceutical quality assessment system" to replace its existing system for reviewing the chemistry, manufacturing, and controls section of INDs and NDAs. To be implemented in 2005, the new system will bring a separation of premarketing and postmarketing chemistry reviews, a new focus on "critical pharmaceutical quality attributes and their relevance to safety and efficacy," the involvement of a so-called pharmaceutical assessment lead (PAL) to conduct a high-level review and focus the chemistry review on the most important quality attributes, and more frequent CMC-focused meetings between FDA chemists and NDA sponsors (see Chapter 8).

- Statistical Reviewer: Evaluates the pivotal clinical data to determine if there exists statistically significant evidence of the drug's safety and effectiveness, the appropriateness of the sponsor's clinical data analyses and the assumptions under which these analyses were performed, the statistical significance of newly submitted nonclinical data, and the implications of stability data for establishing appropriate expiration dating for the product.

- Biopharmaceutics Reviewer: Evaluates pharmacokinetics and bioavailability data to establish appropriate drug dosing.

- Microbiology Reviewer: For certain drugs (anti-infectives, antivirals, and special pathogens), a CDER microbiologist will evaluate the drug's effects on target viruses or other microorganisms. For sterile drugs and certain non-sterile drug products (e.g., aqueous dosage forms that can support microbial growth), a microbiologist will conduct a product quality assessment.

- *Bioresearch Monitoring Reviewer*: A reviewer from CDER's Division of Scientific Investigations (DSI) provides an assessment of the "usability" of the clinical, nonclinical, and biopharmaceutics data in the NDA.

Based on an NDA's content, the review team may involve "consult" reviewers to assess, as necessary, a risk minimization action plan, the environmental assessment, a drug's abuse potential, and the trade name/package insert/patient package insert, MedGuide or other consumer information.

In the past, the filing decision has also triggered a division request that the relevant FDA field office undertake what is called a "preapproval inspection" of the sponsor's manufacturing facilities. Under its draft GRMPs, however, CDER recommends that requests for manufacturing facility inspections and clinical investigator inspections "be made early in the review cycle and, optimally, prior to the filing date." During preapproval inspections, FDA investigators visit the applicant's production facilities to audit manufacturing-related statements and commitments made in the NDA against actual manufacturing practices employed by the sponsor or contract manufacturer.

When the primary technical reviews are completed, each discipline reviewer must prepare a written evaluation that presents his or her conclusions and recommendations regarding the application. In most cases, the medical reviewer is responsible for evaluating and reconciling the conclusions of reviewers in the other scientific disciplines. This process, and the development of what CDER calls an "institutional decision" on an NDA's approvability, is likely to involve considerable dialogue between the medical reviewer and reviewers in the other disciplines.

During the drug review process, the review division assessing the NDA can seek advice and comment from one of its prescription drug advisory committees (see Chapter 10). When called upon, these expert committees provide the agency with independent, non-binding advice and recommendations. In addition, the review division can also request input from an internal panel of senior CDER managers under the so-called "regulatory briefing" program.

At the completion of its review, CDER must issue an action letter—an approval, approvable, or not-approvable letter. This action letter communicates the results of the review to the applicant and, if necessary, identifies what issues or deficiencies must be addressed before the application can be approved. Under a proposed regulation released in mid-2004, CDER proposed to replace both approvable and not-approvable letters with the so-called "complete response" letter. Acknowledging that its current system of approvable and not approvable letters often sent unclear and misleading messages regarding a drug application's current status and ultimate approvability, the FDA said that the complete response letter will represent "a consistent and more neutral mechanism to convey that we cannot approve a drug marketing application in its current form...."

During PDUFA III's term (FY2003-FY2007), the FDA must review and act on 90% of NDAs for "priority" drugs (i.e., drugs representing a significant improvement over marketed products) within 6 months and 90% of NDAs for "standard" drugs within 10 months (see Chapter 9). As noted above, FDA officials have also established a non-PDUFA-related benchmark through which the agency will seek a 10% reduction in the median review time for certain NDAs.

Under the user-fee program, the center also committed to specific review timeframes for taking action on sponsor resubmissions (i.e., formal company responses to approvable/not-approvable or complete response letters). Applicable review performance goals are based on the type and amount of data provided in these resubmissions (see Chapter 9).

CHAPTER 2

Nonclinical Drug Testing

For most new molecular entities (NME) and other drugs whose clinical safety and efficacy have not been established previously, preclinical *in vitro* and *in vivo* animal testing represents the first major step toward regulatory approval. According to recent estimates by Bain & Co., 31 percent of the drugs tested in formal preclinical studies fail to progress into clinical trials. Preclinical screening and testing will show that the discarded compounds are unsafe, are poorly absorbed, lack pharmacological activity, or have some other flaw that makes them unworthy of further development.

For those drugs that are researched further, animal studies play several roles in drug development. First, the studies provide the basic toxicological and pharmacological information necessary to support a submission notifying the FDA that the sponsor seeks to initiate clinical trials. While the FDA's decision to approve a new pharmaceutical for marketing is based largely on the results of clinical studies, the agency will not allow an entirely unknown and uncharacterized compound to be administered to human subjects in such studies. Before clinical work begins, the agency requires that the drug be administered to, and its short-term effects be studied in, laboratory animals. The FDA uses data from these studies to decide if the drug is sufficiently safe for initial administration to humans.

Once clinical trials begin, further *in vitro* and *in vivo* animal studies provide information essential to the continued clinical use and, ultimately, the approval of the drug. Long-term and specialized animal tests are needed to support the safety of testing a compound in larger patient populations and over longer periods. These tests also allow researchers to evaluate effects that are impractical or unethical to study in humans, such as drug effects over an entire animal life span, on pregnancy and reproduction, and on animal development.

Although nonclinical research results are imperfect predictors of clinical responses, laboratory animals remain the best practical experimental models for identifying and measuring a compound's biological activity, and for predicting a drug's clinical effects. (Because animal studies are performed before and during clinical studies, the term "nonclinical" generally is preferable to "preclinical" when discussing the full spectrum of *in vitro* and non-human *in vivo* tests associated with drug development.) By studying a drug's dose-response characteristics, adverse and residual effects, and mechanism, site, degree, and duration of action, drug sponsors and the FDA gain valuable insights on the compound's probable action and effects in humans.

The FDA plays at least four principal roles in the nonclinical testing of drugs:

- the agency determines, sometimes on a case-by-case basis, what nonclinical test data are needed to show that a drug is sufficiently safe for initial and continued testing in humans;

- the agency, when asked, provides advice to drug sponsors on the adequacy of nonclinical testing programs developed for specific drugs before the animal studies are initiated;

- the agency provides independent analyses of nonclinical test results and conclusions; and

- the agency sets minimum standards for laboratories conducting nonclinical toxicity testing through good laboratory practice (GLP) regulations (see discussion below).

Trends in Nonclinical Testing

Although there are few, if any, studies that measure it directly, nonclinical testing has been affected by industry's need to streamline the drug development process. While most efforts to streamline drug development times have focused on the clinical research process, new benchmarks for preclinical drug development have begun to emerge over the last several years. In mid-1999, for example, Hoffmann-La Roche reported that it had established "a new benchmark" for preclinical development in taking a new compound from a "proof of concept" study to the start of clinical trials in 18 months.

Further, under its March 2004 Critical Path Initiative, the FDA will be focusing on drug safety assessments and other areas in an effort to address what it calls "the pipeline problem," which the agency blames on the inability of the applied sciences necessary for product development to keep pace with the tremendous advances in the basic sciences. Unfortunately, the agency notes, the traditional tools used to assess product safety—animal toxicology and outcomes from human studies—"have changed little over many decades and have largely not benefited from recent gains in scientific knowledge."

The centerpiece of the new initiative will be the development of a so-called "product development toolkit" that will comprise "powerful new scientific and technical methods such as animal or computer-based predictive models, biomarkers for safety and effectiveness, and new clinical evaluation techniques...[and which will be used] to improve predictability and efficiency along the critical path from laboratory concept to commercial product." Among the tools that the FDA claims are urgently needed are better predictors of human immune responses to foreign antigens, methods to further enhance the safety of transplanted human tissues, new techniques for assessing drug-induced liver toxicity, methods to identify gene therapy risks based on assessments of gene insertional and promotional events, and efficient protocols for qualifying biomaterials. The agency has also highlighted what it says are a few of the key safety assessment "opportunities" identified by FDA reviewers and outside experts to make the critical path faster, more predictable, and less costly:

- Targeted research aimed at specific toxicity problems should be undertaken. The FDA notes that while proteomic and toxicogenomic approaches may provide important sensitive and predictive safety assessment techniques in the future, their application remains in the early stages and must be expanded.

- As the world's largest repository of *in vitro* and animal results that are linked to actual human outcome data, the FDA's own files could be further data mined and thereby form the basis for useful predictive safety models. These data could be used to feed more powerful *in silico* (computer modeling) analyses for predictive toxicology, the agency notes.

- There is an urgent need to supplement ongoing international efforts to develop and validate nonclinical models useful in predicting human risk, particularly to assess the risk of new drugs that cause heart rhythm abnormalities (see discussion below).

Also as part of its commitment to improving the so-called "critical path" for new product development, CDER was preparing to release a guidance that would, in part, outline the preclinical safety data needed to support exploratory, proof-of-mechanism, and microdose clinical studies (see Chapter 3). In a July 2004 speech touting the mechanisms described in the guidance as an opportunity to study pharmacokinetics and target interacton early in drug development, one senior CDER official noted that "the amount of preclinical safety data for [these studies] will generally be less than for conventional INDs. The reduction in safety date requirements will be scaled to the goals, duration and scope of the proposed clinical trials."

In recent years, factors such as advances in the scientific understanding of disease and drug-related health effects and the goal of regulators and researchers to maximize the utility of nonclinical testing in predicting the likely clinical effects of experimental drugs continued to influence the FDA's requirements for and expectations regarding nonclinical testing programs:

- As global regulators have become increasingly sensitive to certain safety-related drug effects (e.g., QT prologation, hepatic effects) in recent years, they are looking to all forms of testing, including nonclinical testing, to help identify these potential hazards and assess their risks. In September 2004, the FDA released a revised ICH draft guidance entitled, S7B *The Nonclinical Evaluation of the Potential for Delayed Ventricular Repolarization* (QT Interval Prolongation) *by Human Pharmaceuticals*. The draft guidance recommends that researchers employ both *in vivo* and *in vitro* assays in nonclinical testing to develop an integrated assessment of likely clinical QT interval prolongation risk.

- As part of an effort to create a tighter scientific linkage between nonclinical and clinical studies, the FDA is working to identify, evaluate, and establish relevant protein biomarkers in the blood in both animal models and humans. These biomarkers can be used to help detect "the very earliest damage that can be caused by certain drugs to the heart, kidney, immune system and liver." In April 2003, for example, an FDA/industry working group recommended that serum cardiac troponin be used as a biomarker for drug-induced cardiac toxicity in nonclinical trials. Serum cardiac troponins could be "useful in investigating specific cases of concern for drug-induced myocardial injury," according to a paper authored by the working group. FDA officials point out, however, that there is not yet universal agreement on the utility of this endpoint.

- In a push to develop standards for and to benefit from emerging technologies, the FDA released a November 2003 draft guidance on pharmacogenomics in which it outlined situations in which pharmacogenomics data would be required in INDs and NDAs and other situations in which industry could submit such data on a voluntary basis. In the draft guidance, the first of three pharmacogenomics-related guidances expected from the FDA, the agency acknowledged that most pharmacogenomic data currently are exploratory or research-oriented and, therefore, need not be submitted in INDs or NDAs (see Chapters 3 and 7). To help FDA reviewers and scientists understand the relevant scientific issues in the emerging field, however, the draft guidance recommends that sponsors consider submitting the data voluntarily. In addition, the agency notes that certain pharmacogenomic data—such as test results used in an animal trial to support safety—will be required in an IND's pharmacology/toxicology section or previous human use section or in an NDA's pharmacology/toxicology, human pharmacokinetics/bioavailability , or clinical data section. "Pharmacogenomic data relevant to, or derived from, animal or *in vitro* studies should ordinarily be submitted [to the IND's pharmacology/toxicology section] when the sponsor wishes to use these data to make a scientific case, or when the test is well established as a predictive biomarker (i.e., is a known valid biomarker)," the agency states.

- In its continuing initiative to obtain more relevant data and information on drug effects in pediatric patients, CDER released a February 2003 draft guidance entitled, *Nonclinical Safety Evaluation of Pediatric Drug Products*. Although postnatal developmental toxicity is a primary concern because pediatric organ systems at highest risk for drug toxicity are those that undergo significant postnatal development, the draft guidance notes that nonclinical developmental toxicity studies have traditionally focused on prenatal development. When pediatric clinical studies involve long-term exposure, the agency advises that researchers conduct juvenile animal studies before initiating long-term clinical studies. If the indication is for long-term use, but the clinical trials are short-term, the juvenile animal studies should be available before the marketing application is submitted. When pediatric trials do not involve long-term exposure, juvenile animal studies can be conducted in conjunction with the clinical trials. Depending on the species, juvenile studies can utilize many animals and can be expensive and logistically difficult. Sponsors should consult with the appropriate divisions prior to initiating such studies, the agency advises.

- To better ensure the safety of human clinical study volunteers, developers should employ a standardized process for selecting a maximum recommended starting dose (MRSD) for first-in-human clinical trials involving new molecular entities in adult healthy subjects, the FDA recommends in a December 2002 draft guidance entitled, *Estimating the Safe Starting Dose in Clinical Trials for Therapeutics in Adult Healthy Volunteers*. The major elements of this recommended process include the determination of the no observed adverse effect levels (NOAELs) in the tested animal species, the conversion of NOAELs to a human equivalent dose (HED), the selection of the most appropriate species, and the application of a so-called "safety factor" (see Chapter 5). Providing data for the selection of the MRSD is considered one of the key goals of nonclinical testing.

- Under a May 2002 final rule, the FDA provides for the approval of certain new drug and biological products "based on animal data when adequate and well-controlled efficacy studies in humans cannot be ethically conducted because the studies would involve administering a potentially lethal or permanently disabling toxic substance or organism to healthy human volunteers and field trials are not feasible prior to approval." Under the rule, new drugs and biologicals used to reduce or prevent the serious or life-threatening toxicity of chemical, biological, radiological or nuclear substances can be approved based on evidence of effectiveness derived from appropriate and well-controlled efficacy studies in animals.

FDA Guidance on Nonclinical Testing Requirements

Until fairly recently, the FDA's nonclinical testing requirements were described only in very general terms in two now-outdated guidelines, one published in 1968 by the FDA and the other in 1977 by the U.S. Pharmaceutical Manufacturers Association (PMA). In the late 1980s and early 1990s, FDA toxicologists and pharmacologists were developing several guidance documents to address subjects ranging from animal-testing requirements for specific classes of drugs to the use of computer technology for nonclinical data submissions.

Concurrent with the FDA's efforts to produce updated guidance in this area, the European Community (EC) and Japan were developing testing standards that were often similar in principle but different in detail. In an effort to harmonize these and other testing standards, the regulatory authorities and pharmaceutical industries of these three regions organized the International Conferences on Harmonization (ICH).

The harmonization initiative has had fundamental effects on the FDA's own efforts to develop recommendations for nonclinical testing. Most importantly, the FDA has sought to revise its guidelines to reflect the consensus to which the agency has contributed as part of the ICH process.

The ICH process and its effects on the FDA's efforts will continue for some time. By the late 1990s, the FDA had accepted harmonized recommendations on single dose toxicity testing, the nonclinical safety studies needed to support human clinical trials, and the duration of chronic toxicity testing in rodents. It had also adopted harmonized guidelines on reproductive toxicity studies, toxicokinetics, certain aspects of pharmacokinetics, genotoxicity testing, and carcinogenicity studies. Efforts to finalize guidelines on other nonclinical topics continue (see discussion of S7B above), and new topics are poised to enter the process. In addition to outlining the FDA's nonclinical testing requirements, the following discussion analyzes the specific effects that the ICH process has had and is expected to have on these requirements.

FDA officials are always careful to stress the limitations of guidelines, no matter how current. (Note: Under the FDA's 1997 Good Guidance Practices initiative, all new guidelines are being designated as "guidances.") As with any guidances, the agency's nonclinical guidelines are designed only to provide general direction for typical situations; they cannot be applied universally to all drugs and all situations. Therefore, the FDA remains willing to advise sponsors, particularly about unusual cases. FDA staffers will discuss nonclinical testing strategies during the development of these plans, but can usually offer more useful insights if a sponsor develops a nonclinical study program and submits the plan for agency review. Recommendations obtained from such reviews supplement drug sponsors' own expertise and the more general suggestions provided by FDA and ICH guidelines.

Whether or not a sponsor chooses to initiate a dialogue with FDA staff, the types and amount of nonclinical testing ultimately required by the agency will depend on several factors, including:

- a drug's chemical structure, and the similarity of that structure to existing compounds with safety profiles known to the FDA;
- a drug's proposed indication in humans;
- a drug's target patient population (e.g., elderly, infants, women);
- special characteristics of a drug's use pattern (e.g., if a drug is likely to be prescribed as a concomitant medication);
- a drug's proposed route of administration; and
- a drug's proposed duration of administration (i.e., whether for chronic or short-term use).

Types of Nonclinical Studies

When drug sponsors initiate a nonclinical testing program, their first goal is to conduct the studies and collect the data necessary to support the safety of early clinical trials. In the past, these data generally have been limited to short-term animal test results. Today, however, *in vitro* and *in vivo* genotoxicity testing is assuming greater importance during the preclinical phase.

As stated above, preclinical studies represent only part of a drug's nonclinical development. The comprehensive nonclinical testing program necessary to support marketing approval for most new drugs involves years of work and several different types of studies.

The ICH's M3 *Guidance on Nonclinical Safety Studies for the Conduct of Human Clinical Trials for Pharmaceuticals* (November 1997), hereafter referred to as the M3 guidance, discusses the timing of the various components of nonclinical testing and their relation to the conduct of clinical trials. According to this document, the goals of the nonclinical safety evaluation include "characterization of toxic effects with respect to target organs, dose dependence, relationship to exposure, and potential reversibility. The information is important for the estimation of an initial safe starting dose for the human trials and the identification of parameters for clinical monitoring for potential adverse effects. The nonclinical safety studies, although limited at the beginning of clinical development, should be adequate to characterize potential toxic effects under the conditions of the supported clinical trial."

For the purpose of analysis, nonclinical testing is often divided into two areas: pharmacology and toxicology. Together, pharmacology and toxicology studies are designed to provide an integrated overview of a drug's effects in various animal species.

Pharmacology Studies Because insights gained from pharmacological studies—particularly those regarding adverse effects—can influence the direction of later toxicological testing, pharmacologic work is generally conducted first.

Pharmacological Screening. The pharmacological study of a new drug proceeds in phases. The initial phase, pharmacological screening, is really part of the drug discovery process. It involves the use of *in vitro* and *in vivo* assays designed to determine if a compound has any pharmacological activity. Hundreds of compounds may be subjected to these screenings, with those exhibiting measurable pharmacological effects being selected as "lead chemicals" (i.e., substances to be tested further).

Pharmacodynamics. Once a lead chemical is selected, the sponsor generally begins to compile a more complete qualitative and quantitative pharmacological profile of the compound. This profile consists largely of pharmacodynamic studies, which provide an indication of the drug's action on various receptors or physiological systems in animals.

Some pharmacodynamic studies, called "safety pharmacology studies," should be sufficiently extensive to determine dose-response relationships and the drug's duration and mechanism of action. In these studies, researchers explore the drug's potential adverse effects on major physiological systems and activities (i.e., neurologic, cardiovascular, respiratory, gastrointestinal, genitourinary, endocrine, anti-inflammatory, immunoreactive, chemotherapeutic, and enzymatic) in relation to exposure. The studies are designed to investigate all primary and secondary effects related or unrelated to the desired therapeutic effect, extensions of the therapeutic effect that might produce toxicity at higher doses, and effects related to interactions with other drugs. According to the ICH's November 1997 M3 guidance, safety pharmacology studies should be performed prior to human exposure. These assessments may be made as part of independent pharmacology studies or incorporated into appropriate toxicology studies. Additional studies may be appropriate following initial clinical studies or toxicology studies.

In July 2000, the ICH parties released a final guidance entitled, S7 *Guideline on Safety Pharmacology Studies for Human Pharmaceuticals.* Although earlier ICH guidances discussed safety pharmacology studies, the S7 guidance was the first to define this phase of development—"those studies that investigate the potential undesirable pharmacodynamic effects of a substance on physiological functions in relationship to exposure in the therapeutic range and above." (Author's note: The S7 guidance states that pharmacology studies also comprise two other categories of studies—primary pharmacodynamic studies ("studies on the mode of action and/or effects

20

of a substance in relation to its desired therapeutic target") and secondary pharmacodynamic studies ("studies on the mode of action and/or effects of a substance not related to its desired therapeutic target...sometimes referred to as part of general pharmacology studies")). The principal objectives of safety pharmacology studies, the guidance notes, are: (1) to identify undesirable pharmacodynamic properties of a substance that may have relevance to its human safety; (2) to evaluate adverse pharmacodynamic and/or pathophysiological effects of a substance observed in toxicology and/or clinical studies; and (3) to investigate the mechanism of the adverse pharmacodynamic effects observed and/or suspected. Among the tests recommended by the guidance is a "safety pharmacology core battery" designed to "investigate the effects of the test substance on vital functions," which are generally the cardiovascular, respiratory and central nervous systems.

Pharmacokinetics. The pharmacology component of preclinical development also includes pharmacokinetic testing, which is designed to obtain information on the extent and duration of systemic exposure to the drug. Generally, these studies are performed both *in vitro* and *in vivo* in multiple species using both radiolabeled and unlabeled test compound. The results are then compared to identify species-to-species drug-response differences that might affect later nonclinical and clinical studies or their interpretation. Today, these studies are considered to be a much more important aspect of preclinical drug development than they were previously, and serve as the basis for subsequent toxicokinetic assessments (see discussion on toxicity studies below). According to the ICH's M3 guidance, exposure data in animals should be evaluated prior to human trials, and additional information on absorption, distribution, metabolism and excretion should become available by the time that early Phase 1 studies (human pharmacology) are complete so that human and animal metabolic pathways can be compared.

It is worth noting that this is one area in which there is little specific international guidance available, and where the ICH regional-specific guidances differ.

Pharmacokinetic studies are designed to yield information about the drug's absorption, distribution, metabolism, and excretion (ADME) pattern. Analytical methodology employed to generate these data may include ultraviolet absorption, fluorescence, high-pressure liquid chromatography, gas chromatography, immunoassay, liquid scintigraphy, autoradiography and mass spectrometry analysis of the parent compound and/or metabolites in tissues or fluids.

Absorption studies generally involve serial determinations of drug concentration in blood and urine after dosing to indicate the rate and extent of absorption (e.g., following oral administration). Typically, studies using the intravenous route are conducted to serve as a reference. Common pharmacokinetic parameters employed in these assessments include plasma area under the curve (AUC), maximum (peak) plasma concentration (Cmax), and plasma concentration at a specified time after administration of a given dose (C(time)). Bioavailability (i.e., the amount of drug that reaches the systemic circulation) is dependent, in part, on the extent of absorption, but is also influenced by other factors, such as the extent of a drug's metabolism by the liver before it enters the general circulation.

Distribution studies provide information on the extent and time course of tissue accumulation and the elimination of a drug and/or its metabolites. Distribution patterns can be assessed by sacrificing animals at predetermined intervals after dosing, and then measuring the concentration of the drug and/or its metabolites in selected tissues. In general, only single dose studies of distribution are performed. According to the final ICH guideline entitled, S3B *Pharmacokinetics: Guidance for Repeated Dose Tissue Distribution Studies* (March 1995), however, repeat dose distribution studies are appropriate for compounds that have: (1) an apparently long half life; (2) incomplete elimination; or (3) unanticipated organ toxicity.

The "volume of distribution" represents another parameter that is useful in assessing drug distribution. The volume of distribution relates the amount of drug in the body to the concentration of drug in the blood or plasma. For drugs that are extensively bound to plasma proteins but not to tissue components, the volume of distribution will approach that of the plasma volume.

The assessment and quantification of a drug's metabolic pattern is essential for a complete understanding of efficacy and toxicity, since species differences in toxicity may be related to differences in metabolism. To assess the metabolic profile of a drug, the concentration of the drug and its major metabolites are measured in plasma, urine, feces, bile, and/or other tissues as a function of time following dose administration. In some cases, toxicological testing of pharmacologically active metabolites may be necessary in addition to testing on the drug itself.

"Clearance" is a measure of an organism's ability to eliminate a drug. The concept represents the rate of a drug's elimination in relation to its concentration (CL=Rate of elimination/C). This excretion parameter can be determined for individual organs and, when added together, will equal total systemic clearance. In general, decreased toxic potential is associated with rapid and complete excretion.

Toxicity Studies In *vitro* and *in vivo* animal toxicity studies are undertaken to identify and measure a drug's short- and long-term functional and morphologic adverse effects. Depending on the nature of a drug, its intended use, and the extent of its proposed study in clinical trials, a toxicity testing program may comprise some or all of the following elements:

- acute toxicity studies;
- subacute or subchronic toxicity studies;
- chronic toxicity studies;
- carcinogenicity studies;
- special toxicity studies;
- reproductive toxicity studies;
- genotoxicity studies; and
- toxicokinetic studies.

Acute Toxicity Studies. Acute (single dose) toxicity studies are designed to measure the short-term adverse effects of a drug when administered either in a single dose or in multiple doses during a period not exceeding 24 hours. Results from acute toxicity studies should provide information on the following:

- the appropriate dosage for multiple-dose studies;
- the potential target organs of toxicity;
- the time-course of drug-induced clinical observations;
- species-specific differences in toxicity;
- the potential for acute toxicity in humans; and
- an estimate of the safe acute doses for humans.

To determine initial toxicity levels, researchers should evaluate a drug's single dose (acute) toxicity in two mammalian species prior to the first human exposure. These studies should involve dosages that are intended to cause no adverse effects and those intended to cause major (life-threatening) toxicity. The use of vehicle control groups should be considered. According to the ICH's M3 guidance, a dose-escalation study is considered an acceptable alternative to the single-dose design.

The route(s) of administration should include an intravenous route and the route intended for human administration. When intravenous dosing is proposed in humans, use of this route alone in animal testing is sufficient. The animals are then observed for 14 days after drug administration.

The FDA indicates that investigators need to obtain more than just mortality data from acute toxicity studies. At a minimum, researchers should observe and record test animals' clinical signs, and the time of onset, the duration, and the reversibility of toxicity. Gross necropsies should be performed on all animals.

In the past, one type of data derived from acute toxicity studies was the drug's "lethal dose" (LD). LD_{50}, which is calculated using a specific statistical formula, represents the dosage level that kills 50 percent of the test animals. Since 1988, however, the FDA has recommended that classic LD_{50} studies not be conducted (*Federal Register* 53:39650). This action came after the value of the "classic" LD_{50} was seriously questioned internationally for ethical and scientific reasons. Today, in accordance with ICH recommendations for single dose toxicity testing, none of the ICH parties requires or recommends that sponsors determine the "classic" LD_{50}.

The LD_{50} has been replaced by single dose administration, increasing dose tolerance studies that measure toxic response as a function of dose. When relevant, major and pharmacologically significant metabolites should be tested in acute toxicity studies. The tests should employ a testing protocol that maximizes the amount of information that can be derived from the smallest number of animals.

In addition to a universal adoption of this approach by the ICH, the FDA published a revised guidance entitled, *Single Dose Acute Toxicity Testing for Pharmaceuticals* (August 1996). This guidance document indicates that acute toxicity studies, when appropriately designed and conducted, may provide the primary safety data to support single dose pharmacokinetic studies in humans, although nonclinical studies of this nature will require a more comprehensive study design. These toxicity studies should be designed to assess dose-response relationships and pharmacokinetics. Clinical pathology and histopathology should be monitored at an early time and at termination (i.e., ideally, for maximum effect and recovery).

Subacute or Subchronic Studies. Subacute, or subchronic, toxicity testing allows investigators to evaluate a drug's toxic potential and pathologic effects over a longer period. These studies range in length from 14 to 90 days, with the duration generally dependent on the proposed term of clinical use and the duration of proposed clinical trials. According to the ICH's M3 guidance, the duration of the animal toxicity studies conducted in two mammalian species (one non-rodent) should, in principle, equal or exceed the duration of the clinical trial, "up to the maximum recommended duration of the repeated dose toxicity studies" (see exhibit below).

Subacute studies are designed to assess the progression and regression of drug-induced lesions. However, the studies are generally of insufficient duration to identify all secondary effects that may arise during long-term clinical use or during chronic toxicity and carcinogenicity testing.

Independent studies are performed in at least one rodent and one non-rodent species. Typically, the test compound is administered daily at three or more dosage levels. The highest dose used in these studies should be selected to deliberately induce toxic reactions. The lowest dosage should be selected to identify a no-observed adverse (toxic)-effect level (NOAEL)—that is, the dose demonstrating only intended pharmacologi-

ICH's Duration of Repeated Dose Toxicity Studies to Support Phase I and II Trials in the EU and Phase I, II, and III Trials in the United States and Japan[1]

Duration of Clinical Trials	Minimum Duration of Repeated Dose Toxicity Studies	
	Rodents	Nonrodents
Single Dose	2-4 Weeks[2]	2 Weeks
Up to 2 Weeks	2-4 Weeks[2]	2 Weeks
Up to 1 Month	1 Month	1 Month
Up to 3 Months	3 Months	3 Months
Up to 6 Months	6 Months	6 Months[3]
> 6 Months	6 Months	Chronic[3]

[1] In Japan, if there are no Phase II clinical trials of equivalent duration to the planned Phase III trials, conduct of longer duration toxicity studies should be considered as given in the table below.

[2] In the EU and the United States, 2-week studies are the minimum duration. In Japan, 2-week nonrodent and 4-week rodent studies are needed. In the United States, as an alternative to 2-week studies, single dose toxicity studies with extended examinations can support single dose human trials.

[3] Data from 6 months of administration in nonrodents should be available before the initiation of clinical trials longer than 3 months. Alternatively, if applicable, data from a 9-month nonrodent study should be available before the treatment duration exceeds that which is supported by the available toxicity studies.

Source: ICH M3 Guidance

cal effects. When possible, this dose should represent a multiple of the projected average daily clinical dose. Further, each study should employ appropriate control groups (i.e., untreated and/or vehicle, comparative).

During such studies, researchers should collect the following data, as appropriate, for the specific test compound:

- observed effects;
- mortality;
- body weight;
- food/water consumption;
- physical examinations;
- hematology/bone marrow/coagulation;
- blood chemistry/urinalysis;
- organ weights;
- gross pathology; and
- histopathology.

The studies in rodents are often used to establish dosing levels for carcinogenicity studies, such as the maximum tolerated dose (MTD). The MTD is the dose just high enough to elicit signs of minimal toxicity without significantly altering the animal's normal life span due to effects other than carinogenicity.

Chronic Toxicity Testing. Chronic toxicity studies, which are tests of 180 days to a year in duration, are designed to determine the following:

- the potential risk in relation to the anticipated dose and period of drug treatment;
- the potential target organs of toxicity;
- the reversibility of any observed toxicities; and
- the no-observed adverse (toxic)-effect level.

The FDA generally requires that sponsors conduct these studies in one rodent (usually rat) and one non-rodent (usually dog) species for both chronic-use drugs and drugs intended for intermittent use to treat chronic or recurrent diseases. Because there is flexibility in this requirement, sponsors should consult the relevant FDA review division for a product-specific assessment.

In accordance with an ICH consensus, the FDA has reduced its recommended maximum duration of chronic toxicity studies in rodents from 12 to 6 months. The agency continues to recommend 12-month studies, however, when rodent carcinogenicity bioassays are not performed as part of the drug toxicity profile, but when chronic toxicity testing would otherwise be appropriate.

After considerable discussion and debate, the ICH parties reached consensus on the recommended duration of nonrodent studies through the June 1999 release of a final guidance entitled, S4A *Duration of Chronic Toxicity Testing in Animals* (*Rodent and Nonrodent Toxicity Testing*). Although the FDA agreed to reduce the recommended duration of chronic non-rodent studies from 12 months to the ICH-recommended 9 months, the agency included a fairly detailed "note" regarding this consensus: "While FDA considers 9-month studies in nonrodents acceptable for most drug development programs, shorter studies may be equally acceptable in some circumstances and longer studies may be more appropriate in others, as follows:

1. Six-month studies may be acceptable for indications of chronic conditions associated with short-term, intermittent drug exposure, such as bacterial infections, migraine, erectile dysfunction, and herpes.

2. Six-month studies may be acceptable for drugs intended for indications for life-threatening diseases for which substantial long-term human clinical data are available, such as cancer chemotherapy in advanced disease or in adjuvant use.

3. Twelve-month studies may be more appropriate for chronically used drugs to be approved on the basis of short-term clinical trials employing efficacy surrogate markers where safety data from humans are limited to short-term exposure, such as some acquired immunodeficiency syndrome (AIDS) therapies.

4. Twelve-month studies may be more appropriate for new molecular entities acting at new molecular targets where postmarketing experience is not available for the pharmacological class. Thus, the therapeutic is the first in a pharmacological class for which there is limited human or animal experience on its long-term toxic potential."

Dose selection criteria are similar to those described for subacute and subchronic studies, and must reflect the results of these shorter-term studies as well as structure-activity relationships, pharmacology studies, and pharmacokinetic data. Typically, recovery subgroups and, in some cases, interim sacrifice subgroups are included. As specified above for subacute and subchronic studies, researchers must collect the data listed, as appropriate, for the drug under investigation.

ICH's Duration of Repeated Dose Toxicity Studies to Support Phase III Trials in the EU and Marketing in All Regions[1]

Duration of Clinical Trials	Minimum Duration of Repeated Dose Toxicity Studies	
	Rodents	Nonrodents
Up to 2 Weeks	1 Month	1 Month
Up to 1 Month	3 Months	3 Months
Up to 3 Months	6 Months	3 Months
> 3 Months	6 Months	Chronic

[1] The above table also reflects the marketing recommendations in the three regions, except that a chronic nonrodent study is recommended for clinical use > 1 month.

Source: ICH M3 Guidance

Chronic studies are often initiated when Phase 2 trials provide indications of a drug's effectiveness, and are conducted concurrently with Phase 3 trials. Data obtained from chronic toxicity tests are used to support the safety of long-term drug administration in clinical trials and, ultimately, the approval of the drug for general marketing.

Carcinogenicity Studies. Multiple aspects of carcinogenicity testing have been discussed as part of the ICH initiative (i.e., need, dose selection, testing approaches). As stated in ICH proceedings, "...a carcinogenicity study is one of the most resource-consuming in terms of animals and time. In the interests of decreased animal use and protection, but without prejudicing safety, such studies should only be performed once... This could be achieved through harmonisation of the requirements of different regulatory systems."

In the past, the FDA has generally required carcinogenicity studies for any drug intended for use for three months or more, and for drugs intended for intermittent use where the total cumulative lifetime exposure may exceed three months. However, to be consistent with the final ICH guideline entitled, S1A *Guidance on the Need for Long-Term Carcinogenicity Studies of Pharmaceuticals* (March 1996), the agency revised its requirements and now expects carcinogenicity studies for drugs whose use is continuous for six months or is intermittent to treat chronic or recurrent diseases. Consistent with the ICH consensus, completed carcinogenicity studies generally are not needed in advance of clinical trials "unless there is cause for concern." According to the M3 guidance, for drugs designed to treat certain serious diseases, carcinogenicity testing, if needed, may be conducted postapproval.

Today, the FDA generally requires carcinogenicity studies using the mouse and the rat. Carcinogenicity studies in rats are generally two years in duration. If long-term studies are conducted in mice, these are also generally two-year studies.

Ideally, the route of administration selected for carcinogenicity studies should be the intended clinical route. When there is more than one route or there is a change in the proposed clinical route, the carcinogenicity test route should be that which provides the greatest systemic exposure. Similar to chronic toxicity studies, carcinogenicity investigations are not usually initiated until a drug shows some indication of effectiveness in Phase 2 clinical trials.

Also, consistent with the final ICH guidance entitled, S1C *Dose Selection for Carcinogenicity Studies of Pharmaceuticals* (1994) and a final addendum entitled, S1C(R) *Addendum to 'Dose Selection for Carcinogenicity Studies of Pharmaceuticals'*:

Addition of a Limit Dose and Related Notes (December 1997), the FDA no longer views dose selection based on the MTD as the only acceptable practice. As stated in the 1994 guidance, the doses selected "should provide an exposure to the agent that (1) allows an adequate margin of safety over the human therapeutic exposure, (2) is tolerated without significant chronic physiological dysfunction and are compatible with good survival, (3) is guided by a comprehensive set of animal and human data that focuses on the properties of the agent and the suitability of the animal, and (4) permits data interpretation in the context of clinical use."

The guidance proposes that any one of several approaches may be appropriate for dose selection in carcinogenicity studies: (1) toxicity-based endpoints; (2) pharmacokinetic endpoints; (3) saturation of absorption; (4) pharmacodynamic endpoints; (5) maximum feasible dose; and (6) additional endpoints. In all cases, appropriate dose-ranging studies are necessary.

Because the approaches for dose selection adopted by ICH offer flexibility and because the factors to be considered in the use of any specific endpoint are complex, it may be prudent for sponsors to ask the agency for an assessment of appropriate dose-selection criteria in individual cases. The prospect of additional revisions to recommended study designs, as well as the expense associated with this aspect of nonclinical testing, should also motivate sponsors to obtain specific FDA guidance before initiating carcinogenicity studies. CDER offers consultation on dose selection and study design issues for carcinogenicity studies through the work of the Carcinogenicity Assessment Committee.

In a May 2001 draft guidance entitled, *Statistical Aspects of the Design, Analysis, and Interpretation of Chronic Rodent Carcinogenicity Studies of Pharmaceuticals*, the FDA also emphasizes the "particularly critical" importance of dose selection, and advises companies to consult the S1C guidance. The draft document provides sponsors with FDA recommendations on the design and interpretation of animal carcinogenicity studies, methods of statistical analysis of tumor data, and the presentation of data and results in reports. "In a carcinogenicity study of a new drug using a series of increasing dosing levels, statistical tests for positive trends in tumor rates are usually of greatest interest, but..., in some situations, pairwise comparisons are considered to be more indicative of drug effects than trend tests," the draft guidance notes.

In July 1997, the ICH parties also agreed to a final guidance entitled, S1B *Testing for Carcinogenicity of Pharmaceuticals*, which the FDA published in February 1998. This guidance outlines experimental approaches that may obviate the need for the routine conduct of two long-term rodent carcinogenicity studies for those pharmaceuticals that currently require such evaluation. A basic scheme comprising one long-term rodent carcinogenicity study (generally, the rat), plus one additional study for carcinogenic activity *in vivo*, is advanced in the guidance. The additional study could be either a short- or medium-term rodent test system or a long-term carcinogenicity study in a second rodent species. Under the final guidance, the additional study must be scientifically justified and must contribute to the overall assessment of carcinogenic potential.

Because of the time and expense associated with carcinogenicity studies, CDER traditionally has been willing to review and comment on proposed carcinogenicity protocols through its Carcinogenicity Assessment Committee and Executive Carcinogenicity Assessment Committee. Some aspects of this process have been formalized by the special protocol question and assessment process outlined in the FDA's PDUFA II and III commitments. Under this process, CDER must review and respond to specific sponsor questions regarding carcinogenicity, stability, or Phase 3 clinical protocols within 45 days. If CDER's Carcinogenicity Assessment Committee agrees in its response that the protocol data can be used as part of the primary basis for product approval, the user-fee commitments state that the center "will not alter its perspective on the issue of design, execution, or analysis unless public health concerns unrecognized at the time of the protocol assessment...are evident." According to CDER data released in 2004, industry had submitted 274 protocols under the special protocol question and assessment process, most of which were thought to be carcinogenicity protocols. CDER had met its goal to respond within 45 days on almost 92 percent of these protocol submissions.

In December 1999, CDER released a draft guidance entitled, *Special Protocol Assessment* to outline the protocol assessment and agreement process for carcinogenicity, stability, and Phase 3 protocols. According to the draft guidance, "a sponsor interested in Agency assessment and agreement on a carcinogenicity protocol should notify the appropriate review division...and discuss planned carcinogenicity testing at an end-of-phase 2 meeting or should notify the director of the appropriate division of an intent to request special protocol assessment by letter at least 30 days prior to submitting the request. With the notice of intent, the sponsor should submit relevant background information so that the Agency may review (or re-review) reference material related to carcinogenicity protocol design prior to receiving the carcinogenicity protocol." In the draft document, CDER noted that it is developing a guidance to describe the type of information that would be appropriate to submit before requesting a carcinogenicity protocol assessment. Protocols submitted for special protocol assessment should be forwarded to the agency at least 90 days before a study's anticipated commencement, the agency recommends.

A May 2002 guidance entitled, *Carcinogenicity Study Protocol Submissions* specifies the types of information that CDER considers important in evaluating protocols for animal carcinogenicity studies. Although that information will vary with the proposed study design and test approach, CDER notes that the following information, in all cases, will facilitate the protocol-review process: the basis for dose selection; a toxicology study report (usually 90-day); metabolic profiles for the drug in humans and in the species employed for assessing carcinogenic potential; toxicokinetic data; exposure data; plasma protein binding data; and a summary of the investigations on the genotoxic potential of the drug and its major human metabolites.

In late 1998, CDER published a manual of policies and procedures entitled, *Submission of Preclinical Carcinogenicity Protocols and Study Results* (MaPP 7412.3) to provide an administrative mechanism for the submission, and CDER tracking and processing, of proposed carcinogenicity protocols, toxicity data supporting dose selection, and carcinogenicity study results to an existing IND or in advance of a traditional IND submission. This MaPP was to remain in effect until CDER publishes a general MaPP establishing a tracking system for all pre-IND submissions.

In January 2000, CDER released a draft guidance entitled, *Photosafety Testing*, to assist companies in determining whether they should test for photosensitivity and assess the potential human risk for photochemical carcinogenesis and enhancement of UV-induced skin carcinogenesis in the development of topically and systemically administered drug products. According to the draft, the identification of photosensitivity effects before widespread human exposure is preferable to learning of these effects through postmarketing adverse event reports, which CDER claims has been the traditional way that such effects have been discovered.

Special Toxicity Studies. Special toxicity studies include those studies appropriate for a particular formulation or route of administration (e.g., parenteral or local tolerance studies, *in vitro* hemolysis), and studies conducted in a particular animal model relevant to a human disease or age. At this writing, formal FDA guidance pertaining to special toxicity testing was limited largely to a brief discussion provided in the FDA's *Guideline for the Format and Content of the Nonclinical Pharmacology/Toxicology Section of an Application.* Therefore, sponsors should ask the relevant CDER review division if special toxicity testing is considered applicable. The evaluation of local tolerance should be performed prior to human exposure (and in animals using routes relevant to the proposed clinical administration), although this assessment may be part of other toxicity studies.

An October 2002 FDA guidance entitled, *Immunotoxicology Evaluation of Investigational New Drugs* provides recommendations on when additional, specific immunotoxicology studies should be conducted, the parameters that should be routinely assessed in toxicity studies to determine a drug's effects on immune function, and when additional mechanistic information could help characterize the significance of a drug's effect on the immune system. While evidence of immunotoxicity can "usually" be observed in standard nonclinical toxicology studies, additional studies are needed in some cases, the draft guidance notes. Specific immunotoxicity testing is expected (i.e., to complement the standard repeat-dose toxicology studies) when drugs will be administered by the inhalation or topical route, the guidance states. Researchers should also consider specific immunotoxicity studies when there is evidence of drug-induced immunosuppression, when use during pregnancy is likely and the drug has been shown to induce immunosuppression in adults, when adverse reactions of drug-induced hypersensitivity are observed in toxicology studies, when the drug will be used in treating HIV infection, when chronic toxicology studies or rodent bioassays indicate carcinogenic potential, or when drug-induced autoimmunity suspected in toxicology studies is difficult to confirm using current methods.

Reproductive Toxicity Studies. The FDA requires reproductive testing for any drug to be used in women of childbearing potential, regardless of whether the target population is pregnant women. Generally, these studies have been conducted in a three-segment testing protocol previously recommended by the FDA: (1) Segment I-fertility and general reproductive performance (involving the study of both the male and female rat); (2) Segment II-teratology (conducted in the rat and the rabbit); and (3) Segment III-perinatal and postnatal development (conducted in the rat to evaluate drug effects during the last third of pregnancy and the period of lactation).

In an effort to reduce differences in reproductive toxicity requirements between the EC, Japan, and the United States, the ICH parties adopted the final guidance entitled, S5A *Detection of Toxicity to Reproduction for Medicinal Products* (September 1994). As stated in this guideline, "the aim of reproductive toxicity studies is to reveal any effect of one or more active substances(s) on mammalian reproduction." Therefore, the combination of studies selected should "allow exposure of mature adults and all stages of development from conception to sexual maturity." The integrated sequence of testing has been segregated into the following stages: (A) premating to conception; (B) conception to implantation; (C) implantation to closure of the hard palate; (D) closure of the hard palate to the end of pregnancy; (E) birth to weaning; and (F) weaning to sexual maturity.

The guideline suggests that the "most probable" option for investigating reproductive toxicity is a three-study design:

- Fertility and embryonic development. This study comprises stages A and B, and is conducted in at least one species, preferably the rat. Assessments should include maturation of gametes, mating behavior, fertility, preimplantation stages of the embryo, and implantation. In particular, sponsors should note that, in contrast to the previous Segment I study, this study design uses a histological evaluation of testes, epididymis, and sperm counts to assess drug effects on male fertility.

- Pre- and postnatal development, including maternal development. This phase comprises stages C to F, and is conducted in at least one species, preferably the rat. The study is designed to detect adverse effects on the pregnant/lactating female, and on the development of the conceptus and the offspring following exposure of the female from implantation through weaning. Assessments should include toxicity relative to that in nonpregnant females, pre- and postnatal death of offspring, altered growth and development, and functional deficits (e.g., behavior, maturation, and reproduction) in offspring.

- Embryo-fetal development. This study comprises stages C to D, and is usually conducted in two species: a rodent (preferably the rat) and non-rodent (preferably the rabbit). The goal is to detect adverse effects on the pregnant female and the development of the embryo and the fetus consequent to exposure of the female from implantation to closure of the hard palate. Researchers should assess toxicity relative to that in nonpregnant females, embryo-fetal death, and altered growth, including structural changes.

According to the ICH's M3 document, women of childbearing potential may be included in early, carefully monitored studies in the U.S. without the prior conduct of reproduction toxicity studies, provided appropriate precautions are taken (e.g., pregnancy testing, use of highly effective birth control method, and entry after confirmed menstrual period). In the United States, the assessment of female fertility and embryofetal development should be completed before women of childbearing potential using birth control are enrolled in Phase 3 trials. Women not of childbearing potential (i.e., permanently sterilized, postmenopausal) may be included in clinical trials without reproduction studies, provided the relevant repeated dose toxicity studies, including an evaluation of the female reproduction organs, have been completed.

Subsequent to the release of the above guideline, the ICH parties adopted S5B *Addendum on Toxicity to Male Fertility* (1996). This addendum suggests that the following be taken into account to assess effects on male fertility:

- Provided that no precluding effects have been found in repeated dose toxicity studies, a pre-mating treatment interval of four weeks for males and two weeks for females can be used.

- Histopathology of the testis has been shown to be the most sensitive method for the detection of effects on spermatogenesis. Therefore, good pathological and histopathological examination of the male reproductive organs provides a quick and direct means of detection.

- Sperm analysis can be used as a method to confirm findings by other methods and to characterize effects further.

According to the ICH's M3 guidance, a male fertility study should be completed prior to initiating Phase 3 trials. It adds that men may be included in Phase 1 and 2 trials prior to the male fertility study when an evaluation of the male reproductive organs is performed in the repeated dose toxicity studies.

A November 2001 CDER draft guidance entitled, *Integration of Study Results to Assess Concerns About Human Reproductive and Developmental Toxicities* describes a process for estimating human developmental and reproductive risks as a result of drug exposure when definitive human data are unavailable. The integration process is designed to estimate the likelihood that a drug will increase the risk of adverse human development or reproductive effects. Specifically, the process is based on the evaluation of a complete set of reproductive and general toxicology studies conducted in animals, pharmacokinetics, and the absorption and distribution of metabolic elimination studies conducted in humans and animals. The evaluation also compares animal and human drug-induced pharmacodynamic responses, drug metabolism and disposition, drug-induced pharmacologic and toxic effects, and drug exposures in animal studies against those at the highest recommended dose in humans.

Genotoxicity Studies. Also referred to as "mutagenicity studies," genotoxicity studies (now the preferred term) are used to assess a drug's potential to cause genomic damage that could induce cancer (i.e., somatic cell mutation) and/or heritable defects (i.e., germ cell mutation). These short-term studies include a battery of mammalian and non-mammalian, *in vitro* and *in vivo* tests designed to detect a compound's ability to cause an increase in genetic alterations (e.g., primary DNA damage, chromosomal aberrations). Although genotoxicity tests have not been specified as requirements for pharmaceuticals or described in a CDER guideline, these screening tests have been strongly recommended by the FDA, and are required in both the EC and Japan. (Note: Genotoxicity tests have been described in the FDA's Redbook, or *Toxicological Principles for the Safety Assessment of Direct Food Additives with Color Additives Used in Food*.)

The importance and complexity of genotoxicity studies is reflected in CDER's formation of a Genetic Toxicology Review Committee (GTRC) in late 2004. The new committee will perform a tertiary review "when positive genetic toxicology study results serve as the basis for imposition of a full or partial clinical hold on an investigational new drug application (IND) or a request that additional studies be performed to further evaluate the positive findings, the center states in an internal policy document entitled, *Tertiary Review of Genetic Toxicology Studies Resulting in a Recommendation for a Clinical Hold or Conduct of Additional Studies* (MaPP 7400.4). Given that the interpretation of genetic toxicology studies is not always straightforward and given the potential serious impact of a positive genetic toxicology test on a drug's development program, the GTRC "will ensure that clinical division directors are provided with consistent, high-quality information about the genetic toxicology studies on which to base their decisions regarding the safety of allowing the proposed clinical studies to proceed."

The ICH has addressed genotoxicity testing through three final guidances. According to the M3 document, *in vitro* tests for the evaluation of mutations and chromosomal damage "are generally needed" prior to first human exposure. The third test—an *in vivo* test for chromosomal damage—can be conducted during clinical trials. Additional testing should be performed if an equivocal or positive finding is made.

The ICH guidance entitled, S2A *Guidance on Specific Aspects of Regulatory Genotoxicity Tests for Pharmaceuticals* (April 1996) addresses and provides recommendations for the following issues:

- The base set of bacteria strains to be used in bacterial mutation assays;
- Acceptable bone marrow tests for the detection of clastogens *in vivo*;
- Further evaluation of compounds giving positive *in vitro* results;
- Validation of negative *in vivo* tests;
- Definition of the top concentration for *in vitro* tests; and
- Use of male/female rodents in bone marrow micronucleus tests.

In November 1997, the FDA published a companion ICH guidance entitled, S2B A *Standard Battery for Genotoxicity Testing of Pharmaceuticals*. This guidance defines a standard set of genotoxicity tests to be conducted for pharmaceutical registration, and recommends the extent of confirmatory experimentation for *in vitro* genotoxicity tests in the standard battery. The standard test battery calls for the completion of the following tests prior to the initiation of Phase 2 studies:

- a test for gene mutation in bacteria;
- an *in vitro* test with cytogenic evaluation of chromosomal damage with mammalian cells or an *in vivo* mouse lymphoma tk assay; and
- an *in vivo* test for chromosomal damage using rodent hematopoietic cells.

Note: although the test battery must be completed before Phase 2, the two *in vitro* assays must be performed prior to first-in-man studies. In practice, however, the agency generally sees all three elements of the test battery conducted prior to first-in-man studies.

Additional genotoxicity testing may be required if: (1) an equivocal or positive finding is made in the genotoxicity testing battery; or (2) genotoxicity testing is negative, but carcinogenicity testing is positive.

The final ICH guidance also discusses situations in which the standard three-test battery may need modification.

Toxicokinetic Studies. Toxicokinetics is defined as "the generation of pharmacokinetic data, either as an integral component in the conduct of nonclinical toxicity studies or in specially designed supportive studies, in order to assess systemic exposure. These data may be used in the interpretation of toxicological findings and their relevance to clinical safety issues."

In 1994, the FDA released a final ICH guideline entitled, SA3 *Toxicokinetics: The Assessment of Systemic Exposure in Toxicity Studies.* As stated in this ICH guidance, the primary objective of toxicokinetics is to describe the systemic exposure achieved in animals and its relationship to the dose level and the time course of the toxicity study. Secondary objectives are:

- to relate the exposure achieved in toxicity studies to toxicological findings, and contribute to the assessment of the relevance of these findings to clinical safety;
- to support the choice of species and treatment regimen in nonclinical toxicity studies; and
- to provide information that, in conjunction with the toxicity findings, contributes to the design of subsequent nonclinical toxicity studies.

The objectives may be achieved by the derivation of one or more pharmacokinetic parameters from measurements made at appropriate time points during the course of the individual studies. These measurements usually consist of plasma (or whole blood or serum) concentrations for the parent compound and/or metabolite(s), and should be selected on a case-by-case basis. Plasma (or whole blood or serum) AUC, Cmax, and C(time) are the most commonly used parameters for assessing exposure in toxicokinetic studies. For some compounds, it may be more appropriate to calculate exposure based on the (plasma protein) unbound concentration. Toxicokinetic studies should be designed to provide information that may be integrated into the full spectrum of nonclinical toxicity testing and then compared to human data.

Nonclinical Testing and New Drug Excipients

In a September 2002 draft guidance entitled, *Nonclinical Studies for Development of Pharmaceutical Excipients,* the agency acknowledged the need for new drug excipients (e.g., fillers, extenders, diluents, solvents, emulsifiers, flavors, coloring agents) and advocated a "flexible approach" to nonclinical development that considers both the type of use and the biological activity and physical properties of the molecular entity. Since safety data are necessary to support the use of new excipients, the agency recognized that there is a common perception that the development process for new excipients is often resource intensive.

"With proper planning, however, it is often possible to assess the toxicology of an excipient in a relatively efficient manner," the agency emphasizes. "For example, sponsors may be able to develop new excipients concurrently with development of new therapeutic substances by adding groups of animals that receive the excipient to studies that would have been conducted anyway to develop a drug substance. We recognize that existing human data for some excipients can substitute for nonclinical safety data, and an excipient with documented prior human exposure under circumstances relevant to the proposed use may not require evaluation in the full battery of toxicology studies outlined [in this guidance]. For example, we will continue to consider factors such as use in previously approved products or GRAS status as a food additive."

FDA Standards for Nonclinical Testing: Good Laboratory Practice (GLP)

Manufacturers of drugs and other FDA-regulated products are given considerable freedom during the preclinical screening and testing of new products. Provided that they comply with the U.S. Animal Welfare Act and other applicable animal welfare laws, nonclinical testing laboratories at pharmaceutical companies and private contractors are not limited in the use of animals to screen and measure the activity of drugs.

When the sponsor begins to compile safety data for submission to the FDA, however, standards called Good Laboratory Practice (GLP) apply. To ensure the quality and integrity of data derived from nonclinical testing, the FDA requires that nonclinical laboratory studies designed to provide safety data for an IND, NDA, or other regulatory submission comply with GLP standards. GLP regulations apply to product sponsor laboratories, private toxicology laboratories, academic and government laboratories, and all other facilities involved in animal testing and related analyses whose results will be submitted to the FDA in support of a product's safety.

GLP regulations establish basic standards for the conduct and reporting of nonclinical safety testing. Specifically, the regulations set standards in such areas as the organization, personnel, physical structure, maintenance, and operating procedures of nonclinical testing facilities.

GLP regulations, which became effective in June 1979, were the FDA's response to finding, in the mid-1970s, that some nonclinical studies submitted to support the safety of new drugs were not being conducted according to accepted standards. After establishing the initial GLP regulations, the FDA's confidence in the work of nonclinical laboratory facilities increased markedly. As a result, in October 1987, the agency published revised GLP regulations that sought to reduce regulatory and paperwork burdens facing laboratories conducting animal studies.

The Applicability of GLP

On one level, GLP applicability is fairly straightforward. According to FDA regulations, GLP applies to facilities conducting "nonclinical laboratory studies that support or are intended to support applications for research or marketing permits for products regulated by the Food and Drug Administration, including food and color additives, animal food additives, human and animal drugs, medical devices for human use, biological products, and electronic products."

What at times seems more difficult is identifying which nonclinical tests are subject to GLP requirements. The FDA states that GLP applies to "nonclinical laboratory studies," which the regulations define as "*in vivo* or *in vitro* experiments in which test articles are studied prospectively in test systems under laboratory conditions to determine their safety. The term does not include studies utilizing human subjects or clinical studies or field trials in animals. The term does not include basic exploratory studies carried out to determine whether a test article has any potential utility or to determine physical or chemical characteristics of a test article."

As currently interpreted, GLP applies to all "definitive" nonclinical safety studies, including key acute, subacute, chronic, reproductive, genetic toxicology, and carcinogenicity studies. Preliminary pharmacological screening and metabolism studies are exempt from GLP requirements, as are initial pilot studies such as dose-ranging, absorption, and excretion tests.

The Major Provisions of GLP

The core provisions of GLP establish standards for the nonclinical laboratory's organization, physical structure, equipment, and operating procedures. For purposes of analysis, these standards may be grouped into seven general areas:

- organization and personnel;
- testing facility;
- testing facility operation;
- test and control article characterization;
- the protocol and conduct of the nonclinical laboratory study;
- records and reporting; and
- equipment design.

Organization and Personnel GLP regulations regarding a nonclinical laboratory's organization and personnel address four areas: general personnel, testing facility management, study director, and quality assurance unit. Aside from the general qualifications and responsibilities of personnel and management, however, this aspect of GLP focuses primarily on issues regarding the study director and quality assurance unit.

Study Director. GLP requires that the management of the testing facility conducting a nonclinical program designate a scientist or other professional to serve as the study director. This individual has overall responsibility for the "technical conduct of the study, as well as for the interpretation, analysis, documentation, and reporting of results and represents the single point of study control." The FDA does not require that the study director be technically competent in all areas of a study, however.

Quality Assurance Unit. GLP also requires that each testing facility have a quality assurance unit (QAU) comprising one or more persons directly responsible to facility management. The QAU monitors each study to "assure management that the facilities, equipment, personnel, methods, practices, records, and controls" are consistent with GLP. To ensure that such evaluations are made objectively, QAU members may not be involved in any animal study that they monitor.

The GLP regulations specify several major QAU responsibilities in the areas of record maintenance, study inspections, and reports to facility management. At the conclusion of a study, the QAU is required to prepare and sign a statement—to be included with the final report—that specifies the dates on which inspections were made and the findings reported to management and the study director.

Current regulations require that the QAU inspect a nonclinical study at intervals the unit considers adequate to ensure the study's integrity. However, the FDA advises that each study, regardless of its length, be inspected in-process at least once, and that, across a series of studies, all phases be inspected to assure study integrity.

Testing Facility Obviously, the laboratory facility in which the testing program takes place is a primary focus of GLP. Animal care and supply facilities, test substance handling areas, laboratory operation, specimen and data storage, administrative and personnel facilities, methods of dosage preparation, and test substance accountability all must meet detailed requirements. Records indicating compliance must be kept.

In general terms, a testing facility and its equipment must be of suitable size and construction to allow for the proper conduct of the nonclinical study. Animal care areas, for example, must provide for sufficient separation of species/test systems and individual projects, isolation of animals, protection from outside disturbances, and routine or specialized animal housing. Regulated environmental controls for air quality—temperature, humidity, and air changes—and sanitation are needed.

Operation of Testing Facility Each laboratory must base its operations on standard operating procedures (SOPs). SOPs, which are in some respects extensions of nonclinical protocols, are written study methods or directions that laboratory management believes are adequate to ensure the quality and integrity of data obtained from animal tests. The description of research procedures provided by protocols and SOP documents makes possible the verification and reconstruction of studies.

The detailed written procedures specified in the SOPs must be maintained for all aspects of the study, including animal care, laboratory tests, data handling and storage, and equipment maintenance and calibration. Each laboratory area must have accessible laboratory manuals and SOPs relevant to the laboratory procedures being performed. Determining the degree to which SOPs are observed is another QAU responsibility. Any deviations from established SOPs must be authorized by the study director and noted in the raw data. On the other hand, the laboratory's management must approve major changes.

Test and Control Article Characterization Under the 1987 GLP revision, testing facilities are not required to characterize test and control articles before toxicity studies begin. This allows companies to screen out many of the useless compounds before investing resources necessary to characterize them: "FDA has concluded that characterization of test and control articles need not be performed until initial toxicology studies with the test article show reasonable promise of the articles reaching the marketplace. In arriving at this conclusion, the agency considered that prior knowledge of the precise molecular structure is not vital to the conduct of a valid toxicology test. It is important, however, to know the strength, purity, and stability of a test or control article that is used in a nonclinical laboratory study." FDA officials point out that either the sponsor or the testing laboratory may perform the test and control article characterization. The current GLP regulations allow facilities to conduct stability testing of test and control articles either before study initiation or, if this is impossible, through periodic analyses of each batch.

The Protocol and the Conduct of Nonclinical Laboratory Studies A protocol, or testing plan, is a vital element in both clinical and nonclinical studies. GLP regulations state that a nonclinical program must have a written protocol that "clearly indicates the objectives and all methods for the conduct of the study." Included in the 12-item protocol, which the sponsor must approve, should be descriptions of the experimental design and the purpose of the study as well as the type and frequency of tests, analyses, and measurements to be made. Changes made to the protocol during the course of the study must be documented by an official protocol amendment signed by the study director. The study director's approval of protocol amendments assures the FDA of the data's integrity.

Although protocols and SOPs may seem similar, the two have different purposes. The protocol is specific to the study being conducted, while laboratory SOPs are standards used for all research projects at a given facility. For example, SOPs would provide "how to" instructions on a facility's routine procedures for obtaining animal blood samples, caring for animals, and using and maintaining equipment. In contrast, the protocol provides study-specific instructions—for example, how often and from what animals blood samples are to be taken, what tests are to be conducted, and the number, species, sex, age, and weight of the animals to be tested in a particular study.

Records and Reporting A final report must be prepared for each nonclinical laboratory study. Comprehensive reports typically include the summary, testing methods, results, and conclusions of a study, as well as all raw data on each of the test animals. These final reports, as well as all raw data, documentation, protocols, and certain specimens generated during the nonclinical study, must be stored in an archive or repository to assure their safety and integrity for specific periods as designated in GLP regulations. Although these regulations state that two to five years is adequate, the FDA sometimes recommends that records be stored indefinitely and that specimens—slides, tissues, and blocks—be stored as long as they can be used to validate data.

Equipment Design GLP regulations specify requirements for the design, maintenance, and calibration of equipment used in nonclinical tests. Equipment used for facility environmental control and automatic, mechanical, or electronic equipment used in the generation, measurement, or assessment of data must be: (1) of appropriate design and adequate capacity to function according to the protocol; (2) suitably located for operation, inspection, cleaning, and maintenance; and (3) adequately tested, calibrated, and/or standardized. SOPs are required to define, in sufficient detail, the methods, materials, and schedules to be used in the routine inspection, cleaning, maintenance, testing, calibration, and standardization of equipment.

CDER's GLP Inspections

To monitor compliance with GLP requirements, the FDA employs a program of on-site laboratory inspections and data audits. According to the agency's Compliance Policy Guide (CPG) 7348.808, the FDA conducts two basic types of GLP compliance inspections: surveillance (or routine) inspections and directed inspections.

Representing the majority of GLP inspections, on-site surveillance inspections are periodic, routine evaluations of a laboratory's GLP compliance. Typically, these evaluations are based on either active or recently completed studies. Routine inspections for monitoring a nonclinical laboratory's GLP compliance are scheduled "approximately every two years" and are unannounced inspections.

Directed inspections are conducted when necessary—when questionable data raise suspicions during an IND or NDA review, for example. The agency may also conduct a directed "data audit" in response to questions or issues that arise during an NDA review (e.g., the NDA review division may request such an inspection when a novel product is under review) or in response to information received from other sources (e.g., complaints). Whenever possible, the FDA will couple directed inspections with routine inspections.

If FDA inspectors find GLP violations within a facility, CDER reviewers will evaluate the violations as described in the establishment inspection report (EIR) and decide on a course of action. When the agency observes noncompliance, it has several options, ranging from the issuance of untitled correspondence, in which CDER would discuss the findings and make recommendations (but not request a formal action or response), to the issuance of a warning letter, in which CDER will generally put a firm on notice regarding noncompliance and establish that specific actions (e.g., action and response) are necessary. In cases involving severe compliance problems, the FDA may disqualify data from an entire nonclinical study.

CHAPTER 3

The IND

The investigational new drug application, or IND, is a submission through which a drug sponsor alerts the FDA of its intention to conduct clinical studies with an investigational drug. The IND is a descriptive notification that the sponsor must submit to the FDA, and that the agency has a brief time to review, prior to the initiation of clinical trials.

In legal terms, the IND is a request for an exemption from the federal statute that prohibits an unapproved drug from being shipped in interstate commerce. Current federal law requires that a drug be the subject of an approved new drug application (NDA) before the product is transported or distributed across state lines. Because a sponsor will probably want to ship the investigational drug to clinical sites in other states, it must seek an exemption from this legal requirement.

In many respects, the IND is a product of a successful preclinical development program. During a new drug's early preclinical development, the sponsor's primary goal is to determine if the compound exhibits pharmacological activity that justifies commercial development and if the product is reasonably safe for initial use in humans. When a product is identified as a viable candidate for further development, the sponsor then focuses on collecting the data and information necessary to establish, in the IND, that the product will not expose human subjects to unreasonable risks when used in limited, early-stage clinical studies. Generally, this includes data and information in three broad areas:

Animal Pharmacology and Toxicology Studies: Preclinical data to permit an assessment as to whether the product is reasonably safe for initial testing in humans.

Manufacturing Information: Information pertaining to the composition, manufacture, and stability of, and the controls used for, the drug substance and the drug product to permit an assessment of the company's ability to adequately produce and supply consistent batches of the drug. Further, information on the compound's structure is used to assess whether the compound is similar to drugs known to be toxic.

Clinical Protocols and Investigator Information: Detailed protocols for proposed clinical studies to permit an assessment as to whether the initial-phase trials will expose subjects to unnecessary risks. Also, information on the qualifications of clinical investigators—professionals (generally physicians) who oversee the administration of the experimental compound—to permit an assessment as to whether they are qualified to fulfill their clinical trial duties.

Federal regulations are clear regarding the IND's purpose and the FDA's role in the application's review. As stated in 21 CFR 312.22, "FDA's primary objectives in reviewing an IND are, in all phases of the investigation, to assure the safety and rights of subjects, and, in Phase 2 and 3, to help assure that the quality of scientific evaluation of drugs is adequate to permit an evaluation of the drug's effectiveness and safety."

Unlike NDAs, INDs are never approved by the FDA. Rather, sponsors are permitted to initiate the clinical trials proposed in an IND 30 days after the FDA receives the application, provided that the agency does not contact the applicant during this 30-day period to alert the company otherwise (see Chapter 4). In all cases, however, sponsors are advised to check with a review division before initiating clinical trials to ensure that the IND was received and reviewed.

Types of INDs

This chapter focuses on submissions that are sometimes called "commercial INDs," which are applications filed principally by companies whose ultimate goal is to obtain marketing approval for new products. An October 2000 CDER guidance document defines commercial IND as "an IND for which a sponsor is usually a corporate entity. Other entities may be designated as commercial if it is clear the sponsor intends the product to be commercialized at a later date." In that same guidance, CDER clarified that IND-related user-fee performance goals (e.g., acting on clinical hold responses) are relevant only to commercial INDs and not other categories of submissions (see discussion below).

There are at least a few types of applications that may be grouped within a second class of filings sometimes referred to as "noncommercial" INDs. Interestingly, the vast majority of INDs are noncommercial research submissions. These include the following types of INDs:

Investigator IND (also called research IND). The investigator IND is submitted by a physician who both initiates and conducts an investigation, and under whose immediate direction the investigational drug is administered or dispensed. In most cases, an investigator IND proposes clinical studies on previously studied drugs. A physician might submit a research IND to propose studying an unapproved drug, or an approved product for a new indication or in a new patient population. Generally, however, the physician's motivation is not commercial in nature—in other words, the goal is not to develop data to support marketing approval for an unapproved product or to support new labeling for an approved product. For example, the investigator may simply want to treat patients or obtain data to publish a research paper. Since the investigator assumes the role and all responsibilities of the sponsor under investigator INDs, the applications are also sometimes called "investigator-sponsor" INDs.

Emergency Use IND. The emergency use IND is a vehicle through which the FDA can authorize the immediate shipment of an experimental drug for a desperate medical situation. According to FDA regulations, "need for an investigational drug may arise in an emergency situation that does not allow time for submission of an IND... In such a case, FDA may authorize shipment of the drug for a specified use in advance of submission of an IND." Emergency use INDs generally are reserved for life-threatening situations in which no standard acceptable treatment is available, and in which there is not sufficient time to obtain institutional review board (IRB) approval. Emergency use INDs are also sometimes called "compassionate use" or "single-patient" INDs. Noting the absence of specific standards for compassionate drug use, FDA officials revealed in mid-2000 that the agency was developing a proposed regulation to outline criteria for a variety of experimental drug access options for patients not enrolled in formal clinical trials. In its June 2004 regulatory agenda, the FDA confirmed that it still plans to release such a proposed regulation, which would be entitled, *Treatment Use of Investigational Drugs* and which would allow the treatment use of investigational drugs in individual patients (including in emergencies), intermediate size patient populations, and larger populations under a treatment protocol or IND (see discussion below).

Treatment IND. Although the treatment IND has a history dating back to the 1960s and 1970s, the FDA took steps to formalize the treatment IND concept in a 1987 regulation. Through the FDA's treatment IND program, experimental drugs showing promise in clinical testing for serious or life-threatening conditions are made widely available while the final clinical work is performed and the FDA review takes place (see Chapter 15). The FDA Modernization Act of 1997 codified the treatment IND concept as well as other expanded use programs (e.g., emergency use) into law, and encouraged the FDA to consider changes that might reduce industry reluctance to participate in expanded drug access programs.

Screening INDs A subcategory of commercial IND submissions, called "screening INDs," gained considerable attention several years ago and seemed destined to once again as part of the FDA's Critical Path Initiative (see Chapter 1). After years seemingly on the fringe of regulatory legitimacy, screening INDs were the subject of a May 2001 Manual of Policies and Procedures document (MaPP 6030.4). In this MaPP, CDER established that a sponsor could, through a screening IND, seek FDA permission to test several closely related chemical entities in initial clinical trials. "In general, CDER policy has been to encourage separate INDs for different molecules and dosage forms," the MaPP notes. "However, in the early phase of drug development, before the developmental path is clear, exploratory studies may be conducted on a number of closely related drugs to choose the preferred compound or formulation. These studies may be best and most efficiently conducted under a single IND.

"Screening INDs are appropriate when single-dose or short-term, repeat-dose clinical trials (≤ 3 days of dosing) are proposed using multiple, closely related compounds. The compounds include different salts or esters and active moieties that are slightly different chemically, but appear to be similar in pharmacodynamic properties. The proposed studies could be a single trial with multiple compounds or similar trials involving only one compound (e.g., several PK studies, one for each compound). The number of compounds tested should usually be ≤ 5. Normally, the intent of the study is to compare the properties of the closely related active moieties to screen for further development." After the early exploratory studies (e.g., Phase 1 tolerance, PK/PD, early pilot efficacy studies) conducted under the screening IND are complete, the application should be withdrawn, MaPP 6030.4 states. When the sponsor plans to conduct further studies for one or more of the moieties or when additional, closely related chemical moieties are to be studied in clinical trials, the sponsor should submit an entirely new IND.

In mid-2004, CDER officials revealed that the agency planned to implement a formal guidance for screening INDs (ScIND) as part of the agency's commitment to improving the "critical path" for medical product development. During a September 2004 speech, Acting FDA Commissioner Lester Crawford, Ph.D., said the anticipated guidance would outline "ways to perform early proof-of-mechanism, screening, and microdose human studies in a safe, efficient manner." A month later, he stated that the guidance's "goal is to facilitate early, small-scale proof-of-concept studies before a drug reaches IND stage."

While it was unclear at this writing whether the ScIND guidance would establish one or multiple routes for exploratory clinical studies, FDA officials indicated that it would, unlike MaPP 6030.4, explicitly state that firms can initiate such studies with less preclinical safety data. In a July 2004 speech touting the new ScIND concept as an opportunity to study pharmacokinetics and target interaction early in drug development, one senior CDER official noted that "the amount of preclinical safety data for ScINDs will generally be less than for conventional INDs. The reduction in safety data requirements will be scaled to the goals, duration and scope of the proposed clinical trials."

In developing the ScIND concept, CDER studied a number of different models, including the European Medicines Evaluation Agency's (EMEA) proposed "microdose IND" concept (January 2003), the Pharmaceutical Research and Manufacturers of America's proposed "exploratory IND" model (May 2004), and the National Cancer Institute's "facilitated IND" proposal.

The Applicability of the IND

The IND is a requirement for all persons and firms seeking to ship unapproved drugs over state lines for use in clinical investigations. For certain types of clinical testing and products, however, the FDA offers exemptions from IND submission requirements:

- Clinical investigations of a drug product that is lawfully marketed in the United States, provided that all of the following conditions apply: (1) the investigation is not intended to be reported to the FDA as a well-controlled study in support of a new indication for use, or is not intended to be used to support any other significant change in the drug's labeling; (2) the investigation is not intended to support a significant change in the advertising for a prescription drug; (3) the investigation does not involve a change in the route of administration, dosage level, patient population, or other factor that significantly increases the risks (or decreases the acceptability of the risks) associated with the use of the drug product; (4) the investigation complies with institutional review board (IRB) evaluation and informed consent requirements; and (5) the study's sponsor and investigator do not represent in a promotional context that the drug is safe or effective for the purposes for which it is under investigation, or unduly prolong the study after finding that the results are sufficient to support a marketing application. The FDA has stated that this exemption is intended primarily for practicing physicians.

- Drugs intended solely for testing *in vitro* or in laboratory research animals, provided the drug labels and shipments comply with FDA regulations applicable to investigational drugs.

- Clinical investigations involving the use of a placebo, provided that the investigations do not involve the use of a new drug or otherwise trigger IND submission requirements.

- Certain *in vivo* bioavailability and bioequivalence studies in humans. FDA regulations state, however, that INDs are required for *in vivo* bioavailability or bioequivalence studies in humans if the test product is a radioactively labeled drug product, is a cytotoxic drug product, or contains a new chemical entity. Further, INDs are required for the following types of human bioavailability studies that involve a previously approved drug that is not a new chemical entity: (1) a single-dose study in normal subjects or patients when either the maximum single or total daily dose exceeds that specified in the labeling of the approved product; (2) a multiple-dose study in normal subjects or patients when either the single or total daily dose exceeds that specified in the labeling of the approved product; or (3) a multiple-dose study on a controlled-release product for which no single-dose study has been completed.

In part an effort to reduce the number of unnecessary IND submissions, particularly investigator INDs (see discussion above), the FDA released a September 2003 final guidance (subsequently revised slightly in February 2004) entitled, IND *Exemptions for Studies of Lawfully Marketed Drug or Biologic Products for the Treatment of Cancer*. Under the guidance, whose principles are thought to apply to INDs in other therapeutic categories as well, planned studies "may be considered exempt from the requirements of an IND if the studies involve a new use, dosage, schedule, route of administration or new combination of marketed cancer products in a patient population with cancer and the following conditions apply: the studies are not intended to support FDA approval of a new indication or a significant change in the product labeling; the studies are not intended to support a significant change in the advertising for the product; investigators and their IRBs determine that based on the scientific literature and generally known clinical experience, there is not a significant increase in the risk associated with the use of the drug product; the studies are to be conducted in compliance with IRB and informed consent regulations...; and the studies will not be used to promote unapproved indications...."

In addition to the IND exemptions mentioned above, FDA regulations provide a mechanism through which individuals and firms can seek an agency waiver from IND requirements. The agency can grant a waiver if certain criteria are met, including that the sponsor's noncompliance will not pose a significant or unreasonable risk to human subjects.

IND Content and Format Requirements

Until the late 1980s, the FDA had less-than-exacting content and format requirements for INDs. A 1987 revision to federal regulations—originally called the "IND Rewrite"—changed this, however, as the FDA sought better organized and more standardized INDs to help expedite reviews.

Another substantive change to IND content requirements came in November 1995, when the FDA clarified its IND data and data presentation requirements in a guidance entitled, *Content and Format of Investigational New Drug Applications* (IND) *for Phase 1 Studies of Drugs, Including Well-Characterized, Therapeutic, Biotechnology-Derived Products*. Although the FDA characterized the guidance as a "clarification," it really represented a shift in policy, particularly in establishing that the agency would accept toxicology data summaries and line listings based upon sponsors' unaudited draft toxicologic reports of completed animal studies. If industry followed the reduced data requirements outlined in the November 1995 guidance, the FDA claimed that "IND submissions for Phase 1 studies should usually not be larger than two to three, three inch, 3-ring binders." This shift was prompted largely by growing concerns that early-stage clinical research projects were moving to other countries, particularly European countries, which often had less-demanding regulatory requirements for initial clinical trials.

In the FDA Modernization Act of 1997, Congress also moved to codify and extend such "clarifications" by adding to the Food, Drug and Cosmetic Act specific language regarding IND submission requirements. The reform legislation states that the IND submission should include: (1) "information on [the] design of the [proposed clinical] investigation and adequate reports of basic information, certified by the applicant to be accurate reports, necessary to assess the safety of the drug for use in clinical investigation;" and (2) "adequate information on the chemistry and manufacturing of the drug, controls available for the drug, and primary data tabulations from animal or human studies."

In the coming years, several regulatory initiatives and scientific advances will drive the continuing evolution of the IND, at least with respect to its content and format:

The ICH's Common Technical Document (CTD) *Initiative*. Although the marketing application (NDA) was the initial focus of the ICH and FDA's CTD initiative (see Chapter 7), the agency has quickly extended the CTD principles and format to other applications, including the IND. In their most recent calls for electronic INDs (see discussion below), for example, CDER officials are encouraging companies to provide these applications in the CTD format. Further, in some of its most recent IND-related guidances—INDs *for Phases 2 and 3 Studies of Drugs, Including Specified Therapeutic Biotechnology-Derived Products: Chemistry, Manufacturing, and Controls Content and Format* (May 2003), for example—CDER is advocating that the content of the IND be presented in the CTD format.

Submission of eINDs. As it is doing for the NDA, the FDA is moving the IND and other applications inexorably toward the electronic submission age. During 2003, in fact, the agency added the IND to the growing list of regulatory submissions that it can accept completely in electronic format (i.e., without an accompanying paper-based version). In an August 2003 draft industry guidance entitled, *Providing Regulatory Submissions in Electronic Format-Human Pharmaceutical Product Applications and Related Submissions,* CDER provided industry with guidance on providing INDs and other applications in the harmonized electronic common technical document (eCTD) format. CDER used the draft guidance to establish its clear interest in promoting electronic submissions, including eINDs, in the eCTD format as early as possible in the development process. "We believe it is most beneficial to begin your eCTD-based submissions with the initial submission of an application," the agency stated. "The maximum benefit will be derived once an application is in electronic format. This is particularly true for the IND, where submissions are provided over a long period of time. You should submit the electronic document information for all documents in the eCTD backbone files following the ICH eCTD specifications and the Comprehensive Table of Contents Headings and Hierarchy" (the comprehensive table of contents and hierarchy is derived from the ICH eCTD specifications as well as the specifications for the CTD's Module 1-U.S. region-specific and administrative information). By mid-2004, CDER officials reported that the center was no longer accepting eINDs in any format other than the eCTD format. While industry's interest in developing such submissions was limited at this writing, CDER officials believe submission rates will increase as they develop new electronic tools. Meanwhile, eINDs are receiving attention under separate initiatives as well: Under a November 2003 NCI/FDA initiative regarding oncology product development, the agencies were working together "to build tools that facilitate electronic interaction, focusing in particular on IND applications."

Pharmacogenomics. Like other elements of the drug development and approval process, the IND will be affected by important scientific advances. In a November 2003 draft guidance, for instance, the agency took its first step in encouraging industry to submit pharmacogenomics information in INDs and other applications to help FDA reviewers and scientists understand the relevant scientific issues in this emerging field (see discussion below). While the FDA planned to release a final guidance in late 2004, agency officials claimed that the agency was actively reviewing and acting on pharmacogenomics data voluntarily submitted by applicants.

Risk Minimization Action Plans. As the result of the FDA's focus on risk management under PDUFA III, certain INDs are likely to feature what are called "risk minimization action plans," or RiskMAPs. In a May 2004 draft industry guidance entitled, *Development and Use of Risk Minimization Action Plans,* the FDA notes that, while routine risk minimization measures (e.g., FDA-approved professional labeling) will be sufficient for most products, "for a small number of products where a [RiskMAP] should be considered...sponsors are encouraged to consider developing a RiskMAP," which the agency defines as "a strategic safety program designed to meet specific goals and objectives in minimizing known risks of a product while preserving its benefits." In the draft guidance, the agency notes that a company can submit a RiskMAP before or after approval, and that the plan should be submitted in either the IND or NDA if it is filed in advance of marketing clearance (see Chapter 7 for a more in-depth discussion on RiskMAPs).

CDER Move to New Risk-Based Pharmaceutical Quality Assessment System. Although it will have more direct implications for the development and FDA review of chemistry sections of NDAs, the FDA's shift to a new "modern, risk-based pharmaceutical quality assessment system" will impact the IND review process (see Chapters 4 and 8). As CDER redefines its expectations for the chemistry section of the NDAs under this new system, which is scheduled for implementation in mid-2005, it is conceivable that the center will seek similar changes in IND submissions in the future.

According to the current IND application form (Form FDA 1571), an IND will consist of as many as 10 principal sections:

1. Cover Sheet (Form FDA 1571).

2. Table of Contents.

3. Introductory Statement.

4. General Investigational Plan.

5. Investigator's Brochure (IB).

6. Clinical Protocols.

7. Chemistry, Manufacturing, and Control Data.

8. Pharmacology and Toxicology Data.

9. Previous Human Experience (if applicable).

10. Additional Information, including plans for pediatric studies.

The nature of the drug and the available product-related information affect the number of sections included in an IND submission. These and other factors also determine the quantity of information to be included in the application. "Sponsors are expected to exercise considerable discretion...regarding the content of information submitted in each section [of the IND], depending upon the kind of drug being studied and the nature of the available information," FDA regulations state. "The amount of information on a particular drug that must be submitted in an IND depends upon such factors as the novelty of the drug, the extent to which it has been studied previously, the known or suspected risks, and the developmental phase of the drug."

Concurrently with an IND filing (or at any later time), a sponsor can request a "fast track" designation for its drug, provided the therapy addresses unmet medical needs related to a serious and life-threatening condition. This "fast track" designation, which was created under the FDA Modernization Act of 1997, makes a product eligible for accelerated approval and other benefits (see Chapter 15).

The following sections discuss the content requirements for each component of the IND. Although not included in the listing of IND content requirements above, many INDs include a cover letter that briefly summarizes the purpose and content of the submission. By providing a general introduction to the submission and identifying any previously reached sponsor/FDA agreements, cover letters are often extremely useful to drug reviewers.

Cover Sheet (Form FDA 1571) Form FDA 1571, the first required element of an IND, serves as the cover sheet for the entire IND submission (see sample form below). By completing and signing, or having an authorized representative complete and sign, this form, the sponsor: (1) identifies itself, the investigational drug, the persons responsible for monitoring the clinical trial and safety-related trial information, and the phase(s) of investigation covered by the application; (2) establishes the nature of the submission (i.e., initial submission, amendment, etc.); (3) identifies any responsibilities that have been transferred to a contract research organization (CRO); and (4) agrees to comply with applicable regulations, including those requiring the sponsor to refrain from initiating clinical studies until an IND covering the investigations is in effect. A completed copy of Form FDA 1571 is also required with each amendment submitted to the IND.

If the person signing the IND form does not reside or maintain a place of business within the United States, "the IND is required to contain the name and address of, and be countersigned by, an attorney, agent, or other authorized official who resides or maintains a place of business within the United States."

Item 12 of Form 1571—Contents of Application—is important because it identifies the various elements that must be addressed in an original IND submission. These elements are discussed below.

Table of Contents FDA regulations offer no guidance on the IND's table of contents. The agency does state, however, that sponsors should follow the specified IND format "in the interest of fostering an efficient review of the application." Obviously, the table of contents should be sufficiently detailed to permit FDA reviewers to locate important elements of the application quickly and easily. The table of contents should provide the location of items by volume and page number.

Introductory Statement The IND's introductory statement should provide a description of the drug, the goals of the proposed clinical investigations, and a summary of the previous human experience with the drug. According to FDA regulations, this section should provide "a brief introductory statement giving the name of the drug and all active ingredients, the drug's pharmacological class, the structural formula of the drug (if known), the formulation of the dosage form(s) to be used, the route of administration, and the broad objectives and planned duration of the proposed clinical investigation(s)." The sponsor must also summarize all previous clinical experience with the drug (with reference to other INDs, if applicable), including "investigational or marketing experience in other countries that may be relevant to the safety of the proposed clinical investigation(s)." If a foreign regulatory authority discontinued the drug's testing or marketing for any reason related to safety or effectiveness, the sponsor must identify the country(ies) in which the withdrawal took place and must describe the reason for the withdrawal.

General Investigational Plan The general investigational plan must provide a brief description of the clinical studies planned for the experimental drug. At a minimum, studies planned for the first year should be described. The FDA has stated that the goal of this section is to provide agency reviewers a brief overview of the scale and nature of clinical studies to be conducted during the following year. This general overview should be no more than two to three pages in length, and should provide the necessary context for FDA reviewers to assess the adequacy of technical information to support future studies and to provide advice and assistance to the sponsor.

According to federal regulations, the "plan should include the following: (a) the rationale for the drug or the research study; (b) the indication(s) to be studied; (c) the general approach to be followed in evaluating the drug; (d) the kinds of clinical trials to be conducted in the first year following the submission (if plans are not developed for the entire year, the sponsor should so indicate); (e) the estimated number of patients to be given the drug in those studies; and (f) any risks of particular severity or seriousness anticipated on the basis of the toxicological data in animals or prior studies in humans with the drug or related drugs."

The FDA does not require rigid adherence to the general investigational plan. Provided that it fulfills protocol and information amendment reporting requirements (see discussion below), a sponsor is free to deviate from the plan when necessary.

Investigator's Brochure With the exception of investigator-sponsored applications, all INDs must include a copy of the investigator's brochure (IB)—an information package providing each participating clinical investigator with available information on the drug, including its known and possible risks and benefits. The most recent discussion of the purpose of, and content requirements applicable to, an IB appear in an addendum to the ICH's final guideline entitled, *Good Clinical Practice: Consolidated Guideline*, which the FDA released in May 1997:

DEPARTMENT OF HEALTH AND HUMAN SERVICES PUBLIC HEALTH SERVICE FOOD AND DRUG ADMINISTRATION **INVESTIGATIONAL NEW DRUG APPLICATION (IND)** **(TITLE 21, CODE OF FEDERAL REGULATIONS (CFR) PART 312)**	Form Approved: OMB No. 0910-0014. Expiration Date: January 31, 2006 See OMB Statement on Reverse. NOTE: No drug may be shipped or clinical investigation begun until an IND for that investigation is in effect (21 CFR 312.40).

1. NAME OF SPONSOR	2. DATE OF SUBMISSION
3. ADDRESS *(Number, Street, City, State and Zip Code)*	4. TELEPHONE NUMBER *(Include Area Code)*
5. NAME(S) OF DRUG *(Include all available names: Trade, Generic, Chemical, Code)*	6. IND NUMBER *(If previously assigned)*

7. INDICATION(S) *(Covered by this submission)*

8. PHASE(S) OF CLINICAL INVESTIGATION TO BE CONDUCTED. ☐ PHASE 1 ☐ PHASE 2 ☐ PHASE 3 ☐ OTHER _____ (Specify)

9. LIST NUMBERS OF ALL INVESTIGATIONAL NEW DRUG APPLICATIONS *(21 CFR Part 312)*, NEW DRUG OR ANTIBIOTIC APPLICATIONS *(21 CFR Part 314)*, DRUG MASTER FILES *(21 CFR 314.420)*, AND PRODUCT LICENSE APPLICATIONS *(21 CFR Part 601)* REFERRED TO IN THIS APPLICATION.

10. IND submission should be consecutively numbered. The initial IND should be numbered "Serial Number: 0000." The next submission (e.g., amendment, report, or correspondence) should be numbered "Serial Number: 0001." Subsequent submissions should be numbered consecutively in the order in which they are submitted.	SERIAL NUMBER: ___ ___ ___

11. THIS SUBMISSION CONTAINS THE FOLLOWING: (Check all that apply)

☐ INITIAL INVESTIGATIONAL NEW DRUG APPLICATION (IND)   ☐ RESPONSE TO CLINICAL HOLD

PROTOCOL AMENDMENT(S):   INFORMATION AMENDMENT(S):   IND SAFETY REPORT(S):
☐ NEW PROTOCOL   ☐ CHEMISTRY/MICROBIOLOGY   ☐ INITIAL WRITTEN REPORT
☐ CHANGE IN PROTOCOL   ☐ PHARMACOLOGY/TOXICOLOGY   ☐ FOLLOW-UP TO A WRITTEN REPORT
☐ NEW INVESTIGATOR   ☐ CLINICAL

☐ RESPONSE TO FDA REQUEST FOR INFORMATION   ☐ ANNUAL REPORT   ☐ GENERAL CORRESPONDENCE

☐ REQUEST FOR REINSTATEMENT OF IND THAT IS WITHDRAWN, INACTIVATED, TERMINATED OR DISCONTINUED   ☐ OTHER _____ (Specify)

CHECK ONLY IF APPLICABLE

JUSTIFICATION STATEMENT MUST BE SUBMITTED WITH APPLICATION FOR ANY CHECKED BELOW. REFER TO THE CITED CFR SECTION FOR FURTHER INFORMATION.

☐ TREATMENT IND 21 CFR 312.35(b)   ☐ TREATMENT PROTOCOL 21 CFR 312.35(a)   ☐ CHARGE REQUEST/NOTIFICATION 21 CFR 312.7(d)

FOR FDA USE ONLY		
CDR/DBIND/DGD RECEIPT STAMP	DDR RECEIPT STAMP	DIVISION ASSIGNMENT:
		IND NUMBER ASSIGNED:

FORM FDA 1571 (1/03)   PREVIOUS EDITION IS OBSOLETE

<table>
</table>

12.	**CONTENTS OF APPLICATION**

CONTENTS OF APPLICATION

This application contains the following items: *(check all that apply)*

- ☐ 1. Form FDA 1571 [21 CFR 312.23 (a) (1)]
- ☐ 2. Table of contents [21 CFR 312.23 (a) (2)]
- ☐ 3. Introductory statement [21 CFR 312.23 (a) (3)]
- ☐ 4. General investigational plan [21 CFR 312.23 (a) (3)]
- ☐ 5. Investigator's brochure [21 CFR 312.23 (a) (5)]
- ☐ 6. Protocol(s) [21 CFR 312.23 (a) (6)]
  - ☐ a. Study protocol(s) [21 CFR 312.23 (a) (6)]
  - ☐ b. Investigator data [21 CFR 312.23 (a) (6)(iii)(b)] or completed Form(s) FDA 1572
  - ☐ c. Facilities data [21 CFR 312.23 (a) (6)(iii)(b)] or completed Form(s) FDA 1572
  - ☐ d. Institutional Review Board data [21 CFR 312.23 (a) (6)(iii)(b)] or completed Form(s) FDA 1572
- ☐ 7. Chemistry, manufacturing, and control data [21 CFR 312.23 (a) (7)]
  - ☐ Environmental assessment or claim for exclusion [21 CFR 312.23 (a) (7)(iv)(e)]
- ☐ 8. Pharmacology and toxicology data [21 CFR 312.23 (a) (8)]
- ☐ 9. Previous human experience [21 CFR 312.23 (a) (9)]
- ☐ 10. Additional information [21 CFR 312.23 (a) (10)]

13. IS ANY PART OF THE CLINICAL STUDY TO BE CONDUCTED BY A CONTRACT RESEARCH ORGANIZATION? ☐ YES ☐ NO

IF YES, WILL ANY SPONSOR OBLIGATIONS BE TRANSFERRED TO THE CONTRACT RESEARCH ORGANIZATION? ☐ YES ☐ NO

IF YES, ATTACH A STATEMENT CONTAINING THE NAME AND ADDRESS OF THE CONTRACT RESEARCH ORGANIZATION, IDENTIFICATION OF THE CLINICAL STUDY, AND A LISTING OF THE OBLIGATIONS TRANSFERRED.

14. NAME AND TITLE OF THE PERSON RESPONSIBLE FOR MONITORING THE CONDUCT AND PROGRESS OF THE CLINICAL INVESTIGATIONS

15. NAME(S) AND TITLE(S) OF THE PERSON(S) RESPONSIBLE FOR REVIEW AND EVALUATION OF INFORMATION RELEVANT TO THE SAFETY OF THE DRUG

I agree not to begin clinical investigations until 30 days after FDA's receipt of the IND unless I receive earlier notification by FDA that the studies may begin. I also agree not to begin or continue clinical investigations covered by the IND if those studies are placed on clinical hold. I agree that an Institutional Review Board (IRB) that complies with the requirements set forth in 21 CFR Part 56 will be responsible for initial and continuing review and approval of each of the studies in the proposed clinical investigation. I agree to conduct the investigation in accordance with all other applicable regulatory requirements.

16. NAME OF SPONSOR OR SPONSOR'S AUTHORIZED REPRESENTATIVE

17. SIGNATURE OF SPONSOR OR SPONSOR'S AUTHORIZED REPRESENTATIVE

18. ADDRESS (Number, Street, City, State and Zip Code)

19. TELEPHONE NUMBER (Include Area Code)

20. DATE

(**WARNING**:A willfully false statement is a criminal offense. U.S.C. Title 18, Sec. 1001.)

Public reporting burden for this collection of information is estimated to average 100 hours per response, including the time for reviewing instructions, searching existing data sources, gathering and maintaining the data needed, and completing and reviewing the collection of information. Send comments regarding this burden estimate or any other aspect of this collection of information, including suggestions for reducing this burden to:

Food and Drug Administration
CBER (HFM-99)
1401 Rockville Pike
Rockville, MD 20852-1448

Food and Drug Administration
CDER (HFD-94)
12229 Wilkins Avenue
Rockville, MD 20852

"An agency may not conduct or sponsor, and a person is not required to respond to, a collection of information unless it displays a currently valid OMB control number."

Please DO NOT RETURN this application to this address.

FORM FDA 1571 (1/03)

"The Investigator's Brochure (IB) is a compilation of the clinical and nonclinical data on the investigational product(s) that are relevant to the study of the product(s) in human subjects," the guidance states. "Its purpose is to provide the investigators and others involved in the trial with the information to facilitate their understanding of the rationale for, and their compliance with, many key features of the protocol, such as the dose, dose frequency/interval, methods of administration, and safety monitoring procedures. The IB also provides insight to support the clinical management of the study subjects during the course of the clinical trial. The information should be presented in a concise, simple, objective, balanced, and nonpromotional form that enables a clinician, or potential investigator, to understand it and make his/her own unbiased risk-benefit assessment of the appropriateness of the proposed trial. For this reason, a medically qualified person should generally participate in the editing of an IB, but the contents of the IB should be approved by the disciplines that generated the described data." The ICH consolidated guidance also offers an example of an IB format.

While not as detailed as the ICH guideline's description of investigator's brochure content requirements, FDA regulations call for IBs to include the following principal elements:

- a brief description of the drug substance and formulation, including the structural formula (if known);

- a summary of the pharmacological and toxicological effects of the drug in animals and, to the extent known, in humans;

- a summary of the pharmacokinetics and biological disposition of the drug in animals and, if known, in humans;

- a summary of information relating to the drug's safety and effectiveness in humans obtained from prior clinical studies (reprints of published articles on such studies may be appended when useful); and

- a description of possible risks and side effects anticipated on the basis of prior experience with the drug under investigation or with related drugs, and precautions to be taken or special monitoring to be performed as part of the drug's investigational use.

As clinical trials advance, the sponsor must inform investigators "of new observations discovered by or reported to the sponsor of the drug, particularly with respect to adverse effects and safe use." Such information may be distributed to investigators by means of periodically revised IBs, reprints of published studies, reports or letters to clinical investigators, or other appropriate means. Copies of these communications should also be submitted to the IND file. According to the ICH's May 1997 consolidated GCP guideline, the IB should be reviewed at least annually and be revised as necessary in compliance with a sponsor's written procedures.

Clinical Protocols FDA regulations state that, along with the general investigational plan, clinical protocols are "the central focus of the initial IND submission." Protocols are descriptions of clinical studies that identify, among other things, a study's objectives, design, and procedures. The FDA reviews clinical protocols to ensure: (1) that subjects will not be exposed to unnecessary risks in any of the clinical trials; and (2) that Phase 2 and Phase 3 clinical study designs are adequate to provide the types and amount of information necessary to show that the drug is safe and/or effective.

In the initial IND submission, the sponsor must provide only protocols for the proposed study or studies that will begin immediately after the IND goes into effect—that is, after the FDA's 30-day review period. Although initial INDs generally include just Phase 1 protocols, some may propose Phase 2 or 3 protocols, particularly if a drug has been studied in clinical trials previously (e.g., in foreign clinical studies).

As stated, the safety of initial Phase 1 studies is the FDA's principal concern in reviewing the original IND submission. Since late-phase clinical studies often are not fully developed until data from Phase 1 studies are obtained, Phase 2 and Phase 3 protocols may be submitted later in the development process (see discussion of protocol amendments below).

In its November 1995 IND guidance document, the FDA highlighted the regulations' more flexible approach to Phase 1 protocols. "Sponsors are reminded that the regulations were changed in 1987 specifically to allow Phase 1 study protocols to be less detailed and more flexible than protocols for Phase 2 and 3 studies. This change recognized that these protocols are part of an early learning process and should be adaptable as information is obtained, and that the principal concern at this stage of development is that the study be conducted safely. The regulations state that Phase 1 protocols should be directed primarily at providing an outline of the investigation: an estimate of the number of subjects to be included; a description of safety exclusions, and a description of the dosing plan, including duration, dose, or method to be used in determining dose. In addition, such protocols should specify in detail only those elements of the study that are critical to subject safety, such as: 1) necessary monitoring of vital signs and blood chemistries and 2) toxicity-based stopping or dose adjustment rules. In addition, the regulations state that modifications of the experimental design of Phase 1 studies that do not affect critical safety assessments are required to be reported to FDA only in the annual report."

In contrast, the FDA requires that Phase 2 and 3 protocols include detailed descriptions of all aspects of the studies. Federal regulations state that these protocols "should be designed in such a way that, if the sponsor anticipates that some deviation from the study design may become necessary as the investigation progresses, alternatives or contingencies to provide for such deviations are built into the protocols at the outset. For example, a protocol for a controlled short-term study might include a plan for an early crossover of nonresponders to an alternative therapy." About such contingency plans, which are optional, the FDA has commented that it "strongly encourages the submission of such plans as it believes there is much to be gained in thinking about the planning for possible alternative courses of action early in the protocol development process. Providing in the initial protocol for possible departures from the study design enhances the value or reviewability of study results. Such advance planning also permits both FDA and the sponsor to raise useful questions about study design and supporting information at the earliest possible time."

Agency reviewers report that the language used in the November 1995 guidance and, perhaps to an even greater extent, FDAMA had, for a time, given some firms the false impression that summary-type protocols were permitted in INDs. Although protocol summaries may be appropriate in some cases and when authorized by a review division, CDER reviewers were frustrated by the number of summary-type protocols that were submitted in INDs following FDAMA's passage.

Although the components and level of detail found in a protocol will depend upon the phase covered and other factors, FDA regulations state that a protocol should include seven elements:

1. A statement of the objectives and purpose of the study.

2. The name and address of, and a statement of qualifications (curriculum vitae or other statement of qualifications) for, each investigator; the name of each subinvestigator (i.e., research fellow, resident) working under the supervision of the investigator; the names and addresses of the research facilities to be used; and the name and address of each institutional review board (IRB) responsible for reviewing the protocols. To provide the FDA with necessary information on clinical investigators, many companies simply forward a copy of the

Form FDA 1572-Statement of Investigator forms that the investigators provided to the sponsor (see sample form below). The submission of the 1572 to the FDA is not a requirement, however, and IND sponsors can opt to provide the necessary investigator-related information in other formats.

To address some of the complexities of providing information on foreign investigators, CDER officials noted several years ago that the agency was developing a new guidance entitled, *Submission to an IND of Investigator Information for Non-U.S. Studies*, which has not yet been released. In 2004, FDA officials revealed that the agency was developing a proposed regulation under which it would establish specific good clinical practice requirements for non-U.S. clinical trials and under which it would be seeking from sponsors more information on how foreign investigators are trained (see Chapter 6).

3. The criteria for patient selection and exclusion, and an estimate of the number of patients to be studied. Sponsors should be aware of a June 2000 regulation that allows the FDA to place certain studies under an IND on clinical hold when the agency determines that a sponsor has categorically excluded otherwise eligible men or women with reproductive potential from participating in a study of a drug for a life-threatening disease or condition that affects both genders (see Chapter 4).

4. A description of the study design, including the type of control group to be used, if any, and a description of the methods to be used to minimize bias on the part of subjects, investigators, and analysts.

5. The method for determining the dose(s) to be administered, the planned maximum dosage, and the duration of individual patient exposure to the drug.

6. A description of the observations and measurements to be made to fulfill the objectives of the study.

7. A description of clinical procedures, laboratory tests, or other means to be employed in monitoring the effects of the drug in human subjects and in minimizing risk.

The ICH's May 1997 consolidated GCP guideline also features a discussion of standards for the content of clinical protocols and protocol amendments. According to the ICH's GCP guideline, a trial protocol should "generally include the following topics":

General Information: the protocol's title and identifying number, the sponsor and monitor's name and address, the name and title of the investigator responsible for conducting the trial, and the name and address of the person authorized to sign the protocol and any protocol amendments for the sponsor.

Background Information: the name and a description of the investigational product, a summary of findings from nonclinical studies, a summary of known and potential risks and benefits to human subjects, and a description of the population to be studied.

Trial Objectives and Purpose: a detailed description of the trial's purpose and objectives.

Trial Design: a statement of the primary and secondary endpoints (if any) to be measured during the trial, a description of the type/design of the proposed trial (e.g., blinding, controls) and a schematic diagram of trial design, procedures, and stages.

Selection and Withdrawal of Subjects: subject inclusion and exclusion criteria and subject withdrawal criteria and procedures.

<table>
<tr>
<td colspan="2">

DEPARTMENT OF HEALTH AND HUMAN SERVICES
PUBLIC HEALTH SERVICE
FOOD AND DRUG ADMINISTRATION
STATEMENT OF INVESTIGATOR
(TITLE 21, CODE OF FEDERAL REGULATIONS (CFR) PART 312)
(See instructions on reverse side.)

</td>
<td>

Form Approved: OMB No. 0910-0014
Expiration Date: January 31, 2006
See OMB Statement on Reverse.

NOTE: No investigator may participate in an investigation until he/she provides the sponsor with a completed, signed Statement of Investigator, Form FDA 1572 (21CFR 312.53(c)).

</td>
</tr>
</table>

1. NAME AND ADDRESS OF INVESTIGATOR

2. EDUCATION, TRAINING, AND EXPERIENCE THAT QUALIFIES THE INVESTIGATOR AS AN EXPERT IN THE CLINICAL INVESTIGATION OF THE DRUG FOR THE USE UNDER INVESTIGATION. ONE OF THE FOLLOWING IS ATTACHED:

☐ CURRICULUM VITAE   ☐ OTHER STATEMENT OF QUALIFICATIONS

3. NAME AND ADDRESS OF ANY MEDICAL SCHOOL, HOSPITAL, OR OTHER RESEARCH FACILITY WHERE THE CLINICAL INVESTIGATION(S) WILL BE CONDUCTED.

4. NAME AND ADDRESS OF ANY CLINICAL LABORATORY FACILITIES TO BE USED IN THE STUDY.

5. NAME AND ADDRESS OF THE INSTITUTIONAL REVIEW BOARD (IRB) THAT IS RESPONSIBLE FOR REVIEW AND APPROVAL OF THE STUDY(IES).

6. NAMES OF THE SUBINVESTIGATORS (e.g., research fellows, residents, associates) WHO WILL BE ASSISTING THE INVESTIGATOR IN THE CONDUCT OF THE INVESTIGATION(S).

7. NAME AND CODE NUMBER, IF ANY, OF THE PROTOCOL(S) IN THE IND FOR THE STUDY(IES) TO BE CONDUCTED BY THE INVESTIGATOR.

FORM FDA 1572 (1/03)   PREVIOUS EDITION IS OBSOLETE

8. ATTACH THE FOLLOWING CLINICAL PROTOCOL INFORMATION:

☐ FOR PHASE 1 INVESTIGATIONS, A GENERAL OUTLINE OF THE PLANNED INVESTIGATION INCLUDING THE ESTIMATED DURATION OF THE STUDY AND THE MAXIMUM NUMBER OF SUBJECTS THAT WILL BE INVOLVED.

☐ FOR PHASE 2 OR 3 INVESTIGATIONS, AN OUTLINE OF THE STUDY PROTOCOL INCLUDING AN APPROXIMATION OF THE NUMBER OF SUBJECTS TO BE TREATED WITH THE DRUG AND THE NUMBER TO BE EMPLOYED AS CONTROLS, IF ANY; THE CLINICAL USES TO BE INVESTIGATED; CHARACTERISTICS OF SUBJECTS BY AGE, SEX, AND CONDITION; THE KIND OF CLINICAL OBSERVATIONS AND LABORATORY TESTS TO BE CONDUCTED; THE ESTIMATED DURATION OF THE STUDY; AND COPIES OR A DESCRIPTION OF CASE REPORT FORMS TO BE USED.

9. COMMITMENTS:

I agree to conduct the study(ies) in accordance with the relevant, current protocol(s) and will only make changes in a protocol after notifying the sponsor, except when necessary to protect the safety, rights, or welfare of subjects.

I agree to personally conduct or supervise the described investigation(s).

I agree to inform any patients, or any persons used as controls, that the drugs are being used for investigational purposes and I will ensure that the requirements relating to obtaining informed consent in 21 CFR Part 50 and institutional review board (IRB) review and approval in 21 CFR Part 56 are met.

I agree to report to the sponsor adverse experiences that occur in the course of the investigation(s) in accordance with 21 CFR 312.64.

I have read and understand the information in the investigator's brochure, including the potential risks and side effects of the drug.

I agree to ensure that all associates, colleagues, and employees assisting in the conduct of the study(ies) are informed about their obligations in meeting the above commitments.

I agree to maintain adequate and accurate records in accordance with 21 CFR 312.62 and to make those records available for inspection in accordance with 21 CFR 312.68.

I will ensure that an IRB that complies with the requirements of 21 CFR Part 56 will be responsible for the initial and continuing review and approval of the clinical investigation. I also agree to promptly report to the IRB all changes in the research activity and all unanticipated problems involving risks to human subjects or others. Additionally, I will not make any changes in the research without IRB approval, except where necessary to eliminate apparent immediate hazards to human subjects.

I agree to comply with all other requirements regarding the obligations of clinical investigators and all other pertinent requirements in 21 CFR Part 312.

INSTRUCTIONS FOR COMPLETING FORM FDA 1572
STATEMENT OF INVESTIGATOR:

1. Complete all sections. Attach a separate page if additional space is needed.

2. Attach curriculum vitae or other statement of qualifications as described in Section 2.

3. Attach protocol outline as described in Section 8.

4. Sign and date below.

5. FORWARD THE COMPLETED FORM AND ATTACHMENTS TO THE SPONSOR. The sponsor will incorporate this information along with other technical data into an Investigational New Drug Application (IND).

10. SIGNATURE OF INVESTIGATOR	11. DATE

(**WARNING**: A willfully false statement is a criminal offense. U.S.C. Title 18, Sec. 1001.)

Public reporting burden for this collection of information is estimated to average 100 hours per response, including the time for reviewing instructions, searching existing data sources, gathering and maintaining the data needed, and completing reviewing the collection of information. Send comments regarding this burden estimate or any other aspect of this collection of information, including suggestions for reducing this burden to:

Food and Drug Administration	Food and Drug Administration	*An agency may not conduct or sponsor, and a person is not required to
CBER (HFM-99)	CDER (HFD-94)	respond to, a collection of information unless it displays a currently valid
1401 Rockville Pike	12229 Wilkins Avenue	OMB control number.*
Rockville, MD 20852-1448	Rockville, MD 20852	

Please DO NOT RETURN this application to this address.

FORM FDA 1572 (1/03)   PAGE 2 OF 2

Treatment of Subjects: the treatment(s) to be administered, including the name, dose(s), dosing schedules, route/mode of administration, and treatment and follow-up periods, procedures for monitoring patient compliance, and other treatments permitted and not permitted before and/or during the trial.

Assessment of Efficacy: specification of the efficacy parameters, and the methods and timing for assessing, recording, and analyzing these parameters.

Assessment of Safety: specification of the safety parameters, a description of the methods and timing for assessing, recording, and analyzing these parameters, a detailing of the procedures for eliciting reports of and for recording and reporting adverse events and intercurrent illnesses, and a description of the type and duration of subject follow-up following adverse events.

Statistics: a description of the statistical methods to be employed, including the timing of any planned interim analyses, the planned subject enrollment, the level of significance to be used, criteria for trial termination, procedures for accounting for missing, unused, or spurious data, and methods for the selection of subjects to be included in the analyses.

Direct Access to Source Documents: the protocol or other written agreements should specify that the investigators/institutions will permit trial-related monitoring, audits, IRB/IEC review, and regulatory inspections by providing direct access to source data and documents.

Quality Control and Quality Assurance.

Ethics: a description of the ethical considerations relating to the trial.

Data Handling and Recordkeeping.

Financing and Insurance: a description of financial- and insurance-related arrangements if not addressed in a separate agreement.

Publication Policy: a description of the publication policy if not addressed in a separate agreement.

Supplements.

The ICH's GCP guideline notes that sponsors may provide site-specific information on separate protocol pages or address these areas in a "separate agreement," and that some of the information may be contained in other documents (e.g., the investigator's brochure) that are referenced in the protocol.

The Submission of Informed Consent Forms in the IND. Although they are not required to do so under FDA regulations, many IND applicants routinely submit informed consent documents (ICD)—a sample of the documents that clinical study subjects will sign to consent to participate in a trial—in their INDs. Under a November 2002 CDER policy, however, the drug center is likely to be asking more applicants to submit ICDs with their INDs.

The new policy appears to represent an increase in CDER's involvement in consent document reviews, a process that is a formal IRB responsibility under agency regulations. The new policy may be a further outgrowth of the Department of Health and Human Services' (HHS) May 2000 "plan of action," which sought to heighten government oversight of clinical research activities, in part by focusing increasing attention on the informed consent and IRB processes.

"Because the IRB is responsible for reviewing ICDs for all clinical investigations under its jurisdiction, the IND regulations do not require that ICDs be routinely submitted to CDER," the CDER policy document states.

"There are situations in which review of an ICD by CDER in addition to IRB review is particularly important to determine whether a clinical investigation may safely proceed under 21 CFR 312... In these situations, CDER will review the ICD if the sponsor has submitted it as part of their IND submission. If the ICD has not been submitted, CDER will request that the sponsor submit it for review."

While the CDER policy leaves ICD review to the discretion of the review division, the policy emphasizes that, "in most cases, ICDs should be reviewed as part of the review of an IND submission when review of the proposed investigational use raises a particular concern about the adequacy of informed consent. For example, review of an ICD is warranted when:

- Unusual toxicity is associated with the study drug.

- The study population is particularly vulnerable.

- The study design is unusual for the therapeutic class.

- CDER is in a better position than the IRB to assess whether the ICD adequately addresses a particular concern based on proprietary data."

In such cases, drug review divisions are instructed to assess the ICD's adequacy in addressing any safety issues or study design matters, and in providing required elements of informed consent. When a division has specific concerns about whether the ICD meets regulatory requirements, it is advised to forward the ICD, the protocol, and relevant supporting documentation to the Division of Scientific Investigations' Human Subject Protection Team for a consultative review.

Due to concerns regarding vulnerable populations, CDER review of the ICD is "always recommended" for treatment INDs and protocols and when exceptions from informed consent requirements are sought for emergency research. For such situations, CDER review divisions are advised to seek an assessment by the Division of Scientific Investigations as well. Many CDER divisions already have such a policy.

The CDER policy establishes for its review divisions that they have the regulatory authority to request an ICD, which is not identified in the IND regulations or Form FDA-1571 as a submission requirement. Under 21 CFR 312.23(a)(11), an IND sponsor must submit "any other relevant information needed for the review of the application" when requested by the FDA.

While the CDER policy document stops short of recommending that drug review divisions call for the submission of and review ICDs in all cases, it emphasizes that such reviews could be beneficial when the documents are otherwise made available. "If a sponsor has submitted an ICD as part of its IND, but the protocol does not fall under any of the situations [in which ICD review and submission is recommended or warranted], it may still be useful to review the ICD to rule out significant deficiencies," the policy states.

Under the policy, CDER provides its review divisions with a range of regulatory options when issues are identified during the ICD review. Generally, review division or DSI comments on ICD content will be what the agency terms "advisory." "They need not specifically prescribe how the sponsor should address the comments, and the investigation need not be put on hold pending submission of a revised ICD," the center states.

"For multicenter trials with local IRB review of the ICD (i.e., for which the content of the ICD may vary somewhat from site to site), the sponsor should be advised to ensure that the ICD for each center is revised to address CDER comments on safety issues."

But the policy does allow CDER review divisions to use the regulatory hammer—a formal clinical hold action (see Chapter 4)—in specific cases. "In some situations, the review division or DSI may find an ICD to be misleading, inaccurate, or incomplete in a way that raises a significant safety concern for potential study subjects and requires that specified revisions be made to address the concern before a trial can proceed. In such cases the review division may place the IND on clinical hold until an acceptable revision of the ICD is received..., or may discuss specific modifications with the sponsor to avoid a clinical hold."

Chemistry, Manufacturing, and Controls Information The purpose of the IND's chemistry, manufacturing, and control (CMC) section is to establish that the methods used to manufacture and assay the investigational product are adequate to ensure the product's safety. Submission requirements for the IND's CMC section are a function of several factors, including the stage of the clinical trial proposed in the application.

The IND's CMC section was one of two sections affected by the FDA's 1995 IND reform initiative. Specifically, the initiative revised the CMC section in two ways: (1) it suggested that IND sponsors include a new "chemistry and manufacturing introduction;" and (2) it suggested that sponsors provide information on the drug substance and drug product in a pair of "summary reports" (see discussions below).

Based on the FDA's November 1995 guidance document, an IND proposing a Phase 1 clinical study should include CMC information comprising the following six components:

Chemistry and Manufacturing Introduction. In this introduction, "the sponsor should state whether it believes: 1) the chemistry of either the drug substance or the drug product, or 2) the manufacturing of either the drug substance or the drug product, presents any signals of potential human risk. If so, these signals of potential risks should be discussed, and the steps proposed to monitor for such risk(s) should be described, or the reason(s) why the signal(s) should be dismissed should be discussed. In addition, sponsors should describe any chemistry and manufacturing differences between the drug product proposed for clinical use and the drug product used in the animal toxicology trials that formed the basis for the sponsor's conclusion that it was safe to proceed with the proposed clinical study. How these differences might affect the safety profile of the drug product should be discussed. If there are no differences in the products, that should be stated."

Drug Substance. The FDA states that information on the drug substance should be provided in a "summary report" comprising five elements: (1) a description of the drug substance, including its physical, chemical, or biological characteristics, along with some evidence to support its proposed chemical structure; (2) the name and address of its manufacturer; (3) a description of the general method of preparation of the drug substance (ideally presented as a detailed flow diagram), including a list of the reagents, solvents, and catalysts used; (4) a brief description of the acceptable limits and analytical methods used to assure the identity, strength, quality, and purity of the drug substance; and (5) information sufficient to support the stability of the drug substance during toxicologic studies and the proposed clinical studies (neither detailed stability data nor the stability protocol should be submitted). Reference to the current edition of the U.S. Pharmacopeia or National Formulary may satisfy relevant requirements in the drug substance subsection.

In manufacturing and packaging their products, applicants often utilize components (e.g., drug substances, nonstandard excipients, containers) manufactured by other firms, such as contract manufacturers. In such cases, the contract manufacturer is likely to want to preserve the confidentiality of its manufacturing processes. Since an IND must provide information on these processes, contract manufacturers often submit this information to the FDA in a drug master file (DMF). This allows drug sponsors that use the company's products to meet submission requirements by incorporating by reference information provided in the master file.

Because the drug sponsor never sees the information in the DMF, the confidentiality of the contract facility's manufacturing processes is maintained. In the IND (or other submission), an incorporation by reference should be made in the section of the application in which the referenced information would normally appear if provided by the applicant.

Traditionally, there have been five different types of DMFs: Type I DMFs, which provide information on manufacturing sites, facilities, operating procedures, and personnel information; Type II DMFs, which provide information on drug substances or drug products, drug substance intermediates, and materials use in preparing them; Type III DMFs, which include information on packaging materials; Type IV DMFs, which provide information on excipients, colorants, flavors, essences, or materials used in their preparation; and Type V DMFs, which include FDA-accepted reference information. In a January 2000 final rule, however, CDER eliminated Type I DMFs, and instructed industry to use the other types of DMFs to submit the information traditionally provided in Type I DMFs. In 1992, a CDER task force on the DMF system had recommended that the agency eliminate Type I DMFs, in part because the information contained in these DMFs was often outdated and was frequently not easily accessible to FDA inspectors, and because more updated information was maintained onsite by manufacturers, where it was more easily available to agency inspectors.

A more detailed discussion of CDER's requirements for, and use of, DMFs can be found in the center's *Guideline for Drug Master Files* (September 1989).

Drug Product. The FDA suggests that the IND provide information on the drug product in a "summary report" comprising as many as six components: (1) a list—usually no more than one or two pages long—of all components, which may include reasonable alternatives for inactive compounds, used in the manufacture of the investigational drug product, including both those components intended to appear in the drug product and those that may not appear, but that are used in the manufacturing process; (2) where applicable, a brief summary of the quantitative composition of the investigational new drug product, including any reasonable variations that may be expected during the investigational stage; (3) the name and address of the drug product manufacturer; (4) a brief, general description of the method of manufacturing and packaging procedures for the product (ideally presented as flow diagrams); (5) a brief description of the proposed acceptable limits and analytical methods used to ensure the identity, strength, quality, and purity of the drug product; and (6) information sufficient to support the stability of the drug substance during the toxicologic studies and the proposed clinical studies (neither detailed stability data nor the stability protocol should be submitted). Reference to the current edition of the U.S. Pharmacopeia or National Formulary may satisfy certain requirements for this section.

A Brief, General Description of the Composition, Manufacture, and Control of any Placebo Used in the Controlled Clinical Trials. The FDA states that this information should be provided in "diagrammatic, tabular, and brief written" form.

Labeling. The labeling section should comprise "a mock-up or printed representation of the proposed labeling that will be provided to investigator(s) in the proposed clinical trial." Investigational labels must carry a "caution" statement required by federal regulations: "Caution: New Drug-Limited by Federal (or United States) law to investigational use."

Environmental Analysis (EA) Requirements. This section should provide either an environmental assessment, or a claim for a categorical exclusion from the requirement for an environmental assessment. Under a July 1997 final regulation, the FDA established that EAs would be required in INDs (and NDAs) only under "extraordinary circumstances" (e.g., when available data indicate that the expected level of exposure could do serious harm to the environment). Because the use of experimental compounds in clinical trials represents a temporary and low-volume release, however, virtually all INDs traditionally have included only a claim for a categorical exclusion in the past.

To provide further insights regarding the changes brought by the July 1997 regulation, CDER released a final guidance document entitled, *Environmental Assessment of Human Drug and Biologics Applications* (July 1998). This guidance superseded CDER's *Guidance for Industry for the Submission of Environmental Assessments for Human Drug Applications and Supplements* (November 1995).

The FDA emphasizes throughout its regulations and guidelines that the amount and detail of information needed in the IND's CMC section depends on several factors, including the scope and phase of the proposed clinical investigation, the proposed duration of the study, the dosage form, and the quantity of information otherwise available. "Modifications to the method of preparation of the new drug substance and dosage form, and even changes in the dosage form itself, are likely as the investigation progresses," the agency states in its November 1995 IND guidance document. "The emphasis in an initial Phase 1 CMC submission should, therefore, generally be placed on providing information that will allow evaluation of the safety of subjects in the proposed study. The identification of a safety concern or insufficient data to make an evaluation of safety is the only basis for a clinical hold based on the CMC section."

FDA regulations add that "the emphasis in an initial Phase 1 submission should generally be placed on the identification and control of the raw materials and the new drug substance. Final specifications for the drug substance and drug product are not expected until the end of the investigational process." However, when final specifications are not established until just prior to Phase 3 studies, comparability with preceding studies may be necessary. Stability testing should support the duration of use for the proposed clinical studies.

The FDA does require that sponsors comply with Current Good Manufacturing Practices (cGMP) during clinical trials. According to the FDA's *Guideline on the Preparation of Investigational New Drug Products* (Human and Animal) (March 1991), the "FDA recognizes that manufacturing procedures and specifications will change as clinical trials advance. However, as research nears completion, procedures and controls are expected to be more specific because they will have been based upon a growing body of scientific data and documentation.... When drug development reaches a stage where the drugs are produced for clinical trials in humans...then compliance with the CGMP regulations is required. For example, the drug product must be produced in a qualified facility, using laboratory and other equipment that has been qualified, and processes must be validated. There must be written procedures for sanitation, calibration, and maintenance of equipment, and specific instructions for the use of the equipment and procedures used to manufacture the drug. Product contamination and wide variations in potency can produce substantial levels of side effects and toxicity, and even produce wide-sweeping effects on the physiological activity of the drug. Product safety, quality, and uniformity are especially significant in the case of investigational products. Such factors may affect the outcome of a clinical investigation that will, in large part, determine whether or not the product will be approved for wider distribution to the public."

In October 2001, the FDA released a final ICH guidance entitled, Q7A *Good Manufacturing Practice Guide for Active Pharmaceutical Ingredients*, which included a brief section on GMP issues for clinical trial-stage drugs. "The controls used in the manufacture of APIs for use in clinical trials should be consistent with the stage of development of the drug product incorporating the API," the guidance states. "Process and test procedures should be flexible to provide for changes as knowledge of the process increases and clinical testing of a drug product progresses from pre-clinical stages through clinical stages. Once drug development reaches the stage where the API is produced for use in drug products intended for clinical trials, manufacturers should ensure that APIs are manufactured in suitable facilities using appropriate production and control procedures to ensure the quality of the API."

In late 2004, the FDA revealed that it was developing a new draft guidance on the application of cGMP requirements to compounds used in Phase 1 clinical trials. The document, FDA officials claimed, is designed "to ease the progress of new drugs through the early stages of drug development."

As the testing and drug development process advances, sponsors must submit IND information amendments to the CMC section of the IND (see discussion below). Most importantly, the amendments must describe the effects of the transition from pilot scale production used for early clinical studies to the larger-scale production methods used for expanded clinical investigations. In May 2003, CDER released a final guidance entitled, INDs for Phases 2 and 3 Studies of Drugs, Including Specified Therapeutic Biotechnology-Derived Products: Chemistry, Manufacturing, and Controls Content and Format to clarify the difference between "CMC safety information," which should be submitted in information amendments, and "corroborating information," which can be submitted in an annual report. By specifying the chemistry, manufacturing, and controls information that is needed during Phase 2 and 3 clinical trials, the guidance claims that it provides IND sponsors with "regulatory relief" in four specific areas "by providing flexibility in the collecting and reporting of data and by avoiding redundant submissions. Certain information that traditionally has been submitted in information amendments would be identified as corroborating information, [which is less likely to affect the safe use of the drug but should be submitted to ensure the proper identity, strength or potency, quality, and purity of the investigational drug], and can be submitted in an annual report. The limited phase 2 corroborating information recommended...need not be submitted before initiation of phase 2 studies and can be generated during phase 2 drug development. The phase 3 corroborating information recommended...need not be submitted before the initiation of phase 3 studies and can be generated during phase 3 drug development. The corroborating information and a summary of CMC safety information submitted during a subject-reporting period would be included in the annual report. Therefore, there should be no need for general CMC updates at the end of phase 1 or phase 2."

In addition to the documents referenced above, the agency has published several guidelines that provide insights regarding the submission of chemistry, manufacturing, and control information in both INDs and NDAs. These include the following: Guideline for the Format and Content of the Chemistry, Manufacturing, and Controls Section of an Application (February 1987), Guideline for Submitting Documentation for the Manufacture of and Controls for Drug Products (February 1987), Guideline for Submitting Supporting Documentation in Drug Applications for the Manufacture of Drug Substances (February 1987), Guidance for Industry: Container Closure Systems for Packaging Human Drugs and Biologics-Chemistry, Manufacturing, and Controls Documentation (May 1999), Documentation for Packaging for Human Drugs and Biologics (February 1987), Draft Guidance on the Stability Testing of Drug Substances and Drug Products (June 1998), Guideline for Submitting Documentation for the Stability of Human Drugs and Biologics (February 1987), and Guidance for Industry for the Submission of Chemistry, Manufacturing, and Controls for Synthetic Peptide Drug Substances (November 1994).

ICH guidelines, such as the December 2003 revised final guideline entitled, Q1A(R2) Stability Testing of New Drug Substances and Products and the final guidance entitled, Q6A Specifications: Test Procedures and Acceptance Criteria for New Drug Substances and New Drug Products: Chemical Substances, now provide more updated guidance in certain areas than is available in FDA guidances. While many of the ICH's manufacturing-related guidelines apply more directly to marketing submissions, they may offer insights to IND applicants as well (see Chapter 7).

To assist companies in seeking and participating in productive pre-IND submission meetings on CMC-related issues, CDER issued a February 2000 draft document entitled, IND *Meetings for Human Drugs and Biologics: Chemistry, Manufacturing, and Controls Information.* The meetings, which sponsors must pursue by submitting to the FDA a formal request outlining the specific meeting objectives or desired outcomes, might focus on the drug's physical or chemical characteristics, the source and method of preparation, toxic reagent removal, formulation issues, sterility, or drug stability. As part of the Pharmaceutical cGMPs for the 21st Century Initiative, CDER chemists plan to hold more CMC-specific sponsor meetings during the development process.

Animal Pharmacology and Toxicology Information The principal focus of the FDA's 1995 IND reform initiative was the application's pharmacology and toxicology section. The agency's "clarification" of its requirements for this section was designed to permit sponsors to scale back data submissions and to submit INDs months earlier than they could have previously.

In the absence of data derived from previous clinical testing or marketing use, data from animal studies serve as the basis for concluding that a drug is sufficiently safe for initial administration to humans. Therefore, this IND section must include information from the preclinical pharmacology and toxicology studies (animal and *in vitro*) sufficient to establish that the investigational product is reasonably safe for initial use in clinical studies. As is true for the IND's other technical sections, the data and information necessary in the pharmacology and toxicology component depend on several factors, including the nature of the product and the nature and duration of the clinical studies proposed in the IND (see Chapter 2).

The FDA's November 1995 IND guidance document provides the most detailed and current analysis of content requirements for this section. The guideline suggests that the section comprise four elements:

Pharmacology and Drug Disposition. This section should provide, if known: (1) a description of the pharmacologic effects and mechanism(s) of actions of the drug in animals; and (2) information on the absorption, distribution, metabolism, and excretion of the drug. "A summary report, without individual animal records or individual study results, usually suffices," the agency states in the 1995 IND guidance. "In most circumstances, five pages or less should suffice for this summary. If this information is not known, it should simply be so stated. To the extent that such studies may be important to address safety issues, or to assist in evaluation of toxicology data, they may be necessary; however, lack of this potential effectiveness information should not generally be a reason for a Phase 1 IND to be placed on clinical hold."

Integrated Toxicology Summary. Requirements for the IND's integrated summary of toxicologic effects were the most significantly affected by the FDA's 1995 IND reform initiative. At that time, the agency pointed out that its regulations did not specify whether toxicology data and the study reports should be "final fully quality-assured" individual study reports or earlier, unaudited draft toxicologic reports of completed studies. The agency conceded that most sponsors had concluded that the former were required in INDs.

In clarifying its policy, the FDA stated that, "if final, quality-assured individual study reports are not available at the time of IND submission, an integrated summary report of toxicologic findings based on the unaudited draft toxicologic reports of the completed animal studies may be submitted... Usually, 10 to 15 pages of text with additional tables (as needed) should suffice for the integrated summary."

The FDA guidance document adds that the integrated summary of toxicologic findings should comprise five elements: (1) a brief description of the trial design and any deviations from the design in the conduct of the trials (in addition, the dates of the performance of the trials should be included); (2) a systematic presentation of the findings from the animal toxicology and toxicokinetic studies (i.e., from a systems review perspective); (3) identification and qualifications of the individual(s) who evaluated the animal safety data and concluded that it is reasonably safe to begin the proposed human study; (4) a statement of where the animal studies were conducted and where the records of the studies are available for inspection should an inspection occur; and (5) a declaration that each study subject to good laboratory practice (GLP) regulations was performed in full compliance with GLPs or, if the study was not conducted in compliance with those regulations, a brief statement of the reason for the noncompliance and the sponsor's view on how such noncompliance might affect the interpretations of the findings.

The last three information elements identified above may be supplied as part of the integrated summary or as part of the full data tabulations section.

If an IND includes an integrated summary based on unaudited draft reports, the sponsor should submit an update to the summary within 120 days "after the start of the human study(ies)," the FDA states in an October 2000 guidance entitled, Q&A: *Content and Format of* INDs *for Phase 1 Studies for Drugs, Including Well-Characterized, Therapeutic Biotechnology-Derived Products*. "The Agency measures the 120-day period based on the Agency's receipt (date receipt stamped on the IND submission) of the *integrated study report* including the toxicology information. If the sponsor does not submit the final, quality-assured report and update at this time, the sponsor should make the final, quality-assured report available upon the request of the Agency and update the Agency on any changes in the findings. In any case, the final, quality-assured report should be submitted with the NDA. The Agency believes that 120 days from submission of an integrated toxicology summary should provide sponsors with adequate time to complete a final, quality-assured document."

Full Toxicology Data Tabulation. For each animal toxicology study that is intended to support the safety of the proposed clinical investigation, the sponsor should submit a full tabulation of data suitable for a detailed review. The agency states that this section should consist of "line listings of the individual data points, including laboratory data points, for each animal in these trials along with summary tabulations of these data points." To facilitate interpretation of the line listings, they should be accompanied by "either: 1) a brief (usually a few pages) description (i.e., a technical report or abstract including a methods description section) of the study or 2) a copy of the study protocol and amendments."

Toxicology GLP Certification. A declaration that each study subject to good laboratory practice (GLP) regulations was performed in full compliance with GLPs or, if the study was not conducted in compliance with those regulations, a brief statement of the reason for the noncompliance.

Previous Human Experience with the Investigational Drug If an investigational drug, or any of its active ingredients, has been marketed or tested in humans previously, the sponsor must provide specific information about any such use that may be relevant to the FDA's evaluation of the safety of either the drug or the proposed investigation. In such cases, the information should be presented in an integrated summary report. If the drug has been marketed outside the United States, the IND must provide a list of the countries in which the drug has been marketed or withdrawn.

Additional Information Any other information that would aid in the evaluation of the proposed clinical study should be included in this section. For example, the section might include information on a drug's dependence and abuse potential (if applicable), or data from special tests on radioactive drugs. Often, the section contains published literature, scientific meeting abstracts, or related materials.

For certain drugs (see Chapter 16), the applicant must provide in this section of the IND its plans for assessing the drug's pediatric safety and efficacy. Currently, CDER is developing a new guidance document entitled, *Pediatric Safety and Efficacy Data in INDs*, which it hopes to release by late 2004.

Pharmacogenomic Data and the IND

As noted above, the FDA used a draft November 2003 guidance entitled, *Pharmacogenomic Data Submissions* to lay the groundwork for encouraging and, in some cases, requiring IND applicants to submit pharmacogenomic data that they develop as part of the drug development process. While the agency acknowledges that most pharmacogenomic data currently are exploratory or research-oriented and, therefore, need not be submitted in an IND or NDA, sponsors should consider submitting the data voluntarily to help FDA reviewers and scientists understand the relevant scientific issues in this emerging field, the agency states. While the agency prepared to release a final guidance document in late 2004, CDER officials claimed that center reviewers were actively reviewing and making decisions based on voluntarily submitted pharmacogenomic data.

When the submission of pharmacogenomic data is not otherwise required—and it will be required in some cases (see discussion below)—companies should submit what the agency calls "voluntary genomic data submissions" (VGDS), which will be evaluated by a cross-center interdisciplinary pharmacogenomic review group within the agency. Although the agency pledges not to use VGDSs for "regulatory decision making," voluntary submissions will provide the FDA with access to emerging pharmacogenomic data "so that a foundation can be built for developing sound regulatory policies."

In the November 2003 draft guidance, the FDA makes the case that the submission of pharmacogenomic data may be required under two sections of the IND—the pharmacology/toxicology data section and the previous human experience section. "Pharmacogenomic data relevant to, or derived from, animal or *in vitro* studies should ordinarily be submitted [to the IND's pharmacology/toxicology section] under CFR 312.23(a)(8) when the sponsor wishes to use these data to make a scientific case, or when the test is well established as a predictive biomarker (i.e., is a known valid biomarker)," the draft guidance states.

Because IND sponsors are required, in the previous human experience section, to summarize trials or human experience relevant to the evaluation of a drug's safety/efficacy, "sponsors must submit human data of known relevance (e.g., known valid pharmacogenomic biomarkers)," the draft guidance states. In addition, sponsors must submit human pharmacogenomic data "intended to be used in decision making in the drug development process... In cases when the validity of the test is not well established, such data will be viewed by the FDA as supportive only for the purposes of regulatory decision making."

The FDA notes in the guidance that "data from a VGDS submission to an IND will not be used for regulatory decision making." If, following the submission of the VGDS, the sponsor develops additional information that makes the initial submission something that must be reported under an NDA or BLA, the sponsor must then submit the data to the appropriate application, the agency notes. The draft guidance adds that VGDSs may be submitted in advance of the IND submission for "candidate drugs."

Given the lack of standards for presenting/exchanging genomic data, the agency does not recommend a specific VGDS format. The agency notes, however, that the data provided and level of detail in VGDSs should be sufficient to allow FDA reviewers to interpret the information and independently analyze the data, verify the results, and explore possible genotype-phenotype correlations across studies.

An Algorithm for Pharmacogenomic Submissions to INDs

IND holders that generate or possess pharmacogenomic data related to an investigational drug "can comply with FDA requirements using the following algorithms," the agency states in the November 2003 draft guidance:

"**Pharmacogenomic data must be submitted to the IND under CFR 312.23 if ANY of the following apply:**

1. The test results will be used for decision making in any clinical trial, or in an animal trial used to support safety. (For example, the results will affect dose selection, entry criteria, safety monitoring, or subject stratification.)

2. The sponsor is using the test results to support scientific arguments pertaining to, for example, the safety, effectiveness, dosing and pharmacology of the drug.

3. The test results constitute a known valid biomarker for physiologic, pathophysiologic, pharmacologic, toxicologic, or clinical states or outcomes in humans, or is a known valid biomarker for a safety outcome in animal studies. If the information on the biomarker (example, human P450 2D6 status) is *not* being used for purposes 1 or 2 above, the information can be submitted to the IND as an abbreviated report.

Submission to an IND is NOT needed, but voluntary submission is encouraged (i.e., information does not meet the criteria of CFR 312.23) if:

4. Information is from exploratory studies or is research data, such as from general gene expression analyses in cells/animals/humans, or single-nucleotide polymorphism (SNP) analysis of trial participants.

5. Information consists of results from test systems where the validity of the biomarker is not established."

As the agency reviewed public comments in developing a final guidance, FDA officials attempted to allay industry concerns regarding the submission of pharmacogenomic data. With the exception of cancer therapies, for which tumors can provide gene sequence expression data, experimental products are unlikely to face new FDA requirements under the pharmacogenomics guidance in the near term, CDER Director Janet Woodcock, M.D., claimed at a November 2003 workshop.

Submitting the IND

FDA regulations state that "the sponsor shall submit an original and two copies of all submissions to the IND file, including the original submission and all amendments and reports." In some cases, additional copies may be needed.

The sponsor must provide an accurate and complete English translation for any information originally written in a foreign language. In addition, the applicant must submit the original foreign language document or literature article on which the translation is based.

Maintaining/Updating the IND

Given that clinical development takes place over a multi-year period, a single IND may be "in effect," or "active," for several years or even decades. Because of this, the IND is a "living document" that must be updated continually so that the safety of ongoing and upcoming clinical trials may be periodically reassessed in light of the latest information. Any document submitted to an active IND (i.e., after FDA receipt of an original submission) is referred to as an IND amendment. Each amendment must be accompanied by a completed and signed Form 1571, which identifies the purpose and contents of the submission.

Federal regulations require sponsors of active INDs to update their filings through four types of amendments: protocol amendments, information amendments, IND safety reports, and annual reports.

Protocol Amendments Protocol amendments are necessary when a sponsor wants to change a previously submitted protocol or to add a study protocol not submitted in the original IND. New protocols and most protocol changes must have been submitted to the FDA and have received IRB approval before being initiated. Some sponsors may choose to obtain FDA comments before implementing new protocols or protocol changes, however.

Protocol amendments that introduce a new protocol should contain the protocol itself along with a brief description of the most clinically significant differences between the new and previous protocols. In explaining this requirement, the FDA writes that "...a detailed and undiscriminating enumeration of the differences would defeat the purpose of this requirement, which is to identify the most important differences between the old and new protocols and to alert FDA reviewers to major changes that may require additional supporting data, such as changes in dose, route of administration, or indication."

Amendments that specify changes to previously submitted protocols are required when a sponsor seeks: (1) to modify a Phase 1 protocol in a manner that significantly affects the safety of clinical subjects; or (2) to modify a Phase 2 or Phase 3 protocol in a manner that significantly affects the safety of the subjects, the scope of the investigation, or the scientific quality of the study. Federal regulations provide the following examples of protocol changes requiring amendments:

- any increase in drug dosage or the duration of individual subject exposure to the drug beyond that in the current protocol, or any significant increase in the number of study subjects;

- any significant change in the design of a protocol, such as the addition or deletion of a control group;

- the addition of a new test or procedure that is intended to improve monitoring for, or reduce the risk of, a side effect or adverse event, or the elimination of a test intended to monitor safety;

- the elimination of an apparent, immediate hazard to subjects (such a change may be implemented prior to an amendment submission, provided that the FDA is subsequently notified through a protocol amendment and that the IRB is properly notified); and

- the addition of a new investigator to carry out a previously submitted protocol (the investigational drug may be shipped to the investigator and the investigator may participate in the study prior to the submission of the amendment, provided the sponsor notifies the FDA within 30 days of the investigator's first participation in the study).

Amendments for changes to existing protocols must provide a "brief description of the change and reference (date and number) to the submission that contained the protocol." Amendments for a new investigator must include "the investigator's name, the qualifications to conduct the investigation, reference to the previously submitted protocol, and all additional information as is required [for other investigators]."

For certain protocol amendments, the FDA requires sponsors to reference the specific technical information that supports the new protocol or protocol change. According to FDA regulations, a protocol amendment must contain a reference, if necessary, to specific technical information in the IND or in a concurrently submitted information amendment to the IND that the sponsor relies on to support any clinically significant change in the new or amended protocol.

Protocol amendments must be prominently identified in one of three ways: "Protocol Amendment: New Protocol," "Protocol Amendment: Change in Protocol," or "Protocol Amendment: New Investigator." Amendments for new protocols or changes in existing protocols must be submitted to the FDA before their implementation. The FDA states, however, that "when several submissions of new protocols or protocol changes are anticipated during a short period, the sponsor is encouraged, to the extent feasible, to include these all in a single submission." Amendments to add new investigators or to provide additional information about investigators may be batched and submitted at 30-day intervals.

IND Safety Reports Sponsors must submit IND safety reports to inform the FDA and all participating investigators of any adverse experience (AE) that is associated with the use of a product and that is both serious and unexpected. The goal of this requirement is to ensure the timely communication of the most important new information about experiences with the investigational drug.

Through a long-awaited October 1997 final rule, the FDA's AE and IND safety reporting requirements were revised in several important ways. Designed to standardize the FDA's pre- and postmarketing AE reporting rules and to harmonize the agency's requirements with international standards, the regulation redefines many of the terms crucial to AE reporting, recasts the reporting timeframes for expedited pre- and postmarketing AE reports, and codifies the use of the MedWatch Form (Form 3500A) for expedited AE reports (i.e., the regulation permits the use of Form 3500A for IND AE reporting, but requires its use for postmarketing AE reporting).

For the purpose of AE reporting, FDA regulations require sponsors to "promptly review all information relevant to the safety of the drug obtained or otherwise received by the sponsor from any source, foreign or domestic, including information derived from any clinical or epidemiological investigations, animal investigations, commercial marketing experience, reports in the scientific literature, and unpublished scientific papers, as well as reports from foreign regulatory authorities that have not already been previously reported to the agency by the sponsor."

Once a sponsor's employee has knowledge of safety-related data, the sponsor is considered to have received that information. Therefore, sponsors must develop efficient mechanisms to ensure that such information is communicated internally (e.g., from subsidiaries, other departments within the company, and CROs).

The reporting requirements applicable to adverse experiences are based on factors such as the nature, severity, and probable cause of the experience. The definitions of several terms, some of which were revised by the October 1997 regulation, are critically important in AE reporting:

Serious Adverse Drug Experience. A "serious" AE is "any adverse drug experience occurring at any dose that results in any of the following outcomes: Death, a life-threatening adverse drug experience, inpatient hospitalization or prolongation of existing hospitalization, a persistent or significant disability/incapacity, or a congenital anomaly/birth defect. Important medical events that may not result in death, be life-threatening, or require hospitalization may be considered a serious adverse drug experience when, based upon appropriate medical judgment, they may jeopardize the patient or subject and may require medical or surgical intervention to prevent one of the outcomes listed in this definition. Examples of such medical events include allergic bronchospasm requiring intensive treatment in an emergency room or at home, blood dyscrasias or convulsions that do not result in inpatient hospitalization, or the development of drug dependency or drug abuse."

Unexpected Adverse Drug Experience. An unexpected adverse drug experience is "any adverse drug experience, the specificity or severity of which is not consistent with the current investigator brochure; or if an investigator brochure is not required or available, the specificity or severity of which is not consistent with the risk information described in the general investigational plan or elsewhere in the current application, as amended. For example, under this definition, hepatic necrosis would be unexpected (by virtue of greater severity) if the investigator brochure only referred to elevated hepatic enzymes or hepatitis. Similarly, cerebral thromboembolism and cerebral vasculitis would be unexpected (by virtue of greater specificity) if the investigator brochure only listed cerebral vascular accidents. 'Unexpected,' as used in this definition, refers to an adverse drug experience that has not been previously observed (e.g., included in the investigator brochure) rather than from the perspective of such experience not being anticipated from the pharmacological properties of the pharmaceutical product."

Associated with the Use of the Drug. The phrase "associated with the use of the drug" is interpreted by the regulations to mean "that there is a reasonable possibility that the experience may have been caused by the drug." To harmonize the definition of this phrase with ICH guidances, CDER proposed, as part of a March 2003 proposed regulation designed to harmonize FDA requirements with ICH and international standards (see discussion below), to substitute the phrase "suspected adverse drug reaction" (SADR) for the phrase "associated with the use of the drug." Under the proposed rule, SADR is defined as "a noxious and unintended response to any dose of a drug [or biologic] product for which there is a reasonable possibility that the product caused the response. In this definition, the phrase, 'a reasonable possibility' means that the relationship cannot be ruled out."

Life-Threatening Adverse Drug Experience. A "life-threatening" AE is "any adverse drug experience that places the patient or subject, in the view of the investigator, at immediate risk of death from the reaction as it occurred, i.e., it does not include a reaction that, had it occurred in a more severe form, might have caused death."

Disability. A "disability" is "a substantial disruption of a person's ability to conduct normal life functions." The FDA considers only a persistent or significant or incapacitating disability to be serious. Therefore, experiences of relatively minor medical significance, such as a headache, nausea, vomiting, diarrhea, influenza, and accidental trauma (e.g., sprained ankle), would not be considered serious.

The October 1997 AE final rule revised the reporting timeframes applicable to the two types of IND safety reports that sponsors must make: telephone/facsimile IND safety reports and written IND safety reports.

Telephone/fax reports are required for any unexpected fatal or life-threatening experience associated with the use of the drug. Sponsors must submit these reports within 7 calendar days of their initial receipt of the AE-related information. Companies may make these reports via telephone or facsimile transmission.

Written IND safety reports must be issued to the FDA and participating investigators for any AE that is associated with the use of the drug and that is both serious and unexpected. Such reports must also be made after any finding from animal tests suggesting a significant risk for human subjects. These reports must be issued within 15 calendar days of the sponsor's initial receipt of the information.

The written IND safety reports must identify all safety reports previously filed with the IND concerning a similar adverse experience, and must provide an analysis of the adverse experience's significance in light of the previous, similar reports. Adverse experiences that require telephone/facsimile safety reports must also be the subject of a written IND safety report.

The FDA advises sponsors to submit in written IND safety reports "as much information as possible on a case. In some instances, information for final description and evaluation of a case report may not be available within 15 calendar days. Nevertheless, initial reports should be submitted within this timeframe when the following minimum criteria are met: An identifiable patient; a suspected medicinal product; an identifiable reporter; and an adverse event or outcome that can be identified as serious and unexpected, and for which, in clinical investigation cases, there is a reasonable suspected causal relationship between the investigational product and the adverse event (i.e., the causal relationship cannot be ruled out)."

A safety report to an IND does not necessarily represent the sponsor's concession that there is a relationship between the product and the adverse experience. In fact, the sponsor may state this fact explicitly in the safety report.

The October 1997 final rule also permits the use of the MedWatch Form—FDA Form 3500A—for written IND safety reports. Alternatively, sponsors can submit the reports in a narrative form, or attach a page or pages featuring a narrative description with FDA Form 3500A. Under the regulation, the FDA also permits companies, without agency pre-approval, to make written IND safety reports for foreign AEs on the CIOMS I form.

The agency may request that a sponsor submit IND safety reports in a particular format or at a frequency different than those required by regulations. In April 2003, CDER Office of Medical Policy Director Robert Temple, M.D., stated that CDER's review divisions may, in some cases, reach agreements under which IND holders are permitted not to collect and report certain types of adverse event data. In recent years, some have raised concerns regarding the burdens placed on sponsors, IRBs, the FDA and others in collecting, reporting, and reviewing certain AE-related data, some of which are for insignificant drug responses.

Anticipated Changes to IND Safety Reporting Requirements. When the FDA finalizes a March 2003 proposed regulation entitled, *Safety Reporting Requirements for Human Drug and Biological Products*, it will implement important changes designed to harmonize its IND safety reporting requirements with ICH and international standards. As noted above, the proposed regulation would revise or replace definitions ("associated with the use of the drug," see discussion above) that are essential for IND safety reporting, define minimum content requirements for safety reports, and establish new provisions regarding which types of safety issues require expedited reporting.

Annual Reports Within 60 days of the anniversary date on which the initial IND "went into effect," the sponsor must submit an overview of information collected on the subject product during the previous year. Described by regulations as "a brief report of the progress of the investigation," the annual report should provide the following:

Information on Individual Studies. The FDA requires "a brief summary of the status of each study in progress and each study completed during the previous year. The summary must include the following information on each study: (1) the title of the study (with any appropriate study identifiers such as protocol number), its purpose, a brief statement identifying the patient population and a statement as to whether the study is completed; (2) the total number of subjects initially planned for inclusion in the study, the number entered into the study to date, the number whose participation in the study was completed and planned, and the number who dropped out of the study for any reason; and (3) if the study has been completed or if the interim results are known, a brief description of any available study results."

Summary Information. This section should include all additional product-related information collected during the previous year, as well as summary data from all clinical studies: (1) a narrative or tabular summary showing the most frequent and most serious adverse experiences by body system; (2) a summary of all IND safety reports submitted during the past year; (3) a list of subjects who died while participating in the investigation, with the cause of death for each subject (this list must identify all deaths, including those persons whose cause of death is not believed to be product related); (4) a list of subjects who dropped out during the study due to an adverse experience, regardless of whether the experience is thought to be drug related; (5) a brief description of any information that is pertinent to an understanding of the drug's actions (e.g., information from controlled trials and information about bioavailability); (6) a list of the preclinical studies (including animal studies) completed or in progress during the past year, and a summary of the major preclinical findings; and (7) a summary of any significant manufacturing or microbiological changes made during the past year.

General Investigational Plan. A brief description of the general investigational plan for the coming year must be provided. This plan should be as descriptive as the earlier plans submitted in the original IND and subsequent annual reports. If the plans are not yet formulated, the sponsor must indicate this fact in the report.

Investigator's Brochure Revisions. When the investigator's brochure has been revised, the sponsor must include a description of the revision and a copy of the new brochure.

Phase 1 Modifications. The sponsor must describe any significant Phase 1 protocol modifications that were implemented during the previous year and that were not reported previously to the FDA through a protocol amendment.

Foreign Marketing Developments. According to the IND regulations, this section should provide a "brief summary of significant foreign marketing developments with the drug during the past year, such as approval of marketing in any country or withdrawal or suspension from marketing in any country."

Request for an FDA Response. If the sponsor requests an FDA meeting, reply, or comment, a log of any relevant outstanding business with respect to the IND should be included.

The FDA revised its IND annual report regulations in February 1998 to require that sponsors tabulate in annual reports the numbers of subjects currently enrolled in their clinical trials according to age group, gender, and race. This requirement, which became effective in August 1998, was designed to alert sponsors and the FDA to possible demographic deficiencies in trial enrollment that could result in NDA deficiencies.

Information Amendments Often representing the majority of IND amendments, information amendments are used to report to the FDA new information that would not ordinarily be included in a protocol amendment or IND safety report, and information whose importance dictates that it must be reported before the next IND annual report. Information amendments commonly include new data from animal studies, changes or additions to the IND's chemistry, manufacturing, and controls section, and reports on discontinued clinical trials. Such information is more immediately critical than that included in the annual report. The amendments can also be used to provide administrative information, including responses to CDER requests, changes in IND contact persons, and letters of cross reference. Information amendments should be submitted as necessary, but preferably not more frequently than every 30 days.

The principal content requirements for information amendments are: (1) a statement of the nature and purpose of the amendment; (2) an organized submission of the data in a format appropriate for scientific review; and (3) a request for FDA comment on the information amendment (i.e., if the sponsor seeks agency comment).

In May 2003, CDER released a final guidance entitled, INDs *for Phases 2 and 3 Studies of Drugs, Including Specified Therapeutic Biotechnology-Derived Products: Chemistry, Manufacturing, and Controls Content and Format* to provide guidance on the proper submission of CMC information in information amendments and annual reports. Specifically, the guidance clarified the difference between "CMC safety information," which should be submitted in information amendments, and "corroborating information," which can be submitted in an annual report. In specifying the chemistry, manufacturing, and controls information that is needed during Phase 2 and 3 clinical trials, the guidance claims that it provides IND sponsors with "regulatory relief" in four specific areas "by providing flexibility in the collecting and reporting of data and by avoiding redundant submissions. Certain information that traditionally has been submitted in information amendments would be identified as corroborating information, [which is less likely to affect the safe use of the drug but should be submitted to ensure the proper identity, strength or potency, quality, and purity of the investigational drug], and can be submitted in an annual report. The limited phase 2 corroborating information recommended...need not be submitted before initiation of phase 2 studies and can be generated during phase 2 drug development. The phase 3 corroborating information recommended...need not be submitted before the initiation of phase 3 studies and can be generated during phase 3 drug development. The corroborating information and a summary of CMC safety information submitted during a subject-reporting period would be included in the annual report. Therefore, there should be no need for general CMC updates at the end of phase 1 or phase 2."

CHAPTER 4

CDER and the IND Review Process

Although most analyses of the U.S. Food and Drug Administration (FDA) focus on the agency's authority to decide which new treatments reach the American market, the FDA plays a regulatory gatekeeper role at another key point in the drug development process. In reviewing investigational new drug applications (IND), the FDA determines which experimental therapies advance from the preclinical to the clinical development phase.

When a drug sponsor submits an IND, the FDA assumes an important role in the development of a new product: From this point forward, the sponsor can do little without at least submitting documents to, and in some cases awaiting the review and approval of, the agency. And, under such programs as PDUFA III's Pilot 2-Scientific Feedback and Interactions During Development of Fast Track Products (see Chapter 5), the agency may be interacting with sponsors more closely than ever during the clinical development process.

In fact, most sponsor activities beyond the preclinical development phase are subject to some form of FDA oversight. This reality is highlighted in the following statement that a sponsor must sign in the IND: "I agree not to begin clinical investigations until 30 days after FDA's receipt of the IND unless I receive earlier notification by FDA that the studies may begin. I also agree not to begin or continue clinical investigations covered by the IND if those studies are placed on clinical hold. I agree that an Institutional Review Board (IRB) that complies with [federal regulations] will be responsible for the initial and continuing review and approval of each of the studies in the proposed clinical investigation. I agree to conduct the investigation in accordance with all other applicable regulatory requirements."

While virtually all other FDA drug review processes have been reformed under the Food and Drug Administration Modernization Act of 1997 (FDAMA) and the reauthorized Prescription Drug User Fee Act (PDUFA I, II, and III), the agency's long-standing IND review process has largely survived the wave of regulatory reform initiatives over the last decade or so. In contrast to the NDA review process, which has seen everything from its review timelines to its sponsor communication processes redefined, tightened, or tweaked, it is arguable that only peripheral aspects of the IND review process have been influenced by reform efforts.

Still, regulatory initiatives and scientific advances stand to affect some aspects of the IND review process. CDER efforts to extend the common technical document (CTD) format for marketing applications to IND submissions and the center's increasing interest in receiving electronic INDs in the CTD format will certainly impact the IND review process. In addition, INDs will be expected to include different types of data—for example, pharmacogenomics data—in the future (see discussions below).

The FDA's Center for Drug Evaluation and Research (CDER) is the regulatory and scientific body that oversees the development and marketing of all new drugs, including the review of IND submissions. Therefore, before outlining the IND review process, it is appropriate to profile CDER, one of several primary program centers within the FDA.

The FDA's Center for Drug Evaluation and Research (CDER)

CDER has functioned in many forms during its history. Several recent restructuring initiatives were undertaken to better distribute workload throughout the center, reflect evolving philosophies and approaches to the drug review process, and respond to emerging issues such as risk management. In mid-2005, the center was scheduled to implement another significant restructuring designed to improve the balance of the center's workload and resources across its new drug review divisions and to improve the "logical grouping" of products within the center's offices and divisions.

CDER's current structure is largely the product of a series of reorganizations in the mid-1990s, the most important of which was a sweeping center-wide restructuring initiative that fundamentally changed the offices and divisions responsible for reviewing INDs and NDAs. Center management stated in 1995 that the initiative was designed to flatten what had become a "pyramidal system" of drug review and approval, to create smaller and more focused and cohesive review teams, and to facilitate intra-center communication.

This October 1995 reorganization created what CDER officials have called two "super offices" that continue to form the core of the center today:

Office of Review Management (now the Office of New Drugs). Within its Office of Review Management (ORM), which has subsequently been renamed the Office of New Drugs (OND), CDER concentrated virtually all the offices and units essential for new drug reviews. In addition, the center reconfigured its ten previous new drug review divisions into 14 review units, and spread these over five Offices of Drug Evaluation (ODE), instead of the previous two (see organizational chart below). This chapter focuses largely on these new drug review divisions and their activities related to IND reviews. It is important to note, however, that CDER added a sixth ODE as part of a recent intercenter consolidation, under which review responsibility and staffing for so-called therapeutic biological products were shifted from the Center for Biologics Evaluation and Research (CBER) to the drug center. Although this new ODE is discussed further below, the office and its activities will not be profiled in this text because they focus on biological products rather than drugs. At the office director level today, OND includes several teams that provide office-level expertise and support to all of the office's drug review groups and that reflect emerging priorities at the center, including the pharmacology/toxicology staff, the study endpoints and labeling team, and the pregnancy labeling team.

Office of Pharmaceutical Science. The Office of Pharmaceutical Science (OPS) was created, in part, to bring all of CDER's generic and new drug review chemists under a single management structure, thereby promoting a greater degree of consistency in chemistry reviews, policies, and approaches. Today, the office oversees four separate offices, including the Office of New Drug Chemistry, the Office of Generic Drugs, the Office of Testing and Research, and the new Office of Biotechnology Products (relocated to OPS as part of the CDER/CBER consolidation, see discussion below). In March 2004, the Office of Clinical Pharmacology and Biopharmaceutics was moved from OPS to the Office of the Center Director.

CDER has tweaked its structure considerably over the past several years. In May 2001, then-CDER Director Janet Woodcock, M.D., proposed a series of organizational changes designed to streamline several center units that she felt had become too large to manage, ORM in particular. The most significant element of this restructuring, which was implemented in early 2002, was to shift the Office of Postmarketing Drug Risk

Center for Drug Evaluation and Research

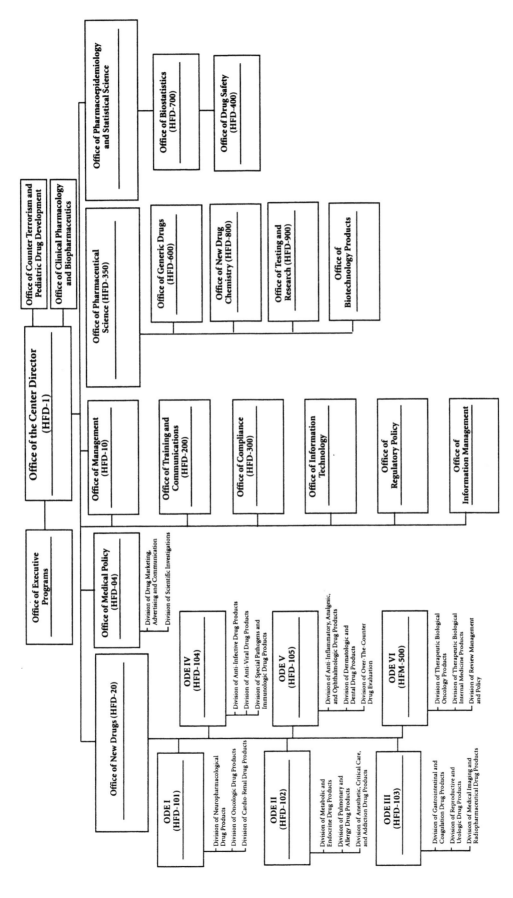

As of October 2004

Assessment and the Office of Biostatistics from the Office of Review Management (ORM) (as well as CDER's MedWatch Program) to a new Office of Pharmacoepidemiology and Statistical Science (OPSS). The shifting of OPDRA and MedWatch (see Chapter 11) under OPSS reflected CDER's intensifying focus on drug safety and risk management, which continues today. Under the reorganization, OPDRA's name was also changed to the Office of Drug Safety to better reflect its role in monitoring the safety of marketed medicines. During the term of PDUFA III (FY2003-FY2007), ODS is expected to grow anywhere from 50% to 150% from its pre-PDUFA III base of 80 to 90 persons.

At this writing, CDER comprised several principal offices in addition to the Office of Pharmaceutical Science, the Office of New Drugs (see discussion below), and the Office of Pharmacoepidemiology and Statistical Science:

The Office of Compliance. CDER's Office of Compliance monitors the quality of marketed drugs through product testing, surveillance inspections, and compliance programs; develops policies and standards for drug labeling and current good manufacturing practice (cGMP); and coordinates actions between CDER's center and field offices (e.g., for cGMP inspections). In January 2003, CDER reorganized the Office of Compliance to "improve coordination and communication and to enhance the office's capacity to implement risk management approaches to compliance activities." The reorganized office includes three divisions: the Division of New Drugs and Labeling Compliance, which is responsible for compliance and enforcement issues related to approval and labeling requirements for OTC and prescription drugs; the Division of Manufacturing and Product Quality, which is responsible for CDER's oversight of foreign and domestic investigations and inspections, drug recalls, and imports/exports; and the newly created Division of Compliance Risk Management and Surveillance, which is responsible for guiding the office's risk-management approach, including leading the office's data analysis, information management, and post-market surveillance activities.

The Office of Medical Policy. Led by Robert Temple, M.D., who is also the director of the Office of Drug Evaluation I, CDER's Office of Medical Policy houses the Division of Drug Marketing, Advertising and Communications and the Division of Scientific Investigations, which is responsible for CDER's Bioresearch Monitoring Program (see Chapter 14).

Office of Clinical Pharmacology and Biopharmaceutics. As noted, the Office of Clinical Pharmacology and Biopharmaceutics was moved from OPS in March 2004 and was placed directly under the Office of the Center Director. The office helps to assure the safety and effectiveness of new drugs by reviewing clinical pharmacology and biopharmaceutics information (e.g., dosing) in INDs and NDAs.

The Office of Counter-Terrorism and Pediatric Drug Development. The center has upgraded its former Office of Pediatric Drug Development and Program Initiatives, which was established in October 2001 and was placed under OND, to the Office of Counter-Terrorism and Pediatric Drug Development at the CDER director level. At the same time, CDER consolidated its increasingly important counter-terrorism efforts within this new office.

The Office of Regulatory Policy. This office is responsible for developing and issuing draft and final regulations and policies, handling Freedom of Information Act requests and citizen's petitions, and coordinating center policies in several areas, including user fees.

The Office of Training and Communications. CDER's Office of Training and Communications was created in 1995 to spearhead the center's various training/personnel development and internal and external communications programs.

The Office of Information Management and Office of Information Technology. These two offices spearhead the center's IT programs and fulfill a critical role in many CDER initiatives, including the electronic submission program.

Office of Management. The Office of Management leads the center's planning, budgeting, facilities management, and program management efforts.

Office of Executive Programs. The Office of Executive Programs houses CDER's Quality Assurance Staff, Advisors and Consultants Staff (i.e., advisory committee issues), executive operations staff, international program, and the CDER ombudsman.

Recent and Upcoming Changes in CDER Structure As noted above, the most recent significant change in CDER's structure is one that, at least initially, did not affect drug reviews in any significant way. The so-called CDER/CBER "consolidation" in 2003 did bring new responsibilities (for therapeutic biological products) and new staffing (over 200 staffers) to the drug center. Today, these responsibilities and staffers reside in two offices that are, at least for now, independent from other CDER offices—OND's Office of Drug Evaluation VI (ODE VI), which reviews INDs and biological license applications (BLA) for monoclonal antibodies, therapeutic proteins, and other therapeutic biological products, and the Office of Pharmaceutical Science's new Office of Biotechnology Products, which primarily addresses manufacturing issues regarding therapeutic biological products.

When CDER formed these new biologics-only groups, however, senior center officials quickly characterized the center's structure as "interim," and noted that CDER's drug and biological product reviewers would be integrated more fully as part of a "comprehensive reorganization" initiative to be implemented in spring 2005, when the drug center will consolidate all its offices within a single facility. The restructuring, which will affect many of CDER's existing new drug review divisions, is also designed to improve the balance of workload and resources across divisions and to improve the "logical groupings" of products regulated by CDER's offices and divisions.

At this writing, many of the details of OND's proposed reorganization had been released. As part of the reorganization, OND will trade its current structure, which features six offices of drug evaluation (ODE), for a five-ODE structure (see exhibit below). In addition to four reconstituted ODEs, each of which will house three new drug review divisions, OND will establish a new Office of Oncology Products, which will bring under one office the two divisions responsible for reviewing drug and biological oncology products. The formation of the new oncology office was widely anticipated, since harmonizing standards for drug and biologic cancer treatments was one of the primary motivations behind the initial transfer of biological oncology review functions and staff from CBER to CDER. The office will also have a third division whose review responsibilities will include medical imaging agents used in the diagnosis of cancer.

Among the most notable changes to be implemented under the pending reorganization will be the split of CDER's long-standing Division of Neuropharmacological Drug Products. Probably because the division has become what is easily CDER's busiest (in terms of NDA workload), CDER will split the division's two key therapeutic areas—neurology and psychiatry—into separate review divisions. Among the other changes will be a newly constituted division—the Division of Analgesic, Anesthetic and Rheumatology Drug Products—that will be responsible for all analgesic products, which are spread among multiple divisions currently.

Office of New Drugs: Proposed Restructuring

(planned for implementation in April 2005)

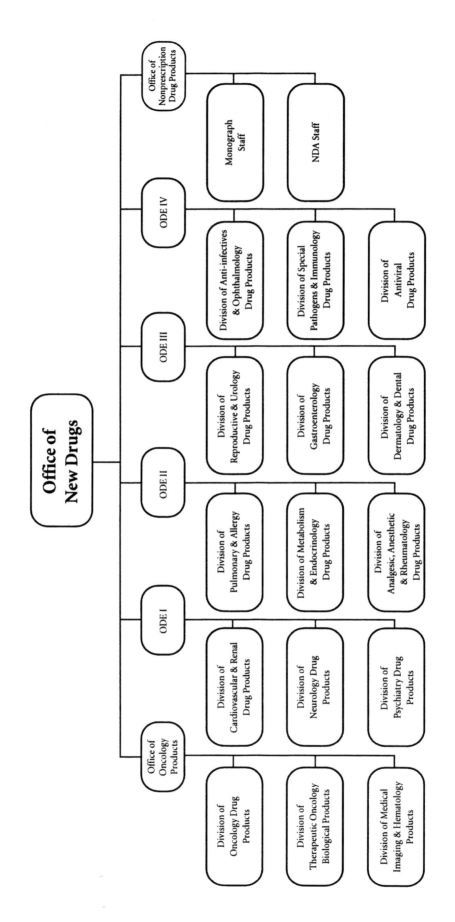

Source: CDER

CDER will implement other organizational changes and approaches simultaneously with those discussed above. Consistent with its so-called *Pharmaceutical cGMPs for the 21st Century Initiative*, CDER will establish what it calls "a modern, risk-based pharmaceutical quality assessment system" in mid-2005. In implementing this system, the drug center will reorganize its Office of New Drug Chemistry (ONDC) to make the office more efficient and flexible in managing chemistry-related review workloads and to revise its approach to IND, NDA, and supplemental NDA reviews (see discussions below).

CDER's Drug Review Divisions

Although each of CDER's offices plays an essential role in drug regulation, this chapter focuses on the Office of New Drugs' five drug-related Offices of Drug Evaluation (ODE), which house the 14 new drug review divisions that process and evaluate INDs and NDAs for new drugs. Since their decisions determine the fates of therapeutically and commercially significant new drugs, these divisions are certainly among the most closely monitored and highly pressured offices within the FDA. With the advent of PDUFA I/II/III, the industry, congressional, and public scrutiny under which the divisions have traditionally operated has intensified considerably over the last decade or so. To meet the review goals established under the user-fee program, these divisions have absorbed several hundred additional staffers since the early 1990s. Maintaining manageable divisional workloads and creating review groups that evaluate "more focused groups of products" were among CDER's primary motivations in its 1995 restructuring and in several divisional shifts that have taken place since.

As the division titles indicate, the reviewing responsibilities are apportioned to CDER's 14 new drug review divisions by therapeutic area. Each unit has its own areas of expertise, and reviews all new drugs proposed for use in these areas. Not surprisingly, this separation of responsibility creates disparities in the workloads facing the divisions and fundamental differences in the scientific and medical issues the divisions address in reviewing new drugs.

CDER's 14 new drug review divisions differ in other ways. Although the groups function under the same legal and regulatory framework, each division traditionally has had considerable autonomy to establish its own policies and procedures within that general framework. And while the center's drug review groups continue to function independently, at least some of their autonomy has been minimized over the years by efforts to standardize policies and processes. Since the mid-1990s, for example, the center has maintained a Manual of Policies and Procedures (MaPP), which now comprises dozens of detailed center-wide policies on issues ranging from CDER/sponsor meetings to IND clinical hold procedures. Under its Good Review Practices (GRP) initiative (see Chapter 8), the center is also developing internal guidances and tools designed to add consistency to drug application reviews, particularly NDA clinical data reviews. Although the movement toward standardization is more focused on NDA reviews, it is likely to affect other reviews as well.

The following sections provide brief profiles of CDER's five drug-related ODEs and 14 new drug review divisions, with particular emphasis on the therapeutic categories of drugs that each unit regulates.

CDER's Office of Drug Evaluation I

ODE I comprises the three new drug review divisions profiled below.

Division of Cardio-Renal Drug Products Since the division's long-time director, Raymond Lipicky, M.D., retired from the agency in early 2002, the division has had a few directors. Today, the division is led by Acting Director Norman Stockbridge, M.D. Based on information released at this writing, the Division of Cardio-

Renal Drug Products will remain in ODE I and retain its current product responsibilities when CDER reorganizes in spring 2005.

The primary classes of drugs for which the Division of Cardio-Renal Drug Products is responsible include antihypertensives, agents for the prevention of restinosis, agents for treating renal disease, agents for intermittent claudication, agents used for hypotension and shock, angiographic diagnostic agents, angiotensin converting enzyme inhibitors, antianginal agents, anti-arrhythmics, angiotensin II receptor antagonists antiplatelet drugs, b-blockers B1 selective, beta blocking agents, botanical products for cardiovascular indications, calcium channel blockers, cardiovascular diagnostics, central alpha-2 agonists, coronary vasodilators, diuretics and renal tubule inhibitors, neutral endopeptidase/angiotensin converting enzyme inhibitors peripheral vasodilators, potassium channel openers, and potassium salts.

From 1995 through 1999, the division had approved more new molecular entities (NME) than all but one other CDER division, although the division's output of NME approvals has been inconsistent since. The division approved two NMEs in 2001 and four in 2002, but did not approve any new drugs in either 2000 or 2003. The unit's average NME review time was 15.6 months in 2001 and 18.5 months in 2002. As of January 2004, the unit had one of CDER's more modest pending NDA workloads—8 NDAs.

Division of Oncologic Drug Products Since 1999, the Division of Oncologic Drug Products has been led by Director Richard Pazdur, M.D. As part of CDER's pending reorganization, this unit will be renamed the Division of Drug Oncology Products and moved into the center's new Office of Oncology Products.

One of CDER's more visible and busy review units, the Division of Oncologic Drug Products reviews all oncology drugs, including drugs to treat AIDS patients with Kaposi's sarcoma and lymphoma, drugs to treat chronic graft-versus-host disease, antineoplastic hormones, biological response modifiers for cancer treatment cancer chemotherapeutic agents with or without monoclonal antibodies, cytoxic alkylating agents, cytoxic antimetabolics, cytotoxics, immunomodulators, radiosensitizers, and miscellaneous multi-drug resistance modulators.

Various controversies and initiatives regarding oncology therapies have had fundamental effects on the division, its staffing, and focus over the years. In large part due to a 1996 controversy that ultimately brought a greater focus on cancer drug reviews, the division saw its review staff grow by roughly 20 percent in the late 1990s. After patient advocacy groups questioned why the agency was expending so many more resources on the review of AIDS treatments than on therapies for cancer or heart disease, CDER unveiled the Oncology Initiative, which the Clinton Administration estimated would reduce cancer drug development times by at least a year and cut oncology NDA review times from an average of 12.4 months to 6 months (see Chapter 15) While the political intensity of cancer drug approvals faded somewhat in the years that followed, the various elements of the Oncology Initiative either have been incorporated into division practice or were legislated by FDAMA provisions, division staffers point out.

More recently, however, oncology drug development and reviews have again become an FDA and government priority. In November 2003, the FDA and National Cancer Institute (NCI) announced that their Interagency Oncology Task Force would launch two new initiatives to facilitate the development and use of cancer drugs One of the initiatives involves the development of a new system for the electronic submission of INDs. "The FDA has agreed to work with NCI to develop clinical trial management software that makes it easier for cancer research groups and the FDA to work collaboratively," the agencies announced. As a first step, the NCI and FDA are working together to build tools that facilitate "electronic interaction, focusing in particular on IND applications." FDA officials claimed that the electronic submission of INDs and data during the clinical development process could cut "at least months" off the ultimate review times for cancer agents. Under the second initiative, a new Fellowship Training Program, research fellows will work in the NCI's clinical oncology programs and the FDA's technical and regulatory review programs so that these physicians and scientists can bring state-of-the-art knowledge to the design, conduct, and review of clinical trials.

After improving its average NME review times substantially in recent years, the division saw its mean review time jump to 16.0 months in 2003, due largely to a single lengthy NME review. In the previous five years, the division's average NME review time was well under a year. The unit has averaged roughly two to three NME approvals annually since the mid-1990s. The division had only six pending NDAs under review as of January 2004.

Division of Neuropharmacological Drug Products The Division of Neuropharmacological Drug Products has been led by Director Russell Katz, M.D., since late 1999. As noted, CDER plans to split this division as part of the pending reorganization, due largely to workload issues. Because the unit had become what was easily CDER's busiest in recent years (in terms of NDA workload), the drug center plans to split the division's two key therapeutic areas—neurology and psychiatry—into separate review divisions under ODE I.

The Division of Neuropharmacological Drug Product's current responsibilities can be divided into two general therapeutic categories:

Neurology Drugs. Anticonvulsants, antiemetics, antinauseants, anti-Parkinson agents, antispasticity agents, cerebral stimulants, vascular agents, drugs to assist memory (Alzheimer's/senility/dementia), and drugs to treat migraine, movement disorders, multiple sclerosis, narcolepsy/sleep apnea, stroke, and tardive dyskinesia.

Psychiatric Drugs. Anorexigenic agents/CNS stimulants, antianxiety agents/anxiolytics, antidepressants, antimanics, antipsychotics, hypnotics, sedatives, and drugs to treat schizophrenia, eating disorders, learning disabilities (dyslexia), minimal brain dysfunction, obsessive compulsive disorder, and panic.

Over the last several years, the division has maintained CDER's highest mean NME review time—roughly two years in 2000, 2001, and 2002. CDER's most productive review group in terms of NME approvals since 1996, the division approved only one NME in 2003, although it did so in just 9.9 months.

Office of Drug Evaluation II

ODE II comprises the three new drug review divisions profiled below.

Division of Metabolic and Endocrine Drug Products David Orloff, M.D., has been the permanent director of the Division of Metabolic and Endocrine Drug Products since 2000. Although it seemed to be a likely candidate for restructuring based on workload issues, the division will remain intact under CDER's proposed reorganization plan.

The Division of Metabolic and Endocrine Drug Products classifies its review responsibilities into about a dozen drug and disease areas: adrenal/ACTH, anabolic steroids, bone calcium and phosphorus metabolism developmental disorders, drugs for diabetes (miscellaneous), dopamine agonists, growth hormone and analogs, hyperglycemic agents, oral hypoglycemic agents, oral insulins, large volume parenterals (LVP), lipid-altering agents, metabolic studies and inborn errors of metabolism, nutrients/amino acids, nutritional LVPs, obesity drugs (anorectics), somatostatin, thyroid agents, vasopressin, and vitamins (other than vitamin D).

Despite its considerable NDA workload, which was CDER's third toughest as of January 2004 (12 pending NDAs), the Division of Metabolic and Endocrine Drug Products had, until 2003, maintained one of the center's most consistent average new drug review times over the past several years. From 1994 through 2002, for example, its average NME review time seldom strayed far from the 12-month mark. In 2003, the division cleared four NMEs, the most within CDER, but did so in a mean time of 21.4 months, its highest mark since 1993.

Division of Pulmonary and Allergy Drug Products Led by Division Director Badrul Chowdhury, M.D., the Division of Pulmonary and Allergy Drug Products is responsible for a wide variety of pulmonary and anti-allergic drugs. These include anti-allergy nasal sprays, antiasthmatic dry powder inhalers, antiasthmatic metered dose inhalers, antiasthmatics (nonsteroidal), antihistamines, antitussives, decongestants, beta-2 agonists, bronchodilators, bronchoconstrictors, cough-cold-allergy preparations, inhaled corticosteriods, pulmonary anti-inflammatory agents, antitussives, mucolytic agents, and pulmonary surfactants.

After being founded in May 1995, the division grew to manage one of CDER's larger NDA workloads, although that workload has moderated at least somewhat more recently (10 pending NDAs as of January 2004). Given that the division has approved only two NMEs over the last four years (2000-2003) and none in 2002 or 2003, it is difficult to provide meaningful statistics on recent NME review times for the group.

Under CDER's reorganization proposal, the Division of Pulmonary and Allergy Drug Products will remain intact under ODE II.

Division of Anesthetic, Critical Care, and Addiction Drug Products Created in 1995, the Division of Anesthetic, Critical Care, and Addiction Drug Products is led by Robert Rappaport, M.D. Although it will remain under ODE II, this unit will be reconstituted as the Division of Analgesics, Anesthetics, and Rheumatology Drug Products under CDER's restructuring plan. By forming this new unit, which will also include anti-inflammatory (systemic corticosteroids) and neurological (non-narcotic analgesics, muscle relaxants) drugs now regulated by CDER's Division of Anti-Inflammatory, Analgesic, and Ophthalmic Drug Products, CDER will effectively group all analgesic drugs under one unit.

The division's current responsibilities can be categorized into two general product groups:

Abusable Drugs. Drugs to treat alcoholism and drug abuse, enkephalin analgesics, hallucinogenic agents, marijuana studies, methadone and other addictives, narcotic antagonist/agonists/analgesics, narcotics in addiction research, and drugs to treat nicotine addiction.

Anesthetic Drugs. Epidural and intrathecal analgesics, neuromuscular blocking agents, preanesthetic sedatives, and general, local, and regional anesthetic agents.

The Division of Anesthetic, Critical Care, and Addiction Drug Products approves few NMEs. The division, which lacked an NME approval in 2001, 2002, and 2003, cleared just three new drugs from 1997-2003.

Office of Drug Evaluation III

Like ODE I and II, ODE III oversees three new drug review divisions.

Division of Reproductive and Urologic Drug Products Led by Division Director Daniel Shames, M.D., the Division of Reproductive and Urologic Drug Products is responsible for oral and non-oral contraceptives, dopamine agonists, estrogens, gonadotropins, GnRH agonists and antagonists, oxytocics, androgens/testosterone, progestins, uterine-acting agents, drugs to treat benign prostate disease, drugs for sexual dysfunction, drugs for treatment of preterm labor, IUDs, sclerosing agents, prostaglandins (abortifacients), drugs for premenstrual syndrome, subdermal pellets (testosterone and estrogen), and androgens/anabolic steroids.

The division, which should not be affected by CDER's pending reorganization, continues to maintain one of CDER's more challenging NDA workloads. As of January 2004, the division had 11 pending NDAs, the third most within CDER.

Division of Medical Imaging and Radiopharmaceutical Drug Products One of CDER's smaller drug review units, the Division of Medical Imaging and Radiopharmaceutical Drug Products is led by Director George Mills, M.D. The division oversees a relatively homogeneous group of imaging and therapeutic products, including magnetic resonance image enhancement agents, radioactive diagnostic agents, radioactive therapeutic agents, radiopaque contrast agents, ultrasound imaging agents, positron emission tomography products, and adjuvants used with all of these products (e.g., potassium perchlorate).

The division has cleared a single NME in each of the past three years. In 2001 and 2002, the unit's NME review times were among the highest in the center (31.7 months and 31.6 months, respectively), although the division cleared an NME in just 6.7 months during 2003.

In April 2003, the Division of Medical Imaging and Radiopharmaceutical Drug Products will be consolidated under CDER's new Office of Oncology Drug Products. Most, if not all, of the division's staffing and product responsibilities will be shifted to a new Division of Medical Imaging and Hematology Products.

Division of Gastrointestinal and Coagulation Drug Products The Division of Gastrointestinal and Coagulation Drug Products is led by Robert Justice, M.D., who was appointed as the unit's director in 2003. Under CDER's reorganization plan, the unit's coagulation products will be shifted to the new Division of Medical Imaging and Hematology Products, and the group will be renamed the Division of Gastroenterology Drug Products.

The division's current review responsibilities can be broken down into two principal therapeutic areas:

Coagulation Drugs. Anti-anemia drugs, anticoagulants, antifibrinolytics, antiplatelet agents, antithrombin drugs, coagulants, fibrinolytics, hematologics, heparin inhibitors (including protamine sulfate and heparinase), metal chelators, miscellaneous blood drugs (including drugs for hemoglobinopathies, thrombocytopenia, and peripheral vascular disease), prostaglandins, and Vitamin K.

Gastrointestinal Drugs. Antacids, anticholinergics, antidiarrheals, antiemetics, cathartics and laxatives, cholelitholytic agents, GI diagnostics, GI motility modifying agents, H2 receptor antagonists, inflammatory bowel disease agents, irritable bowel syndrome agents, liver agents, metal chelators, miscellaneous gastric secretory agents, miscellaneous GI drugs (including hemorrhoidal preparations), pancreatitis agents, pancreatic enzymes, prostaglandins, proton pump inhibitors, sclerosing agents, and sucralfate.

The division's NME approval output and mean new drug review times have varied greatly in recent years. The division's recent mean review times have ranged from 23.4 months in 2000, when it cleared six new drugs, to 7.9 months in 2003, when it cleared two NMEs.

Office of Drug Evaluation IV

After a May 1997 restructuring, ODE IV comprised three new drug review divisions.

Division of Anti-Infective Drug Products The Division of Anti-Infective Drug Products is led by Janice Soreth, M.D., a former medical team leader who was named the division's director in December 2001. Under CDER's reorganization plan, the division will assume responsibilities over ophthalmology drug products (from the current Division of Anti-Inflammatory, Analgesic and Ophthalmologic Drug Products), and will be renamed the Division of Anti-Infective and Ophthalmologic Drug Products.

Today, the Division of Anti-Infective Drug Products regulates aminoglycoides, antibacterial agents, sulfon-amides, topical antibiotics, antigonorrheal agents, anti-resistant antimicrobials, antitumor antibiotics, cephalosporins, clindamycins, dermatologics, detergents, erythromycins/systemic macrolides, other topical anti-infectives, other systemic antimicrobial drugs, otic antibiotics in combination, penem antibiotics, peni-cillins, antibiotic peptides, sulfonamides, gram positive systemic antibiotics, and tetracyclines.

With only one NME approval in 2003 and 2002 combined and only four over the past six years, the division has not been one of CDER's more productive review groups. To be fair, the unit has one of CDER's smaller NDA workloads, with only four pending NDAs in January 2004.

Division of Antiviral Drug Products Under an ODE IV restructuring in 1997, the Division of Antiviral Drug Products' responsibilities were narrowed almost exclusively to antiviral products for AIDS and AIDS-related indications. Today, the Division of Antiviral Drug Products is focused largely on HIV therapies, although it does review immunomodulators and immunostimulants, and has responsibilities for other indications, such as herpes, hepatitis, CMV, respiratory syncytial virus, and influenza.

Not surprisingly given the nature of the products it regulates, the Division of Antiviral Drug Products main-tains CDER's best average new drug review times. In 2003, for example, the division cleared three NMEs in a mean of 7.3 months.

CDER's pending reorganization is not expected to affect the Division of Antiviral Drug Products.

Division of Special Pathogen and Immunologic Drug Products When it was created in May 1997, the Division of Special Pathogen and Immunologic Drug Products assumed responsibility for several drugs and drug groups previously handled by the two other ODE IV review groups. Today, the division is responsible for aminoglycosides, anthelmintic agents (general), antibacterials (bacterial vaginosis), antibacterial quinolones, antifungal candidiasis, systemic antifungals, systemic anti-infectives, antimycobacterials, antiparasitic agents, antiprotozoal agents, antitrichomonads, antituberculosis, chronic fatigue syndromes, immunomodu-lators, immunostimulatory agents, macrolides, other drugs for AIDS-related illnesses, other antiparasitic, antimicrobial drugs, drugs to prevent the rejection of transplanted organs, spiramycin, systemic antibiotics (H. pylori indication), and thalidomide.

Although the division had maintained a mean NME review time of a year or less from 1999 through 2002, the division saw that mark jump to 39.6 months in 2003. The 2003 figure was based on a single lengthy NME review, however.

The division is expected to remain intact and under ODE IV following CDER's planned restructuring.

Office of Drug Evaluation V

ODE V comprises the two new drug review divisions profiled below, in addition to the Division of Over-the-Counter Drug Products, which generally is not considered a new drug review division but which is involved in nonprescription drug issues, including the reviews of NDAs for prescription-to-OTC switches. In early 2003, CDER announced the formation, within ODE V, of a new Botanical Review Team to consolidate OND's scientific and regulatory expertise in botanical products and to serve as a resource to all review divisions and offices in evaluating botanical product INDs and NDAs. The review team is not a separate division, but is a unit within the ODE V office and reports to the ODE V director.

ODE V will be disbanded under CDER's reorganization plan. One division will be moved into ODE III, while another will be split into a pair of reconstituted divisions that will be moved under other ODEs. Meanwhile, the Division of Over-the-Counter Drug Products will form the core of a new Office of Nonprescription Drugs within the Office of New Drugs. Through a group called the NDA Staff, the new OTC office will continue to participate in the reviews of prescription-to-OTC switches proposed in NDAs.

Division of Dermatologic and Dental Drug Products Led by Division Director Jonathan Wilkin, M.D., a dermatologist, the Division of Dermatologic and Dental Drug Products regulates three drug categories:

Dermatological Drugs. Systemic and topical anti-acne drugs, antibacterials for acne, topical antihistamines, topical antimicrobial burn preparations, topical antimicrobials, oral antifungals, antiperspirants, topical antipruritics, anti-seborrheics, topical astringents, topical aural drugs, topical corticosterioids, hair and scalp preparations, miscellaneous topical and systemic immunosuppressants, modulators, pediculicides, pigmenting agents, drugs to treat psoriasis, retinoids, soaps/cleansers, steriods, sunscreens/photoprotectants, thalidomide, and wound cleansing/disinfection agents.

Topical Vaginal Drugs.

Dental Drugs. Anticaries preparations (fluorides, etc.), antigingivitis and antiplaque agents, antifibrinolytics, chelating agents, dental tissue adhesives, dental implants, lozenges, mouthwashes, and periodontal treatments, toothpastes, and drugs to treat xerostomia.

Although the division's responsibilities will not change under CDER's restructuring plan, it will be moved into ODE III (see exhibit above).

Division of Anti-Inflammatory, Analgesic, and Ophthalmic Drug Products Led by Acting Director Brian Harvey, M.D., the Division of Anti-Inflammatory, Analgesic, and Ophthalmic Drug Products is responsible for the three drug categories identified in its title:

Anti-Inflammatory Drugs. Systemic corticosteroids, nonsteroidal cyclooxygenase inhibitors, enzyme blockers, anti-gout drugs, metalloproteinase inhibitors, and immunomodulators for rheumatic diseases.

Neurological Drugs. Non-narcotic analgesics, antipyretics, counterirritants, and muscle relaxants.

Ophthalmics. Alpha adrenergic agonist/blockers, antibiotics, antifungals, antiprotozoals, antivirals, beta adrenergic blockers, carbonic anhydrase inhibitors, corticosteroids, immune system regulators, mast cell inhibitors, nonsteroidal anti-inflammatory agents, prostaglandins, and proteolytic enzymes.

Over the last several years, the division has maintained one of CDER's most consistent mean NME review times. From 1998 to 2003, the unit's mean NME review time has ranged between 5.9 months and 9.9 months Entering 2004 with 16 pending NDAs, the division had CDER's second heaviest NDA review burden.

Under CDER's restructuring proposal, this division essentially will be disbanded, with much of its responsibilities and staff being shifted to a new Division of Analgesics, Anesthetics and Rheumatology Drug Products under ODE II (see exhibit above). Responsibility for ophthalmic drugs would be moved to a new Division of Anti-Infectives and Ophthalmology Drug Products in ODE IV.

Inside the FDA's Drug Review Divisions

Although CDER's 14 new drug review divisions differ in many ways, they are similar in nature and structure. Each unit is led by a division director who is generally a physician, and has, at its core, a three- or four-discipline review structure. IND and NDA reviews are conducted by individuals from each of the following technical disciplines, who are assisted by consult review disciplines when necessary: medical/clinical; nonclinical pharmacology/toxicology; chemistry; and microbiology (e.g., for anti-infective drugs, sterile products):

Medical/Clinical Discipline Often called medical officers, medical/clinical reviewers are almost exclusively physicians. In some instances, such as in the review of psychiatric and dental products, non-physicians are used as medical officers to evaluate drug efficacy.

Medical reviewers are responsible for evaluating the clinical sections of submissions, such as the safety of the clinical protocols in an IND or the results of clinical testing as submitted in an NDA. Within most divisions, clinical reviewers also take the lead role in IND and NDA reviews, and are responsible for reconciling the results of the chemistry, pharmacology, and clinical reviews to formulate the basis upon which a drug will be approved for marketing or used in early clinical testing. Generally, medical reviewers are assigned to one or more drug groups, or therapeutically focused teams.

Chemistry Discipline Each review division has a group of assigned chemists responsible for reviewing the chemistry, manufacturing, and control sections of drug applications. In general terms, chemistry reviewers address issues related to drug identity, manufacturing and control, and analysis.

Technically, CDER's chemists report into the center's Office of New Drug Chemistry (ONDC) rather than the review divisions in which they work. For practical reasons, however, the chemists traditionally have been housed within the respective review divisions.

In mid-2005, however, CDER's move to "a modern, risk-based pharmaceutical quality assessment system" will bring substantive changes to ONDC's structure and approach to chemistry reviews for INDs, NDAs, and supplemental NDAs (sNDA). While CDER's traditional review process has relied on a single chemistry reviewer to evaluate the chemistry, manufacturing, and controls (CMC) aspects of a drug throughout the entire product lifecycle (IND to NDA to postmarketing manufacturing changes), ONDC will be establishing three premarketing chemistry divisions to handle IND/NDA submissions and a postmarketing chemistry division to address sNDA submissions (for postmarketing manufacturing changes).

As part of the reorganization, the chemists that have been housed within the respective drug review divisions will now be housed together under ONDC's new premarketing and postmarketing divisions. Since these chemists will continue to be dedicated to specific new drug review divisions and will, within CDER's new facility, be working adjacent to these divisions, this is not likely to represent a significant change.

Each premarketing chemistry division will feature what is called a "pharmaceutical assessment lead" (PAL), a high-level reviewer who will serve as a "dedicated scientific liaison" to the new drug review divisions. A PAL will conduct an initial assessment of an NDA's CMC section to identify critical issues for the review, and will assign the application to a chemistry reviewer or a small team of interdisciplinary scientists (e.g., chemists, pharmaceutical scientists, engineers) based on the findings of this assessment. Although the PAL will conduct only this initial assessment of NDAs, he or she will likely serve as the primary chemistry reviewer for INDs, according to current CDER plans.

Pharmacology Discipline The pharmacology review team is staffed by pharmacologists and toxicologists who evaluate the results of animal studies in attempting to relate nonclinical drug effects to potential effects in humans.

Microbiology Discipline Within certain divisions, including the Division of Anti-Infective Drug Products and the Division of Antiviral Drug Products, there is a fourth technical review discipline—microbiology. Since antimicrobial and antiviral drug products are designed to affect microbial or viral—rather than human—physiology, the groups employ microbiologists to evaluate the products' effects on viruses or other microorganisms. In addition, the Office of Pharmaceutical Science maintains the New Drug Microbiology Team to consult with other divisions on specific drugs (e.g., sterile products).

Project Management Staff/Consumer Safety Officers Within CDER's new drug review divisions, there is at least one other group of individuals critical to the application review process—project management staff. Called consumer safety officers (CSO) in the past, these individuals are now called project managers, or regulatory health project managers, to better reflect their role in the review management process.

CDER's project managers serve as a drug sponsor's primary contact with a division during the product development and application review processes. In addition to a reviewer from each of the primary technical disciplines, a project manager is assigned to each IND and NDA upon its submission.

Since most project managers have scientific backgrounds (i.e., primarily in pharmacy), they can provide informed reports on technical issues that arise during the application review process. Their real expertise, however, is their knowledge of the drug review process, and of the policies, procedures, and idiosyncrasies of their respective divisions.

The IND Review Process

The IND review is unique among the FDA's application review processes. In many respects, this process and the FDA's treatment of INDs represent a delicate balance between the federal government's responsibility to protect clinical trial subjects from unnecessary risks and its desire to avoid becoming an impediment to the advance of medical research. Given these dual goals, the FDA must perform a safety review of an IND prior to clinical trials, but is given only 30 days in which to reach an initial decision on the application.

The FDA's principal goals during the IND review are: (1) to determine if the preclinical test data show that the drug is reasonably safe for administration to humans; and (2) to determine if the protocol for the proposed clinical studies would expose clinical subjects to unnecessary risks (assuming the protocol proposes only Phase 1 studies).

Although some aspects of the IND review process were addressed by the Food and Drug Administration Modernization Act of 1997, the process has been largely shielded from reform efforts, perhaps due to its efficiency. Because of industry sensitivities regarding the IND clinical hold process, however, FDAMA introduced provisions designed to streamline that process (see discussion below). FDAMA and PDUFA II/III do attempt to further increase CDER's role as a drug development collaborator with industry, largely by formalizing the process through which early-stage (e.g., pre-IND) meetings are scheduled and held.

In coming years, several regulatory initiatives and scientific advances are likely to affect the IND review process to varying degrees:

The ICH's Common Technical Document (CTD) Initiative. Although the marketing application (NDA) was the initial focus of the ICH and FDA's CTD initiative (see Chapter 7), the agency has quickly extended the CTD principles and format to other applications, including the IND. In their most recent calls for electronic INDs (see discussion below), for example, CDER officials are encouraging companies to provide these applications in the CTD format. Further, in some of its most recent IND-related guidances—INDs *for Phases 2 and 3 Studies of Drugs, Including Specified Therapeutic Biotechnology-Derived Products: Chemistry, Manufacturing, and Controls Content and Format* (May 2003), for example—CDER is advocating that the content of the IND be presented in the CTD format.

Submission of eINDs. As it is doing for the NDA, the FDA is moving the IND and other applications inexorably toward the electronic submission age. During 2003, in fact, the agency added the IND to the growing list of regulatory submissions that it can accept completely in electronic format (i.e., without an accompanying paper-based version). In an August 2003 draft industry guidance entitled, *Providing Regulatory Submissions in Electronic Format-Human Pharmaceutical Product Applications and Related Submissions*, CDER provided industry with guidance on providing INDs and other applications in the harmonized electronic common technical document (eCTD) format. CDER used the draft guidance to establish its clear interest in promoting electronic submissions, including eINDs, in the eCTD format as early as possible in the development process. "We believe it is most beneficial to begin your eCTD-based submissions with the initial submission of an application," the agency stated. "The maximum benefit will be derived once an application is in electronic format. This is particularly true for the IND, where submissions are provided over a long period of time. You should submit the electronic document information for all documents in the eCTD backbone files following the ICH eCTD specifications and the Comprehensive Table of Contents Headings and Hierarchy" (the comprehensive table of contents and hierarchy is derived from the ICH eCTD specifications as well as the specifications for the CTD's Module 1-U.S. region-specific and administrative information). As of mid-2004, in fact, CDER officials reported that the center was not accepting eINDs in any format other than the eCTD format. While industry's interest in developing such submissions was limited at this writing, CDER officials believe submission rates will increase as they develop new electronic tools. Meanwhile, eINDs are receiving attention under separate initiatives as well: Under a November 2003 NCI/FDA initiative regarding oncology product development, the agencies were to work together "to build tools that facilitate electronic interaction, focusing in particular on IND applications."

Pharmacogenomics. As scientists and regulators learn more about how to use new sciences, such as pharmacogenomics, for decision making in the drug development process, the IND review process will increasingly involve the review of new types of data. In a November 2003 draft guidance, for instance, the agency took its first step to encourage industry to submit pharmacogenomics information in INDs and other applications to help FDA reviewers and scientists understand the relevant scientific issues in this emerging field (see Chapter 3). While the agency prepared to release a final guidance document in late 2004, CDER officials claimed that center reviewers were actively reviewing and making decisions based on voluntarily submitted pharmacogenomic data in advance of a final guidance.

CDER *Standardization of Review Processes.* CDER officials continue to push to standardize the application review process through the ongoing good review practices (GRP) initiative, which includes the development of discipline review templates. In July 2003, CDER and CBER issued a draft GRP guidance entitled, *Good Review Management Principles for PDUFA Products* to identify the current best review practices and future initiatives for the first-cycle review of NDAs. Earlier, in May 2001, CDER released a reviewer guidance document entitled, *Pharmacology/Toxicology Review Format*, to provide the pharmaceutical industry and others "with an understanding of the standard format and content of primary pharmacology/toxicology reviews." The center states that it uses a standardized format for IND and NDA pharmacology/toxicology reviews for several reasons, including that the format provides for unified communication among multiple audiences, and that it ensures that the most important information is captured in all reviews. In mid-2004, CDER released a pair of internal guidances—*Clinical Pharmacology and Biopharmaceutics Review Template* (May 2004) and *Clinical Review Template* (July 2004) to establish standardized "review templates" for different aspects of the clinical reviews for NDAs (see Chapter 8). In fiscal year 2004, the agency was also planning to release other standards-related guidances, including documents on the safety review of clinical data and standards for the electronic submission of clinical data. Although many of these standards-related guidance documents and initiatives focus on the NDA review, it is likely that at least some of the principles and practices espoused in these documents and initiatives will extend to IND reviews at some point.

Initial Processing of the IND The FDA's early processing of an IND depends on the manner in which the application is shipped to the agency. INDs arriving by regular mail, for example, are forwarded to the general FDA mailroom, while applications shipped by courier are sent directly to CDER's Central Document Room.

Once within CDER's Central Document Room, an IND is stamped with the date of receipt, an extremely important event since it starts the 30-day review clock. Staffers within this office assign an identification number to the IND, and then log information about the filing into a computer database-the sponsor's name, the drug's name, and the application's identification number. They will also capture certain information, such as the type of IND (commercial, research, emergency use) and the nature of the filing (paper, electronic, or mixed), on a form that will accompany the IND to the division. Finally, staffers package the application (e.g., in review jackets if necessary) before forwarding it to the review division. Generally, sponsors package the INDs in appropriately colored jackets that can be purchased from the federal government.

Given the tight IND review time frame, this initial processing occurs extremely quickly. After arriving and being processed by CDER's Central Document Room, most INDs will be forwarded to the relevant review division by the next business day. For treatment INDs, however, the staffers attempt to forward the applications even sooner, when possible.

The IND within the Review Division Once within the relevant review division, the IND is sent to a file or document room, where a staffer creates an electronic file containing the applicant's name, the IND's date of receipt and identification number, and other information (*note:* some divisions share document rooms today). The division then develops and forwards an "acknowledgment letter," which tells the applicant that the FDA has received the IND. This letter also specifies the IND's identification number and receipt date, and provides the name of the project manager who will act as the sponsor's FDA contact person on matters involving the application.

The assigned project manager will then serve as the unofficial coordinator of the review, seeing that the application is forwarded to the relevant individuals. At this stage, the project manager will review the contents of the IND to identify any deficiencies.

As noted previously, an IND faces reviews by the three or four technical review disciplines within a division—medical/clinical, pharmacology, chemistry, and, in two divisions, microbiology. The first copy of the IND is usually forwarded to a supervisory medical officer, sometimes called a "group leader," who has expertise in the subject drug's therapeutic category. In some review divisions, it is the group leader who analyzes the results of the medical, pharmacology, and chemistry reviews, and recommends whether or not the IND contents are adequate to allow the initiation of clinical trials.

Obviously, each review discipline focuses on the aspect of the IND relevant to its expertise:

Pharmacology Review. The reviewing pharmacologist focuses on the results of animal pharmacology and toxicology testing, and attempts to relate these test results to human pharmacology. As noted above, CDER has provided some insights into the IND pharmacology review in its May 2001 reviewer guidance entitled, *Pharmacology/Toxicology Review Format.*

Chemistry Review. The reviewing chemist evaluates the manufacturing and processing procedures for a drug to ensure that the compound is adequately reproducible and stable in its pure form. If the drug is either unstable or not reproducible, then the validity of any clinical testing would be undermined and, more importantly, the studies may pose significant risks. The chemistry reviewer also evaluates the drug's characterization and chemical structure, and compares the product's structure and impurity profile to those of other drugs (i.e., drugs known to be toxic). As noted above, CDER's transition to a new "pharmaceutical quality assessment system" in mid-2005 will affect the center's structure for conducting IND chemistry reviews. Upon this transition, the IND's chemistry evaluation will be conducted or led by a pharmaceutical assessment lead (PAL), who will be a high-level chemistry reviewer within the Office of New Drug Chemistry rather than a reviewing chemist within the new drug review division.

Clinical Review. The medical reviewer evaluates the clinical trial protocol to determine: (1) if the subjects will be protected from unnecessary risks (for all clinical trials proposed in the IND); and (2) if the study design will provide relevant data on the safety and effectiveness of the drug (if Phase 2 or 3 trials are proposed in the initial IND filing). Since the late 1980s, FDA reviewers have been instructed to provide drug sponsors with greater freedom during Phase 1, as long as the investigations do not expose subjects to undue risks. In evaluating Phase 2 and 3 investigations, however, FDA reviewers also must ensure that these studies are of sufficient scientific quality, and that they are capable of yielding data that can support marketing approval.

Microbiology Review. When relevant, a microbiologist evaluates data on the drug's *in vivo* and *in vitro* effects on the physiology of the target virus or other microorganism.

During the drug evaluation process, reviews in the three or four technical areas are supplemented by what are called "consultative reviews" in biostatistics and clinical biopharmaceutics. At the IND review stage, agency biostatisticians may evaluate animal data to determine the statistical significance of drug effects in animals, including tumor rates and dose-response relationships. Further, while FDA biopharmaceutics staffers may not become directly involved in the IND review (except for AIDS drugs and other critical therapies), these staffers can review biopharmaceutics and pharmacokinetic data (i.e., drug concentrations in blood and urine) from initial clinical studies to provide advice on dosing, dosing intervals, and other drug-administration issues for later trials.

As new types of data are required or provided voluntarily in INDs and other regulatory submissions, other groups may become involved in the application review process. In mid-2004, for example, CDER was in the process of establishing a pharmacogenomics advisory committee that will, in some cases, become involved in the review of pharmacogenomics data submitted voluntarily by IND and NDA sponsors (see discussion above and Chapter 3). At press time, however, it was unclear if such a committee would become directly involved during the 30-day IND review period.

During the review process, IND reviewers may contact the applicant via phone, fax, e-mail, or letter to seek clarifications or more information or data (see discussion below). When the reviewers complete their evaluations, each submits a report summarizing his or her findings to the group leader, who is left to reconcile these findings and to make a final recommendation to the division director. Alternatively, some divisions may not typically have written IND assessments from each reviewer developed by the end of the 30-day review, but may instead choose to discuss and document all relevant concerns and issues at a group meeting called a "safety meeting" during the 30-day IND review. Ultimately, however, all reviewers must document their findings in a written review.

While a division must complete its safety evaluation within the 30-day period, reviewers may continue to evaluate the IND after the period expires. If new safety concerns arise from this continuing review, the FDA may order that ongoing clinical trials be discontinued until these concerns are addressed and resolved.

The 30-Day Review Clock Except for a narrow class of INDs for emergency research (see discussion below), the FDA has no uniform procedures for informing applicants about the results of routine IND reviews. Most drug review divisions, for instance, do not contact the sponsor if they do not identify any problems with drug safety and the proposed clinical trials. Rather, the divisions just allow the 30-day review period to expire, thereby permitting the sponsor to initiate clinical studies immediately. In this way, INDs are never formally approved, but are allowed to proceed (i.e., the clinical studies proposed in the IND can be initiated) through the center's "administrative silence." Although they are not required to do so, sponsors should contact the agency before beginning clinical trials to confirm that studies may be initiated.

CDER staffers caution that a firm that has not received an acknowledgement letter should not initiate trials, no matter how long the company believes that an IND has been at the agency. Because INDs can be lost during shipment or misplaced at the agency, applicants should contact the FDA if they have not received an acknowledgement letter within a reasonable period.

When deficiencies are found in an IND, the FDA may place the IND on clinical hold (see discussion below) or permit clinical studies to begin. If the review division decides that an IND deficiency is not sufficiently serious to justify delaying clinical studies, the division may either telephone, or forward an information request letter to, the sponsor. Whichever form the communication takes, the division informs the sponsor that it may proceed with the planned clinical trials, but that additional information is necessary to complete or correct the IND file.

Although there can be considerable variability in the ways that CDER's 14 drug review divisions communicate deficiencies to applicants during the initial IND review process and while clinical studies are being conducted under an IND, center officials have been attempting to standardize these communications. Because the initial IND review period is so brief, however, most division/applicant communications regarding IND deficiencies take place via the telephone and less-formal fax communications. If there are problems that reviewers believe must be addressed before an IND can proceed, the division often will call or fax the applicant to request an amendment (e.g., a protocol amendment) or additional information during the 30-day review period. In many cases, issues can be resolved during this 30-day period, thereby circumventing the need for a formal clinical hold. In certain cases, some divisions also claim that they will permit applicants to begin studies before the submission and agency review of a requested change or information, provided that a company has given its commitment to implement the change or submit the information prior to study initiation. Although such informal processes are being discouraged by CDER management, they may still be undertaken in selected situations.

Once an IND becomes "active," meaning that studies are being conducted under that application (i.e., following the initial 30-day review), there will likely be instances in which a sponsor and CDER will have to communicate to address emerging issues in response to new preclinical and clinical data and the submission of new clinical protocols. The drug center has attempted to standardize such communications by classifying them into the following categories:

Deficiency Letters. Typically, a deficiency letter is sent when a review division identifies problems or deficiencies that might, if not resolved, justify the use of a clinical hold. Rarely is there time during the initial 30-day IND review period to allow for the use of deficiency letters.

Information Request Letters. An information request letter is sent when a review division wants a response from the sponsor (e.g., a clarification or more information on an issue), but when the absence of the information would not typically justify a clinical hold. In virtually all cases, the types of issues that trigger an information request letter can be addressed quickly. For the development and issuance of IND information request letters regarding chemistry/manufacturing/control issues, CDER has developed and released an internal policy manual entitled, *Drafting, Circulating, and Signing Chemistry, Manufacturing, and Controls Letters* (MaPP 5310, October 1998).

Advice Letter. An advice letter is an FDA communication in which a division makes comments to the applicant (e.g., regarding an ongoing or proposed clinical study or protocol), but when the agency is not seeking any type of response from the clinical sponsor.

Under a 1997 regulation, the FDA established that sponsors of INDs for a special class of studies—emergency research conducted under an exemption from informed consent requirements—would require prior FDA authorization before trial initiation (see Chapter 5). For any IND proposing such research, the FDA must provide a written determination before study initiation. In contrast to the submission and review scenario for a traditional IND, therefore, the applicant must await the agency's authorization before it can initiate a study in this special class, even if such authorization is not granted within 30 days.

The Clinical Hold

When CDER discovers serious deficiencies that cannot be addressed before or during the IND review process, the center will contact the sponsor within the 30-day review period to delay the clinical trial. The clinical hold is the mechanism that CDER uses to accomplish this.

Through a clinical hold order, the agency can delay the initiation of an early-phase trial on the basis of information submitted in the IND. Later in the development process, clinical hold orders can be used to suspend an ongoing study based on either a re-review of the original IND or a review of newly submitted clinical protocols, safety reports, protocol amendments, or other information. When a clinical hold is issued, a sponsor must address the issue that is the basis of the hold before it can be removed.

The FDA's authority regarding clinical holds is outlined in federal regulations, which specify the clinical hold criteria that the agency applies to the various phases of clinical testing. In addition, CDER has developed a policy guide entitled, IND *Process and Review Procedures* (MaPP 6030.1) to describe the center's policies and procedures for issuing IND clinical holds.

Although Congress addressed clinical holds under the FDA Modernization Act of 1997, the regulation seemed, in most respects, to codify existing FDA practice regarding holds. The law's provisions allow the FDA to issue a clinical hold when it determines that: (1) "the drug involved represents an unreasonable risk to the safety of persons who are the subjects of the clinical investigation, taking into account the qualifications of the clinical investigators, information about the drug, the design of the clinical investigation, the conditions for which the drug is to be investigated, and the health status of the subjects involved;" or (2) for such other reasons as the FDA may by regulation establish.

Clinical Holds and Phase 1 Trials One of the principal goals of the FDA's 1987 IND regulations was to give sponsors "greater freedom" during the initial stages of clinical research. Therefore, the regulations state that the FDA should not place a clinical hold on a Phase 1 study "unless it presents an unreasonable and significant risk to test subjects." In the regulation's preamble, the FDA establishes that it will "defer to sponsors on matters of Phase 1 study design," and will not consider a Phase 1 trial's scientific merit in deciding whether it should be allowed to proceed.

The regulation specified four situations in which the FDA can either delay a Phase 1 study proposed in an IND or discontinue an ongoing Phase 1 trial:

- if human subjects are or would be exposed to an unreasonable and significant risk of illness or injury;
- if the clinical investigators named in the IND are not qualified by reason of their scientific training and experience to conduct the investigation described in the IND;
- if the investigator's brochure (i.e., material supplying drug-related safety and effectiveness information to clinical investigators) is misleading, erroneous, or materially incomplete; or
- if the IND does not contain sufficient information as required under federal regulations to assess the risks that the proposed studies present to subjects.

A June 2000 regulation provided an additional circumstance in which CDER could impose a clinical hold on clinical studies. Under that regulation, CDER can place a clinical hold on a study for a drug intended to treat a life-threatening disease or condition if it finds that the study sponsor has "categorically excluded" otherwise eligible men or women of reproductive potential because of a perceived risk or potential risk of reproductive or developmental toxicity. The regulation is a government response to the previous practice of excluding women of childbearing potential from early clinical trials.

Since the new requirement does not apply to studies that are conducted exclusively in healthy volunteers, it will be irrelevant for many Phase 1 studies. Studies that are pertinent only to one gender (e.g., to evaluate a drug's excretion in semen or its effects on menstrual function) are also exempt from such requirements.

The fact that CDER may be reviewing more informed consent documents (ICD) as part of the IND review process could also increase the situations in which the center might issue clinical holds. Under a November 2002 CDER policy, the drug center could ask more applicants to submit ICDs with their INDs. Although many IND applicants routinely submit ICDs in their INDs on a voluntary basis, the new policy will encourage CDER reviewers to request the submission of the ICD if "the proposed investigational use raises a particular concern about the adequacy of informed consent" (see Chapter 3). The new policy recommends that ICDs be submitted for all treatment INDs and protocols and cases in which a sponsor requests exceptions from informed consent requirements. When a division has specific concerns about the ICD, it is advised to forward the ICD the protocol, and relevant supporting documentation to the Division of Scientific Investigations' Human Subject Protection Team for a consultative review. In particularly problematic cases, the new policy allows for the use of a clinical hold order until "an acceptable revision of the ICD is received."

Clinical Holds and Phase 2 and 3 Studies The FDA has greater discretionary powers to delay and discontinue Phase 2 and Phase 3 trials. Current regulations allow the agency to place a clinical hold on a Phase 2 or Phase 3 trial if: (1) any of the Phase 1 clinical hold criteria outlined above are met; or (2) the "plan or protocol for the investigation is clearly deficient in design to meet its stated objectives."

How Clinical Holds Work The FDA acknowledges that the imposition of a clinical hold is a relatively informal and flexible process. Given the nature of product development, the agency has resisted suggestions that it formalize the clinical hold process.

Current regulations state that the hold process will, in many cases, begin with an FDA-sponsor discussion: "Whenever FDA concludes that a deficiency exists in a clinical investigation that may be grounds for the imposition of a clinical hold, FDA will, unless patients are exposed to immediate and serious risk, attempt to discuss and satisfactorily resolve the matter with the sponsor before issuing the clinical hold order." The agency claims that most potential holds, particularly those based on inadequate patient monitoring, can be resolved through such discussions.

In certain situations (e.g., when CDER cannot complete an initial review within 30 days), a division may ask sponsors, on an informal basis, to voluntarily agree to an extension of the 30-day review to avoid a clinical hold order. Called an "informal clinical hold," this mechanism allows the FDA and the sponsor alike to avoid complications associated with formal clinical hold orders (e.g., paperwork). In such cases, the division typically promises to contact the sponsor as soon as a decision is reached. Because increased sponsor/agency communications and development-stage meetings have provided more opportunities for issues to be addressed, FDA officials claim that informal clinical holds are now less common than they once were. Beginning several years ago, senior CDER officials began to discourage the use of informal clinical holds, largely because of uncertainty regarding the regulatory implications of such informal concepts. In addition, industry has proposed that CDER eliminate informal holds because they are not subject to the time and procedural requirements established for formal clinical holds. Although there are no CDER data on the use of informal clinical holds, most within the center assume that they are less common today.

CDER's October 2000 *Guidance for Industry: Submitting and Reviewing Complete Responses to Clinical Holds* and its May 1998 MaPP 6030.1 define two types of clinical holds:

Complete clinical hold: "A delay or suspension of all clinical work requested under an IND. If a sponsor submits an initial IND and within the first 30-day period FDA and the sponsor agree on an alternative protocol that is allowed to proceed, this does not constitute a clinical hold provided there are no specific FDA contingencies that require FDA review/approval before further studies are started."

Partial clinical hold: "A delay or suspension of only part of the clinical work requested under the IND (e.g., a specific protocol or part of a protocol is not allowed to proceed; however, other protocols or parts of the protocol are allowed to proceed under the IND). If FDA requires that progress to the next study is contingent (1) on FDA review of additional data and (2) subsequent specific permission for the study to proceed, this represents a partial clinical hold. On the other hand, if the sponsor does not need to wait for FDA review and authorization to proceed before initiating a new protocol, then this is not a partial hold, even if additional data have been requested." In a September 2004 guidance entitled, *The Use of Clinical Holds Following Clinical Investigator Misconduct*, CDER establishes circumstances (e.g., data falsification, serious protocol violations, failure to obtain IRB review and informed consent, failure to report serious adverse experiences) under which it might consider suspending a particular clinical investigator's participation in a clinical trial through a partial clinical hold order (see Chapter 14).

Under CDER policy, the division's relevant medical team leader (i.e., the reviewing medical officer's supervisor) is responsible for leading discussions of safety concerns regarding the planned protocol. If these concerns cannot be resolved through the discussions, however, the review division director must be involved in the decision to impose a clinical hold.

According to CDER's MaPP 6030.1, "clinical holds of commercial INDs should be communicated to the appropriate sponsor representative by a telephone call from the division director (or acting division director)." A letter clearly identifying the reasons for the clinical hold must be sent to the sponsor within seven calendar days of this telephone call.

When the hold order is issued, identified studies must be delayed or discontinued immediately. If the study has not yet begun, no subjects may be administered the investigational drug. Ongoing studies placed on clinical hold must be discontinued immediately, and no new subjects may be recruited to the study or placed on the treatment. CDER may, however, permit subjects already on the treatment to continue receiving the experimental drug.

To facilitate CDER's timely review of sponsor responses to clinical holds, applicants should forward their responses by courier to the division document room and fax a copy of the cover letter to the division project manager responsible for the IND. This communication should be clearly identified as a "Clinical Hold Complete Response." When CDER uses a clinical hold letter to communicate issues that are unrelated to the imposition of the clinical hold (i.e., in addition to those issues that are relevant), sponsors should address such issues in a separate amendment to the IND and not in a formal response to the hold, current center guidance states.

CDER policies and regulations call for divisions to respond to complete sponsor responses within 30 calendar days of their receipt. If the division is not able to do so, division staffers must telephone the sponsor and discuss "the review progress to date and what is being done to facilitate completion of the review." Division directors make the final decisions on issuing and lifting all clinical holds. The FDA's PDUFA III commitments also include performance standards affecting this goal: In fiscal years 2003 through 2007, 90 percent of FDA responses must be sent within 30 calendar days.

An applicant must await an FDA response before beginning or resuming a trial placed on clinical hold. According to CDER's October 2000 guidance document, "After an IND has been placed on clinical hold, until the applicant has received a communication (via phone, fax, letter, e-mail) from the Agency allowing the study to proceed, the study may not be initiated."

IND Clinical Hold Rates Within CDER It is well known that CDER's clinical hold rates on commercial INDs declined dramatically in the mid- and late 1990s, and that they have remained relatively low since that time. The agency issued clinical holds on just 8 to 9 percent of commercial INDs submitted in each of the last four fiscal years (2000-2003) (note: these figures can rise slightly over time, since INDs can be placed on clinical hold even after the initial 30-day review period).

Clinical Holds* on Commercial IND Submissions by CDER Drug Review Division, 1994–2003
(# INDs placed on hold/# of IND receipts)

	1994	1995**	1996**	1997**	1998**	1999**	2000**	2001**	2002**	2003
Cardio-Renal Drug Products	0%	3%	0%	8%	5%	0%	19%	7%	4%	3%
	(0/23)	(1/30)	(0/26)	(2/26)	(1/22)	(0/23)	(5/26)	(2/30)	(1/28)	(1/35)
Neuropharmacological Drug Products	37%	45%	20%	22%	35%	29%	11%	29%	19%	26%
	(17/46)	(19/42)	(8/41)	(14/65)	(19/55)	(15/52)	(6/56)	(14/48)	(10/54)	(14/54)
Oncologic Drug Products	-	4%	3%	1%	4%	5%	3%	5%	4%	2%
		(2/55)	(2/58)	(1/94)	(4/105)	(3/64)	(2/74)	(3/62)	(2/55)	(1/62)
Pulmonary Drug Products	-	9%	8%	4%	4%	5%	4%	5%	0%	14%
		(2/22)	(2/26)	(1/25)	(1/23)	(1/21)	(1/25)	(1/19)	(0/20)	(4/28)
Medical Imaging and Radiopharm. Drug Products	-	20%	0%	0%	29%	0%	0%	0%	0%	0%
		(2/10)	(0/5)	(0/9)	(2/7)	(0/11)	(0/5)	(0/20)	(0/6)	(0/5)
Gastrointestinal and Coagulation Drug Products	5%	8%	17%	5%	12%	10%	9%	0%	11%	0%
	(1/19)	(2/24)	(6/35)	(1/22)	(3/25)	(2/20)	(3/32)	(0/22)	(3/28)	(0/30)
Anesthetic, Critical Care and Addiction Drug Products	-	7%	0%	0%	6%	12%	0%	4%	14%	13%
		(1/15)	(0/17)	(0/23)	(1/18)	(3/25)	(0/11)	(1/24)	(4/29)	(3/23)
Metabolic and Endocrine Drug Products	18%	4%	6%	9%	3%	5%	18%	18%	19%	11%
	(8/45)	(1/28)	(2/34)	(3/33)	(1/36)	(2/37)	(9/49)	(8/44)	(8/43)	(1/11)
Anti-Infective Drug Products	5%	29%	0%	15%	0%	9%	0%	17%	0%	9%
	(1/19)	(4/14)	(0/7)	(2/13)	(0/14)	(1/11)	(0/11)	(1/6)	(0/4)	(1/11)
Anti-Inflammatory, Analgesic and Ophthalmic Drug Products	-	3%	9%	3%	5%	21%	0%	9%	10%	16%
		(1/30)	(3/35)	(1/37)	(2/39)	(7/34)	(0/39)	(3/34)	(4/40)	(5/32)
Antiviral Drug Products	7%	9%	5%	9%	10%	16%	4%	10%	7%	0%
	(2/28)	(2/22)	(1/20)	(2/22)	(3/30)	(6/37)	(1/25)	(2/20)	(2/28)	(0/17)
Reproductive and Urologic Drug Products	-	5%	6%	9%	8%	12%	11%	7%	3%	4%
		(1/19)	(2/29)	(3/35)	(3/40)	(6/52)	(4/36)	(2/29)	(1/37)	(1/26)
Special Pathogens and Immunologic Drug Products	-	6%	6%	0%	0%	7%	0%	0%	0%	0%
		(1/17)	(1/18)	(0/15)	(0/11)	(1/14)	(0/8)	(0/11)	(0/13)	(0/12)
OTC Products	-	-	-	-	-	-	-	-	-	-
Dermatological and Dental Drug Products	7%	7%	12%	19%	13%	3%	10%	0%	9.0%	0%
	(2/30)	(2/30)	(3/25)	(5/27)	(6/46)	(1/29)	(4/42)	(0/41)	(4/43)	(0/24)
Totals	13%	12%	8%	8%	10%	11%	8%	8%	9%	9%
	(43/333)	(41/358)	(30/376)	(35/446)	(46/471)	(48/430)	(35/459)	(34/410)	(39/428)	(34/396)

* Holds column in 1995–2003 represents number of INDs received in FY that were placed on hold (full or partial) at any point. Data from previous years represent holds on initial IND submissions.

** 1995–2003 data are for fiscal years.

Source: FDA

It is important to note, however, that hold rates can vary considerably from division to division. This variability is at least partially influenced by the nature of the drugs that the various divisions review. The Division of Neuropharmacological Drug Products, for example, issued holds on 26 percent (14 of 54) of the commercial INDs submitted in FY2003, according to CDER data. The Division of Special Pathogen and Immunologic Drug Products, on the other hand, has not issued a single clinical hold order for any of the commercial IND submissions filed over the last four fiscal years (see exhibit below).

There are several potential reasons why IND hold rates declined during the 1990s and have remained low relative to previous periods. Some maintain that all industry submissions have improved in recent years. Others point to CDER's Clinical Holds Peer Review Committee, which now meets regularly to evaluate a sample of the center's IND hold decisions. Divisions and reviewers that issue IND holds must be prepared to discuss and defend these actions before the committee, which comprises largely senior CDER officials. In addition, sponsors are given the opportunity to appear before the committee to discuss the holds placed on their INDs.

IND Status

Once the FDA's 30-day review period expires and clinical investigations are initiated, an IND may be classified into any one of five status categories:

Active Status. Generally, an active IND is one under which clinical investigations are being conducted—in other words, the FDA has decided not to delay or suspend the clinical studies proposed under the initial IND or subsequent protocol amendments. An IND may remain on active status for extended periods even though no trials are being conducted under the application, however. In such cases, clinical studies may be re-initiated under the IND without further notification to the FDA.

Inactive Status. An IND on inactive status is one under which clinical investigations are not being conducted. There are two ways through which an IND can be put on inactive status. First, the IND sponsor may ask CDER to place the application on inactive status, thereby eliminating the IND updating and submission requirements applicable to the sponsor. Also, the FDA may place the application on inactive status if the agency finds either: (1) that no subjects are entered into an IND's clinical studies for a period of two years or more; or (2) that all investigations under an application remain on clinical hold for one year or more. CDER may seek to terminate INDs that remain on inactive status for five years or more (see discussion below).

Clinical Hold. As previously discussed, a clinical hold is an FDA order to delay a proposed investigation or to suspend an ongoing investigation. If all investigations covered by an IND remain on clinical hold for one year or more, CDER may place the IND on inactive status.

Withdrawn Status. The sponsor of an IND can withdraw an IND at any time and for any reason. When the sponsor withdraws an IND, all clinical investigations under the IND must be discontinued, the FDA and all investigators must be notified, and all stocks of the drug must be returned to the sponsor or otherwise disposed of at the request of the sponsor.

IND Termination. The FDA will seek to terminate an IND if the agency is unable to resolve deficiencies in an IND or in the conduct of an investigation through a clinical hold order or through a more informal alternative. For example, the agency would pursue IND termination if a sponsor failed to delay a proposed investigation under an IND that had been placed on clinical hold. Except when continuing an investigation would present an immediate danger to clinical subjects, the FDA will issue a proposal to terminate and will offer the sponsor an opportunity to respond before finalizing a termination.

CHAPTER 5

The Clinical Development of New Drugs

Virtually all preclinical work—animal pharmacology/toxicology testing and the development of the IND—is undertaken to obtain the FDA's tacit permission to initiate clinical trials, the ultimate premarketing testing ground for unapproved drugs. During these trials, an investigational compound is administered to human subjects and is evaluated for its safety and effectiveness in treating, preventing, or diagnosing a specific disease or condition. The results of this testing will comprise the single most important factor in the FDA's approval or disapproval of a new drug.

As they have in the past, emerging socio-political trends and scientific advances are placing new demands on, and offering new opportunities to, companies undertaking clinical development programs for experimental drugs. Given the push toward personalized medicine, for example, pharmacogenomics has become a significant new consideration in drug development. Under a November 2003 draft guidance document, the agency is now seeking and receiving voluntary pharmacogenomic data submissions so its reviewers can accelerate their understanding of the scientific issues in this emerging field (see Chapters 3 and 7).

Further, the FDA's increased focus on risk management and drug safety under PDUFA III means that drug developers must consider both the need for and the appropriate characteristics of so-called "risk minimization action plans" as their products advance through clinical trials. The intensifying focus on drug safety by both the American public and U.S. policy makers continues to pressure clinical development programs and pharmacovigilance activities (e.g., Phase 4 programs and adverse experience reporting efforts) to assure a drug's safety. Scientific advances in the understanding of specific drug effects continue to spotlight certain adverse drug effects—liver toxicities and QTc prolongation in particular—in the drug development and approval process. This has put growing pressure on drug sponsors to better characterize drug effects in these and other areas during the development process and, when necessary, to more fully characterize such effects following approval.

Meanwhile, FDA initiatives designed to modernize and streamline product development may usher in the next significant evolutionary stage in clinical development. Under its March 2004 "Critical Path Initiative," the FDA will be focusing on drug safety and efficacy assessments to address what it calls the "pipeline problem"—the recent slowdown, instead of the expected acceleration, in innovative medical therapies reaching patients. "Not enough applied scientific work has been done in creating new tools to get fundamentally better answers about how the safety and effectiveness of new products can be demonstrated, in faster time frames, with more certainty, and at lower costs," the agency stated in unveiling the program. "As a result, the vast majority of investigational products that enter clinical trials fail... In many cases, developers have no choice but to use the tools and concepts of the last century to assess this century's candidates."

The centerpiece of the Critical Path Initiative, which will no doubt be a multi-year effort, is the development of a so-called "product development toolkit" that will comprise "powerful new scientific and technical methods such as animal or computer-based predictive models, biomarkers for safety and effectiveness, and new clinical evaluation techniques...[and which will be used] to improve predictability and efficiency along the critical path from laboratory concept to commercial product." The toolkit's goal will be to allow researchers to better predict eventual product failures early during clinical trials and to reduce developmental uncertainties in three critical areas—product safety, medical utility, and manufacturing potential (see exhibit below).

At the same time that the FDA, under the Critical Path initiative, is looking outside the agency for assistance in identifying the areas that will most benefit from innovative approaches and emerging technologies, it is also undertaking a number of internal programs and initiatives that are designed to streamline and improve clinical development programs:

- Under its January 2003 "Innovation Initiative," the FDA is attempting to facilitate new product development by providing clearer and up-to-date guidances on priority diseases and emerging technologies. To provide a clearer understanding of key review questions, required scientific evidence, target clinical endpoints for establishing efficacy in clinical trials, and FDA expectations of NDAs, the agency is creating working groups that will draw on experts from across the agency and from the broader community to develop guidances, initially for priority diseases such as oncology, diabetes, and obesity.

- As part of the agency's commitment to improving the critical path for medical product development, CDER officials revealed in mid-2004 that they planned to implement a formal guidance to facilitate the conduct of exploratory clinical studies. During a September 2004 speech, Acting FDA Commissioner Lester Crawford, Ph.D., said the anticipated guidance would outline "ways to perform early proof-of-mechanism, screening, and microdose human studies in a safe, efficient manner." A month later, he stated that the guidance's "goal is to facilitate early, small-scale proof-of-concept studies before a drug reaches IND stage." In theory, such studies will permit sponsors to obtain an initial assessment of a drug's effects before committing to full-scale clinical development. While it was unclear at this writing whether the guidance would establish one or multiple routes for exploratory clinical studies, FDA officials indicated that it would, unlike an existing policy on screening INDs (ScIND, see Chapter 3), explicitly state that firms can initiate such early clinical studies with less preclinical safety data. In a July 2004 speech touting the new ScIND concept as an opportunity to study pharmacokinetics and target interaction early in drug development, one senior CDER official noted that "the amount of preclinical safety data for ScINDs will generally be less than for conventional INDs. The reduction in safety data requirements will be scaled to the goals, duration and scope of the proposed clinical trials." In developing the ScIND concept, CDER studied a number of different models, including the European Medicines Evaluation Agency's (EMEA) proposed "microdose IND" concept (January 2003), the Pharmaceutical Research and Manufacturers of America's proposed "exploratory IND" model (May 2004), and the National Cancer Institute's "facilitated IND" proposal.

- To formally assess the value of sponsor/agency meetings in improving the drug development and approval process, the FDA has undertaken at least two pilot programs that involve meetings during the clinical development process. Under a new voluntary pilot program, the FDA is participating in so-called end-of-Phase 2A meetings in an effort to address drug-dosing issues earlier in a product's development process. Also, under a PDUFA III pilot, the FDA and sponsors of eligible products can enter into an agreement to engage in frequent scientific feedback and interactions during the clinical development phase (see discussions below for more on FDA/sponsor meetings).

- To promote clinical trial safety and improve the predictive value of the data derived from all types of testing, the agency is attempting to create a "tighter scientific linkage" between non-clinical and clinical studies. The FDA is identifying, evaluating and establishing relevant protein biomarkers in blood in both animal models and humans to help detect the very earliest damage that certain drugs can do to the heart, kidney, immune system and liver. To enhance safety within broad segments of patient populations and enable safe development of new drug classes, the agency is working to identify and elucidate associated serum biomarkers and mechanisms responsible for the development of vascular inflammation in specific organ systems. Agency scientists continue to examine noninvasive imaging technology to extend the FDA's long-standing interest in applying accurate dose-concentration-response principles by viewing drugs and their actions directly at the level of the drug target, rather than indirectly via plasma concentrations. Finally, the agency is developing a pediatric pharmacokinetics study design template to facilitate the implementation of sparse sample strategies in pediatric drug development as well as a standardized approach for using exposure-response information to help evaluate the risks/benefits of drugs and for recommending dose adjustments in special populations.

- Under its Critical Path Initiative, the FDA has expressed its interest in examining computer-based predictive models, including computerized clinical trial simulation tools, to improve the efficiency and predictability of product development. In fact, even before unveiling the initiative, then-FDA Commissioner Mark McClellan, M.D., Ph.D., appointed Don Stanski, M.D., to serve as a scientific advisor to CDER and to spearhead the agency's computer simulation policies. By mid-2004, the agency had begun educating its clinical reviewers on computer simulation models, and was meeting with firms such as the Pharsight Corporation to learn about available tools for computer modeling, clinical trial simulation, and quantitative decision-making methodologies in the drug development process. Further, through an upcoming guidance on key considerations following Phase 2A studies, the agency is expected to encourage firms to use innovative tools, including computer-based clinical trial simulation technology, in such tasks as selecting doses for late-stage clinical studies and predicting possible adverse reactions, including QT prolongation and acute liver damage.

- CDER's Office of New Drugs has established a Study Endpoints and Label Development Team to support the center's drug review divisions in their deliberations regarding the choice of clinical endpoints used to support product effectiveness claims. The team responds to divisional consult requests for the review of the development, modification, or validation of measurement instruments. The unit also coordinates policy development to promote the consistency and quality of labeling content and the incorporation of labeling goals in early product development decisions.

- Under a November 2003 agreement, the FDA and National Cancer Institute launched an Interagency Oncology Task Force whose goal is to facilitate the development and use of cancer drugs. Under the agreement's new Fellowship Training Program, research fellows are working in the NCI's clinical oncology programs and the FDA's technical and regulatory review programs so that these physicians and scientists can bring state-of-the-art knowledge to the design, conduct, and review of clinical trials. The agencies will also work together to further develop biomarkers and create an oncology bioinformatics infrastructure to support clinical development programs.

Clinical Trials and the FDA's "Critical Path" Initiative

Because the "applied sciences" necessary for medical product development have failed to keep pace with the tremendous advances in the basic sciences that have led to the discovery of many new products, the FDA's March 2004 Critical Path Initiative will attempt to develop a "product development toolkit" that will help researchers move a product along more efficiently from laboratory concept to commercial product. The initiative, says the agency, is not a "fundamental departure" for the FDA, but rather builds on the agency's proven "best practices" for expediting the availability of promising medical technologies.

The product development toolkit, says the agency, will comprise "powerful new scientific and technical methods such as animal or computer-based predictive models, biomarkers for safety and effectiveness, and new clinical evaluation techniques." The goal of the product development toolkit will be to help predict eventual product failures early during clinical trials and to reduce developmental uncertainties in three critical areas: product safety; medical utility (efficacy); and manufacturing potential. The first two of these areas, which are important to clinical development, are discussed further below.

Safety Assessment The traditional tools used to assess product safety—animal toxicology and outcomes from human studies—"have changed little over many decades and have largely not benefited from recent gains in scientific knowledge," the FDA claims. The resultant inability to more effectively assess and predict product safety leads to clinical development failures and marketing failures, the agency notes.

Among the tools that the FDA claims are urgently needed are better predictors of human immune responses to foreign antigens, methods to further enhance the safety of transplanted human tissues, new techniques for assessing drug liver toxicity, methods to identify gene therapy risks based on the assessment of gene insertional and promotional events, and efficient protocols for qualifying biomaterials. The FDA also highlights what it says are a few of the key safety assessment "opportunities" identified by FDA reviewers and outside experts to make the critical path faster, more predictable, and less costly:

- Targeted research aimed at specific toxicity problems should be undertaken. The FDA notes that while proteomic and toxicogenomic approaches may provide important sensitive and predictive safety assessment techniques in the future, their application remains in the early stages and must be expanded.

- As the world's largest repository of *in vitro* and animal results that are linked to actual human outcomes data, the FDA's own files could be further "datamined," and thereby form the basis for useful predictive safety models. These data could be used to inform more powerful *in silico* (computer modeling) analyses for predictive toxicology, the agency notes.

- There is an urgent need to supplement ongoing international efforts to develop and validate nonclinical models useful in predicting human risk, particularly to assess the risk of new drugs that cause heart rhythm abnormalities.

Evaluation of Medical Utility This second dimension—establishing that a product will actually benefit people—"is the source of innumerable failures late in product development" and represents one of the most difficult and important challenges in product development, the agency notes. To develop better tools necessary to select useful products and eliminate failures more effectively and earlier in the development process, the FDA claims that a more systematic and dynamic understanding of human disease will be nec-

–continued–

98

—continued—

essary, something that the agency says will require "major additional scientific efforts as well as significant advances in bioinformatics." The development of better tools will also "require strengthening and rebuilding the relevant disciplines (e.g., physiology, pharmacology, clinical pharmacology) and working to identify ways to bridge between the laboratory and the whole organism and correlate early markers of safety and benefit with actual outcomes in patients." In addition, the FDA notes that it is working to facilitate more interest in earlier "proof-of-concept" trials designed to confirm a product's activity in humans before commitments to full-scale development are made.

The development of a better efficacy toolkit, says the agency, must be supported by targeted efforts in a variety of areas, including the following:

- New biomarkers (quantitative measure of biological effects that provide informative links between mechanism of action and clinical effectiveness) and additional surrogate endpoints (quantitative measures that can predict effectiveness) will be needed to guide product development. In some cases, the agency notes, "datamining and analysis, with possibly a single additional clinical trial, may be all that is necessary to confirm the surrogacy of a particular marker." The agency cautions that, for biomarkers that appear promising today, specific projects are necessary to assemble existing data on the association of the marker with clinical outcomes, assemble existing data on the performance of the marker during intervention trials compared to the performance of current outcome measures, identify any data gaps or remaining uncertainties, and identify clinical trials under development in which the remaining questions could be addressed in a straightforward manner.

- Because effectiveness criteria for many therapeutic products are best defined by the practitioners and patients who use the products, the agency notes that "much work needs to be done on clinical trial design and patient-driven outcome measures to ensure that endpoints in new therapeutic areas accurately reflect patient needs and values."

- While the agency fully expects new imaging techniques to contribute "important biomarkers and surrogate endpoints," the speed with which these new tools become available will depend on the effort invested in developing them for this purpose. The predictive value of various imaging technologies requires further study and evaluation, the agency notes.

Agency officials hope the new initiative will permit a retrospective analysis of why late-stage trials fail so frequently. "One of the things that need to be done is to help explain the high failure rate," noted CDER's Associate Director for Medical Policy Director Robert Temple, M.D. at the time the Critical Path Initiative was introduced. "The most striking thing to me is that PhRMA reports that more than half of the drugs that enter Phase 3 don't come out the other end with a successful application. Every one of those drugs had an animal model or some type of human model that someone thought was plausible and had clinical trials in the Phase 2 category that someone found encouraging enough to proceed. And yet almost half the time they were wrong. One of the things we need to do is to go back and figure out why the error rate was so high. Is it because the animal models were flawed and there should have been some better ones? Is it because they didn't do proper dose finding? Is it because there's more variability from one person to another than anybody anticipated? Because there are now potential methods for assessing that variability,

—continued—

–continued–

whether it's genomically or some other way. Part of this opportunity is to go back and look, which will obviously require a lot of people's help."

The Next Steps

While acknowledging that there are many public and private groups with expertise necessary to develop solutions to critical path challenges, the FDA holds that it "is ideally positioned to bring together the stakeholders to identify and address the most significant problems." The first significant milestone in the Critical Path Initiative was scheduled for late fall 2004, when the agency hoped to release a so-called National Critical Path Opportunities List, which will identify those areas of product development that could benefit most from innovative approaches and emerging technologies. The agency is developing the list through extensive consultation with all public and private stakeholders, a process that began with an FDA Science Board meeting in April 2004 and that also involved a series of workshops and meetings. Lastly, the FDA notes that it "will make internal changes to intensify its ability to surface crucial issues and to support high-priority critical path research efforts."

Even as the agency pursued initiatives to leverage emerging technologies and medical knowledge, new analyses seemed to confirm that earlier industry efforts to streamline drug development processes in response to spiraling product development costs and an increasingly competitive marketplace (i.e., due to managed care, generic competition, etc.) were working. These streamlining efforts first appeared to take hold in the late 1990s, reversing a seemingly inexorable rise in clinical development times during the 1980s and 1990s. A November 2003 Tufts Center for the Study of Drug Development analysis showed that the mean clinical development time for new chemical entities (NCE) approved from 1999-2001 (5.5 years) declined 14% from the prior three-year period and 24% from the high of 7.2 years observed in 1993-1995. It is important to note, however, that mean clinical development times varied greatly by therapeutic class—times ranged from 7.9 years for gastrointestinal drugs to just 3.8 years for anti-infective and respiratory agents during the 1999-2001 period.

Today, industry continues to innovate in this, the most complex and costly element of the drug development process. Some major companies, for example, are now undertaking ultra-small, limited human trials during a drug's development to obtain an earlier-than-ever assessment of the therapy's clinical potential and risks. Although such companies obviously cannot abandon nonclinical testing, they emphasize that the emerging approach, called "experimental medicine" by some, provides substantively better predictive information than animal studies. Meanwhile, Pfizer and Lilly are funding university-based research designed to develop tools that will permit companies to identify likely placebo responders, who can make experimental therapies seem less effective in the context of clinical trials, particularly those for antidepressants. And, after using its diagnostics expertise to develop a genotyping screen to identify likely responders to its investigational cancer therapy Zarnestra, Johnson & Johnson saw the clinical trial subject response rate climb from 20% to 80%.

In addition to those initiatives highlighted above, clinical development programs continue to be influenced by several continuing FDA and international efforts to better characterize clinical data and testing requirements as well as at least a few blossoming controversies:

FDA Guidance on Clinical Standards for Drug Approval. Although the clinical testing process has long been the focus of the plurality of FDA guidelines, the agency added several important guidance documents to this corpus over the past several years, including *Providing Clinical Evidence of Effectiveness for Human Drug and Biological Products* (May 1998), which offers the agency's latest and most detailed views regarding the "quantitative and qualitative standards" for establishing drug effectiveness, and *Cancer Drug and Biological Products—Clinical Data in Marketing Applications* (October 2001), in which CDER clarifies the clinical data necessary for oncology drugs and notes that those requirements may be less than those for less-serious diseases. As noted above, however, the FDA in now focused, under new agency initiatives, on forming working groups with outside experts to develop guidances that will provide a clearer understanding of required scientific evidence and clinical end-points in establishing efficacy in clinical trials for specific high-priority therapeutic categories, such as oncology, diabetes, and obesity. In July 2004, the agency also adopted the so-called Study Data Tabulation Model (SDTM), which is a standard format in which clinical trial sponsors can submit data to the agency and which the agency claims will lead to greater efficiencies in clinical research by helping to "automate the largely paper-based clinical trials research process." As part of its effort to standardize drug reviews, CDER also released a July 2004 internal "clinical review template" to establish procedures that its medical reviewers are to use in documenting the primary clinical reviews of NDAs.

International Guidance on Clinical Trials. Supplementing FDA guidance documents are about a dozen clinically oriented guidelines developed under the International Conference on Harmonization (ICH) initiative, including a final guidance entitled, E8 *General Considerations for Clinical Trials* (December 1997), and another guidance entitled, *Statistical Principles for Clinical Trials* (September 1998). In August 2000, the ICH parties released a draft guideline entitled, *Principles for Clinical Evaluation of New Antihypertensive Drugs*, what is thought to be the first in what ultimately will be a series of ICH guidances that will address clinical testing issues specific to individual therapeutic categories. The ICH effort is also assuming a lead role in developing clinical trial-related guidances addressing cutting-edge issues presented by advances in scientific understanding. In September 2004, for instance, the FDA released a draft ICH guidance entitled, E14 *Clinical Evaluation of QT/QTc Interval Prolongation and Proarrhythmic Potential for Non-Antiarrhythmic Drugs*, which states that, "in general drugs should receive an electro-cardiographic evaluation, beginning early in clinical development, typically including a single trial dedicated to evaluating their effect on cardiac repolarization." Earlier, in June 2003, CDER's Cardiovascular and Renal Drugs Advisory Committee echoed a 2002 FDA/Health Canada concept paper by agreeing that the FDA should consider requiring clinical data to characterize drug effects on the QT interval for all new molecular entities.

Initiatives for Testing in Special Populations. Legislative and regulatory initiatives continue to pressure industry to include special populations in clinical trials, including children, women, the elderly, and racial and ethnic subgroups. In a January 2003 draft guidance entitled, *Collection of Race and Ethnicity Data in Clinical Trials*, the agency recommends that sponsors collect clinical trial race and ethnicity data using standardized Office of Management and Budget categories because such efforts will enhance the early identification of differences in physiological response among racial and ethnic subgroups and facilitate FDA comparisons across studies. In mid-2002, Division for Oncologic Drug Products Director Richard Pazdur, M.D., encouraged industry to incorporate foreign clinical sites earlier in drug development programs to assess whether intrinsic ethnic differences exist and to better address such differences in Phase 3 studies. After being invalidated by an October 2002 court ruling, the FDA's authority to require pediatric studies in certain cases was re-established by a new law signed in 2003 (see Chapter 16). In mid-2000, the FDA implemented a regulation establishing its authority to issue clinical holds on any studies that "automatically excluded," because of a possible risk of reproductive or developmental toxicity, women of reproductive potential who suffer from a life-threatening disease. After releasing the results of a 2001 study on the inclusion of gender-related information in new drug applications approved from 1995 to 1999, FDA officials further encouraged clinical trial sponsors to include women in Phase 1 and 2 pharmacodynamic and pharmacokinetic studies on a more routine basis to provide more information on how drugs work differently in men and women and on drug dosing issues. Although the agency issued a February 1998 regulation mandating that IND and NDA sponsors submit efficacy and safety subset analyses based on gender, age, and race, it was to use the results of this study, which found that women represent "a relatively small percentage" (just 22%) of subjects enrolled in Phase 1 and 2 studies, to determine the need for further regulations to ensure the inclusion of women and other groups in clinical trials. Overall, however, the study found that women are participating in clinical trials "in approximate proportion to their representation in the population."

The Public Availability of Clinical Trial Information for Serious and Life-Threatening Diseases. Although they do not directly affect clinical trial conduct, the availability of information on ongoing clinical trials and industry's practices for releasing the results of completed clinical trials were at the center of blossoming controversies during 2004. In a May 2004 congressional hearing, the FDA expressed concern regarding industry's comparatively low compliance rates with certain provisions of The Food and Drug Administration Modernization Act of 1997 (FDAMA), which requires that companies post certain information on all open Phase 2 through Phase 4 clinical trials for serious and life-threatening diseases on an NIH-maintained clinical trials data bank (clinicaltrials.gov). Industry groups have reassured Congress that industry's compliance rates have improved and will continue to improve now that the FDA has finalized its guidance document on the program—*Information Program on Clinical Trials for Serious and Life-Threatening Diseases: Establishment of a Data Bank* (March 2002 and further revised in February 2004). Separately, a June 2004 lawsuit filed by New York Attorney General Eliot Spitzer charged that GlaxoSmithKline "concealed and suppressed" clinical study results that showed an increased pediatric suicide risk associated with its antidepressant Paxil (paroxetine). Soon after, two House and Senate subcommittees began examining the assessment of antidepressant suicidality clinical data within both the FDA and drug companies. In the face of this growing controversy, PhRMA expressed its support for the creation of a comprehensive national database to publish both positive and negative results from all industry clinical trials, and revised its clinical trials principles document to establish that all "meaningful results of clinical trials...must be reported in an objective, accurate, balanced and complete manner" and that "study sponsors will not suppress or veto publications." Further, in October 2004, PhRMA established a central, comprehensive database (www.clinicalstudyresults.or) to provide both positive and negative results of all controlled clinical trials (mainly Phase 3 and Phase 4) completed by PhRMA-member companies. Meanwhile, major firms were moving to establish or expand their company websites to provide more information on their clinical trials. Despite this, several U.S. senators introduced a bill entitled The Fair Access to Clinical Trials Act in October 2004 to require that all drug, biologic, and device clinical trials be registered on clinicaltrials.gov as a prerequisite for IRB approval, and to require that sponsors post summaries of results (e.g., primary and secondary outcomes, important adverse events) once the studies are completed.

Today, the clinical development program remains, without question, the most complex, time-consuming, and costly element in the pharmaceutical development process. At a minimum, it requires a coordinated effort that involves a sponsor willing to assume the financial, legal, and regulatory responsibilities associated with the program, the commitment and expertise of physicians, nurses, and other health-care professionals who play key roles in executing the clinical development protocol, and patients willing to make a contribution to clinical research or to take the chance that an experimental drug will do more for them than either existing therapies or no therapy at all.

The FDA's Role in Clinical Trials

Traditionally, the FDA has played at least three major roles in the clinical testing of a drug. As it does for animal studies, the FDA sets general standards for clinical studies to ensure that data derived from clinical trials are valid and accurate. The agency accomplishes this goal essentially by maintaining and enforcing a set of related guidelines and regulations called Good Clinical Practices, or GCP (see Chapter 6). These documents define the responsibilities of the key figures involved in clinical trials.

The FDA's second role is to protect the rights and, to the degree possible, the safety of subjects participating in clinical trials. Obviously, since such testing involves the administration of pharmacologically active drugs to humans, the agency cannot guarantee the safety of clinical subjects. The FDA's role, then, is to ensure: (1) that clinical subjects are not exposed to any unnecessary risks; (2) that clinical subjects are exposed to the least possible risk given the benefit anticipated from the use of an experimental therapy; and (3) that all clinical subjects provide their informed consent before entering a trial. The FDA does this not only through GCP regulations and guidances, but also by reviewing clinical protocols and changes to the protocols that may affect the safety of the subjects, and by exercising its right to delay or discontinue clinical trials when necessary (see Chapter 4). The agency also fulfills this role by monitoring the performance of clinical trial sponsors and monitors, clinical investigators and institutional review boards (see Chapter 14).

Lastly, by deciding the nature and quantity of clinical data necessary to establish a drug's safety and effectiveness, the FDA participates actively in determining what testing is necessary in a clinical development program. Because the scientific and medical issues differ so significantly between various drugs and medical conditions, the agency works with the sponsor to reach such determinations on a case-by-case basis. Ideally, the sponsor initiates this process by providing the FDA with its optimal and comprehensive global development plan for a new drug. At each subsequent meeting, this plan should be reviewed and updated to refine the sponsor's recommended plan of study.

As noted above, however, under various initiatives, including the so-called Critical Path Initiative, the FDA is today assuming a much more proactive role to promote the translation of medical innovations and scientific advances into new medical products. As the agency pushes forward in attempting to make the "critical path" of drug development faster, more predictable, and less costly, much of the emphasis will be on issues related to perhaps the most important element along this critical path—clinical trials.

To help drug sponsors design clinical trials that are based upon sound scientific principles and that provide for the protection of clinical subjects, the FDA has developed and published dozens of general and therapeutic area-specific clinical guidelines over the past two decades. In the last decade, however, FDA guidances have been supplemented by several ICH guidelines that are directly relevant to, and that represent the agency's latest thinking on, the design and conduct of clinical trials, including:

- Final E1A *The Extent of Population Exposure Required to Assess Clinical Safety for Drugs Intended for Long-Term Treatment of Non-Life-Threatening Conditions* (March 1995);

- Final E2A *Clinical Safety Data Management: Definitions and Standards for Expedited Reporting* (March 1995);

- Final E2B *Guidance on Data Elements for Transmission of Individual Case Safety Reports* (January 1998);

- Final E2C *Clinical Safety Data Management: Periodic Safety Update Reports for Marketed Drugs* (May 1997) and E2C *Addendum to ICH E2C Clinical Safety Data Management: Periodic Safety Update Reports for Marketed Drugs* (February 2004);

- Draft E2E *Pharmacovigilance Planning* (November 2003);

- Final E3 *Guideline on the Structure and Content of Clinical Study Reports* (July 1996);

- Final E4 *Dose-Response Information to Support Drug Registration* (November 1994);

- Final E5 *Ethnic Factors in the Acceptability of Foreign Clinical Data* (June 1998) and E5 *Questions and Answers* (June 2004);

- Final E6 *Good Clinical Practice: Consolidated Guideline* (May 1997);

- Final E7 *Studies in Support of Special Populations: Geriatrics* (August 1994);

- Final E8 *General Considerations for Clinical Trials* (December 1997);

- Final E9 *Statistical Principles for Clinical Trials* (September 1998);

- Final E10 *Choice of Control Group in Clinical Trials* (July 2000);

- Final E11 *Clinical Investigations for Medicinal Products in the Pediatric Population* (July 2000);

- Final M3 *Nonclinical Safety Studies for the Conduct of Human Clinical Trials for Pharmaceuticals* (November 1997); and

- Draft *Principles for Clinical Evaluation of New Antihypertensive Drugs* (August 2000).

The Structure of Clinical Trials

The design of a clinical trial will differ significantly from one drug and disease state to another. The nature of a drug, the product's proposed use, the results of the preclinical testing, principles of medical practice, patient preferences, biostatistical considerations, and the availability and quality of existing standard treatments are among the factors considered in designing a clinical trial or a global drug development program.

Although clinical trials for different drugs can vary greatly in design, they are often similar in structure. Since researchers may know little about a new compound prior to its use in humans, testing the drug through serially conducted investigations permits each phase of clinical development to be carefully designed to use and build upon the information obtained from the research stage preceding it. In its October 1988 *Plan for Accelerated Approval of Drugs to Treat Life-Threatening and Severely Debilitating Illnesses*, the FDA discussed the structure of clinical trials and the basis for this structure:

"[The clinical] drug development process is generally thought of, in simplified terms, as consisting of three phases of human testing to determine if a drug is safe and effective: Phase 1 with 10 to 50 patients to study how the drug is tolerated, metabolized, and excreted; Phase 2 with 50 to 200 patients in which the safety and efficacy of the drug are first evaluated in controlled trials; and Phase 3 with 200 to 1,000 or more patients to confirm and expand upon the safety and efficacy data obtained from the first two phases... The three phases describe the usual process of drug development, but they are not statutory requirements. The basis for marketing approval is the adequacy of the data available; progression through the particular phases is simply the usual means the sponsor uses to collect the data needed for approval. The statute itself focuses on the standard of evidence needed for approval, as derived from adequate and well-controlled clinical investigations with no mention of phases 1, 2, and 3."

While acknowledging that clinical testing is often classified into these primary "temporal phases," the ICH's final E8 *Guidance on General Considerations for Clinical Trials* (December 1997) also points out that the phases are descriptive rather than prescriptive. For some drugs, this "typical sequence" may be inappropriate or unnecessary, the guidance states (see exhibit below).

Phases of Clinical Investigation

(from the ICH's December 1997 Final Guideline on General Considerations for Clinical Trials)

Phase 1 (Most typical type of study: Human Pharmacology). Studies in Phase 1 typically involve one or a combination of the following assessments:

- *Estimation of initial safety and tolerability.* The initial and subsequent administration of an investigational new drug into humans is usually intended to determine the tolerability of the dose range expected to be needed for later clinical studies and to determine the nature of adverse reactions that can be expected. These studies typically include both single and multiple-dose administration.

- *Determination of pharmacokinetics* (PK). Preliminary characterization of a drug's absorption, distribution, metabolism, and excretion is almost always an important goal of Phase 1. PK studies are undertaken to assess the clearance of the drug and to anticipate the possible accumulation of parent drug or metabolites and potential drug-drug interactions.

- *Assessment of pharmacodynamics* (PD). Depending on the investigational drug and the endpoint under study, PD studies and studies relating drug blood levels to response (PK/PD studies) may be conducted in healthy volunteer subjects or in patients with the target disease. In some studies involving patients, PD data can provide early estimates of drug activity and potential effectiveness and can guide the dosage and dose regimen in later studies.

- *Early measurement of activity.* Preliminary studies of activity or potential therapeutic benefit may be conducted in Phase 1 as a secondary objective. Such studies may be appropriate when effectiveness is readily measurable with a short duration of drug exposure.

Phase 2 (Most typical kind of study: Therapeutic exploratory). Generally, Phase 2 is considered to comprise studies in which the primary objective is to explore therapeutic effectiveness in patients. Initial therapeutic exploratory studies may use a variety of study designs, such as concurrent controls and comparisons with baseline status. Subsequent trials are usually randomized and concurrently controlled to evaluate the efficacy of the drug and its safety for a particular therapeutic indication. The goals of Phase 2 studies include determining the dose(s) and regimen for Phase 3 studies and the evaluation of potential study endpoints, therapeutic regimens (including concomitant medications), and target populations (e.g., mild versus severe disease) for further study in Phase 2 or Phase 3 trials.

Phase 3 (Most typical kind of study: Therapeutic confirmatory). Usually, Phase 3 is considered to begin with the initiation of studies in which the primary objective is to demonstrate, or confirm, therapeutic benefit. Phase 3 studies are designed to support marketing approval by confirming the preliminary evidence collected in Phase 2 that shows the drug to be safe and effective for use in the intended indication and population. Studies in Phase 3 may also further explore the dose-response relationship, or explore the drug's use in a broader population, in different disease stages, or in combination with another drug.

Phase 4 (Variety of studies: Therapeutic Use). Phase 4 includes all postapproval studies (other than routine surveillance) related to the approved indication. These studies, which are not considered necessary for approval but are often important for optimizing the drug's use, include additional drug-drug interaction, dose-response, or safety studies and studies designed to support use under the approved indication (e.g., mortality/morbidity studies).

Phase 1 Clinical Trials

The earliest Phase 1 clinical trials, sometimes called "first-in-man studies," represent the first introduction of a new drug into human subjects. While the focus at this stage is the assessment of clinical safety, researchers usually obtain pharmacokinetic data as well and frequently assess a drug's effect on a well-established bio-marker (e.g., ACE inhibition, blood pressure). Except for extrapolations based on the safety profile obtained from animal studies, investigators may know little about the drug's possible clinical effects prior to these studies.

Phase 1 testing of a new drug is considered highly exploratory because there are often no human safety data available. For this reason, these studies are entered into very cautiously, with the drug being used in an esca-lating fashion and at fractions of the predicted therapeutic doses in small numbers of subjects, each of whom must submit to close clinical observation for drug effects. While healthy adults whose schedules permit short-term confinement are ideal subjects, stable patients with the target disease or condition can also be studied in Phase 1 trials. Although male volunteers have dominated Phase 1 study populations traditionally, the FDA continues to push for as much as an equal number of females in early-stage trials, unless there is a specific reason to exclude females (see discussion above).

Phase 1 clinical trials provide an initial clinical indication of whether a drug is sufficiently well tolerated to be used in further human testing. According to FDA regulations, "Phase 1 includes the initial introduction of an investigational new drug into humans... These studies are designed to determine the metabolism and phar-macologic actions of the drug in humans, the side effects associated with increasing doses, and, if possible, to gain early evidence on effectiveness. During Phase 1, sufficient information about the drug's pharmacoki-netics and pharmacological effects should be obtained to permit the design of well-controlled, scientifically valid Phase 2 studies. The total number of subjects and patients included in Phase 1 studies varies with the drug, but is generally in the range of 20 to 80. Phase 1 studies also include studies of drug metabolism, struc-ture-activity relationships, and mechanism of action in humans, as well as studies in which investigational drugs are used as research tools to explore biological phenomena or disease processes." These studies can also provide basic pharmacokinetic information, which allows for the comparison of human drug disposition to that of animals so that nonclinical findings can be correlated and verified.

It is worth noting that the term Phase 1 can refer not only to a stage of development (i.e., earliest human expo-sure), but also to a type of study (i.e., generally any clinical pharmacology study). This type of study may occur at various times throughout a drug's clinical development, and sometimes after the drug has been introduced into the market.

Testing certain drugs in healthy adults is not considered ethical. Because of the known toxicity of certain classes of drugs, such as those used in treating AIDS and cancer, some Phase 1 studies are conducted with patients who have, or are at risk of having, the condition for which the drug is being studied. Because healthy volunteers have no opportunity to benefit from a treatment, the administration of highly toxic compounds to such individuals is considered an unacceptable risk. Even if the subjects are patients, Phase 1 trials are not efficacy studies, but focus on safety/tolerability and effects on preclinical biomarkers.

The FDA advises that investigators performing Phase 1 tests involving "normal" volunteers should be skilled in the "initial evaluation of a variety of compounds for safety and pharmacological effect." In those cases in which diseased patients are studied under a Phase 1 protocol, investigators should be, or should work with co-investigators who are, experts in either the particular disease categories to be treated or in the evaluation of drug effects on the disease process. It is also important that such investigators carefully consider the influence of any active disease state on the pharmacokinetic and pharmacodynamic findings.

PK/PD and Phase 1 Trials Based on the FDA's review experience in the early 1990s, the selection of the starting dose for clinical trials was recognized as a weakness of many clinical programs. Traditional dose-based comparisons between animals and humans are considered inadequate largely because of major differences between species in the disposition and metabolism of drugs. Thus, calculations based on animal half-lives and dosing intervals and their relationship to toxicity often led to errors in selecting the starting dose for Phase 1 trials. For these reasons, the "first-in-man" dose is usually a fraction (often as small as one-tenth) of the highest no-effect dose in pertinent animal toxicity studies.

In a December 2002 draft guidance, however, the agency outlines a process, or algorithm, for deriving the maximum recommended starting dose (MRSD) for "first in human" clinical trials of new molecular entities in adult healthy volunteers, and recommends a standardized process through which researchers can select the MRSD. The MRSD selection process advocated under the guidance, entitled *Estimating the Safe Starting Dose in Clinical Trials for Therapeutics in Adult Health Volunteers*, employs observed toxicities, administered doses, and an algorithmic approach, and involves five key steps:

Step 1: Determine the No Observed Adverse Effect Level (NOAEL) by evaluating available animal data. For the purposes of the MRSD-selection process, the FDA defines NOAEL as "the highest dose level that does not produce a significant increase in adverse effects."

Step 2: Convert the NOAELs in the relevant animal studies to human equivalent doses (HED). Researchers must determine the most appropriate method for extrapolating the animal dose to the equivalent human dose, although the agency notes that toxic endpoints for therapeutics administered systemically to animals, such as the maximum tolerated dose (MTD) or NOAEL, "are usually assumed to scale well between species when doses are normalized to body surface area."

Step 3: Select the most appropriate species. After the HEDs have been determined (based on the NOAEL from all toxicology studies relevant to the proposed human trial), the next step is to select one HED for subsequent derivation of the MSRD. The HED should be chosen from the "most appropriate species," the FDA states. "In the absence of data on species relevance, a default position is that the most appropriate species for deriving the MRSD for a trial in adult healthy volunteers is the most sensitive species (i.e., the species in which the lowest HED can be identified)."

Step 4: Application of safety factor. After the HED of the NOAEL in the most appropriate species has been determined, researchers must apply a safety factor to provide a margin of safety for the protection of human subjects receiving the initial clinical dose. The safety factor allows for variability in extrapolating from animal toxicity studies to studies in humans due to such factors as difficulty in detecting certain toxicities in animals. Although the agency notes that the historically accepted safety factor of 10 (the HED derived from the animal NOAEL is divided by the safety factor) "can generally be considered adequate for protection of human subjects participating in initial clinical trials, this safety factor may not be appropriate for all cases," the agency states. The safety factor should be raised when there is reason for increased concern and lowered when available data result in reduced concern.

Step 5: Consideration of the pharmacologically active dose (PAD). After the MRSD has been determined, the agency notes that "it may be of value" to compare it to the pharmacologically active dose (PAD) derived from pharmacodynamic models. "If the PAD is from an in vivo study, an HED can be derived from a PAD estimate by using a body surface area conversion factor (BSA-CF)," the FDA states. "This HED value should be compared directly to the MRSD. If this *pharmacologic* HED is lower than the MRSD, it may be appropriate to decrease the clinical starting dose for pragmatic or scientific reasons. Additionally, for certain classes of drugs or biologics (e.g., vasodilators, anticoagulants, monoclonal antibodies, or growth factors), toxicity may arise from *exaggerated pharmacologic* effects. The PAD in these cases may be a more sensitive indicator of potential toxicity than the NOAEL and might therefore warrant lowering the MRSD."

An FDA focus on early-stage pharmacokinetic/pharmacodynamic studies, which was championed under former CDER Director Carl Peck, M.D., has continued many years after Peck's departure from CDER. In the 1994 final guideline entitled, *E4 Dose-Response Information To Support Drug Registration*, the ICH parties stated that dose-response data "are desirable for almost all new chemical entities," and that "assessment of dose-response should be an integral component of drug development with studies designed to assess dose-response as an inherent part of establishing the safety and effectiveness of the drug."

The FDA's efforts to develop additional guidelines provide further evidence of the agency's continuing interest in promoting the importance of dose-response studies during Phase 1 and Phase 2 clinical trials. In April 2003, for example, the agency supplemented the ICH's E4 guidance with its own guidance entitled, *Exposure-Response Relationships—Study Design, Data Analysis, and Regulatory Applications* to provide recommendations to IND and NDA sponsors on the use of exposure-response information in the development of new drugs.

In a pair of guidances—*In Vivo Drug Metabolism/Drug Interaction Studies-Study Design, Data Analysis, and Recommendations for Dosing and Labeling* (November 1999) and *Drug Metabolism/Drug Interaction Studies in the Drug Development Process: Studies In Vitro* (April 1997)—the agency encourages sponsors to develop information on a drug's metabolic profile early in clinical trials. A May 1998 CDER guidance entitled, *Pharmacokinetics and Pharmacovigilance in Patients with Impaired Renal Function: Study Design, Data Analysis, and Impact on Dosing and Labeling* specifies when PK studies of patients with impaired renal function should be performed, and discusses the design and conduct of PK/PD studies in such individuals. In a November 1999 draft guidance entitled *Pharmacokinetics in Patients with Impaired Hepatic Function: Study Design, Data Analysis, and Impact on Dosing and Labeling*, CDER provides recommendations to companies planning to conduct studies to assess the influence of hepatic impairment on the pharmacokinetics and, where appropriate, the pharmacodynamics of experimental drugs. In a February 1999 guidance entitled, *Population Pharmacokinetics*, the agency offers recommendations on the use of population pharmacokinetics to identify differences in safety and effectiveness among population subgroups in drug development programs.

Sponsor Information/Data Submissions During Clinical Trials Although the clinical program becomes the primary focus of a drug's development once Phase 1 trials begin, other activities continue to support these trials. As clinical trials progress, FDA reviewers continually reassess the safety of these studies. Because the FDA wants these assessments to be based on the latest available data and information, the agency requires that sponsors submit periodic reports on completed and upcoming research. During clinical trials, at least four important types of data and information flow regularly from the sponsor to the FDA:

- New Animal Data. As mentioned previously, animal testing continues during clinical development. Submitted in the form of information amendments to the IND, additional toxicology and pharmacokinetic data may be needed from animal studies to support the safety of new and/or modified clinical studies. For example, longer-term toxicology studies are required as the duration of treatment in humans is extended.

- Protocols and Protocol Amendments. Because protocols for Phase 2 and Phase 3 trials are not normally included in the original IND, protocols for these studies must be forwarded to the FDA subsequently (see Chapter 3). Also, whenever sponsors want to make changes to previously submitted protocols, they must submit protocol amendments.

- Annual Reports. Current regulations require sponsors to submit brief annual reports on the progress of the investigations. These reports must include information on individual studies, provide a summary of the clinical experience with the drug, and provide information on the general investigational plan for the upcoming year, changes in the investigator's brochure, and foreign regulatory and marketing developments (see Chapter 3).

- IND Safety Reports. The drug sponsor must notify the FDA and all participating investigators about information that the company receives from any source indicating or suggesting significant hazards, contraindications, side effects, or precautions that are associated with the use of the drug. All significant safety findings must be reported (see Chapter 3).

Ideally, trial sponsors will establish a collegial relationship with the FDA reviewing team, participate in frequent, informal communications to keep the reviewers apprised of developing data, and engage in a progressive exchange of ideas to facilitate the execution of the clinical development program.

Phase 2 Clinical Trials

Phase 2 clinical trials represent a shift away from testing focused on safety to testing designed to provide a preliminary indication of a drug's effectiveness. In Phase 2 studies, a drug is used, often for the first time, in patients who suffer from the disease or condition that the drug is intended to prevent, diagnose, or treat.

FDA regulations state that "Phase 2 includes the controlled clinical studies conducted to evaluate the effectiveness of the drug for a particular indication or indications in patients with the disease or condition under study and to determine the common or short-term side effects and risks associated with the drug. Phase 2 studies are typically well-controlled, closely monitored, and conducted in a relatively small number of patients, usually involving no more than several hundred subjects."

Typical Phase 2 studies are well-controlled and randomized trials that compare the experimental drug, often at several different doses, to placebo or, in some cases, to an active drug. The studies can provide evidence of effectiveness, a preliminary look at dose-response for effectiveness and the more common adverse drug reactions, and a firm basis for selecting the dose or, ideally, the dose-range to be studied in Phase 3.

In many ways, Phase 2 studies provide the foundation for several key aspects of the study design for the all-important Phase 3 trials. The observed magnitude of the treatment effect in Phase 2 trials is a critical factor in Phase 3 sample size calculations, for example.

Given the costs associated with Phase 3 studies and the perception that Phase 3 success rates have declined for new drugs, some firms have announced that they are focusing more intently on Phase 2 studies—for example, to characterize or fine-tune the dose for the pivotal studies. In fact, agency officials such as CDER's Associate Director for Medical Policy Robert Temple, M.D., have criticized industry for not taking full advantage of Phase 2 trials in designing pivotal Phase 3 studies. Too frequently, says Temple, sponsors fail to conduct comprehensive Phase 2 studies that explore a complete dose range and a drug's effects on biomarkers and then confirm the Phase 2 impressions in well-designed Phase 3 studies that examine the dose range of interest. Instead, he notes, companies tend to "do a little bit" of Phase 2 work and then simultaneously conduct multiple Phase 3 studies, sometimes at a single selected dose and sometimes at a number of doses, but rarely using several doses in a trial to obtain a good picture of dose-response for favorable and unfavorable effects. Temple argues that companies, by obtaining more complete data from Phase 2 trials in advance, could focus on the appropriate dose range in Phase 3 and, therefore, increase the likelihood of success.

While FDA officials concede that they are not absolutely certain of the reasons for declining Phase 3 success rates, many suspect that it can be traced directly to insufficient exposure-response work in Phase 2 studies. Because of this, agency reviewers are now making themselves available to consult with sponsors following the conclusion of so-called "Phase 2A studies," which examine a drug's absorption, metabolism, and pharmacodynamics in patients. Under the new pilot program (see discussion of end-of-Phase 2A meetings below), the agency will provide input on drug-dosing issues before a sponsor initiates Phase 2B studies, which will study a drug's safety and effectiveness in a somewhat larger patient population.

As noted above, Phase 2 trials that are well-controlled studies may provide the basis on which certain drugs are approved for marketing either under the traditional full approval or the accelerated approval model (Subpart H, see Chapter 15). When a new drug is the first effective treatment for, or is a significant advance in the treatment of, a serious or life-threatening disease, the sponsor may file an NDA at the completion of Phase 2. In such cases, however, the data must be statistically sound, and a post-marketing surveillance requirement may be a condition of approval. In recent years, this model has been used several times for antiviral treatments directed against the human immune deficiency virus (HIV) as well as for some cancer drugs, whose accelerated approvals have been based on reasonable surrogate endpoints (e.g., tumor response, 24-week viral load).

Since Phase 2 trials also involve the first meaningful assessment of a drug's effects on key clinical endpoints (i.e., clinical events or measurements used to assess drug effectiveness), these studies can provide valuable information on the utility of a variety of clinical endpoints and markers. Sponsors and investigators then can use this information to select the most appropriate endpoints—those most reflective of the disease and responsive to therapy, for example—for Phase 3 trials (see discussion of clinical endpoints below).

Generally, Phase 2 study objectives should also include developing a description of the dose-response for favorable and unfavorable effects. This information is critical to dose selection (e.g., a very well-tolerated drug may be dosed on the plateau of the dose-response curve, while a drug with toxicity might be given at a lower dose or started at a lower dose). Well-conducted Phase 2 studies of pharmacokinetic and pharmacodynamic parameters may provide useful insights as to whether different subpopulations (e.g., defined by gender, age, or concomitant illness) require different dosing regimens. It is critical to note that the relatively small numbers of patients in Phase 2 studies will usually not allow definitive conclusions about dose-response. Phase 3 studies are necessary to confirm Phase 2 findings and to detect less-common dose-related events.

Because a drug's short-term side effects remain primary concerns during Phase 2 investigations, the compound is administered to a limited number of patients who are closely monitored by the investigators. The use of the drug in larger numbers of subjects (i.e., compared to Phase 1) may reveal less-frequent side effects and provide for better estimates of the dose-toxicity relationships for the more frequently observed adverse effects. Dose-ranging may reveal type 1 target-organ toxicity at the higher doses. Such findings are used to refine the safety surveillance monitoring plans for Phase 3.

Generally speaking, given the comparatively small numbers of patients enrolled in Phase 2 trials, these studies usually are unable to provide the definitive evidence of efficacy and safety necessary to support approval. Under the FDA's expedited development (Subpart E) program, however, Phase 2 trials for products designed to treat life-threatening and severely debilitating diseases may be prospectively designed to support marketing approval (see Chapter 15).

End-of-Phase 2 Meetings and Other FDA-Sponsor Communication During Clinical Trials Under FDAMA and FDA/industry agreements associated with the user-fee program, the FDA has committed to several goals relevant to both end-of-Phase 2 meetings and other important meetings and communications (e.g., protocol reviews). In addition, the agency is actively participating in two pilot programs regarding agency/sponsor interactions during the clinical development process—an end-of-Phase 2A pilot program and a frequent scientific interaction pilot program (see discussions below).

End-of Phase 2 Meetings Although the agency had emphasized in the past that end-of-Phase 2 meetings were designed primarily for sponsors of NMEs and important new uses of marketed products, the FDA has since made the conferences available to all new drug sponsors, regardless of the classification of their products. Federal regulations state that the purposes of end-of-Phase 2 meetings are to determine the safety of proceeding to Phase 3, to evaluate the Phase 3 plan and protocols and the adequacy of current studies and plans to assess pediatric safety and effectiveness, and to identify any additional information necessary to support a marketing application for the uses under investigation. The ultimate goal of such a meeting is for the sponsor and the FDA to reach agreement on plans for the conduct and design of Phase 3 trials.

Under PDUFA III, the FDA has agreed to respond to meeting requests and hold requested meetings, including end-of-Phase 2 meetings, within specified timeframes. Within 14 calendar days of receiving a formal meeting request (i.e., a scheduled face-to-face meeting, teleconference, or videoconference), CDER should notify the sponsor by letter or fax of the date, time, and place for the meeting, as well as the expected CDER participants. The center will attempt to meet this goal for at least 90% of such requests during the PDUFA III years (FY2003-FY2007).

The agency's new meetings management system requires CDER to meet with sponsors within specific timeframes based on the type of meeting requested:

Type A Meeting: "A meeting which is necessary for an otherwise stalled drug development program to proceed (a 'critical path' meeting)." These meetings should take place within 30 days of CDER's receipt of a sponsor's request.

Type B Meeting: An end-of-Phase 2, pre-IND, end-of-Phase 1 (i.e., for Subpart E or Subpart H or similar products), or pre-NDA meeting. Type B meetings should occur within 60 calendar days of the agency's receipt of a meeting request.

Type C Meeting: Any other type of meeting. Type C meetings should be held within 75 calendar days of the agency's receipt of a meeting request.

For a meeting request to qualify under these performance goals, it must be made in writing and fulfill certain informational standards (e.g., statement of purpose, approximate schedule for submission of supporting documentation). In addition, CDER must agree that the meeting "will serve a useful purpose (i.e., it is not premature or clearly unnecessary)." The agency notes, however, that Type B meetings will be honored "except in the most unusual circumstances."

As its name implies, the end-of-Phase 2 meeting takes place after the completion of Phase 2 clinical trials and before the initiation of Phase 3 studies. Since agency recommendations may bring about significant revisions to a sponsor's Phase 3 trial plans, the agency suggests that these meetings be held before "major commitments of effort and resources to specific Phase 3 tests are made." The FDA adds, however, that such meetings are not intended to delay the transition from Phase 2 to Phase 3 studies.

As they should in all such communications with the FDA, sponsors should attempt to obtain from agency reviewers and officials specific recommendations during the meeting. Agency staffers advise that sponsors develop highly specific questions or well-formulated proposals, and that they focus questions not only on safety issues regarding Phase 3 protocols, but on what studies and data will be necessary for the ultimate approval of the drug as well. Under PDUFA III commitments, the FDA has agreed to prepare the meeting minutes and make them available to the sponsor within 30 days after the meeting (i.e., for at least 90% of meetings). The minutes should "clearly outline the important agreements, disagreements, issues for further discussion, and action items from the meeting in bulleted form and need not be in great detail," the agency states.

End-of-Phase 2A Meetings. Under a new voluntary pilot program, CDER is participating in so-called end-of-Phase 2A meetings in an effort to address drug-dosing issues earlier in a product's development process. Specifically, such meetings are designed "to improve the design and use of dose-response and pharmacokinetics-pharmacodynamics studies and data, and to discuss the overall biopharmaceutics and clinical pharmacology development strategy needed to support drug dosing and NDA approval."

In a November 2003 concept paper, the agency said that such meetings would take place after the completion of Phase 1 and the first set of exposure-response studies in patients, but before the initiation of Phase 2B and Phase 3 clinical studies. An outgrowth of the FDA's strategic action plan, the pilot program is designed to provide for FDA/sponsor discussions at a critical juncture—before a company has initiated definitive dose-ranging studies and before it has started planning for the all-important Phase 3 trials.

Continuous Marketing Application Pilot 2—Frequent Scientific Feedback/Interaction. Under PDUFA III's so-called Pilot 2 program, the FDA and applicants of eligible fast track products can enter into an agreement to engage in "frequent scientific feedback and interactions during the IND (or clinical development) phase of a product's development." To qualify for frequent scientific feedback and interactions with FDA under PDUFA III's Pilot 2, companies must submit a Pilot 2 application describing how their fast track products could significantly benefit the public health and how their proposed clinical development program could benefit from frequent FDA communication.

Given the resources and level of commitment anticipated in Pilot 2 programs, the FDA established that each product review division could participate in only a single Pilot 2 project over the course of PDUFA III. As of mid-2004, only 7 of CDER's 17 new drug and biologics review divisions had received an "acceptable" application and enrolled a Pilot 2 project, however.

After a division accepts a Pilot 2 project, the division and the applicant will finalize an agreement on the nature of and timelines for feedback and interactions. The FDA outlines Pilot 2 further in an October 2003 guidance entitled, *Continuous Marketing Applications: Pilot 2—Scientific Feedback and Interactions During Development of Fast Track Products Under PDUFA.*

Special Protocol Assessment and Agreement Process. As part of its "special protocol question assessment and agreement" process introduced under PDUFA II and continued under PDUFA III, the agency also agreed to evaluate

Phase 3 clinical trial protocols (as well as carcinogenicity and stability protocols) to determine whether a trial's design and size are adequate to meet scientific and regulatory requirements identified by the sponsor. Within 45 days of receiving such a protocol and specific sponsor questions, the agency will provide a written response that includes "a succinct assessment of the protocol and answers to the sponsor's questions." Under PDUFA III, the agency has committed to responding to at least 90% of such requests within the 45-day timeframe.

According to text that accompanied the agency's original commitments, "the fundamental agreement here is that having agreed to the design, execution, and analyses proposed in protocols reviewed under this process, the Agency will not later alter its perspective on the issues...unless public health concerns unrecognized at the time of protocol assessment under this process are evident." Related language in the FDA Modernization Act of 1997 seemed to be even stronger: "Any agreement regarding the parameters of the design and size of clinical trials of a new drug...that is reached between the [FDA] and a sponsor or applicant shall be reduced to writing and made part of the administrative record...[and] shall not be changed after the testing begins, except-(i) with the written agreement of the sponsor or applicant; or (ii) pursuant to a decision...by the director of the reviewing division, that a substantial scientific issue essential to determining the safety or effectiveness of the drug has been identified...."

In a May 2002 final guidance entitled, *Special Protocol Assessment*, the FDA attempts to establish the process through which special protocol assessments will be conducted and agreements will be reached. CDER generally recommends that a sponsor submit a protocol intended for a special protocol assessment to the agency at least 90 days prior to the study's anticipated start date. A separate request in the form of an IND amendment should be forwarded for each protocol that the sponsor wants to have reviewed under this process.

To ensure that the CDER review division "is aware of both the developmental context in which the protocol is being reviewed and the questions that are to be answered," the sponsor should seek a meeting with the agency. In the request for protocol assessment, the sponsor should pose focused questions concerning specific issues regarding the protocol, protocol design (including proposed size), study conduct, study goals, and/or data analysis for the proposed investigation. The request should also discuss, in reasonable detail, all data, assumptions, and information needed for an adequate evaluation of the protocol.

Within 45 calendar days of receiving an applicant's request for a special protocol assessment, the review team responsible for the drug product should forward its comments to the applicant. If the applicant wants to discuss any remaining issues (e.g., disagreements) or issues regarding the protocol following the special assessment, it can request a meeting (i.e., a Type A meeting). All agency/sponsor agreements and disagreements should be documented clearly in the special protocol assessment letter and/or the minutes of the Type A meeting.

According to the May 2002 guidance, "documented special protocol assessments should be considered binding on the review division and should not be changed at any time, except as follows:"

- Failure of a sponsor to follow a protocol that was agreed upon with the agency will be interpreted as the sponsor's understanding that the protocol assessment is no longer binding on the agency.
- If the relevant data, assumptions, or information provided by the sponsor in a request for special protocol assessment change are found to be false statements or misstatements or are found to omit relevant facts, the agency will not be bound by any assessment that relied on such data, assumptions, or information.

- A documented special protocol assessment can be modified if (1) the FDA and the sponsor agree in writing to modify the protocol (section 505(b)(4)(C) of the Act) and (2) such modification is intended to improve the study. A special protocol assessment modified in this manner will be considered binding on the review division, except under the circumstances described in the bullet below.

- A clinical protocol assessment will no longer be considered binding if the director of the review division determines that a substantial scientific issue essential to determining the safety or efficacy of the drug has been identified after the testing has begun (section 505(b)(4)(C) of the Act). If the director of the review division makes such a determination, (1) the determination should be documented in writing for the administrative record and should be provided to the sponsor, and (2) the sponsor should be given an opportunity for a meeting at which the review division director will discuss the scientific issue involved (section 505(b)(4)(D) of the Act).

Phase 3 Clinical Trials

In Phase 3 investigations, a drug is tested under conditions more closely resembling those under which it would be used if approved for marketing. During this phase, an investigational compound is administered to a significantly larger patient population (i.e., from several hundred to several thousand subjects) to, in the FDA's words, "gather additional information about effectiveness and safety that is needed to evaluate the overall benefit-risk relationship of the drug and to provide an adequate basis for physician labeling."

The larger patient pool and the genetic, lifestyle, environmental, and physiological diversity that it brings allow the investigators to identify potential adverse drug reactions and to determine the appropriate dosage of the drug for the more diverse general population. Patient population criteria for Phase 3 trials may also be expanded to include those with concomitant therapies and conditions.

Even with the expanded eligibility criteria, the patient population studied in Phase 3 trials will always be a subset of the overall population with a particular disease or condition. The study population in Phase 3 must be sufficiently homogeneous so that variability in response(s) is minimized and so that the study has adequate power to demonstrate an effect. At the same time, the study population must be adequately representative to enable the generalization of the results to the patient population at large.

For certain drugs, principally those for serious and life-threatening illnesses, Phase 3 also marks the point at which clinical trial sponsors must make another important decision: The sponsor often must consider whether to make the study drug available to patients who desperately need therapeutic alternatives and who are unable to enroll in the formal clinical trials. Such availability, sometimes called "expanded access" or "compassionate use," can be provided under several mechanisms that the agency has established, including treatment INDs and emergency use INDs (see Chapter 15). Reached in consultation with the FDA, the decision to make a drug available in this manner is a function, first and foremost, of what is known about a drug's safety and, secondly, what is known about its efficacy. This decision is also based upon the availability of satisfactory therapeutic alternatives in the marketplace and the severity of the disease and its potential for causing disability or death.

Pivotal Clinical Studies Phase 3 testing may produce data from controlled and uncontrolled trials conducted at several hospitals, clinics, or other sites outlined in the protocol. But the clinical data that the FDA will review most closely and upon which the agency will base its approval/disapproval decision are those derived from tests specified in federal regulations as "adequate and well-controlled studies."

The focus on adequate and well-controlled studies as the criterion for assessing the effectiveness of new drugs flows directly from the Federal Food, Drug and Cosmetic Act, which states that "the term 'substantial evidence' means evidence consisting of adequate and well-controlled investigations...on the basis of which it could fairly and responsibly be concluded by...experts that the drug will have the effect it purports or is represented to have under the conditions of use prescribed, recommended, or suggested in the labeling or proposed labeling thereof."

The concept of substantial evidence has a second important component. With rare exceptions, at least two adequate and well-controlled studies are necessary to obtain FDA approval for a new drug. According to the FDA's *Guideline for the Content and Format of the Clinical and Statistical Sections of an Application*, "the requirement for well-controlled clinical investigations has been interpreted to mean that the effectiveness of a drug should be supported by more than one well-controlled trial and carried out by independent investigators. This interpretation is consistent with the general scientific demand for replicability. Ordinarily, therefore, the clinical trials submitted in an application will not be regarded as adequate support of a claim unless they include studies by more than one independent investigator who maintains adequate case histories of an adequate number of subjects."

It is important to note, however, that the adequate and well-controlled studies submitted in support of a drug need not be identical. In some cases, for example, they might be carried out in patient populations with different expressions of the same target illness to be treated by the investigational drug.

In late 1997 and early 1998, an FDA guidance document and the FDA Modernization Act clarified the concept of the "substantial evidence" of effectiveness necessary for approval. In the November 1997 reform legislation, Congress established that data from a single adequate and well-controlled study, together with confirmatory evidence, may, at the FDA's discretion, comprise substantial evidence of effectiveness.

Then, with its release of a May 1998 *Guidance for Industry - Providing Clinical Evidence of Effectiveness for Human Drug and Biological Products*, the FDA took another important step in clarifying—some might say evolving—this standard. The agency stated that it was appropriate to re-articulate its current thinking concerning the "quantitative and qualitative standards for demonstrating effectiveness of drugs" because "the science and practice of drug development and clinical evaluation have evolved significantly since the effectiveness requirement for drugs was established, and this evolution has implications for the amount and type of data needed to support effectiveness in certain cases... At the same time, progress in clinical evaluation and clinical pharmacology has resulted in more rigorously designed and conducted clinical efficacy trials, which are ordinarily conducted at more than one clinical site. This added rigor and scope has implications for a study's reliability, generalizability, and capacity to substantiate effectiveness.

"The usual requirement for more than one adequate and well-controlled investigation reflects the need for independent substantiation of experimental results..., [which is] often referred to as the need for 'replication' of the finding. Replication may not be the best term, however, as it may imply that precise repetition of the same experiment in other patients by other investigators is the only means to substantiate a conclusion. Precise replication of a trial is only one of a number of possible means of obtaining independent substantiation of a clinical finding and, at times, can be less than optimal as it could leave the conclusions vulnerable to any systematic biases inherent to the particular study design. Results that are obtained from studies that are of different design and independent in execution, perhaps evaluating different populations, endpoints, or dosage forms, may provide support for a conclusion of effectiveness that is as convincing as, or more convincing than, a repeat of the same study."

This important guidance also identifies situations in which the agency will consider approving new drugs, or new uses of approved medicines, without data from two adequate and well-controlled studies. To the pharmaceutical industry, the guidance's most intriguing aspect was a discussion of the situations in which a single pivotal study could provide the basis for marketing approval. Although the agency had issued a 1995 statement specifying when a single, multicenter study could support approval, the FDA points out that it had not "comprehensively described the situations" in which a single study might be used or the characteristics of a single study that would make it adequate to support approval.

While the FDA contends that none of the characteristics "is necessarily determinative," the presence of one or more of five characteristics can contribute to a conclusion that a single pivotal study would be adequate to support approval: certain large multicenter studies; consistency across study subsets; multiple "studies" in a single study; multiple endpoints involving different events; and statistically very powerful findings.

The guidance also offers several caveats regarding the use of a single pivotal trial for approval. Reliance on a single study, the agency points out, generally will be limited to situations in which a trial has demonstrated a clinically meaningful effect on mortality, irreversible morbidity, or prevention of a disease with a potentially serious outcome, such that confirmation of the result in a second trial would be ethically difficult or impossible.

Although they concede that the use of a single clinical trial is more common or even typical in certain cases (e.g., oncology drugs, outcome studies), senior FDA officials note that the approach is employed only in a "tiny minority" of all cases today.

A 2001 Tufts Center for the Study of Drug Development (CSDD) found that over 80 percent of major pharmaceutical companies surveyed had used or planned to employ regulatory provisions allowing the use of a single controlled trial to gain product approval. The study found that 8 of the 15 top worldwide pharmaceutical companies surveyed used the single controlled trial (SCT) approach for product applications submitted in 1998 and 1999. The Tufts CSDD identified ten approved drug applications employing the SCT approach—six NDAs, four of which were NDAs for new molecular entities, and four supplemental NDAs. Two of the NME-NDAs were submitted to and approved by the Division of Oncologic Drug Products, while the Division of Gastrointestinal and Coagulation Drug Products received four applications using the SCT approach—three supplemental NDAs and one original NDA. Many, but not all, of the drugs employing the SCT approach were products for indications for which SCTs "were expected to be acceptable to FDA," including orphan drugs, pediatric indications, and drugs reviewed under the accelerated approval process.

The Tufts CSDD study also noted that nine of the 12 identified applications (i.e., ten NDAs and two biologics applications) supplemented the SCT data with confirmatory evidence from related adequate and well-controlled studies. Five of these nine applications included data from studies on different doses, regimens, or dosage forms. A third of the applications used just one type of related study, 55 percent used two or three types of related studies, and 11 percent used as many as five types of related studies to support the SCT. Interestingly, all three of the applications that included data from an SCT alone (i.e., without confirmatory evidence) had been approved. Tufts CSDD noted that the sponsors of these three applications all self-rated their SCTs as being very strong in regard to two of the five study characteristics that the FDA claims are of particular importance when an SCT is used: (1) no single site was disproportionately responsible for the positive effect; and (2) there was consistency of important covariates across study subsets.

Standards for Pivotal Trials Because of their central importance to the FDA's approval decision, pivotal studies must meet particularly high scientific standards: "The purpose of conducting clinical investigations of a drug is to distinguish the effect of a drug from other influences, such as spontaneous change in the course of the disease, improvements in supportive care, placebo effect, or biased observation," the agency states. Therefore, adequate and well-controlled trials are designed to isolate the drug's effects from extraneous factors that might otherwise undermine the validity of the trials' results.

Generally, a study must meet four criteria to be considered pivotal:

1. A pivotal study must be a controlled trial. As previously discussed, a controlled trial, in many cases, compares a group of patients treated with a placebo or standard therapy against a group of patients treated with the investigational drug. The FDA specifies in federal regulations, and the ICH parties recognize in a July 2000 guidance (E10 *Choice of Control Group and Related Issues in Clinical Trials*), five types of controls: placebo concurrent controls; dose-comparison concurrent controls; no treatment concurrent controls; active (positive) treatment concurrent controls; and historical (external) controls. The E10 guidance notes that, "the choice of control group is always a critical decision in designing a clinical trial. That choice affects the inferences that can be drawn from the trial, the ethical acceptability of the trial, the degree to which bias in conducting and analyzing the study can be minimized, the types of subjects that can be recruited and the pace of recruitment, the kind of endpoints that can be studied, the public and scientific credibility of the results, the acceptability of the results by regulatory authorities, and many other features of the study, its conduct, and its interpretation" (see exhibit below). The guidance also notes that it is increasingly common for more than one type of control group to be used in a development program. The 2000 guidance was criticized by industry, principally because it failed to harmonize the various control group preferences of the ICH regions (e.g., the FDA's preference for placebo controls and European regulators' preference for active comparators). The FDA has acknowledged that the guidance, although it discusses the appropriateness of the various controls in specific situations, does not address the requirements in any of the three regions.

2. A pivotal study must have a blinded design when such a design is practical and ethical. According to the ICH's September 1999 final guideline entitled, *Statistical Principles for Clinical Trials*, "blinding, or masking, is intended to limit the occurrence of conscious and unconscious bias in the conduct and interpretation of a clinical trial arising from the influence that the knowledge of treatment may have on the recruitment and allocation of subjects, their subsequent care, the attitudes of subjects to the treatments, the assessment of end points, the handling of withdrawals, the exclusion of data from analysis, and so on. The essential aim is to prevent identification of the treatments until all such opportunities for bias have passed." Double-blind trials are those in which the subjects and the investigator and sponsor staff involved in treating and evaluating patients are kept from knowing which subjects are receiving the experimental drug and which are receiving the placebo/standard therapy. When double-blind trials are not feasible (e.g., because the pattern of administration differs), studies may employ single blinds, in which only the subjects are kept from knowing which treatment is administered. In some cases, however, only an open-label study is possible because of ethical or practical factors. In certain instances, studies employ a mechanism of blinding often referred to as a "double dummy" design that is intended to eliminate the biases that might otherwise result from the comparison of different formulations or routes of administration. In such a design, each study subject receives two formulations, only one of which contains the active moiety. This might be used, for example, when an intravenous antibiotic is being compared to an oral antibiotic. Half the subjects might

receive the active oral formulation and a placebo intravenous formulation, while the remaining subjects would receive the oral placebo and the active intravenous formulation.

3. A pivotal study must be randomized. This means that clinical subjects are assigned randomly to the treatment and control groups. Therefore, each subject has an equal chance of being assigned to the various treatment and control groups to be studied in a particular trial. In combination with blinding, randomization helps prevent potential bias in the selection and assignment of trial subjects.

4. A pivotal study must be of adequate size (see discussion below). The study must involve enough patients to provide statistically significant evidence of a new drug's safety and effectiveness. According to the FDA's *General Considerations for the Clinical Evaluation of Drugs*, the size of a pivotal study is dependent upon factors such as: (1) the degree of response one wishes to detect; (2) the desired assurance against a false positive finding; and (3) the acceptable risk of failure to demonstrate the response when it is present in the population. Sample size calculations require many assumptions about the results to be obtained with the treatment and the population being studied. Because considerable clinical judgment is employed in making these assumptions, FDA officials warn that faulty presumptions frequently result in studies of inadequate statistical power. Most recently, the FDA and ICH have discussed the difficulties and factors involved in study sample sizes, largely from the safety perspective, in guidance documents such as the ICH's E1A *The Extent of Population Exposure to Assess Clinical Safety: For Drugs Intended for Long-term Treatment of Non-Life-Threatening Conditions* (March 1995) and the FDA's May 2004 *Premarketing Risk Assessment* (see discussion below).

These criteria also are included in FDA regulations, which add that the "characteristics" of adequate and well-controlled studies include the following:

- a clear statement of the objectives of the study;

- a design that permits a valid comparison with a control to provide a quantitative assessment of the drug effect;

- a method of subject selection that provides adequate assurance that subjects have the disease or condition being studied, or that they show evidence of susceptibility and exposure to the condition against which prophylaxis is directed;

- a method of assigning patients to treatment and control groups that minimizes bias and that is intended to assure comparability of the groups with respect to pertinent variables such as age, sex, severity of disease, duration of disease, and the use of drugs or therapy other than test drugs (*Author's note*: It is important to note that significant improvements in concomitant therapies or mortality rates may drastically alter the conditions of a long-term treatment study involving a chronic disease. The population characteristics of those enrolled near the end of a study may be entirely different from those found in patients enrolled at the beginning of the study);

- adequate measures to minimize bias by the subjects, observers, and analysts of the data;

- well-defined and reliable methods for objectively assessing subjects' responses; and

- an adequate analysis of the study results to assess the effects of the drug (this should not involve so called "data-dredging" to find a positive effect).

The FDA wrote in 1987 that it "has long considered [these] characteristics as the essentials of an adequate and well-controlled study... In general, the regulation on adequate and well-controlled studies has two overall objectives: (1) To allow the agency to assess methods for minimizing bias; and (2) to assure a sufficiently detailed description of the study to allow scientific assessment and interpretation of it."

It is worth noting that federal regulations do not provide a comprehensive discussion of the testing conditions necessary for pivotal trials. Mentions of other standards that the FDA sees as necessary for pivotal studies are scattered throughout a variety of agency guidelines. Although it does not address pivotal trials directly, the ICH's September 1998 guideline entitled, E9 *Statistical Principles for Clinical Trials* offers a useful discussion regarding important aspects of later-phase study design issues, including study configuration (e.g., cross-over and parallel group), trial comparisons (e.g., superiority, equivalence), and sample size.

Determining Adequate Study Sizes

Against the backdrop of high clinical study costs and difficulties in recruiting study subjects, determining adequate trial sizes remains a complex and problematic process that continues to bedevil many product development programs. In mid-2003, for example, Division of Oncologic Drug Products Director Richard Pazdur, M.D., warned that undersized, or statistically "underpowered," clinical trials for oncology drugs were rapidly becoming a larger problem. "Many times, patient populations and number of patients are calculated more or less from a practical perspective of how many patients one can realistically accrue [within a specific time period], rather than putting a true estimation of what is the treatment effect or what is the proposed effect," Pazdur said at the time.

Over the last several years, a handful of international and FDA guidance documents have addressed the trial-size issue. Under a March 1995 ICH guidance entitled, E1A *The Extent of Population Exposure to Assess Clinical Safety: For Drugs Intended for Long-Term Treatment of Non-Life-Threatening Conditions*, the FDA and ICH generally recommended that 1,500 subjects be exposed to an investigational product (with 300 to 600 exposed for six months, and 100 exposed for one year) intended for the long-term treatment (e.g., chronic or recurrent intermittent) of non-life-threatening conditions. For those products that the E1A guidance characterized as chronic use products, the FDA recommends that the 1,500 subjects include only those who have been exposed to the product in multiple doses, since many adverse events of concern (e.g., hepatotoxicity, hematologic events) do not appear with single doses or very short-term exposure. Also, the 300 to 600 subjects exposed for six months and 100 patients exposed for one year should be exposed to "relevant doses," with a reasonable representation of subjects exposed at the highest proposed dose.

The E1A guidance, however, specifies a number of circumstances in which a safety database larger than 1,500 may be appropriate, including:

1. When there is concern that the drug would cause late-developing adverse events, or cause adverse events that increase in severity or frequency over time. Such concern could be triggered by data from animal studies, clinical information on other agents with related chemical structures or from a related pharmacologic class, or pharmacokinetic or pharmacodymamic properties known to be associated with such adverse events.

2. When there is a need to quantitate the occurrence rate of an expected specific low-frequency adverse event. Examples would include situations in which a specific serious adverse event has been identified in similar products or when a serious event that could represent an alert event is observed in early clinical trials.

3. When a large database would help make risk-benefit decisions in situations in which the benefit from the product is small (e.g., symptomatic improvement in less-serious medical

conditions), will be experienced by only a fraction of the treated patients (e.g., certain preventive therapies administered to healthy populations), or is of uncertain magnitude (e.g., efficacy determination on a surrogate endpoint).

4. When there this concern that a product may add to an already significant background rate of morbidity or mortality, and clinical trials should be designed with a sufficient number of patients to provide adequate statistical power to detect prespecified increases over the baseline morbidity or mortality.

More recently, the agency provided its perspectives on the appropriate size of premarketing safety databases in a May 2004 draft guidance entitled, *Premarketing Risk Assessment*, which it developed as part of its push in the risk management area under PDUFA III. In this draft guidance, the agency acknowledges the complexities of determining an adequate size for safety databases and the practical limitations of clinical development programs.

"Providing detailed guidance on what constitutes an adequate safety database for all products is impossible," the agency notes. "The nature and extent of safety data that would provide sufficient information about risk for purposes of approving a product are individualized decisions based on a number of factors... Even large clinical development programs cannot reasonably be expected to identify all risks associated with a product. Some risks become apparent only when a product is used in tens of thousands or even millions of patients in the general population. However, the larger and more comprehensive a preapproval database, the more likely it is that serious adverse events will be detected."

The Choice of Clinical Trial Controls

(from the ICH's July 2000 guidance entitled, *The Choice of Control Group and Related Issues in Clinical Trials*)

Placebo Concurrent Control "In a placebo-controlled study, subjects are randomly assigned to a test treatment or to an identical-appearing treatment that does not contain the test drug. The treatments may be titrated to effect or tolerance, or may be given at one or more fixed doses. Such trials are almost always double-blind. The name of the control suggests that its purpose is to control for "placebo" effect (improvement in a subject resulting from thinking that he or she is taking a drug), but that is not its only or major benefit. Rather, the placebo control design, by allowing blinding and randomization and including a group that receives an inert treatment, controls for all potential influences on the actual or apparent course of the disease other than those arising from the pharmacologic action of the test drug. These influences include spontaneous change (natural history of the disease and regression to the mean), subject or investigator expectations, the effect of being in a trial, use of other therapy, and subjective elements of diagnosis and assessment. Placebo-controlled trials seek to show a difference between treatments when they are studying effectiveness, but may also seek to show lack of difference (of specified size) in evaluating a safety measurement."

No-Treatment Concurrent Control "In a no-treatment controlled study, subjects are randomly assigned to test treatment or to no (i.e., absence of) study treatment. The principal difference between this design and a placebo-controlled trial is that subjects and investigators are not blind to treatment assignment. Because of the advantages of double-blind designs, this design is likely to be needed and suitable only when it is difficult or impossible to double-blind (e.g., treatments with easily recognized toxicity) and only when there is reasonable confidence that study endpoints are objective and that the results of the study are unlikely to be influenced by [any of the problems associated with knowledge of treatment assignment (e.g., unblinded subjects on active drug might report more favorable outcomes because they expect a benefit or might be more likely to stay in the trial)]. Note that it is often possible to have a blinded evaluator carry out endpoint assessment, even if the overall trial is not double-blind. This is a valuable approach and should always be considered in studies that cannot be blinded, but it does not solve the other problems associated with knowing the treatment assignment...."

Dose-Response Concurrent Control "In a randomized, fixed-dose, dose-response trial, subjects are randomized to one of several fixed-dose groups. Subjects may either be placed on their fixed dose initially or be raised to that dose gradually, but the intended comparison is between the groups on their final dose. Dose-response studies are usually double-blind. They may include a placebo (zero dose) and/or active control. In a concentration-controlled trial, treatment groups are titrated to several fixed-concentration windows; this type of trial is conceptually similar to a fixed-dose, dose-response trial."

Active (Positive) Concurrent Control "In an active control (or positive control) trial, subjects are randomly assigned to the test treatment or to an active control treatment. Such trials are usually double-blind, but this is not always possible; many oncology trials, for example, are considered difficult or impossible to blind because of different regimens, different routes of administration, and different toxicities. Active control trials can have two distinct objectives with respect to showing efficacy: (1) To show efficacy of the test treatment by showing it is as good as a known effective treatment or (2) to show efficacy by showing superiority of the test treatment to the active control. They may also be used with the primary objective of comparing the efficacy and/or safety of the two treatments. Whether the purpose of the trial is to show efficacy of the new treatment or to compare two treatments, the question of whether the trial would be capable of distinguishing effective from less effective or ineffective treatments is critical."

External Control (Including Historical Control) "An externally controlled study compares a group of subjects receiving the test treatment with a group of patients external to the study, rather than to an internal control group consisting of patients from the same population assigned to a different treatment... External (historical) control groups, regardless of the comparator treatment, are considered together as the fifth type [of control group] because of serious concerns about the ability of such trials to ensure comparability of test and control groups and their ability to minimize important biases, making this design usable only in exceptional circumstances. The external control can be a group of patients treated at an earlier time (historical control) or a group treated during the same time period but in another setting. The external control may be defined (a specific group of patients) or nondefined (a comparator group based on general medical knowledge of outcome). Use of this latter comparator is particularly trecherous (such trials are usually considered uncontrolled) because general impressions are so often inaccurate. So-called baseline-controlled studies, in which subjects' status on therapy is compared with status before therapy (e.g., blood pressure, tumor size), have no internal control and are thus uncontrolled or externally controlled."

The ICH guidance also notes that it is often possible and "advantageous" to employ more than one type of control in a single study (e.g., using both an active control and a placebo). Some trials might use several doses of a test drug and several doses of an active control with or without placebo. Such a design, says the guidance, may be useful for active drug comparisons when the relative potency of the two drugs is not well established, or when the trial's purpose is to establish relative potency.

The appropriate size of a safety database supporting a new product, the agency notes, will depend on a number of product-specific factors, including:

- The product's novelty (i.e., whether it represents a new treatment or is similar to available treatment)
- The product's potential advantages over existing therapies
- The intended population
- The product's intended duration of use.

Safety databases for products intended to treat life-threatening disease are "usually" smaller than those for products supporting symptomatic treatment of a nonserious disease, the agency emphasizes. A larger safety database may be appropriate if a product's preclinical assessment or human clinical pharmacology studies identify signals of risk that warrant clinical data to properly define the risk.

In its *Premarketing Risk Assessment* draft guidance, the FDA notes that it is "difficult" to offer general guidance on the appropriate target size of clinical safety databases for products intended for short-term or acute use. "This is because of the wide range of indications and diseases (e.g., acute strokes to mild headaches) that may be targeted by such therapies," says the agency.

Although the FDA uses the *Premarketing Risk Assessment* draft guidance to emphasize E1A's provisions regarding clinical database sizes for products intended for the long-term treatment of non-life-threatening conditions (see discussion above), it specifies additional circumstances in which a larger database may be appropriate:

"1. The proposed treatment is for a healthy population (e.g., the product under development is for chemoprevention or is a preventive vaccine).

2. A safe and effective alternative to the investigational product is already available."

"The FDA is not suggesting that development of a database larger than that described in E1A is required or should be the norm," the agency points out. "Rather, the appropriate database size would depend on the circumstances affecting a particular product... Therefore, FDA recommends that sponsors communicate with the review division responsible for their product early in the development program on the appropriate size of the safety database. FDA also recommends that sponsors revisit the issue at appropriate regulatory milestones (e.g., end-of-phase 2 and pre-NDA meetings)."

The agency also uses the May 2004 draft guidance to emphasize that premarketing safety databases should include, to the extent possible, "a diverse population" in Phase 3 studies. "We recommend that, to the extent feasible, only patients with obvious contraindications be excluded from study entry in phase 3 trials," says the agency. "Inclusion of a diverse population allows for the development of safety data in a broader population that includes patients previously excluded from clinical trials, such as the elderly (particularly the very old), patients with concomitant diseases, and patients taking usual concomitant medications. Broadening inclusion criteria in phase 3 studies enhances the generalizability of study findings and may, therefore, allow the product to be labeled for broader use. Although some phase 3 efficacy studies may target certain demographic or disease characteristics (and hence have narrower inclusion and exclusion criteria), it may be useful to conduct controlled safety and/or efficacy studies in less restricted populations."

Emerging Clinical Trial Enrollment Benchmarks: Trial Size Statistics for New Drugs Approved in 2003

The clinical development programs conducted to support the new molecular entities (NME) approved in 2003 had a mean total enrollment of 4,608 patients and a median total enrollment of 2,452 patients, according to a new survey of 12 of the 21 NMEs cleared by the FDA during the year.

These statistics are based on each sponsor's assessment of the total Phase 1 through Phase 3 trial enrollments in all study treatment arms (active drug, placebo, active controls). In other words, the counts upon which the mean and median are based are thought to represent the total patient databases submitted in the NDAs for these new drugs.

Key Clinical Trial Enrollment Statistics for NMEs Approved in 1999–2003

	2003	2002	2001	2000	1999
Mean Patients Per NDA	4,608	4,749	5,144	6,659*	4,980
Median Patients per NDA	2,452	5,175	4,186	3,840	5,435
Range	282-15,248	710-9,167	832-17,000	1,345-35,696	202-14,300

* drops to 4,723 without Mobic

The results of this analysis, which is our sixth annual effort to analyze the clinical trial sizes for new molecular entities, can be compared with similar analyses released over the last several years. In a study of 23 marketing dossiers submitted between February 1995 and April 1999, CMR International found no discernable trend in the size (i.e., number of subjects enrolled) of clinical programs submitted over this span, despite finding that the median number of clinical trials conducted for these dossiers fell sharply—from 40 for dossiers submitted in 1995/6 to 39 in 1997 to 21 in 1998/9. Over this same period, the median number of subjects was 3,864 for 1995/6, 5,582 for 1997, and 3,750 for 1998/9 submissions. CMR International found that the 23 dossiers had an average of 35 trials and a mean of 4,387 patients.

Similar to last year, the range of total Phase 1 through Phase 3 trial enrollments for the 12 drugs in our survey was considerable. Trial sizes ranged from 282 patients for the orphan drug Velcade to approximately 15,248 patients for Factive, an anti-infective.

Although it had two large clinical trial programs (over 14,000 patients each), the sample of 2003 NME approvals also had an extremely high number (7) of clinical programs that enrolled less than 2,500 patients each (three for HIV treatments)—equaling

the high in our multi-year survey. This helped to produce the lowest mean and median clinical trial enrollment figures in the six years in which we have conducted this study. While the mean patients per NDA declined for the third consecutive year in 2003, the figure was off only 3% from the 2002 mark. The median NME trial size dropped by more than half in 2003, however.

For each drug in the sample, the sponsoring company was asked for the total Phase 1 through Phase 3 trial enrollment, irrespective of treatment arm. In a few cases, when companies could not provide exact trial enrollment figures, we worked with the firms to develop estimates based on the figures that were available, such as the number of subjects who received the experimental therapy during clinical trials or the number enrolled in Phase 3 pivotal trials. In a few other cases, we calculated trial sizes based on study-specific data in product labeling.

Obviously, the results of any such analysis on a cohort of drugs approved in a single year are a function of the nature of the drugs in the cohort. And, since this survey includes just over half of the NMEs approved in the 2003 NME cohort, the statistics are at least in part of function of the absense of drugs that were not included because their clinical trial enrollments could not be confirmed.

Clinical Trial Enrollments (Phase 1-Phase 3, including all treatment arms) for Selected NMEs Approved in 2003

Emtriva	HIV	~2,100
Factive	Pneumonia/bacterial exacerbations of bronchitis	15,248
Fuzeon	HIV-1	~1,100
Levitra	Erectile dysfunction	~5,750
Reyataz	HIV-1	2,425
Velcade	Multiple myeloma	282
Cubicin	Bacterial skin infections	~2,480
Crestor	Various lipid disorders	~14,000
Cialis	Erectile dysfunction	~4,200
Uroxatral	Benign prostatic hyperplasia	~1,808
Boniva	Osteoporosis	~3,925
Aloxi	Chemo-induced nausea/vomiting	~1,978

Source: PAREXEL's Pharmaceutical R&D Statistical Sourcebook 2004/2005

Completing a Drug's Clinical Study

It is in the best interest of the sponsor, the clinical subjects, and, in many cases, the public that a drug's clinical study be completed as soon as sufficient safety and efficacy data are obtained. If a drug is found to be unsafe or ineffective during the development process, then continuing a trial only exposes more clinical subjects to a dangerous or useless compound, and in some cases, keeps study subjects from using better or safer therapies. On the other hand, if the drug is clearly shown to be safer or more effective than existing therapies, delaying the submission of an NDA to gain additional data needlessly prolongs the development process and denies patients access to a needed drug.

Clinical trials may be discontinued before reaching their subject accrual targets for any one of several reasons, including the following:

- the studies clearly establish a drug's safety and effectiveness;
- an unacceptable adverse effect is discovered; or
- it becomes apparent that the studies are unlikely to establish a drug's safety or effectiveness, or that a drug's apparent safety and effectiveness are less than that of a standard therapy.

When designing the trial, statisticians will establish what are called "stopping rules." These are rigorous statistical criteria or goals that, if met at some point during the study of a drug, will trigger the end of the clinical trial. To justify discontinuing the trial, the data generally must meet stringent standards to show, for example, that the drug's effects are: (1) statistically significant (i.e., that the drug was tested in a large enough patient population to ensure that observed effects were not due to chance); and (2) clinically significant (i.e., that the test results are sufficient to show that there is a perceptible difference in the clinical effect between the investigational drug and the placebo and/or a standard therapy).

The periodic analysis of accrued data—interim analysis—is undertaken during the clinical trial to determine if any of the pre-established stopping criteria have been met. Because interim analyses can affect the interpretation of the clinical trial, they must be planned and scheduled in advance and disclosed in the clinical protocol. According to the ICH guideline entitled, E9 *Statistical Principles for Clinical Trials*, "most clinical trials intended to support the efficacy and safety of an investigational product should proceed to full completion of planned sample size accrual; trials should be stopped early only for ethical reasons or if the power is no longer acceptable. However, it is recognized that drug development plans involve the need for sponsor access to comparative treatment data for a variety of reasons, such as planning other trials. It is also recognized that only a subset of trials will involve the study of serious life-threatening outcomes or mortality which may need sequential monitoring of accruing comparative treatment effects for ethical reasons. In either of these situations, plans for interim statistical analysis should be in place in the protocol or in protocol amendments prior to the unblinded access to comparative treatment data in order to deal with the potential statistical and operational bias that may be introduced."

For many clinical trials, particularly those involving drugs with major public health significance, the responsibility for monitoring comparisons of efficacy and/or safety outcomes should be assigned to an independent and external group often called a data safety monitoring board (DSMB), the ICH guidance states. The guidance, which calls the boards independent data monitoring committees (IDMC), says that such panels "may be established by the sponsor to assess at intervals the progress of a clinical trial, safety data, and critical efficacy variables and recommend to the sponsor whether to continue, modify or terminate a trial [based on its findings]."

In a November 2001 draft document entitled, *Guidance for Clinical Trial Sponsors on the Establishment and Operation of Clinical Trial Data Monitoring Committees*, the FDA establishes that data monitoring committees (DMC) should be used in all controlled trials employing mortality or major morbidity as a primary or secondary endpoint. DMCs, the agency notes, may also be useful "in settings where trial participants may be at elevated risk of such outcomes even if the study intervention addresses lesser outcomes such as relief of symptoms." The draft guidance defines DMCs, which the FDA formally requires only when informed consent requirements are waived in studies conducted in emergency settings, as panels of individuals "with pertinent expertise that review on a regular basis accumulating outcome data in certain ongoing clinical trials [and that] advise the sponsor regarding the continuing safety of current participants and those yet to be recruited, as well as the continuing validity and scientific merit of the trial."

In addition to safety considerations (e.g., mortality/major morbidity endpoints, trials in fragile populations, and large/long-duration/multi-center studies), two other factors—practicality and assurance of scientific validity—are relevant in determining whether a sponsor should establish a DMC for a particular trial, says the agency. A DMC may not be practical, for example, for short-term trials in which the trial duration will not give the committee an opportunity to contribute. If a short-term trial presents important safety considerations that justify a DMC, the guidance says that sponsors must develop mechanisms allowing the committee to be informed and convened rapidly when unexpected results are found.

A DMC's likely ability to assure a trial's scientific validity is the third key consideration, the guidance establishes. Trials "of any appreciable duration," the FDA notes, can be affected by changes over time in the understanding of a disease, the affected population, and standard treatments, all of which are changes that may trigger an interest in study modifications as the trial advances. "When a DMC is the only group reviewing unblinded interim data, the trial organizers are free to make changes in the ongoing trial that may be motivated by newly available data outside the trial or by accumulating data from within the trial (e.g., overall event rates)," the guidance states. "In general, recommendations to change the inclusion criteria, the trial endpoints, or the size of the trial are most credibly made by those without knowledge of the accumulating data. When the trial organizers are the ones reviewing the interim data, their awareness of interim comparative results cannot help but affect their determination as to whether these changes should be made. Such changes would inevitably impair the credibility of the study results."

For these reasons and others, the draft guidance touts the advantages of the *independent* DMC, which is defined as "a committee whose members are considered to be independent of those sponsoring, organizing, and conducting the trial" (i.e., have no previous involvement in the trial's design, no current involvement in its conduct other than as the DMC, and have no financial or other important connections to the study sponsor or other trial organizers). A DMC will be considered independent, for example, if the sponsor has no representation on the committee or if the sponsor has a representative only in open meetings, during which enrollment, compliance, and event rates are presented and discussed but during which no study arm-specific data are discussed. The draft guidance acknowledges that DMCs are rarely, if ever, entirely independent of sponsors, given that sponsors typically select and pay the members and establish committee goals and responsibilities.

The independence of other individuals interacting with both the sponsor and DMC is equally important, the FDA states. Trial integrity is best maintained when the statistician preparing unblinded data (i.e., interim analyses) for the DMC is external to the sponsor, especially for studies designed to provide the definitive evidence of efficacy, the draft guidance notes. The statistician should have no responsibility for managing the trial and should have "minimal" contact with those who have such involvement.

Although DSMBs have been receiving greater attention in recent years, they have been in use for more than 25 years. One of the earliest uses of DSMBs may have been in conjunction with placebo-controlled herpes encephalitis studies conducted by the NIAID Collaborative Antiviral Substances Study Group in the early 1970s. In these studies, which involved drugs from a historically toxic class of chemicals, it was essential for researchers to know, as early as possible, that the ancient dictum, "First do no harm," was being honored. The ethical dilemma was that the disease itself was highly lethal while the proposed treatment was potentially highly toxic. This clinical study was carefully designed to incorporate monitoring by a DSMB, which would be in a position to detect unacceptable risks in the ongoing trial and to immediately call for the discontinuation of any or all study treatment arms when such risks were identified. So the board could be truly independent, none of the DSMB members had any interest in, or connection to, the drug sponsors, investigators or study sites; rather, the board answered only to the FDA. The DSMB's pre-defined, statistical evaluation of the mortality data revealed a 70% mortality in the placebo group (this disease had, prior to these findings, been considered "uniformly fatal"), a suggestion of efficacy with a 50% mortality in one of the investigational drug groups and a whopping 96% mortality in the other investigational drug group. Retrospectively from these findings, it could be concluded that anecdotal use of the "lethal" investigational drug for the preceding nine years may have inadvertently caused 26% more patient deaths than if the disease had been left to take its natural course. Ever since, the DSMB's role has been valued whenever there is the possibility of serious toxicity in a controlled clinical trial program.

Phase 4 Clinical Studies

In a very real sense, the clinical development process continues long after a product's approval. The further collection and analysis of adverse experience information and other data provide the sponsor and the FDA with a continuing flow of information so that a drug's safety and effectiveness can be reassessed periodically in light of the latest data.

PDUFA III and several agency initiatives have brought a renewed regulatory focus on the postapproval phase of a product's life cycle. Although the two earlier iterations of the FDA's user-fee program focused largely on the clinical testing and FDA review stages of product development, a primary focus of PDUFA III was on the postapproval phase and drug safety. Among other concepts, PDUFA III introduced the concept of the "risk minimization action plan" (RiskMAP), a strategic safety program designed to minimize a product's "known risks," and the so-called "peri-approval period," a two-year period (following a product's approval) during which the FDA can monitor an applicant's implementation of a RiskMAP (see Chapter 7). Meanwhile, both the ICH and the FDA have released separate draft guidances on pharmacovigilance practices and planning in 2003 and 2004, respectively.

Today, Phase 4 clinical studies have become almost a standard element of the development programs for new drugs, as companies and the FDA seek to further characterize a drug's effects following approval. A Tufts Center for the Study of Drug Development analysis showed that the FDA formally requested postmarketing studies for 73% of the new molecular entities (NME) approved from 1998 through 2003 (see Chapter 11), for example. Further, a U.S. *Regulatory Reporter* study of the approval letters for the 50 NMEs approved from 2001 through 2003 showed that the prevalence of Phase 4 postmarketing commitments has risen from 75% to almost 90% over this three-year period.

Phase 4 clinical trials, which are studies initiated after a drug's marketing approval, have become an increasingly important and common method through which sponsors obtain new information about their marketed drugs. A drug manufacturer may undertake postmarketing clinical studies for any one of several reasons, including the following:

- To satisfy an FDA request made prior to an NDA's approval that Phase 4 trials be conducted following approval (see Chapter 11). For example, the FDA may want the sponsor to better characterize the drug's safety and/or effectiveness in patient groups that may not have been widely represented in pivotal trials (e.g., children, pregnant women, persons using concomitant medications). Sponsor commitments made at the time of a drug's approval may also become, in effect, postmarketing requirements. Often called "Phase 4 commitments," these commitments—and sponsors' progress in fulfilling them—are actively tracked by the FDA following approval (see Chapter 11).

- To develop pharmacoeconomic, or cost-effectiveness, data that can be used to support marketing claims highlighting the advantages of a drug over competing therapies. Given the emergence of managed care and the increased focus on health care costs, however, growing numbers of companies are incorporating the study of pharmacoeconomic parameters into their premarketing studies.

- Other post-marketing studies are carried out to support the publication of articles in different medical specialty journals and presentations at medical specialty meetings. The goal of these studies, which are often conducted by opinion leaders in various specialties, is to provide information to less-experienced practitioners. These studies are sometimes called "Phase 5" studies.

- Finally, there are Phase 4 studies that characterize new formulations, dose regimens and routes of administration for already proven therapeutic indications.

Aside from the fact that they are conducted after approval, Phase 4 studies may differ in a number of important respects from Phase 1, 2, and 3 trials. Phase 4 studies are often of a larger scale than are pre-marketing studies. Also, they may be less rigorously controlled than key, pre-approval studies, although the FDA is monitoring the scientific integrity of these studies, particularly those to be used in support of comparative efficacy and pharmacoeconomic claims (see Chapter 11) and those that become the basis for articles that company sales forces use to promote drug products.

In August 2004, both the Pharmaceutical Research and Manufacturers of America (PhRMA) and the Biotechnology Industry Organization (BIO) asked the FDA to reassess the necessity of Phase 4 postmarketing testing requirements in many cases. With the increase in Phase 4 studies required by the FDA as part of new drug approvals, the organizations claim that firms will initiate fewer development projects. PhRMA asked the agency to consider establishing "a process for ongoing review by therapeutic area to distinguish necessary Phase IV studies from those that are informative but not required for the safe use of a drug... Absent this process, sponsors can be faced with escalating Phase IV programs with little or no offsetting reduction in the Phase III testing program."

CHAPTER 6

Good Clinical Practices (GCP)

Because the FDA's approval of a new drug is based largely on clinical data, the agency has a vested interest in these data and the conditions under which they are obtained. Through a set of regulations and guidelines collectively known as "good clinical practices" (GCP), the FDA sets minimum standards for clinical trials.

By identifying and defining the responsibilities of the key personnel involved in clinical trials, the FDA's GCP regulations are designed to accomplish two primary goals: (1) to ensure the quality and integrity of the data obtained from clinical testing so that the FDA's decisions based on these data are informed and responsible; and (2) to protect the rights and, to the degree possible, the welfare of clinical subjects.

Traditionally, GCP has been a term of convenience used by those in government and industry to identify a collection of related regulations and guidelines that, when taken together, define the clinical study-related responsibilities of sponsors, clinical investigators, monitors, and institutional review boards (IRB). For many years, these responsibilities were found primarily in four documents released in the 1980s:

- a 1981 regulation on the informed consent of clinical subjects;

- a 1981 regulation on the responsibilities of IRBs;

- the 1987 IND Rewrite regulations, which define the responsibilities of the investigator and the sponsor; and

- the 1988 *Guideline for the Monitoring of Clinical Investigations*, which outlines the responsibilities of monitors.

While these documents formed the core of GCP, several more recent FDA documents have provided additional information on GCP standards. Among these is a set of so-called *Information Sheets for Institutional Review Boards and Clinical Investigators* and the FDA's compliance program guidance manuals, which specify how FDA investigators ensure that clinical sponsors, monitors, institutional review boards, and clinical investigators comply with GCP. The information sheets were updated and republished under the title, *Guidance for Institutional Review Boards and Clinical Investigators* in September 1998 . In part to further emphasize the importance of the informed consent process (see discussion below), CDER was in the process of updating these guidance documents. Although a few updated guidances, including one on the acceptance of foreign clinical studies, have been released more recently, most were still being updated as of late 2004.

A more recent and significant addition to the FDA's corpus of GCP documents is the International Conference on Harmonization's (ICH) *Good Clinical Practice: Consolidated Guideline*, which was adopted by the ICH parties in 1996 and then as an FDA guidance in May 1997. Designed to provide "a unified standard for designing, conducting, recording, and reporting trials that involve the participation of human subjects," this harmonized document provides guidance on IRB, sponsor, investigator, monitoring, and auditing requirements, and offers helpful guidance on the content and format of clinical protocols. Integrated into the consolidated ICH guideline are two guidelines that were issued as separate draft documents in 1994: *Guideline for the Investigator's Brochure*, which specifies the minimum information required in, and recommends a format for, the investigator's brochure; and *Guideline for Essential Documents for the Conduct of a Clinical Study*, which identifies the essential documents that "individually and collectively permit evaluation of the conduct of a clinical study and the quality of the data produced."

FDA officials emphasized at the time of its release that the ICH GCP guideline is entirely consistent with the FDA's established GCP requirements, and that the harmonized documents will supplement, rather than replace, existing regulations and guidelines. Agency officials conceded that, in a few areas, the ICH GCP guideline clarified current U.S. practices and requirements better than the FDA's regulations and earlier guidelines. Other analysts stated that the ICH guideline offers several recommendations that, despite not being mentioned specifically in current FDA documents, reflect typical FDA expectations and industry practices.

Over time, the differences in emphasis and specificity between the FDA GCP standards and the ICH GCP guideline should become less evident. FDA officials have stated that the agency will "take into account the ICH GCPs" in developing new or revising existing regulations and guidances as part of routine GCP maintenance activities. In the meantime, the agency maintains that it will "consider clinical studies conducted under ICH GCP as meeting GCP standards acceptable to FDA." In practice, FDA inspectors evaluate clinical studies for their compliance with FDA regulations rather than either the ICH GCP or FDA guidance documents.

Recent Developments in GCP Several developments during the late 1990s brought intense scrutiny on all of the key figures involved in the clinical research process, namely whether they were fulfilling their respective roles under GCP and other applicable standards. This scrutiny, particularly the federal government's desire to study and propose action in this area, has not waned in the intervening years, as discussions over possible legislation on human research protections and over revising government guidances on standards for informed consent, clinical trial monitoring, and other GCP areas remain active.

It is important to note, however, that the adequacy of the GCP standards themselves generally was not criticized or questioned because of these developments. More often than not, the discussions have focused not necessarily on developing new standards, but on developing new and clearer guidances to clarify existing standards for those involved in the clinical research process. Still, the developments have had, over the last several years, a variety of implications for the FDA's oversight of investigators, sponsors, monitors, and IRBs, particularly as they relate to research subject protection, adverse experience reporting, informed consent, and patient recruitment efforts (see Chapter 14 for a more detailed discussion of these issues):

- In the late 1990s, a series of disclosures shook CDER's confidence in clinical investigators and in the pharmaceutical industry's practices designed to detect investigator noncompliance and even fraud. Chief among these was the case of Southern California Research Institute President and Principal Investigator Robert Fiddes, M.D., who was sentenced in 1998 to 15 months in prison and was fined $800,000 for falsifying and fabricating clinical trial data used in multiple approved NDAs. This case and at least one other like it prompted a series of congressional inquiries into CDER's actions in the Fiddes case, the agency's efforts to detect research fraud and the extent of fraud-related problems in clinical research, the agency's authorities to conduct oversight of, and to discipline, clinical investigators, and the general practices that clinical investigators employ to recruit patients for trials.

- Then, in late 1999, what some FDA officials characterized as "grave and disturbing" clinical investigator noncompliance (e.g., non-reporting of adverse experiences to regulators) in several gene therapy studies, one of which resulted in the well-publicized death of a teenage study participant, galvanized the government to take further action. In May 2000, the FDA and the Department of Health and Human Services (HHS) unveiled a "plan of action" in response to what then-FDA Commissioner Jane Henney, M.D., called the failure of some researchers at prestigious institutions...to follow the most basic elements of what it takes to properly conduct clinical studies." As part of this plan, which sought to heighten government oversight of clinical research and to reinforce to research institutions their responsibility to oversee their clinical researchers and IRBs, HHS was to pursue legislation authorizing the FDA to levy civil monetary penalties of up to $250,000 per clinical investigator and $1 million per research institution for violations of informed consent and "other important research practices." Although this legislative proposal was later dropped, the FDA/HHS action plan comprised several other moves focused largely on upgrading training and guidance for clinical investigators: (1) HHS will undertake an "aggressive effort" to improve the education and training of clinical investigators, IRB members, and associated IRB and institutional staff (FDA and NIH will work together to ensure that all clinical investigators, research administrators, IRB members and IRB staff receive "appropriate research bioethics training and human subjects research training"); (2) NIH and the FDA will issue specific guidance on informed consent, clarifying that "research institutions and sponsors are expected to audit records for evidence of compliance with informed consent requirements" (for risky or complex trials, IRBs will be expected to take additional measures, which might include requiring third-party observation of the informed consent process); (3) the FDA will issue guidelines for Data and Safety Monitoring Boards (DSMB)—something the agency did in November 2001 (see discussion below)—to define the relationship between DSMBs and IRBs and to establish when DSMBs are appropriate, that they should be independent, and what their responsibilities should be; and (4) the FDA and NIH will develop new conflict of interest policies for the biomedical community, including a requirement "that any researcher's financial interest in a clinical trial be disclosed to potential participants." Although the FDA has issued the guidance on DSMBs and HHS has issued a conflict of interest guidance (see discussion below), the FDA continued to work in other areas. The agency, for example, continues to develop an updated information sheet on informed consent to offer additional clarifications on the informed consent process and standards.

- In the late 1990s, CDER's Division of Scientific Investigations (DSI) took steps to examine more closely industry's monitoring practices in a now-completed effort to educate itself about, and establish a baseline of, industry's current monitoring activities. Specifically, all CDER site inspectional assignments contained instructions for FDA field inspectors to examine specific aspects of sponsor monitoring during inspections of clinical investigators. Today, DSI physicians are participating in increasing numbers of end-of-Phase 2 meetings with sponsors to review and comment on sponsors' planned monitoring and quality assurance programs for Phase 3 trials. Through such efforts, which began under a pilot program in 1999, DSI hopes to help build quality into the pivotal clinical trial process up front.

- Fueled in part by the HHS "plan of action," government agencies continue to focus on potential conflicts of interest in the clinical research process. In a May 2004 final guidance entitled, *Financial Relationships and Interests in Research Involving Human Subjects: Guidance for Human Subject Protection*, HHS attempts to assist institutions, investigators, and IRBs involved in FDA-regulated and HHS-conducted/sponsored research to determine whether specific financial interests affect the rights and welfare of human subjects and, if so, what actions should be considered to protect these subjects. The guidance recommends that "investigators conducting human subjects research consider the potential effects that a financial relationship of any kind might have on the research or on interactions with research subjects," whether the informed consent document should include information on the source of funding for the conduct and review of research, and whether the informed consent process should be modified when a potential or actual financial conflict exists (e.g., having another individual conduct the informed consent process, using independent monitoring of the research). Under a regulation that went into effect in early 1999, CDER now requires NDA sponsors to submit information concerning the financial interests of, and compensation paid to, investigators responsible for key clinical studies. This regulation resulted from concerns regarding the effects of investigators' financial interests on the validity of their research data. When medical reviewers responsible for evaluating NDAs determine that such interests or compensation "raise a serious question about the integrity of the data," CDER can order an audit of the data collected by the clinical investigators in question or take any other action it deems necessary to ensure the data's reliability (see Chapter 7).

- In 2000, the HHS and FDA contracted with the Institute of Medicine (IoM) to form an independent panel to examine, and make recommendations for improving, the human subject protection systems in clinical trials. After beginning its work in December 2000, the panel issued its first report, which focused on IRBs and which recommended an accreditation system for such boards. In the second and final phase of its work, the panel issued an October 2002 report recommending that all clinical research be made subject to federal oversight and that IRBs be relieved of burdens associated with "organizational responsibilities" (such as compliance with relevant regulations). The IoM committee advocated a concept called the "Human Research Participant Protection Program" (HRPPP), which embraces a set of complementary elements and activities "necessary to ensure that comprehensive protection is afforded to every research participant." In addition to making all research subject to federal oversight and refocusing the mission of IRBs, which the committee advocated renaming "research ethics review boards" (research ERBs), the committee recommended that no protocol be approved without at least a three-quarters majority, that scientific and conflict of interest reviews for protocols be undertaken and summarized for the research ERB's ethics-focused deliberations, and that the degree of scrutiny, extent of continuing oversight, and the safety monitoring procedures for research protocols be calibrated to a study's degree of risk.

Again, while such developments have not changed the core GCP standards, they have certainly helped to sharpen the federal government's focus on human subject protections and CDER's focus on the degree to which sponsors and investigators are fulfilling their responsibilities under GCP requirements.

At this writing, there were multiple emerging initiatives and proposals that stood to affect the scope, application, and enforcement of GCP standards:

- The next entry in the FDA's corpus of GCP documents will likely be a regulation that more definitively defines the FDA's GCP-related expectations for non-U.S. clinical trials. Under a June 2004 proposed rule, the agency would no longer accept any data from foreign trials that are not conducted under an IND as support for efficacy claims unless the trials comply with the FDA's GCP standards. In essence, the proposed rule would explicitly establish GCP as the standard for the agency's acceptance of data from non-IND foreign trials, replacing its long-time standard—that such trials conform to the Declaration of Helsinki (DoH) or national requirements, whichever affords the greater protection to study subjects. Under the proposed rule, the agency would accept as support for an IND or NDA a well-designed and well-conducted non-IND foreign clinical study only if two conditions are met: (1) the study was conducted in accordance with GCP; and (2) the agency can validate the data from the study through an onsite inspection if the agency deems such an inspection necessary.

- Due in part to rising government concerns about the abilities of IRBs to fulfill their responsibilities in the growing and increasingly complicated clinical research market, the FDA stepped up its inspections of the estimated 1,600 IRBs in the late 1990s. Although CDER inspections of IRBs have subsided somewhat (154 IRB inspections in 2003, compared to 223 in 1999), the FDA and other regulatory agencies are taking steps to upgrade their oversight of IRBs. To help the agency track, inspect, monitor, and communicate with IRBs, the agency proposed in July 2004 to require that IRBs register on a website maintained by the U.S. Department of Health and Human Services. In registering, IRBs would be required to provide contact information, the number of active protocols involving FDA-regulated products reviewed in the previous calendar year, an indication of whether the IRB is accredited, and a description of the types of FDA-regulated products involved in the protocols reviewed.

- As the center has in other areas, CDER's clinical trial compliance program continues to adopt more of a risk-based approach that focuses limited resources on high-risk and likely problem areas. In recent years, for example, CDER's DSI has encouraged the voluntary submission of clinical trial-related complaints regarding regulatory noncompliance, fraud, and other issues. In FY2003, voluntary complaints regarding clinical investigators, IRBs, sponsors, and other entities involved in the trial process rose 26%, while FDA inspections initiated to respond to such complaints rose even more. According to CDER data, almost a third of CDER's 33% increase in clinical investigator inspections during FY2003 was driven by the agency's response to voluntary complaints. During FY2003, CDER's "directed" inspections (i.e., non-routine inspections generally undertaken in response to a specific concern) of clinical study sites surged 70%, to an all-time high of 109 inspections. Overall, CDER claims that virtually a third of its clinical investigator inspectional assignments were triggered by voluntary complaints in FY2003, up from 23% in FY2002 and 8% in 1999. CDER continues to increase the visibility of its voluntary clinical trial compliance program, which it has identified as being "of vital strategic importance." In addition, during July 2004, FDA officials noted that the agency's inspectional focus would continue to shift toward studies in vulnerable populations and high-risk products and protocols.

- In September 2004, CDER released a revised draft guidance entitled, *Computerized Systems Used in Clinical Trials* to reflect international harmonization efforts and changes in agency policy relevant to electronic records and electronic signatures (in August 2003, the agency issued guidance clarifying that it intended to interpret its Part 11 regulations for electronic records/signatures "narrowly," and to exercise enforcement discretion with regard to validation, audit trail, record retention, and record copying requirements while the FDA reassessed the Part 11 requirements). The guidance addresses how FDA expectations and regulatory requirements regarding data quality might be satisfied when computerized systems are used to create, modify, maintain, archive, retrieve, or transmit data. When the September 2004 draft guidance is finalized, it will supersede an existing April 1999 guidance under the same title.

Responsibilities of the Sponsor

Federal regulations define "sponsor" as "a person who takes responsibility for and initiates a clinical investigation. The sponsor may be an individual or pharmaceutical company, governmental agency, academic institution, private organization, or other organization."

In general, the term "sponsor" refers to a commercial manufacturer that has developed a product in which it holds the principal financial interest. A sponsor may also be a physician, commonly called a "sponsor-investigator," which federal regulations define as "an individual who both initiates and conducts an investigation and under whose immediate direction the investigational drug is administered or dispensed."

The FDA defines sponsor responsibilities in Part 312, Subpart D in the *Code of Federal Regulations* (CFR), which states: "Sponsors are responsible for selecting qualified investigators, providing them with the information they need to conduct an investigation properly, ensuring proper monitoring of the investigation(s), ensuring that the investigation(s) is conducted in accordance with the general investigational plan and protocols contained in the IND, maintaining an effective IND with respect to the investigations, and ensuring that the FDA and all participating investigators are promptly informed of significant new adverse effects or risks with respect to the drug." Sponsor responsibilities can be divided into the following general areas:

- selecting qualified investigators and monitors;
- informing investigators;
- reviewing ongoing studies for compliance with study plans and applicable regulations;
- recordkeeping and record retention; and
- ensuring the return or disposition of unused investigational drug supplies.

Selecting Investigators and Monitors *Investigator Selection.* The sponsor must select investigators—physicians and other professionals contracted by the sponsor to conduct the clinical study, including supervising the administration of the drug to human subjects—"qualified by training and experience as appropriate experts to investigate the drug" (21 CFR 312.53(a)). Sponsors may ship investigational product only to investigators participating in the study (i.e., for studies under an IND, an investigator must have completed and signed a Form FDA-1572 before the sponsor may ship investigational product to the investigator).

To ensure that a clinical investigator is qualified, the sponsor must obtain certain information from the investigator:

- A Completed and Signed Statement of Investigator Form (Form FDA-1572). This form contains information about the investigator, the site of the investigation, and the subinvestigators (e.g., research fellows and residents) who assist the investigator in the conduct of the investigation by directly treating or evaluating study subjects. By signing the form, the investigator also pledges: (1) to conduct the study in accordance with the clinical protocol(s) and to take proper actions should deviations become necessary; (2) to comply with all requirements regarding the obligations of clinical investigators (as described later in this chapter) and other relevant requirements; (3) to personally conduct or supervise the described investigation; (4) to inform patients, or any persons used as controls, that the drug is being used for investigational purposes and to ensure that the requirements related to obtaining informed consent and IRB review and approval (as described elsewhere in this chapter) are met; (5) to report to the sponsor adverse experiences that occur in the course of the investigation in accordance with regulatory requirements; (6) to review and understand the information in the investigator's brochure, including the drug's potential risks and side effects; and (7) to ensure that all associates, colleagues, and employees assisting in the conduct of the studies are informed about their obligations in meeting the above commitments. Through the form, the investigator also pledges that an IRB operating in compliance with regulatory requirements (described later in this chapter) will be responsible for the initial and continuing review and approval of the clinical investigation. In addition, the investigator promises to report to the IRB all changes in the research activity and all unanticipated problems involving risks to human subjects and to not implement any such changes without IRB approval, except when necessary to eliminate apparent immediate hazards to study subjects.

- Curriculum Vitae. The sponsor must obtain a curriculum vitae or other statement of qualifications of the investigator showing the education, training, and experience that qualify the investigator as an expert in the clinical investigation of the drug.

- Clinical Protocol. For Phase 1 investigations, the sponsor must obtain from the investigator a general outline of the planned investigation, including the estimated duration of the study and the maximum number of subjects that will be involved. For Phase 2 or 3 investigations, the sponsor must obtain an outline of the study protocol, including an approximation of the number and characteristics of investigational subjects and controls, the clinical uses to be investigated, the types of clinical observations and laboratory tests to be conducted, the estimated duration of the study, and copies or a description of case report forms to be used. Although the regulations read differently, in practice it is the sponsor that provides the study protocol to the investigator and not vice versa. According to the ICH GCP guideline, the protocol (or other protocol-referenced documents) must identify "any data to be recorded directly on the [subjects' case report forms] (i.e., no prior written or electronic record of data), and to be considered to be source data."

While the FDA's GCP regulations make no reference to a medical degree or other specific education or training as prerequisites for clinical investigators, the ICH GCP guideline is somewhat more definitive. Under a section entitled, "The Principles of GCP," the guideline states that "the medical care given to, and medical decisions made on behalf of, subjects should always be the responsibility of a qualified physician or, when appropriate, a qualified dentist." In informal correspondence on this issue, the FDA stated, in *Good Clinical Practice: A Question and Answer Reference Guide* (www.barnettinternational.com) that, "while technically a non-physician can be a principal investigator, this requires that the non-physician be qualified to personally conduct or personally supervise all aspects of the study. In practice, we have found it very rare that a non-physician can comply with this requirement. In general, where we have seen non-physicians listed on the 1572 as a principal investigator we usually find an M.D. as a subinvestigator to perform those study functions requiring the appropriate level of medical expertise. For example, a Ph.D. pharmacologist may be listed as a principal investigator on a pharmacokinetic study, with an M.D. as a subinvestigator. Another example might be a clinical psychologist principal investigator with an M.D. subinvestigator."

As noted above, a regulation (21 CFR Part 54) that went into effect in early 1999 requires sponsors to collect certain financial information from clinical trial investigators prior to study initiation. Although this requirement is not considered a factor in determining an investigator's qualifications to participate in a clinical study, the sponsor must collect certain information regarding the investigator's financial interests to permit the company to make a certification or financial disclosure statement in its NDA (see Chapter 7). Specifically, the

February 1999 regulations require: (1) that clinical investigators involved in covered clinical studies provide study sponsors with sufficient and accurate financial information to allow a subsequent disclosure or certification by the sponsor; (2) that sponsors maintain complete and accurate records of the financial interests of investigators who are subject to the disclosure regulation; and (3) that applicants submit lists of all clinical investigators who conducted covered clinical studies and that applicants completely and accurately disclose or certify the financial interests of these clinical investigators. Because it addresses potential sources of bias and specifies the above requirements, the FDA's financial disclosure regulation is considered an element of GCP, FDA officials emphasize. To provide further recommendations in this area, the FDA released a March 2001 industry guidance entitled, *Financial Disclosure by Clinical Investigators*.

Selecting Monitors and Monitoring the Clinical Trial. Sponsors are required to monitor clinical investigations to ensure: (1) the quality and integrity of the clinical data derived from clinical trials; and (2) that the rights and welfare of human subjects involved in a clinical study are preserved. The monitoring function may be performed by the sponsor or its employees, or may be delegated to a contract research organization (CRO).

Specific FDA recommendations on proper monitoring duties and procedures are provided in the agency's *Guideline for the Monitoring of Clinical Investigations* (January 1988). In this document, the FDA identifies six different monitoring responsibilities:

- Selection of a Monitor. According to the guideline, a sponsor may designate one or more appropriately trained and qualified individuals to monitor the progress of a clinical investigation. Physicians, clinical research associates, paramedical personnel, nurses, and engineers may be acceptable monitors depending on the type of product involved in the study.

- Written Monitoring Procedures. A sponsor should establish written procedures for monitoring clinical investigations to assure the quality of the study, and to assure that each person involved in the monitoring process carries out his or her duties.

- Preinvestigation Visits. Through personal contact between the monitor and each investigator, a sponsor must assure that the investigator, among other things, clearly understands and accepts the obligations involved in undertaking a clinical study. The sponsor also must determine whether the investigator's facilities are adequate for conducting the investigation, and whether the investigator has sufficient time to honor his or her responsibilities in the trial.

- Periodic Visits. A sponsor must assure, throughout the clinical investigation, that the investigator's obligations are fulfilled and that the facilities used in the clinical investigation are acceptable. The monitor must visit the clinical site frequently enough to provide such assurances (see discussion below). In the past, David Lepay, M.D., the FDA's senior advisor for clinical science and also the director of the FDA's Good Clinical Practice Program, has emphasized that industry's clinical monitoring efforts should not ignore the trial-related activities of clinical research staff at the various research sites being inspected. Traditionally, sponsors' monitoring programs have focused largely on the activities of clinical investigators, he noted. Further, FDA officials are examining the possibility of making regulatory changes to require that other key individuals involved in a trial (research coordinators, subinvestigators) sign the Form FDA 1572-Statement of Investigator, thereby making these persons directly subject to regulatory action if they fail in their trial-related responsibilities.

- Review of Subject Records. A sponsor must assure that safety and effectiveness data submitted to the FDA are accurate and complete. The FDA recommends that the monitor review individual subject records and other supporting documentation and compare these records with the reports prepared by the investigator for submission to the sponsor. The ICH's GCP guideline, which the FDA adopted in 1997, states that the monitor should check "the accuracy and completeness of the [case report form (CRF)] entries, source data/documents and other trial-related records against each other." Specifically, the guideline states that the monitor should verify that: (1) the data required by the protocol are reported accurately on the CRFs and are consistent with the source data/documents; (2) any dose and/or therapy modifications are well documented for each trial subject; (3) adverse events, concomitant medications and intercurrent illnesses are reported in accordance with the protocol on the CRFs; (4) visits that the subjects fail to make, tests that are not conducted, and examinations that are not performed are clearly reported as such on the CRFs; and (5) all withdrawals and dropouts of enrolled subjects from the trial are reported and explained on the CRFs.

- Record of On-Site Visits. The monitor or sponsor should maintain a record of the findings, conclusions, and actions taken to correct deficiencies for each on-site visit.

Informing Investigators The sponsor is responsible for keeping all investigators involved in the clinical testing of its drug fully informed about the investigational product and research findings. Before the investigation begins, a sponsor must supply participating clinical investigators with an investigator's brochure (see Chapter 3), which provides the following: a description of the product; summaries of its known pharmacological, pharmacokinetic, and biological characteristics; potential adverse effects as indicated by animal tests; and, if available, data on clinical use.

Once clinical trials begin, regulations require that sponsors "keep each participating investigator informed of new observations discovered by or reported to the sponsor on the drug, particularly with respect to adverse effects and safe use." This information may be distributed through periodically revised investigator's brochures, reprints or published studies, reports or letters to clinical investigators, or other appropriate means. Safety information must be relayed to all participating investigators and the FDA through written or verbal IND safety reports (see Chapter 3). The sponsor must provide the FDA and all participating investigators a written IND safety report (see Chapter 3) on any adverse experience that is associated with the use of a new drug and that is both serious and unexpected. The sponsor must report any such adverse experience within 15 calendar days of receiving information about the experience. If an unexpected adverse drug experience is fatal or life-threatening, the sponsor must also notify the FDA by telephone or facsimile transmission within 7 calendar days.

Review of Ongoing Investigations. There are many reasons why the FDA requires sponsors to closely monitor the conduct and progress of their clinical trials. Two of the most important such reasons are to determine whether the investigator is conducting the study in compliance with the protocol, applicable federal regulations, and an acceptable standard of good clinical practice, and whether the new drug study is presenting unreasonable and significant risks to the study subjects.

Unfortunately, neither FDA GCP nor ICH GCP documents are helpful in determining an adequate monitoring frequency. Industry and even FDA officials often speak of an informal industry standard under which each clinical trial site should be visited, on average, every four to six weeks. Even FDA compliance officials concede, however, that it is extremely difficult for the agency to prospectively determine, for each and every trial, how often monitors should visit sites. As a practical matter, in fact, the agency only truly scrutinizes monitoring frequency when agency inspections uncover specific problems at a clinical trial site.

Perhaps the greatest determinant of appropriate monitoring frequency is the rate of enrollment. Sites that enroll a large number of patients in a short period of time need to be monitored far more frequently than sites that are low, slow enrollers, FDA officials advise.

When a sponsor discovers that an investigator is not in compliance, the company must promptly either secure compliance or discontinue product shipments to the investigator and terminate the investigator's participation in the study. If the latter course is chosen or is necessary, the sponsor must require that the investigator return or dispose of the product in accordance with applicable requirements and must report this action to the FDA.

In mid-2001, FDA officials first revealed that they were developing a proposed regulation that would require sponsors to report all cases of investigator noncompliance or misconduct, including fraud, data falsification and human subject protection abuses. Under existing regulations, a sponsor is required to report investigator misconduct only when the investigator is discontinued from a study. According the federal government's latest Unified Agenda (June 2004), the FDA projects that it will publish a notice of proposed rulemaking by February 2005 to require "sponsors to promptly report any information indicating that any person has or may have falsified data in the course of proposing, designing, performing, recording, supervising, or reviewing research, or in reporting research results."

In a September 2004 guidance, CDER stated that data falsification, serious protocol violations, and failure to seek IRB reviews of protocol changes, obtain adequate informed consent, or report serious or life-threatening adverse events are among the reasons why it may decide to suspend a clinical investigator's participation in a clinical trial immediately through a clinical hold order. The agency will consider using clinical hold orders "where the investigator's misconduct appears to pose an ongoing threat to the safety and welfare of [clinical trial] subjects," CDER states in the guidance entitled, *The Use of Clinical Holds Following Clinical Investigator Misconduct.*

The sponsor must review and evaluate safety and effectiveness data as they are supplied by the investigator. In addition to providing IND safety reports, the sponsor must supply to the FDA annual reports on the progress of the investigation.

Sponsors finding that their drugs or studies present unreasonable and significant risks to subjects must: (1) discontinue the investigations that present the risks; (2) notify the FDA, all IRBs, and all investigators who have at any time participated in the investigations that the studies are being discontinued; (3) assure that the disposition of all outstanding stocks of the drug complies with federal regulations; and (4) furnish the FDA with a full report of its actions.

Recordkeeping and Record Retention A sponsor must maintain adequate records showing the receipt, shipment, or other disposition of the investigational product. The records must include, as appropriate, the name of the investigator to whom the drug is shipped and the date, quantity, and batch or code mark of each shipment. Regulations require that the sponsor retain all specified records and reports for two years after either: (1) the approval of its marketing application; or (2) the discontinuation of drug shipment and delivery and the notification of the FDA.

Disposition of Unused Drug Supplies The sponsor must ensure the return of all unused supplies of the drug from each investigator whose participation is discontinued or eliminated. A sponsor may authorize alternative plans, provided that these do not expose humans to risks from the product. In June 1997, CDER published an updated version of Compliance Policy Guide 7132c.05, entitled, *Recovery of Investigational New Drugs from Clinical Investigators.*

In this and other areas, the ICH GCP guideline provides additional guidance, including the following:

- Recommendations that the sponsor/monitor verify that the disposition of unused investigational product at the trial sites complies with regulatory and sponsor requirements.

- Recommendations that "electronic trial data handling and/or remote electronic trial data systems" conform to the sponsor's established requirements for completeness, accuracy, reliability, and consistent intended performance (i.e., validation).

- Recommendations that sponsors obtain "all required documentation" (e.g., IRB approval, a signed Form 1572) before providing an investigator with the investigational product. Again, this has been common practice in the United States.

- Recommendations that the sponsor's designated representative document the review and follow-up of the monitoring reports.

Sponsors and Data Safety Monitoring Boards Given the release of several ICH and FDA guidance documents, employing a data safety monitoring board, or what the FDA calls a Data Monitoring Committee, may increasingly be viewed as a GCP-related requirement for certain trials. For many clinical trials, particularly those involving drugs with major public health significance, the responsibility for monitoring comparisons of efficacy and/or safety outcomes should be assigned to an independent and external group often called a data safety monitoring board (DSMB), the ICH's E9 *Statistical Principles for Clinical Trials* guidance states. The guidance, which calls such boards independent data monitoring committees (IDMC), says that such panels "may be established by the sponsor to assess at specific intervals the progress of a clinical trial, safety data, and critical efficacy variables and recommend to the sponsor whether to continue, modify or terminate a trial [based on its findings]."

In a November 2001 draft document entitled, *Guidance for Clinical Trial Sponsors on the Establishment and Operation of Clinical Trial Data Monitoring Committees*, the FDA establishes that data monitoring committees (DMC) should be used in all controlled trials employing mortality or major morbidity as a primary or secondary endpoint. DMCs, the agency notes, may also be useful "in settings where trial participants may be at elevated risk of such outcomes even if the study intervention addresses lesser outcomes such as relief of symptoms." The draft guidance defines DMCs, which the FDA requires only when informed consent requirements are waived in studies conducted in emergency settings, as panels of individuals "with pertinent expertise that review on a regular basis accumulating outcome data in certain ongoing clinical trials [and that] advise the sponsor regarding the continuing safety of current participants and those yet to be recruited, as well as the continuing validity and scientific merit of the trial."

In addition to safety considerations (e.g., mortality/major morbidity endpoints, trials in fragile populations, and large/long-duration/multi-center studies), two other factors—practicality and assurance of scientific validity—are relevant in determining whether a sponsor should establish a DMC for a particular trial, says the agency. A DMC may not be practical, for example, for short-term trials in which the trial duration will not give the committee an opportunity to contribute. If a short-term trial presents important safety considerations that justify a DMC, the guidance says that sponsors must develop mechanisms allowing the committee to be informed and convened rapidly when unexpected results are found.

A DMC's likely ability to assure a trial's scientific validity is the third key consideration, the guidance establishes. Trials "of any appreciable duration," the FDA notes, can be affected by changes over time in the understanding of a disease, the affected population, and standard treatments, all of which are changes that may trigger an interest in study modifications as the trial advances. "When a DMC is the only group reviewing unblinded interim data, the trial organizers are free to make changes in the ongoing trial that may be motivated by newly available data outside the trial or by accumulating data from within the trial (e.g., overall event rates)," the guidance states. "In general, recommendations to change the inclusion criteria, the trial endpoints, or the size of the trial are most credibly made by those without knowledge of the accumulating data. When the trial organizers are the ones reviewing the interim data, their awareness of interim comparative results cannot help but affect their determination as to whether these changes should be made. Such changes would inevitably impair the credibility of the study results."

For these reasons and others, the draft guidance touts the advantages of the *independent* DMC, which is defined as "a committee whose members are considered to be independent of those sponsoring, organizing, and conducting the trial" (i.e., have no previous involvement in the trial's design, no current involvement in its conduct other than as the DMC, and have no financial or other important connections to the study sponsor or other trial organizers). A DMC will be considered independent, for example, if the sponsor has no representation on the committee or if the sponsor has a representative only in open meetings, during which enrollment, compliance, and event rates are presented and discussed but during which no study arm-specific data are discussed. The draft guidance acknowledges that DMCs are rarely, if ever, entirely independent of sponsors, given that sponsors typically select and pay the members and establish a committee's goals and responsibilities.

The independence of other individuals interacting with both the sponsor and DMC is equally important, the FDA states. Trial integrity is best maintained when the statistician preparing unblinded data (i.e., interim analyses) for the DMC is external to the sponsor, especially for studies designed to provide the definitive evidence of efficacy, the draft guidance notes. The statistician should have no responsibility for managing the trial and should have "minimal" contact with those who have such involvement.

Responsibilities of Investigators

A clinical investigator is the individual who actually conducts, or who is the responsible leader of a team that conducts, a clinical investigation. The product is administered or dispensed to a clinical subject under the immediate direction of this individual.

Federal regulations state that an "investigator is responsible for ensuring that an investigation is conducted according to the signed investigator statement, the investigational plan, and applicable regulations; for protecting the rights, safety, and welfare of subjects under the investigator's care; and for the control of drugs under investigation." As part of the investigator's responsibilities in protecting the rights of study subjects, he or she must obtain legally effective informed consent from prospective subjects or their legally authorized representatives prior to involving these subjects in a clinical study. Specific investigator responsibilities detailed in GCP provisions include the following:

Control of the Product. The investigator can administer the product only to subjects under his or her personal supervision or under the supervision of a subinvestigator. Regulations do not allow an investigator to supply the drug to persons not authorized to receive it.

Recordkeeping and Record Retention. The investigator must keep adequate drug accountability records, and must prepare and maintain, for each subject, adequate and accurate records of all observations and data pertinent to the investigation. These records must be kept for two years after either a marketing application's approval or a sponsor has discontinued an IND and so notified the FDA. The FDA must be allowed access to these records.

The ICH GCP guideline calls for the investigator to maintain a list of appropriately qualified persons to whom significant trial-related responsibilities have been delegated. In addition, the guideline calls for clinical sites to maintain, and sponsors to document the existence of, a confidential list of the names of all subjects allocated to trial numbers upon trial enrollment.

Investigator Reports. The investigator must provide to the sponsor: (1) reports (e.g., up-to-date CRFs) on the progress of the clinical study; (2) safety reports on all adverse experiences that may reasonably be regarded as caused by, or probably caused by, the drug; and (3) adequate reports shortly after the completion of the investigator's participation in the study (FDA officials indicate that completed case report forms on all subjects usually will suffice). As mentioned above, the FDA has been under some pressure to clarify, and educate clinical investigators on, clinical trial adverse experience reporting requirements following disclosures that certain investigators participating in several gene therapy trials failed to fulfill their responsibilities in this area (see discussion above).

Assurance of IRB Review. The investigator must assure that an IRB complying with regulatory requirements will be responsible for the initial and continuing review and approval of the proposed clinical study. He or she must also promptly report to the IRB all changes in the research activity and all unanticipated problems involving risks to human subjects. The investigator must not make any changes in the research without IRB approval, except when necessary to eliminate apparent and immediate hazards to human subjects.

Handling of Controlled Substances. If the investigational product is subject to the Controlled Substances Act, the investigator must take adequate precautions to prevent theft or diversion of the product.

The Institutional Review Board (IRB)

Except under limited circumstances (e.g., emergency use of a drug or when the FDA exempts a study from IRB review), no clinical study that requires prior agency review (i.e., under an IND) may be initiated unless that study has been reviewed and approved by, and remains subject to continuing review by, an IRB. The IRB's function is to ensure, through prior and periodic review, that: (1) risks to subjects are minimized and are reasonable in relation to any anticipated benefits to subjects; (2) selection of subjects is equitable; (3) informed consent is sought and documented in accordance with federal regulations; (4) adequate monitoring is provided to ensure subject safety; (5) subjects' confidentiality is adequately protected; and (6) safeguards are provided to protect the rights and welfare of vulnerable subjects. Although the board's main concern is not the adequacy of study design, the board can order that a trial be modified for safety or other reasons.

An IRB must have at least five members, each of whom is chosen by the institution (i.e., assuming that the site has an IRB). FDA regulations allow institutions that do not have IRBs to use "independent" or other institutions' IRBs to review their studies. IRB members must have the professional backgrounds necessary to review research activities commonly undertaken by the institution, and have the ability to assess the acceptability of proposed research in terms of institutional commitments and regulations, applicable law, and standards and practices.

IRB members often are physicians, pharmacologists, clergy, and administrative managers from the parent institution. At least one board member must have a primary interest in a nonscientific area. Federal regulations also include several other requirements that are designed to ensure the independence of the IRB and guard against conflicts of interest.

Generally, drug sponsors have limited direct contact with an IRB. The investigator conducting the study at a particular institution usually serves as a liaison between the sponsor and the IRB, and presents the study plans to the IRB for review and approval. Since experienced investigators are often familiar with the particular concerns, priorities, and idiosyncrasies of their IRBs, they are often better prepared to deal with them. The FDA does not prohibit direct sponsor-IRB contact, and acknowledges that such contact may help resolve problems in certain cases.

In a March 2002 notice of proposed rulemaking, CDER announced that it was considering whether to amend its IRB regulations to require sponsors and investigators to inform IRBs about any prior IRB review decisions. This change has been discussed by some officials as a way of reducing the practice of IRB "shopping"—that is, when sponsors submit study protocols to multiple IRBs until an IRB approval is gained. Such disclosures, says the agency, could help ensure that sponsors and clinical investigators who submit protocols to more than one IRB will not be able to ignore an unfavorable IRB review decision and that IRBs reviewing a protocol will be aware of what other IRBs reviewing similar protocols have concluded. Industry has encouraged the agency to drop the proposal, in part because the submission of earlier IRB decisions will further burden already stressed IRBs.

Aside from safety concerns, an IRB may address several issues—including specific standards of the institution, state, and locality—in reviewing a study. To fulfill its responsibilities, an IRB will review research protocols and related materials, including informed consent documents and investigator brochures. Any research program that the board approves must meet several criteria specified in FDA regulations:

- risks to subjects must be minimized;
- risks to subjects must be reasonable in relation to the anticipated benefits and the importance of the knowledge that may be expected to be gained;
- subject selection must be equitable;
- informed consent must be sought from each prospective subject or the subject's legally authorized representative;
- informed consent must be appropriately documented (see discussion below);
- when appropriate, the research plan must make adequate provisions for monitoring the data collected to ensure the safety of subjects; and
- when appropriate, there must be adequate provisions to protect the privacy of subjects and to preserve the confidentiality of data.

As are sponsors, monitors, and investigators, IRBs are subject to operating, reporting, and recordkeeping requirements. An IRB must retain adequate minutes of its meetings and copies of all study proposals reviewed, sample approved consent documents, correspondence with investigators, board procedures, and other documents. IRB meeting minutes and records are subject to FDA inspection, and an IRB under FDA jurisdiction may be subject to administrative action for failing to comply with federal regulations.

As noted above, government agencies and oversight boards asked to evaluate the state of clinical trials have acknowledged the difficulties IRBs are experiencing in fulfilling all of their responsibilities due to the increasing demands being placed on them. In recent years, such assessments have raised concerns regarding possible safety and welfare risks to study subjects and prompted government studies, hearings, and proposals to make IRB workloads more reasonable (see discussion above).

Due in part to rising government concerns about the abilities of IRBs to fulfill their responsibilities in the growing and increasingly complicated clinical research market, the FDA stepped up its inspections of the estimated 1,600 IRBs in the late 1990s. Although CDER inspections of IRBs have subsided somewhat (154 IRB inspections in 2003, compared to 223 in 1999), the FDA and other regulatory agencies are taking steps to upgrade their oversight of IRBs.

To help the agency track, inspect, monitor, and communicate with IRBs, the agency proposed in July 2004 to require that IRBs register on a website maintained by the U.S. Department of Health and Human Services. In registering, IRBs would be required to provide contact information, the number of active protocols involving FDA-regulated products reviewed in the previous calendar year, an indication of whether the IRB is accredited, and a description of the types of FDA-regulated products involved in the protocols reviewed.

Informed Consent

Informed consent is a concept or process designed to ensure that subjects do not enter a clinical study against their will or without an adequate understanding of the study or the risks involved in the study. Federal regulations require that, except under special circumstances, "...no investigator may involve a human being as a subject in research...unless the investigator has obtained the legally effective informed consent of the subject or the subject's legally authorized representative. An investigator shall seek such consent only under circumstances that provide the prospective subject or the representative sufficient opportunity to consider whether or not to participate and that minimize the possibility of coercion or undue influence. The information that is given to the subject or the representative shall be in language understandable to the subject or the representative."

Clearly, informed consent is a function of an informed subject. Any subject volunteering for a study must be adequately aware of his or her medical condition, alternative treatments, and the purpose of and risks involved in the clinical study.

As noted, upgrading the informed consent process has been a centerpiece of the federal government's efforts to improve subject protection in clinical research. In 2004, the FDA continued to revise its guidance on informed consent to better focus the process on helping subjects understand issues related to the trial and their participation rather than just the mechanical documentation of informed consent itself. Further, as part of its May 2000 "plan of action" on research subject protection, the FDA and NIH announced that they would issue specific guidance on informed consent, clarifying that "research institutions and sponsors are expected to audit records for evidence of compliance with informed consent requirements" (for "risky" or "complex" trials, IRBs will be expected to take additional measures, which might include requiring third-party observation of the informed consent process).

Federal regulations regarding the protection of clinical subjects state that, at a minimum, the following "basic elements of informed consent" must be provided to clinical subjects before involving them in the study:

- a statement that the study involves research, an explanation of the purposes of the research and the expected duration of the subject's participation, a description of the procedures to be followed, and identification of any procedures that are experimental;

- a description of any reasonably foreseeable risks or discomforts to the subject;

- a description of any benefits that the subject or others may reasonably expect from the research;

- a disclosure of appropriate alternative procedures or courses of treatment, if any, that might be advantageous to the subject;

- a statement that describes the extent, if any, to which confidentiality of records identifying the subject will be maintained and that notes the possibility that the FDA may inspect the records;

- an explanation as to whether any compensation or medical treatments are available if injury occurs during research involving more than minimal risk, and, if so, what the treatments and/or compensation consist of, or where further information may be obtained;

- the identity of the person to contact for answers to pertinent questions about the research and research subject's rights, and the person to contact if the subject suffers a research-related injury; and

- a statement that participation is voluntary, that refusal to participate will involve no penalty or loss of benefits to which the subject is otherwise entitled, and that the subject may discontinue participation at any time without penalty or loss of benefits to which the subject is otherwise entitled.

When appropriate, one or more of the following must also be provided to subjects:

- a statement that a particular treatment or procedure may involve risks to the subject (or to the embryo or fetus, if the subject is or may become pregnant) that are currently unforeseeable;

- anticipated circumstances under which the subject's participation may be terminated by the investigator without regard to the subject's consent;

- any additional costs to the subject that may result from participation in the research;

- the consequences of a subject's decision to withdraw from the research and procedures for ordering termination of participation by the subject;

- a statement that significant new research findings that may affect the subject's willingness to continue his or her participation will be provided to the subject; and

- the approximate number of subjects involved in the study.

While the investigator is directly responsible for obtaining a subject's informed consent and seeing that the subject is truly informed, the IRB and the sponsor/monitor also play roles in ensuring that informed consent requirements are met. The IRB, for example, is responsible for evaluating the adequacy of the informed consent documents. It is worth noting that CDER has released a policy under which it is encouraging its review divisions to play a greater role in evaluating informed consent documents during the IND review process (see Chapter 3).

In most cases, informed consent must be obtained by having the subject or the subject's representative sign a written, IRB-approved consent form. Except in the case of FDA-approved "emergency research" (see discussion below), the IRB cannot waive informed consent requirements for FDA-regulated research. Unless the IRB waives the informed consent requirements because the research presents "minimal risk," the consent form may take one of two forms: (1) a written consent document that embodies the basic elements of informed consent and that may be read to the subject or the subject's representative, who is then given adequate opportunity to read it before signing; or (2) a "short form" written consent document stating that the basic elements of informed consent have been presented orally to the subject or the subject's representative. If the short form is used, which is rare, there are several other requirements: there must be a witness to the oral presentation; the IRB must approve a written summary of what will be said to the subject or the representative; the witness must sign both the short form and a copy of the summary; the person obtaining the consent must sign a copy of the summary; and the subject or the representative must sign the short form and must be given a copy of the summary and the consent form.

The FDA notes, however, that the subject's signature, although it provides documentation of his or her agreement to participate in the study, is representative of a larger process. "The entire informed consent process involves giving a subject adequate information concerning the study, providing adequate opportunity for the subject to consider all options, responding to the subject's questions, ensuring that the subject has comprehended this information, obtaining the subject's voluntary agreement to participate, and continuing to provide information as the subject or situation requires," the agency states in its *Guidance for Institutional Review Boards and Clinical Investigators* (1998). "To be effective, the process should provide ample opportunity for the investigator and the subject to exchange information and ask questions."

Under an October 1996 final regulation, the FDA established conditions under which experimental products could be used in emergencies without prior informed consent. This exception is permitted only for research involving subjects who require emergency medical intervention, who cannot give informed consent due to a life-threatening condition, and who do not have a legally authorized representative available before the drug must be administered. The FDA has established clear and significant regulatory burdens regarding this waiver of informed consent requirements, including special criteria for IRB review and a requirement for the sponsor to submit the study protocol and related materials under a separate IND, even if one is already in place for studies utilizing the conventional consent process. To provide recommendations in this area, CDER released an April 2000 draft guidance entitled, *Guidance for Institutional Review Boards, Clinical Investigators, and Sponsors: Exemption from Informed Consent Requirements for Emergency Research.* More recently, CDER released an internal policy document entitled, INDs: *Exception from Informed Consent Requirements for Emergency Research* (MaPP 6030.8, February 2003).

Under changes implemented in December 1996, the FDA again revised its informed consent regulations to require that the informed consent form be signed and dated by the subject or the subject's legally authorized representative at the time consent is given. The agency also clarified what adequate case histories must include and that the case histories must document that informed consent was obtained prior to a subject's participation in a study. The agency took this action in response to problems that the FDA has had in verifying that informed consent actually preceded subject participation.

CHAPTER 7

The New Drug Application (NDA)

Since 1938, the new drug application (NDA) has been the vehicle through which drug sponsors formally propose that the FDA approve a new pharmaceutical for marketing and sale in the United States. To obtain this government authorization, a drug manufacturer submits, in an NDA, thousands of pages of nonclinical and clinical test data and analyses, drug chemistry information, and descriptions of manufacturing procedures in a specific and fairly well-defined format that has been revised and refined over the past six decades.

By mid-2001, however, the International Conference on Harmonization (ICH) initiative had produced what many viewed as its most significant achievement, one that had significant implications for the traditional NDA format: the development of a harmonized core "information package of [clinical, pharmacology/toxicology, and manufacturing] technical data" that could be submitted in the same format and with the same content to obtain marketing authorization in any of the three ICH regions—the United States, the European Union, and Japan. And, during a so-called "transition period" that lasted from August 2001 to July 2003, companies submitting marketing dossiers to the FDA had the option of using either the ICH's "common technical document" (or CTD) format or the traditional NDA format.

When this CTD transition period expired in July 2003, the FDA began to "highly recommend" that U.S. marketing dossiers be submitted in the CTD format. Unlike the two other ICH parties (EU and Japan), which now require the CTD format, the FDA will not be able to implement the CTD format as a formal requirement until it undertakes a complete revision of its NDA regulations (CFR Part 314).

While the FDA was anxious to migrate to the new harmonized format for marketing dossiers, industry was a bit more reluctant, at least during the CTD transition period. By mid-2004, however, industry had submitted 101 applications to CDER in the harmonized format. Perhaps more impressive was that growing numbers of CTD submissions were being developed and filed for new molecular entities (NME), which showed that firms were increasingly willing to rely on the emerging CTD format for their most important prospects. From July 2003 through May 2004, CDER received nine NDAs for NMEs.

While the submission of applications in the CTD format continues to grow, it will likely be some time before the harmonized format becomes more common than the traditional NDA format.

It is important to note that the CTD and NDA differ primarily in format and not in content. While it is true that the CTD may provide more information in selected areas than a conventional NDA (see discussion below), the FDA's data and information requirements for drug approval will be unaffected by the CTD. In other words, applications in the CTD format must provide the same data and information as those submitted in the conventional NDA format. In many ways, the CTD simply represents an alternative format or organizational structure into which data and information that otherwise would be provided in the NDA format can be provided to the FDA. For a detailed review of the CTD and the CTD format, see exhibit below.

Today, however, it is impossible to separate the FDA's CTD initiative from another key agency effort with which the CTD program is dovetailing—the move toward electronic submissions (see discussion below). Even as they were taking their first steps to implement the new CTD model, both the FDA and industry were anxiously looking ahead to, and preparing for, the next evolutionary stage for marketing dossiers internationally. In many ways, industry and the FDA viewed the paper-based CTD model simply as a bridging mechanism to the electronic CTD, or eCTD, which both regulators and industry maintain holds the real payoff for the drug review process. In its May 2004 *Report to the Nation*, CDER continued to make its case for eCTDs: "Electronic submissions following the Common Technical Document specifications provide our reviewers significant advantages over paper submissions and electronic submissions following past specifications. The eCTD allows our reviewers to build a cumulative table of contents for viewing the entire life cycle of the applications... It not only improves the efficiency of finding documents but also provides a comprehensive picture of the changes to the application over time." According to CDER statistics, industry had submitted 34 eCTDs by mid-2004 (see discussions below).

While fully recognizing that the CTD and eCTD represent the future of marketing dossiers, this chapter focuses largely, although not exclusively, on the conventional NDA. The NDA remains, at this writing and likely for some time into the future, the more frequently used vehicle for obtaining marketing approval for new drugs in the United States. Since NDA-related requirements are better understood and more defined in current FDA regulations and guidances, and since these requirements must be met by applications regardless of whether they are provided in the CTD or NDA format, such an approach in this text remains preferable at this time. For a detailed discussion of the CTD, its format, and its future, see the exhibit below.

Traditionally a paper colossus, the NDA is the largest and most complex premarketing application that the FDA reviews. Given the demands that assembling this regulatory tome put on industry and the demands that reviewing it put on the FDA, there have been some recent efforts attempting to reduce the NDA's size. Under the Food and Drug Administration Modernization Act of 1997, for instance, CDER released a guidance entitled, *Submission of Abbreviated Reports and Synopses in Support of Marketing Applications*, which clarified when NDA sponsors may submit certain clinical trial information in abbreviated reports and synopses rather than full study reports.

Regardless of its format, size, or complexity, an NDA or CTD must provide sufficient information, data, and analyses to permit FDA reviewers to reach several key decisions, including:

1. Whether the drug is safe and effective in its proposed use(s), and whether the benefits of the drug outweigh its risks.

2. Whether the drug's proposed labeling is appropriate and, if not, what the drug's labeling should contain.

3. Whether the methods used in manufacturing the drug and the controls used to maintain the drug's quality are adequate to preserve the drug's identity, strength, quality, and purity.

The History of the NDA

Given its importance in the drug approval process, the NDA is, as it has always been, a product and a reflection of intersecting medical, political, industry, and public healthcare objectives, priorities, and needs. Because of this, the NDA has evolved considerably during its 62-year history.

For decades, the regulation and control of new drugs in the United States has been based on the NDA. Since 1938, each new drug must have been the subject of an NDA before it could be, for commercial purposes, sold in or imported to the United States.

When the Food, Drug and Cosmetic Act (FD&C Act) was passed in 1938, NDAs were required only to contain information pertaining to the investigational drug's safety. In 1962, the Harris-Kefauver Amendments to the FD&C Act required NDAs to provide evidence that a new drug was effective in its intended use as well. These historic amendments also required, for the first time, that an NDA be approved before a drug could be marketed.

The NDA was again the subject of reform in 1985, when the FDA completed a comprehensive revision of the regulations pertaining to new drug applications. While this revision, commonly called the NDA Rewrite, modified NDA content requirements, it was mainly designed to expedite FDA reviews by restructuring the ways in which information and data were organized and presented in the application.

As noted above, regulatory initiatives and scientific advances were among the factors that were influencing the continuing evolution of the NDA and CTD at this writing:

- *From Paper-based to Electronic NDAs.* CDER has spent the last several years laying the regulatory groundwork for computer-assisted new drug applications, or electronic NDAs (eNDA), to replace the traditional paper-based NDA. This process began with the release of a March 1997 final regulation, which established the agency's criteria for accepting electronic records, including eNDAs, and electronic signatures as equivalent to paper records and handwritten signatures (previously, electronic records and submissions could only supplement paper-based records and filings, which were required by regulation). The migration to electronic submissions accelerated under the prescription drug user fee program (PDUFA II), under which the FDA agreed to develop a paperless electronic submission system for all applications, including INDs and NDAs. With the March 1997 final regulation in place, CDER made various types of applications (e.g., INDs and NDAs) formally eligible for electronic submission by publishing guidances that address each type of submission. In the years since, CDER has released several formal guidances and related documents applicable to electronic NDAs: *Regulatory Submissions in Electronic Format: General Considerations* (January 1999), which discusses general issues associated with electronic submissions, including the formats in which certain data should be provided and the types of media that should be used (when finalized, an October 2003 draft guidance entitled, *Providing Regulatory Submissions in Electronic Format-General Considerations* will replace this guidance); *Regulatory Submissions in Electronic Format: New Drug Applications* (January 1999), which provides recommendations for providing the complete archival copy of the NDA in electronic format; *Example of an Electronic New Drug Application Submission* (February 1999); and a draft guidance entitled, *Providing Regulatory Submissions in Electronic Format—Annual Reports for* NDA and ANDAs (August 2003). While the 1999 guidances established CDER's willingness to accept various elements of the NDA in electronic-only form (the complete archival copy of the NDA, Section 11 (case report tabulations), and Section 12 (case report forms)), an August 2003 guidance entitled *Providing Regulatory Submissions in Electronic Format-Human Pharmaceutical Product Applications and Related Submissions* (see discussion below on eCTDs) eliminated any requirement for paper copies, and established CDER's willingness to accept electronic signatures for NDA-related documents that previously required handwritten signatures (e.g., Form FDA 356h). In recent years, the numbers of eNDAs submitted and the numbers of companies developing them have increased markedly. By early 2003, CDER officials reported that about 75% of all new

NDA submissions were considered electronic filings and, of those, roughly 90% were entirely electronic. In eNDAs, text-based documents are submitted as PDF files, while datasets are provided in SAS transport file format. CDER officials continue to consider new regulations to require electronic submissions in the future due to the high costs of maintaining dual electronic and paper-based review systems. Under a December 2003 final rule (and a February 2004 draft guidance entitled, *Providing Regulatory Submissions in Electronic Format-Content of Labeling*), the agency required, for the first time, that a portion of the NDA—a new "content of labeling" section—be provided in electronic form in all cases (see discussion below). In July 2004, the FDA announced that it had adopted the Clinical Data Interchange Consortium's Study Data Tabulation Model (SDTM), which clinical trial sponsors can use to submit clinical data to the agency. Noting that the SDTM will lead to greater efficiencies in clinical research and NDA reviews, the agency was exploring "regulatory approaches" to require the SDTM standard for regulatory submissions.

- *From eNDAs to eCTDs.* As noted above, the flirtations with eNDAs and even paper-based CTDs were simply precursors to what regulators and industry saw as the true future for international marketing dossiers: the eCTD. In April 2003, the FDA released an ICH guidance entitled, *M2 eCTD: Electronic Common Technical Document Specification.* Then, in an August 2003 draft guidance entitled, *Providing Regulatory Submissions in Electronic Format-Human Pharmaceutical Product Applications and Related Submissions*, the FDA recommended that companies begin submitting "eCTD backbone files" because the agency believes that "having the information in the eCTD backbone files will result in greater efficiency in the future." Although CDER noted that the CTD and eCTD formats were developed for marketing dossiers, it emphasized that industry could unlock the true value of the eCTD by using the format for earlier submissions, particularly INDs. "We believe it is most beneficial to begin your eCTD-based submissions with the initial submission of the application," said the agency. "The maximum benefit will be derived once an application is in electronic format. This is particularly true for the IND, where submissions are provided over a long period of time." Further highlighting CDER's desire to accelerate the eCTD era was a simultaneously released web posting announcing that the center "would like to work closely with people who plan to provide a submission using the" new FDA-detailed eCTD specifications. As of mid-2004, CDER had received 34 eCTD submissions.

- *Pharmacogenomics.* Like other elements of the drug development and approval process, the NDA will be affected by important scientific advances. In a November 2003 draft guidance, for instance, the agency took its first step to encourage industry to submit pharmacogenomics information in NDAs and other applications to help FDA reviewers and scientists understand the relevant scientific issues in this emerging field (see discussion below). While the agency prepared to release a final guidance document in late 2004, CDER officials claimed that center reviewers were actively reviewing and making decisions based on voluntarily submitted pharmacogenomic data.

- In September 2004, CDER announced that it would, by mid-2005, transition to a new "risk-based pharmaceutical quality assessment system" under which it would encourage companies to submit different types of product chemistry-related information in NDAs and under which the center would reorganize its process for reviewing the chemistry section of NDAs (and INDs and sNDAs). As part of the new initiative, the FDA will ask NDA applicants to provide more pharmaceutical development information and to develop comprehensive quality summaries (similar to those provided in CTD-formatted applications) that will support a new review model for chemistry sections within new drug applications (see discussion below and Chapter 8).

- *Pediatric Data.* In late 2003, Congress passed and President Bush signed a new law that put to rest a several-year legal battle under which the FDA's authority to require industry to conduct pediatric studies of new drugs was challenged. In an October 2002 ruling, a U.S. district court had struck down the FDA's 1998 "pediatric rule" by questioning the FDA's statutory authority to require pediatric studies. Instead of pursuing a time-consuming appeal of the ruling, the FDA worked with Congress to craft legislation that would provide the agency with the necessary authority. During this period, the agency was barred from enforcing pediatric testing and submission requirements, although it did encourage industry to continue with its pediatric programs. In November 2003, the Pediatric Research Equity Act (PREA) gave the FDA clear authority to require pediatric studies of drugs when other approaches are not sufficient to ensure that drugs are safe and effective in children. Although the pediatric rule's provisions remain in the agency's regulations, the FDA is now referring companies to PREA until the agency can release a draft guidance consistent with the new law. Meanwhile, the agency is expected to propose minor changes to the current pediatric regulations to make them consistent with the provisions of PREA. Under PREA, all applications for new active ingredients, new indications, new dosage forms, new dosing regimens, and new routes of administration must contain a pediatric assessment unless the sponsor has obtained a waiver or deferral of pediatric studies. This assessment, PREA states, must "contain data, gathered using appropriate formulations for each age group for which the assessment is required, that are adequate (i) to assess the safety and effectiveness of the drug or the biological product for the claimed indications in all relevant pediatric subpopulations; and (ii) to support dosing and administration for each pediatric subpopulation for which the drug or the biological product is safe and effective." Under the original pediatric rule, applicants included in their NDAs a "pediatric use section" to provide a summary of the required pediatric assessment reports (submitted in full with the NDA), in addition to information "describing the investigation of the drug for use in pediatric populations, including an integrated summary of the information (the clinical pharmacology studies, controlled clinical studies, or uncontrolled clinical studies, or other data or information) that is relevant to the safety and effectiveness and benefits and risks of the drug in pediatric populations for the claimed indications, [and] a reference to the full descriptions of such studies provided in the [NDA's Human Pharmacokinetic and Bioavailability Section and Clinical Data Section]."

- *Risk Minimization Action Plans.* As the result of the FDA's focus on risk management under PDUFA III, certain NDAs are likely to feature what are called "risk minimization action plans," or RiskMAPs. In a May 2004 draft industry guidance entitled, *Development and Use of Risk Minimization Action Plans*, the FDA notes that, while routine risk minimization measures (e.g., FDA-approved professional labeling) will be sufficient for most products, "for a small number of products where a [RiskMAP] should be considered...sponsors are encouraged to consider developing a RiskMAP," which the agency defines as "a strategic safety program designed to meet specific goals and objectives in minimizing known risks of a product while preserving its benefits." In the draft guidance, the agency notes that a company can submit a RiskMAP before or after approval, and that the plan should be submitted in either the IND or NDA if it is filed in advance of marketing clearance (see discussion below for more on RiskMAPs).

NDA Content and Format Requirements

Although submission requirements are, to some degree, a function of a drug's nature, the NDA must, in each case, provide all relevant data and information that a sponsor has collected during the product's research and

The Common Technical Document/Electronic Common Technical Document

In mid-1997, the ICH parties agreed to begin work on a project called the common technical document (CTD), what was easily the international harmonization program's most ambitious undertaking. The FDA characterized the CTD as "an information package of [clinical, nonclinical, and manufacturing] technical data, in the same format and with the same content, that would be submitted for registering new drugs in all three ICH regions—the United States, the European Union, and Japan." During the CTD's development, the ICH parties noted that the common format for an application's technical documentation will "significantly reduce the time and resources needed to compile applications for registration of human pharmaceuticals and will ease the preparation of electronic submissions." Further, the CTD's "common elements" will facilitate regulatory reviews and applicant/regulator communications and simplify the exchange of regulatory information between regulatory authorities.

During a two-year voluntary submission "transition period" that ended on July 1, 2003, the CTD format became a regulatory option for registering products in the three ICH regions—firms could submit marketing dossiers in either the CTD or traditional application format within each region. During this period, many companies submitted so-called "hybrid applications," which included some CTD modules and some sections in the traditional NDA format. In the United States, the FDA formally initiated the transition period with its release of a draft guidance entitled, *Submitting Marketing Applications According to the ICH-CTD Format-General Considerations*, although some companies made CTD submissions in advance of the document's release.

It is important to note that the CTD comprises a format in which applicants can submit the data necessary in the marketing dossier, and does not modify the required data and information content for conventional NDAs or the standards traditionally applicable to new drug approval in the United States. Therefore, content requirements for marketing dossiers in the different ICH regions will continue to differ in some respects based on local regulations and laws.

When the transition period expired in July 2003, however, the use of the CTD format became "highly recommended" in the United States and mandatory in both Japan and the European Union. Under the FDA's Good Guidance Practice regulations, the phrase "highly recommended" was the strongest language that the agency could use to encourage the use of the CTD format in a guidance document.

Although industry was slow to employ the CTD format during the two-year transition period, this changed quickly and dramatically in the first year following the transition period. By mid-2004, CDER had received 101 CTD submissions, including CTD-formatted submissions for nine new molecular entities. Just as important, CDER notes that there have been no refuse-to-file actions on submissions in the CTD format, which were made by 52 different companies, 28 large and midsize firms and 33 smaller companies, according to the agency. Among the CDER new drug review divisions that had received the most CTDs as of mid-2004 were the Division of Oncology Drug Products (12 CTDs), the Division of Anti-Inflammatory, Analgesic and Ophthlamic Drug Products (11 CTDs), the Division of Special Pathogen and Immunologic Drug Products (9 CTDs), the Division of Metabolic and Endocrine Drug Products (9 CTDs), and the Division of Neuropharmacological Drug Products (7 CTDs).

As CTD-related activity increased, the FDA was already preparing for what it saw as the next step. As noted above, the agency's flirtations with eNDAs and even paper-based CTDs were simply precursors to what regulators and industry saw as the true future for international marketing dossiers: the eCTD. In April 2003, the FDA released an ICH guidance entitled, *M2 eCTD: Electronic Common Technical Document Specification*. Then, in an August 2003 draft guidance entitled, *Providing Regulatory Submissions in Electronic Format-Human Pharmaceutical Product Applications and Related Submissions*, the FDA recommended that companies begin submitting eCTD "backbone files" because the agency believes that "having the information in the eCTD backbone files will result in greater efficiency in the future." While noting that the CTD and eCTD formats were developed for marketing dossiers, CDER argued that industry could unlock the true value of the eCTD by using the format for earlier submissions, particularly INDs. "We believe it is most beneficial to begin your eCTD-based submissions with the initial submission of the application," said the agency. "The maximum benefit will be derived once an application is in electronic format. This is particularly true for the IND, where submissions are provided over a long period of time." Further highlighting CDER's desire to accelerate the eCTD era was a simultaneously released web posting announcing that the center "would like to work closely with people who plan to provide a submission using the" new FDA-detailed eCTD specifications.

As of mid-2004, CDER had received 34 eCTD submissions. Currently, CDER is asking each applicant to participate in the eCTD program with a single "sample" submission. After CDER uses the sample to establish that the applicant can send and that the center can accept an eCTD from the company, the firm is free to submit as many eCTD submissions as it wishes.

As the unofficial outline below indicates, the CTD format itself comprises five modules: Module 1: Administrative and Prescribing Information, which contains forms and documents specific to each region; Module 2: Common Technical Document Summaries; Module 3: Quality; Module 4: Nonclinical Study Reports; and Module 5: Clinical Study Reports. To establish content requirements and specifications for each section of the CTD and eCTD, the FDA has released a series of ICH guidance documents (in addition to those mentioned above): M4: *Common Technical Document for the Regulation of Pharmaceuticals for Human Use; Submitting Marketing Applications According to the ICH-CTD Format-General Considerations*, which provides FDA recommendations for the U.S.-specific requirements for Module 1; M4: *Organization of the CTD*; M4Q: *The CTD-Quality*; M4S: *The CTD-Safety*; M4E-*Efficacy*; and M4S-*The Safety Appendices*. More recently, the agency has issued a series of question-and-answer documents to address section location and formatting issues and questions: *The CTD-General Questions and Answers* (May 2004); *The CTD-Quality Questions and Answers/Location Issues* (June 2004); *The CTD-Efficacy Questions and Answers* (May 2004); and *The CTD-Safety Questions and Answers* (February 2003).

Given the regulatory momentum toward the eCTD, CDER officials are increasingly using eCTD-related information sources to update both CTD- and eCTD-related specifications. For updated specifications for CTDs and eCTDs, industry should refer to CDER's webpage for eCTDs (http://www.fda.gov/cder/regulatory/ersr/ectd.htm). Also available on CDER's webpage are further details on Module 1 and the latest comprehensive listing of CTD/eCTD section numbering and headings.

With the rising numbers of CTD and eCTD submissions, CDER will be working to determine how the review process is affected by the harmonized submission format. In addition, the center will be working to determine if the CTD format should be modified because of new ICH topics or agency initiatives.

Diagrammatic Representation of the CTD

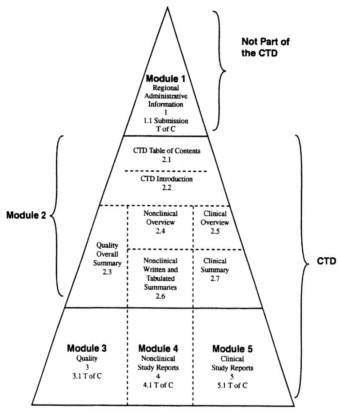

Organization of the CTD: The General Outline*

(Step 4 Guidance)

Module 1: Administrative Information and Prescribing Information

    1.1 Table of Contents of the Submission including Module 1

    1.2 Documents Specific to Each Region (e.g., application forms, prescribing information)

Module 2: Common Technical Document Summaries

    2.1 CTD Table of Contents

    2.2 CTD Introduction

    2.3 Quality Overall Summary

    2.4 Nonclinical Overview

    2.5 Clinical Overview

    2.6 Nonclinical Written and Tabulated Summary
        Pharmacology
        Pharmacokinetics
        Toxicology

    2.7 Clinical Summary
        Biophamaceutics and Associated Analytical Methods

—continued—

Clinical Pharmacology Studies
Clinical Efficacy
Clinical Safety
Synopses of Individual Studies

Module 3: Quality

    3.1 Module 3 Table of Contents

    3.2 Body of Data

    3.3 Literature References

Module 4: Nonclinical Study Reports

    4.1 Module 4 Table of Contents

    4.2 Study Reports

    4.3 Literature References

Module 5: Clinical Study Reports

    5.1 Module 5 Table of Contents

    5.2 Tabular Listing of All Clinical Studies

    5.3 Clinical Study Reports

    5.4 Literature References

*a more detailed version of this general outline appears below

—continued—

Organization of the CTD
(Composite CTD Outline Developed from Various FDA/ICH Guidances)

Module 1: Administrative Information and Prescribing Information* (for U.S. Submissions)

Cover Letter (if applicant wants to submit one, it should be placed here).

FDA Form 356h.

Comprehensive Table of Contents for the Submission Including Module 1. This should include a complete list of all documents provided in the submission, and should specify the location of each document by referring to volume numbers and tab identifiers.

Administrative Documents:

    a. Administrative Documents (e.g., field copy certification, debarment certification)

    b. Prescribing Information (all copies of the labels and all product labeling)

    c. Annotated Labeling Text for NDAs (or labeling comparison for ANDAs).

Module 2: Common Technical Document Summaries

2.1 CTD Table of Contents

2.2 CTD Introduction. This should be "a general introduction to the pharmaceutical, including its pharmacologic class, mode of action, and proposed clinical use. In general, the introduction should not exceed one page."

2.3 Quality Overall Summary. Following the scope and outline of the "Body of Data" in Module 3, the quality overall summary (QOS) should include sufficient information for each section of Module 3 to provide the quality reviewer with an overview of that module. The QOS "should also emphasize critical key parameters of the product and provide, for instance, justification in cases where guidance was not followed... [and] should include a discussion of key issues that integrates information from sections in the Quality module [Module 3] and supporting information from other modules (e.g., qualification of impurities by toxicological studies discussed under the M4S module), including cross-referencing to volume and page numbers in other modules." Generally, the QOS should not exceed 40 pages of text, excluding tables and figures, or 80 pages for biotech products and other products with more complex manufacturing processes.

2.4 Nonclinical Overview. The nonclinical overview, which generally should not exceed 30 pages, should present an integrated and critical assessment of the drug's pharmacologic, pharmacokinetic, and toxicologic evaluation. In contrast to the nonclinical written and tabulated summary, which should be a factual synopsis, the nonclinical overview should provide an interpretation of the nonclinical data, discuss the clinical relevance of the findings, cross-link with the quality aspects of the pharmaceutical, and discuss the implications of the nonclinical findings for the safe use of the drug. It should also discuss and justify the nonclinical testing strategy.

2.5 Clinical Overview. The clinical overview, which should be relatively brief (30 pages, although its length will depend on the application's complexity), should provide a critical analysis of the CTD's clinical data. Although it should refer to data provided in the comprehensive clinical summary, the individual clinical study reports, and other relevant reports, the clinical overview should primarily present the conclusions and implications of those data and should not recapitulate them. In contrast to the clinical summary (see Section 2.7 below), which provides a detailed factual summarization of the CTD's clinical information, the clinical overview should provide "a succinct discussion and interpretation of these findings together with any other relevant information (e.g., pertinent animal data or product quality issues that may have clinical implications)." In other words, the clinical summary focuses on factual summarization, while the clincial overview focuses on critical analysis and interpretation. Specifically, the clinical overview should: (1) present the strengths and limitations of the development program and study results; (2) analyze the benefits and risks of the medicinal product in its intended use; and (3) describe how the study results support critical parts of the prescribing information.

2.6 Nonclinical Written and Tabulated Summaries.** The primary purpose of the nonclinical written and tabulated summaries is to provide a comprehensive, factual synopsis of the nonclinical data. Because, in some ICH regions, "a review of the Tabulated Summaries (in conjunction with the Written Summaries) represents the primary review of the nonclinical information," the M4S: *The CTD—Safety* guidance emphasizes that data presentations in the formats provided as templates and examples "should ensure that a sufficient level of detail is available to the reviewer and should provide concise overviews of related information." In the three written summaries within this section, the applicant should summarize and evaluate the various nonclinical pharmacology, pharmacokinetic, and toxicology studies. The fifth CTD guidance, M4S: *The CTD—Safety Appendices*, provides examples of tables and figures for the written summaries, and templates and examples of tables that comprise the three nonclinical tabulated summaries.

2.6.1 Introduction

2.6.2 Pharmacology Written Summary

2.6.3 Pharmacology Tabulated Summary

2.6.4 Pharmacokinetics Written Summary

2.6.5 Pharmacokinetics Tabulated Summary

2.6.6 Toxicology Written Summary

2.6.7 Toxicology Tabulated Summary

2.7 Clinical Summary.** As noted above, the clinical summary should provide a detailed, factual summarization of all clinical information in the CTD, including clinical study reports, meta-analyses or other cross-study analyses for which full reports have been included in Module 5 (clinical study reports), and postmarketing data for products marketed in other regions. The comparisons and analyses of cross-study results should "focus on factual observations," the CTD guidance documents emphasize. The clinical summary will typically range from 50 to 400 pages (excluding attached tables), although the CTD guidance notes that its size will vary substantially based on the information conveyed.

Biopharmaceutics and Associated Analytical Methods

Clinical Pharmacology Studies

Clinical Efficacy

Clinical Safety

Synopses of Individual Studies

Module 3: Quality

As it does for the QOS, the M4Q:*The CTD—Quality* establishes the Module 3 format for drug substances and drug products, and for biotech products. The guidance is careful to note that, while "the content of [Module 3's] sections should include relevant information described in existing ICH guidances,...harmonized content is not available for all sections... Neither the type nor extent of specific supporting data has been addressed..., and both may depend on regional guidance."

3.1 Module 3 Table of Contents

3.2 Body of Data. Beyond the fact that this section represents the core of the module, Module 3's

Body of Data section is interesting for at least a few reasons. First, it includes the Pharmaceutical Development section (3.2.P.2), which FDA officials have maintained is the CTD's most notable quality- or manufacturing-related departure from traditional NDA submissions. This section, which derives from the development pharmaceutics section in European marketing dossiers, to some degree provides a history of a drug's chemical development and the company's rationale for choosing certain developmental paths (e.g., dosage forms, excipients). In addition, this section includes Section 3.2.R, in which sponsors should provide non-harmonized region-specific information. For U.S. submissions, for example, this would include executed batch records, the methods validation package, and comparability protocols.

3.3 Literature References

Module 4: Nonclinical Study Reports

4.1 Module 4 Table of Contents

4.2 Study Reports

4.3 Literature References

Module 5: Clinical Study Reports

5.1 Module 5 Table of Contents

5.2 Tabular Listing of All Clinical Studies

5.3 Clinical Study Reports. In addition to the clinical study reports, this section should include the integrated analysis of safety summary (ISS) and integrated efficacy summary (ISE), if they are to be included as separate elements of a CTD to be submitted in the United States. Although neither the ISS or ISE are required elements in the CTD, companies can submit them if that is the applicant's preference, or when the information in these analyses are too voluminous to include within the page-count limitations of the clinical overview and summary.

5.4 Literature References

*Although the CTD guidances specify a format and document sequence for Module 1, the individual regions dictate what information is to be included in this module and how it is to be presented. Therefore, standards for Module 1 in the United States are provided in the FDA's *Submitting Marketing Applications According to the* ICH-CTD Format—*General Considerations*. Because of this, the sequencing and numbering of Module 1 as presented above reflects the format specified in FDA's *General Considerations* guidance and not the somewhat different outline in the Step 4 CTD guidances.

**Although the CTD guidance says that "applicants should not modify the overall organization of the CTD," it adds that, "however, in the Nonclinical and Clinical Summaries sections of the CTD, applicants can modify individual formats to provide the best possible presentation of the technical information to facilitate the understanding and evaluation of the results."

development. FDA regulations provide the most fundamental description of NDA content and format requirements: "Applications...are required to be submitted in the form and contain the information, as appropriate for the particular submission... An application for a new chemical entity will generally contain an application form, an index, a summary, five or six technical sections, case report tabulations of patient data, case report forms, drug samples, and labeling. Other applications will generally contain only some of those items and information will be limited to that needed to support the particular submission... The application is required to contain reports of all investigations of the drug product sponsored by the applicant, and all other information about the drug pertinent to an evaluation of the application that is received or otherwise obtained by the applicant from any source. The Food and Drug Administration will maintain guidelines on the format and content of applications to assist applicants in their preparation."

In addition to FDA regulations, a large and growing number of agency and ICH guidance documents drive NDA submission requirements. In many cases, particularly in areas in which the FDA's guidelines are several years old, the ICH guidances provide a better account of the agency's current views on submission requirements. In fact, some of the agency's more recent guidance documents refer directly to ICH guidance documents rather than the relevant FDA guidances that predated them. Some of the newer FDA guidances simply incorporate large sections of text from relevant ICH guidances addressing the same subject. The FDA and ICH guidances relevant to NDA submissions are discussed below.

The Fundamentals of NDA Submissions

Although the quantity of information and data submitted in NDAs can vary considerably, the component parts of drug applications are somewhat more uniform. According to *Form FDA-356h, Application To Market A New Drug, Biologic, or an Antibiotic for Human Use* (see sample form below), NDAs can comprise as many as 20 different sections in addition to the form itself:

1. Index
2. Labeling
3. Summary
4. Chemistry Section
    A. Chemistry, manufacturing and controls information
    B. Samples
    C. Methods validation package
5. Nonclinical Pharmacology and Toxicology Section
6. Human Pharmacokinetics and Bioavailability Section
7. Clinical Microbiology Section
8. Clinical Data Section
9. Safety Update Report
10. Statistical Section
11. Case Report Tabulations
12. Case Report Forms
13. Patent Information on any patent that claims the drug
14. A Patent Certification with respect to any patent that claims the drug
15. Establishment Description
16. Debarment Certification
17. Field Copy Certification
18. User Fee Cover Sheet (Form FDA 3397)
19. Financial Information
20. Other Information

DEPARTMENT OF HEALTH AND HUMAN SERVICES FOOD AND DRUG ADMINISTRATION **APPLICATION TO MARKET A NEW DRUG, BIOLOGIC, OR AN ANTIBIOTIC DRUG FOR HUMAN USE** *(Title 21, Code of Federal Regulations, 314 & 601)*	Form Approved: OMB No. 0910-0338 Expiration Date: August 31, 2005 See OMB Statement on page 2.
	FOR FDA USE ONLY APPLICATION NUMBER

APPLICANT INFORMATION

NAME OF APPLICANT	DATE OF SUBMISSION
TELEPHONE NO. *(Include Area Code)*	FACSIMILE (FAX) Number *(Include Area Code)*
APPLICANT ADDRESS *(Number, Street, City, State, Country, Zip Code or Mail Code, and U.S. License number if previously issued):*	AUTHORIZED U.S. AGENT NAME & ADDRESS *(Number, Street, City, State, ZIP Code, telephone & FAX number)* IF APPLICABLE

PRODUCT DESCRIPTION

NEW DRUG OR ANTIBIOTIC APPLICATION NUMBER, OR BIOLOGICS LICENSE APPLICATION NUMBER (if previously issued)

ESTABLISHED NAME *(e.g., Proper Name, USP/USAN name)*	PROPRIETARY NAME *(trade name)* IF ANY
CHEMICAL/BIOCHEMICAL/BLOOD PRODUCT NAME *(if any)*	CODE NAME *(If any)*

DOSAGE FORM:	STRENGTHS:	ROUTE OF ADMINISTRATION:

(PROPOSED) INDICATION(S) FOR USE:

APPLICATION INFORMATION

APPLICATION TYPE *(check one)* ☐ NEW DRUG APPLICATION (21 CFR 314.50) ☐ ABBREVIATED NEW DRUG APPLICATION (ANDA, 21 CFR 314.94) ☐ BIOLOGICS LICENSE APPLICATION (21 CFR part 601)

IF AN NDA, IDENTIFY THE APPROPRIATE TYPE ☐ 505 (b) (1) ☐ 505 (b) (2)

IF AN ANDA, OR 505(b)(2), IDENTIFY THE REFERENCE LISTED DRUG PRODUCT THAT IS THE BASIS FOR THE SUBMISSION
Name of Drug   Holder of Approved Application

TYPE OF SUBMISSION *(check one)* ☐ ORIGINAL APPLICATION ☐ AMENDMENT TO A PENDING APPLICATION ☐ RESUBMISSION ☐ PRESUBMISSION ☐ ANNUAL REPORT ☐ ESTABLISHMENT DESCRIPTION SUPPLEMENT ☐ EFFICACY SUPPLEMENT ☐ LABELING SUPPLEMENT ☐ CHEMISTRY MANUFACTURING AND CONTROLS SUPPLEMENT ☐ OTHER

IF A SUBMISSION OF PARTIAL APPLICATION, PROVIDE LETTER OF AGREEMENT TO PARTIAL SUBMISSION: _____

IF A SUPPLEMENT, IDENTIFY THE APPROPRIATE CATEGORY: ☐ CBE ☐ CBE-30 ☐ PRIOR APPROVAL (PA)

REASON FOR SUBMISSION

PROPOSED MARKETING STATUS (check one) ☐ PRESCRIPTION (Rx) ☐ OVER THE COUNTER PRODUCT (OTC)

NUMBER OF VOLUMES SUBMITTED | THIS APPLICATION IS ☐ PAPER ☐ PAPER AND ELECTRONIC ☐ ELECTRONIC

ESTABLISHMENT INFORMATION (Full establishment information should be provided in the body of the Application.)
Provide locations of all manufacturing, packaging and control sites for drug substance and drug product (continuation sheets may be used if necessary). Include name, address, contact, telephone number, registration number (CFN), DMF number, and manufacturing steps and/or type of testing (e.g., Final dosage form, Stability testing) conducted at the site. Please indicate whether the site is ready for inspection or, if not, when it will be ready.

Cross References (list related License Applications, INDs, NDAs, PMAs, 510(k)s, IDEs, BMFs, and DMFs referenced in the current application)

FORM 356h (4/03)

This application contains the following items: *(Check all that apply)*

1. Index	
2. Labeling (check one)	☐ Draft Labeling ☐ Final Printing Labeling
3. Summary (21 CFR 314.50 (c))	
4. Chemistry section	
A. Chemistry, manufacturing, and controls information (e.g., 21 CFR 314.50 (d) (1); 21 CFR 601.2)	
B. Samples (21 CFR 314.50 (e) (1); 21 CFR 601.2 (a)) (Submit only upon FDA's request)	
C. Methods validation package (e.g., 21 CFR 314.50 (e) (2) (i); 21 CFR 601.2)	
5. Nonclinical pharmacology and toxicology section (e.g., 21 CFR 314.50 (d) (2); 21 CFR 601.2)	
6. Human pharmacokinetics and bioavailability section (e.g., 21 CFR 314.50 (d) (3); 21 CFR 601.2)	
7. Clinical Microbiology (e.g., 21 CFR 314.50 (d) (4))	
8. Clinical data section (e.g., 21 CFR 314.50 (d) (5); 21 CFR 601.2)	
9. Safety update report (e.g., 21 CFR 314.50 (d) (5) (vi) (b); 21 CFR 601.2)	
10. Statistical section (e.g., 21 CFR 314.50 (d) (6); 21 CFR 601.2)	
11. Case report tabulations (e.g., 21 CFR 314.50 (f) (1); 21 CFR 601.2)	
12. Case report forms (e.g., 21 CFR 314.50 (f) (2); 21 CFR 601.2)	
13. Patent information on any patent which claims the drug (21 U.S.C. 355 (b) or (c))	
14. A patent certification with respect to any patent which claims the drug (21 U.S.C. 355 (b) (2) or (j) (2) (A))	
15. Establishment description (21 CFR Part 600, if applicable)	
16. Debarment certification (FD&C Act 306 (k)(1))	
17. Field copy certification (21 CFR 314.5 (l) (3))	
18. User Fee Cover Sheet (Form FDA 3397)	
19. Financial Information (21 CFR Part 54)	
20. OTHER (Specify)	

CERTIFICATION

I agree to update this application with new safety information about the drug that may reasonably affect the statement of contraindications, warnings, precautions, or adverse reactions in the draft labeling. I agree to submit safety update reports as provided for by regulation or as requested by FDA. If this application is approved, I agree to comply with all applicable laws and regulations that apply to approved applications, including, but not limited to the following:
1. Good manufacturing practice regulations in 21 CFR Parts 210, 211, or applicable regulations, Parts 606, and/or 820.
2. Biological establishment standards in 21 CFR Part 600.
3. Labeling regulations in 21 CFR 201, 606, 610, 660 and/or 809.
4. In the case of a prescription drug product or biological product, prescription drug advertising regulations in 21 CFR 202.
5. Regulations on making changes in application in FD&C Act Section 506A, 21 CFR 314.71, 314.72, 314.97, 314.99, and 601.12.
6. Regulations on reports in 21 CFR 314.80, 314.81, 600.80 and 600.81.
7. Local, state, and Federal environmental impact laws.

If this application applies to a drug product that FDA has proposed for scheduling under the Controlled Substances Act, I agree not to market the product until the Drug Enforcement Administration makes a final scheduling decision.

The data and information in this submission have been reviewed and, to the best of my knowledge are certified to be true and accurate.

Warning: a willfully false statement is a criminal offense, U.S. Code, title 18, section 1001.

SIGNATURE OF RESPONSIBLE OFFICIAL OR AGENT	TYPED NAME AND TITLE	DATE

ADDRESS (Street, City, State, and ZIP Code)	Telephone Number ( )

Public reporting burden for this collection of information is estimated to average 24 hours per response, including the time for reviewing instructions, searching existing data sources, gathering and maintaining the data needed, and completing and reviewing the collection of information. Send comments regarding this burden estimate or any other aspect of this collection of information, including suggestions for reducing this burden to:

Department of Health and Human Services
Food and Drug Administration
CBER, HFM-99
1401 Rockvillle Pike
Rockville, MD 20852-1448

Food and Drug Administration
CDER, HFD-94
12229 Wilkins Avenue
Rockville, MD 20852

An agency may not conduct or sponsor, and a person is not required to respond to, a collection of information unless it displays a currently valid OMB control number.

FORM FDA 356h (4/2003)

Editor's Note: Although not indicated in the listing above, NDAs must now, under a December 2003 final regulation, include a new "content of labeling" section that must be provided in electronic form (see discussion below). The listing on the NDA form also lacks a reference to the need for a pediatric use section, which was originally required under the agency's pediatric rule and is now required under the Pediatric Research Equity Act (see discussion above). The pediatric use section is profiled in the NDA contents discussion below. In addition, Section 15-Establishment Description is relevant only for biological products.

The components of any NDA are, in part, a function of the nature of the subject drug and the information available to the applicant at the time of submission. For example, the safety update report section is not submitted in the original NDA, but is forwarded 120 days after the NDA submission (see discussion below).

An instruction sheet that accompanies Form 356h makes clear that the form's numbered listing of contents constitutes a checklist and is not designed to dictate the NDA's format. "The numbering of the items on [Form 356h's] checklist is not intended to specify a particular order for the inclusion of those sections into the submission," the FDA states. "The applicant may include sections in any order, but the location of those sections within the submission should be clearly indicated in the index." Each NDA section is discussed further below.

The Archival, Review, and Field Copies of the NDA

Since October 1993, drug sponsors have been required to submit three different copies of an NDA to the agency. The NDA's review and archival copies have been long-standing regulatory requirements, while the field copy of the application is a more recent NDA requirement.

The FDA provides specific guidance on content requirements for the archival and review copies in its *Guideline on Formatting, Assembling, and Submitting New Drug and Antibiotic Applications* (February 1987). It is important to note, however, that the NDA has evolved considerably since this guidance was published, and that several new sections (e.g., debarment certification, financial information, field copy certification, pediatric use section, content of labeling section) are now required in the NDA. Although no subsequent agency guidance addresses content requirements as directly as the February 1987 guideline, a January 1999 guidance entitled, *Regulatory Submissions in Electronic Format: New Drug Applications* (see discussion below) does provide a somewhat more up-to-date discussion on the archival and review copies of the NDA.

The roles and content of the archival, review, and field copies of the NDA differ considerably. The archival copy, which is stored by the FDA as a reference document, must contain all the relevant sections identified above. It must also include cover letters confirming FDA-applicant agreements, identifying company contact persons, and providing other information relevant to the NDA review. The purpose of the archival copy is to permit individual reviewers to refer to information not included in their review copies, to give other agency personnel access to the complete application for official business, and to maintain in a single file a complete copy of the entire NDA.

The review copy is a less comprehensive version of the application. It comprises the NDA's five or six technical sections—clinical, nonclinical pharmacology/toxicology, chemistry, statistics, biopharmaceutics, and, for anti-infective drugs, microbiology as well. Each of these technical sections is packaged for distribution to, and evaluation by, reviewers in the corresponding technical discipline. Therefore, these sections must be bound separately, and must be accompanied by a table of contents and a copy of the NDA's application form, index, and summary.

NDA sponsors must also submit what is called a "field" copy of the NDA. To be used by FDA inspectors during preapproval manufacturing inspections, the field copy consists of an NDA's chemistry, manufacturing, and controls section, the NDA application form (Form FDA 356h), and the NDA summary. In addition, the field copy must provide a certification indicating that it includes an exact copy of the chemistry, manufacturing and control section "contained in the archival and review copies of the application." U.S.-based applicants must submit the field copy directly to their respective "home" FDA district offices. Foreign-based applicants should submit field copies to FDA headquarters along with their archival and review copies. In December 2003, however, CDER's Office of Regulatory Affairs issued a notice informing industry that any company submitting an electronic chemistry, manufacturing, and controls section to CDER need not submit an electronic or paper version of the same section to the relevant district office, since the office will be able to access the section through CDER's Electronic Document Room.

In a November 1996 draft guideline, CDER indicated that the NDA's archival copy would be among the first application components that the agency would seek to accept in electronic-only format (i.e., without a paper-based version). Then, in a September 1997 final guideline entitled, *Archiving Submissions in Electronic Format-NDAs*, the FDA provided recommendations on the submission of certain records (i.e., specifically, case report forms and case report tabulations) in electronic form. Subsequently, this final guidance was superseded by a January 1999 guidance entitled, *Regulatory Submissions in Electronic Format: New Drug Applications*.

Although the January 1999 electronic submissions guidance applies only to the NDA's archival copy, a sponsor's decision to submit an electronic version of the archival copy can have implications for the accompanying review copy of the submission. If a company provides the NDA's archival copy in electronic format, for example, the agency will exempt the sponsor from having to submit certain elements of the NDA's review copy in paper format. According to the guidance document, these would include the methods validation reports from the chemistry, manufacturing and controls section, the individual animal line listings from the nonclinical section, and certain study report appendices from the clinical sections. Certain review divisions may permit NDA applicants to avoid submitting other sections of the NDA's review copy, the guidance points out.

Application Form All three versions of the NDA must contain an NDA application form, called Form FDA 356h (see exhibit above). This form, which serves as the NDA's cover sheet, provides a comprehensive checklist of the elements that each application should include. The latest version of the form was implemented in April 2003.

The application form must be completed and signed by the applicant or the applicant's authorized U.S. agent. If the sponsor does not have a residence or place of business within the United States, the application form must provide the name and address of, and be countersigned by, an authorized agent who resides or maintains a place of business in the United States. By signing this form, the sponsor agrees to comply with a variety of legal and regulatory requirements, including current good manufacturing practice (CGMP) standards, advertising and labeling regulations, safety update reporting requirements, and local, state, and federal environmental impact laws.

The Index Perhaps the most critical factor in an NDA's user-friendliness is the speed and ease with which a reviewer can locate specific information during the review process. Since it is the reviewer's "roadmap" to an application that can be hundreds of volumes long and because it can influence the speed and efficiency of the review as well, the NDA's index is an important element of the application.

While the FDA states that the various NDA components may be submitted in any order, the agency emphasizes that the index should clearly indicate the location of each section within the application. Therefore, the agency recommends that, particularly for large submissions, the index "be the first item following the Form FDA 356h."

The archival copy of the NDA must provide a comprehensive index by volume number and page number to the NDA summary, each of the five or six technical sections, and the case report forms and tabulations section. FDA guidelines state that the index should serve as a detailed table of contents for the entire archival NDA.

Each of the separately bound technical sections comprising the review copies must include a copy of the NDA index as well. In addition, each section should include its own individual table of contents based upon the portions of the larger NDA index relevant to that technical section.

Labeling The NDA's archival copy must contain copies of the label and all labeling proposed for the drug product. In the NDA, applicants must submit either 4 copies of a product's draft labeling or 12 copies of the final printed labeling (FPL).

If a sponsor submits draft labeling, one copy should be bound in the archival copy, with single copies placed in the review copies of the clinical, chemistry, and pharmacology sections (labeling in the review sections may be bound separately in the appropriate colored jacket for the respective review sections).

When a sponsor provides FPL and carton labeling, one copy should be mounted, bound, and inserted in the archival copy. The remaining 11 copies should be mounted, bound, and submitted in a separate jacket clearly marked "Final Printed Labeling" (see Chapter 8 for a more detailed discussion of drug labeling requirements).

The New "Content of Labeling" Section. Under a December 11, 2003, final regulation, the FDA is requiring companies submitting NDAs (and NDA supplements and annual reports) to provide what it calls a "content of labeling" section, and that the new section be provided in electronic form. Specifically, this new section of the NDA will comprise the contents of the package insert, and will include all text, tables, and figures.

Interestingly, the new "e-labeling" requirement will not affect any existing components of the NDA—applicants, for instance, still must submit copies of the formatted label and all labeling. In addition, firms will continue to have the option of submitting these existing marketing application components in an electronic or paper-based format. In February 2004, the agency issued a draft guidance entitled, *Providing Regulatory Submissions in Electronic Format-Content of Labeling.*

"The content of labeling is a new labeling type not previously required in the regulations to be submitted," the agency states in the preamble to the final rule. "The content of labeling, defined as the contents of the package insert or professional labeling, including all text, tables and figures for prescription products approved under an ANDA, BLA, or NDA, does not replace any previously required labeling type, including the package insert. In other words, the regulations require the package insert to be submitted in addition to the content of labeling. However, no paper copies of any labeling are required... The applicant has the option of providing the package insert in paper or electronic format under part 11. The package insert, if submitted electronically, must appear as it would in printed form. Submission in this form allows us to evaluate the format of the package insert, such as font size and positioning of the text."

At least initially, the agency required that all e-labeling submissions be provided in portable document format (PDF). "At this time, portable document format (PDF) is the only type of electronic file format that we have the ability to accept for processing, reviewing, and archiving," the agency stated in the final rule. Under a February 2004 draft guidance, however, the agency noted that it ultimately hoped to move to a new "structured product labeling" (SPL) format for e-labeling submissions because the PDF format is not adequate to support related government initiatives on e-prescribing and electronic health records.

The agency's move toward e-labeling was motivated by a few issues, the first of which is an effort to stream-line the drug labeling review process and expedite the approval of postmarketing labeling changes. "Each year FDA conducts a word-for-word comparison of the labeling as part of the review process for more than 1,000 proposed labeling changes for approved NDAs and BLAs," the agency notes. "Because reviewers currently con-duct these comparisons manually using two paper copies of the labeling, the process is slow and subject to error. Requiring the electronic submission of labeling for NDAs, certain BLAs, ANDAs, supplements, and annual reports will greatly enhance the accuracy and speed of labeling review."

FDA officials see this new e-labeling requirement, what seems to be a minor regulatory change on many lev-els, as a key element in the agency's larger and higher-profile "e-health" initiative. In the preamble to the final rule, the agency adds that the new e-labeling regulation is among "a number of changes" that are needed to improve the public's access to drug information. In particular, the FDA notes, the e-labeling initiative will be tied into the DailyMed Initiative, a National Library of Medicine effort to promote patient safety through accessible drug information. "The electronic submission of the content of labeling will allow the agency to provide the DailyMed system with labeling in a comprehensive, reliable, and structured format. The DailyMed can then use this information to make information on medications available to the public...health profes-sionals, and others [who] may use this information in several ways, including to identify drug interactions, contraindications, and possible adverse reactions."

Under a February 2004 final regulation, the FDA also began requiring that the product labels for most pre-scription and OTC drugs feature bar codes that must provide the National Drug Code (NDC) number. The requirement is designed to help reduce the number of medication errors in hospitals and other health care settings.

The NDA Summary In many respects, the NDA summary is an abridged version of the entire application. The summary is designed to provide an overview of the NDA, explaining its intent—to establish the drug's safety and effectiveness for a specific use—and highlighting the studies and analyses that support the product's use.

Given that the summary is one of the few elements of the application that all reviewers receive, its importance cannot be overstated. A well-prepared summary, which should include a balanced, unbiased presentation and analysis of a drug's beneficial and adverse effects, can build a reviewer's confidence in the applicant, the drug, and the validity and completeness of the information in the NDA.

As evidence of the importance that is placed on the NDA summary, the FDA dedicated an entire guideline to the topic—*Guideline for the Format and Content of the Summary for New Drug and Antibiotic Applications* (February 1987). According to this document, "each full application is required...to contain a summary, ordinarily 50 to 200 pages in length, that integrates all of the information in the application and provides reviewers in each review area, and other agency officials, with a good general understanding of the drug product and of the applica-tion. The summary should discuss all aspects of the application and should be written in approximately the same level of detail required for publication in, and meet the editorial standards generally applied by, refer-eed scientific and medical journals... To the extent possible, data in the summary should be presented in tab-ular and graphic forms... The summary should comprehensively present the most important information about the drug product and the conclusions to be drawn from this information. The summary should avoid any editorial promotion of the drug product, i.e., it should be a factual summary of safety and effectiveness data and a neutral analysis of these data. The summary should include an annotated copy of the proposed labeling, a discussion of the product's benefits and risks, a description of the foreign marketing history of the drug (if any), and a summary of each technical section."

Specifically, federal regulations require the NDA summary to provide the following:

- the proposed text of the labeling for the drug, with annotations to the information in the summary and technical sections of the application that support the inclusion of each statement in the labeling, and, if the application is for a prescription drug, statements describing the reasons for omitting a section or subsection of the labeling format;

- a statement identifying the pharmacologic class of the drug and a discussion of the scientific rationale for the drug, its intended use, and the potential clinical benefits of the drug product;

- a brief description of the marketing history, if any, of the drug outside the United States, including a list of the countries in which the drug has been marketed, a list of any countries in which the drug has been withdrawn from marketing for any reason related to safety or effectiveness, and a list of countries in which applications for marketing are pending (the section must describe marketing by the applicant and, if known, the marketing history of other persons);

- a summary of the chemistry, manufacturing, and controls section of the application;

- a summary of the nonclinical pharmacology and toxicology section of the application;

- a summary of the human pharmacokinetics and bioavailability section of the application;

- a summary of the microbiology section of the application (for anti-infectives only);

- a summary of the clinical data section of the application, including the results of statistical analyses of the clinical trials; and

- a concluding discussion that presents the benefit and risk considerations related to the drug, including a discussion of any proposed additional studies or surveillance the applicant intends to conduct following approval.

Chemistry Section In the chemistry section, the NDA's first technical component, the sponsor describes, and provides data regarding, the composition, manufacture, and specifications of both the drug substance (i.e., the active ingredient) and the final drug product, including their physical and chemical characteristics and stability.

A 1997 revision to the Form 356h restructured this NDA section to some degree. Essentially, the outline provided in Form 356h folds the NDA's samples and methods validation package sections into the chemistry section. Under the previous iteration of the form, these components were independent of the chemistry section.

Historically, deficiencies have been more common in the NDA's chemistry, manufacturing, and controls (CMC) section than in other aspects of the application. This is probably due to several factors, including the fact that sponsors cannot develop final product formulations and commercial-scale manufacturing processes until late in the drug development process. In response to this, CDER announced, in mid-2004, that it would initiate more purely CMC-focused meetings with NDA applicants to address chemistry and manufacturing issues and to streamline the review of resubmitted and supplemental NDAs in an effort to free chemistry resources for original NDA submissions.

As noted, CDER's expectations for the NDA's CMC section are likely to evolve as the center shifts to a new "risk-based pharmaceutical quality assessment system" in spring 2005. Under the emerging system, the agency is expected to seek more "pharmaceutical development information" in the CMC section, and to ask sponsors to develop comprehensive CMC summaries (such as those found in CTD-formatted submissions), which are now often developed by CDER's chemistry reviewers. The CMC section will be designed to support CDER's new review approach for the NDA's chemistry section (see exhibit below and Chapter 8).

Recognizing the complexity of the NDA's CMC section, the FDA released, in the mid-1980s, a spate of guidelines that provide agency advice on preparing chemistry, manufacturing, and controls sections for NDAs and other applications: *Guideline for the Format and Content of the Chemistry, Manufacturing, and Controls Section of an Application* (February 1987); *Guideline for Submitting Documentation for the Manufacture and Controls for Drug Products* (February 1987); *Guideline for Submitting Documentation for Packaging for Human Drugs and Biologics* (February 1987); *Guideline for Submitting Documentation for the Stability of Human Drugs and Biologics* (February 1987); and *Guideline for Submitting Supporting Documentation in Drug Applications for the Manufacture of Drug Substances* (February 1987). A few years later, these were supplemented by the agency's *Draft Guideline for Submitting Supporting Chemistry Documentation in Radiopharmaceutical Drug Applications* (November 1991), *Guidance for the Submission of Chemistry, Manufacturing, and Controls for Synthetic Peptide Drug Substances* (November 1994), and *Guideline for Drug Master Files* (September 1989).

Although the FDA has invested much of its more recent CMC guidance development effort into the ICH harmonization process (see discussion below), the agency did publish a handful of formal and draft guidances in the late 1990s, including: *Guidance for Industry: Container Closure Systems for Packaging Human Drugs and Biologics* (May 1999) (the agency also released a May 2002 question-and-answer guidance based on this guidance); *Environmental Assessment of Human Drug and Biologics Applications* (July 1998), which superseded the *Guidance for Industry for the Submission of an Environmental Assessment in Human Drug Applications and Supplements* (1995); *Draft Guidance for Industry on Stability Testing of Drug Substances and Drug Products* (June 1998), which will, when it is published as a new guidance, supersede CDER's *Guideline for Submitting Documentation for the Stability of Human Drugs and Biologics* (February 1997); *Draft Guidance for Industry: NDAs: Impurities in Drug Substances* (December 1998); *Draft Guidance for the Submission of CMC Information for Nasal Spray and Inhalation Solution, Suspension, and Spray Drug Products* (June 1999); and *Draft Guidance for the Submission of CMC Information for Metered Dose Inhaler* (MDI) *and Dry Powder Inhaler* (DPI) *Drug Products* (September 1999).

As noted, the ICH initiative has produced numerous guidelines relevant to the NDA's chemistry section. These documents are cited in the more detailed discussions below.

Form 356h's listing of the NDA contents indicates that the chemistry section should comprise three elements:

> A. Chemistry, manufacturing and control information;
>
> B. Samples; and
>
> C. Methods validation package.

A. Chemistry, Manufacturing, and Control Information. According to FDA regulations, an NDA's chemistry, manufacturing, and control section should comprise four principal elements: (1) a description of the drug substance; (2) a description of the drug product; (3) an environmental impact analysis report (or request for a waiver); and (4) a field copy certification.

The NDA's CMC Section and CDER's New Quality Assessment System

Under the *Pharmaceutical cGMPs for the 21st Century Initiative*, CDER's Office of New Drug Chemistry (ONDC) is establishing "a modern, risk-based pharmaceutical quality assessment system to replace the current CMC review system." Scheduled for full implementation in spring 2005, the new quality assessment system "is intended to address the multiple challenges and difficulties facing the ONDC and to establish a framework to facilitate continuous CMC improvement and innovation in the pharmaceutical industry."

According to an FDA document entitled, ONDC's *New Risk-Based Pharmaceutical Quality System* (September 2004), the challenges and difficulties facing ONDC include the following:

- Inconsistencies in application quality combined with a lack of adequate pharmaceutical development information in NDA submissions, which prevent the agency from taking full advantage of risk-based assessments, and lead to multiple CMC review cycles and an increase in the number of postmarketing manufacturing supplements submitted.

- A lack of process understanding on the part of the applicant and the submission of insufficient product knowledge information in NDAs, which could lead to tight product specifications at the time of approval.

- Due to heavy FDA workload and lack of resources, there is insufficient scientific dialogue between CMC reviewers and applicants during drug development and prior to the submission of NDAs.

- The reliance on a single chemistry reviewer to evaluate the entire CMC section of a drug application throughout the entire product life cycle does not facilitate the optimal use of ONDC's limited resources or available expertise.

- Valuable FDA resources are being used to generate comprehensive CMC summaries and analyze raw data in CMC submissions, which are tasks that could be done more efficiently by NDA applicants.

The new quality assessment system encompasses several initiatives, whose objectives are to allow the rapid integration of new technologies into pharmaceutical manufacturing and to expedite the review of NDAs and supplemental NDAs. The new system will focus on critical pharmaceutical quality attributes (chemistry, pharmaceutical formulation, manufacturing process, product performance), and will rely "more on the information provided by the applicant (e.g., the comprehensive quality overall summary (QOS) and the pharmaceutical development report) and less on the voluminous raw data currently being submitted (e.g., the executed batch records, raw stability data, methods validation package)," the FDA states.

NDAs, Risk-based Assessment, and the First-Cycle Review

In many cases, the agency says that NDAs provide "insufficient pharmaceutical development information," including that needed to support process validation during pre-approval inspections (held at the facility and never shared with the agency). The agency adds that submissions often describe few design considerations that clearly identify critical variables and their relationship to clinical performance.

–continued–

–continued–

Because this lack of detail often leaves agency reviewers uncertain about whether a change in a critical process parameter or end-product specification will adversely affect product performance, the FDA has often had to adopt a "conservative regulatory approach...that often results in specification and controls being based very narrowly on clinical trial lots" and the approval of tests or restrictive acceptance criteria that may not be directly relevant to product performance.

The new assessment system will focus on "critical pharmaceutical quality attributes and their relevance to safety and efficacy," the agency notes. Assessments will be risk-based, depending on the degree of understanding of the product and process demonstrated by the applicant, and will be question-based and peer-reviewed. The risk-based management approach will require that ONDC meet with industry more frequently on CMC-only issues during product development, and this should improve the probability that all CMC issues are addressed during the first-cycle NDA review and possibly lessen the need for postapproval supplements.

Implications for the NDA

The FDA's new risk-based assessment model could have several implications for NDA submissions. First, the agency wants to shift the burden of generating comprehensive CMC summaries and analyzing raw data in CMC submissions from CDER chemists to applicants, who can do it "more efficiently," the agency claims. The drug center is now considering different strategies to use comprehensive QOSs in pharmaceutical quality assessments, since a comprehensive QOS can facilitate the development of a "Big Picture" assessment protocol by the pharmaceutical assessment lead (PAL), a high-level chemistry reviewer who will examine each NDA before forwarding the application to a review chemist. If properly documented, the QOS can "serve as a comprehensive summary of the NDA, thus eliminating the need to use ONDC's valuable resources to generate a summary as part of the NDA review," says the agency. It can also facilitate the establishment of a database to track CMC reviews and identify critical CMC issues and review outcomes.

The FDA says the new system will rely "more on the information provided by the applicant (e.g., the comprehensive quality overall summary (QOS) and the pharmaceutical development report), and less on the voluminous raw data currently being submitted (e.g., the executed batch records, raw stability data, methods validation package)." While the agency wants to continue to receive the raw data, it wants to have NDA applicants develop comprehensive CMC summaries, which are often developed by FDA reviewers currently. Although the FDA is receiving such information in the QOSs within CTD-formatted applications, it is likely to seek such summaries from all NDA applicants, which will be helpful to PALs conducting the initial assessment of CMC sections of NDAs under the FDA's new quality assessment system.

FDA documents released in September 2004 provide other hints as to changing FDA expectations. "We also recommend that pharmaceutical manufacturers always provide evidence that they have conducted appropriate risk analyses of the entire manufacturing process and that they have developed control strategies to mitigate the risk of producing a poor-quality product," the agency notes in ONDC's *New Risk-Based Pharmaceutical Quality Assessment System*. "CMC specifications for a new drug product should be set as a result of a risk-based assessment, clinical relevance, process knowledge, and better use of modern statistical tools," the agency adds.

A *Description of the Drug Substance.* According to slight revisions made to FDA regulations relevant to the NDA's chemistry section under an April 2004 final rule, the applicant should provide the following in this subsection:

"A full description of the drug substance including its physical and chemical characteristics and stability; the name and address of its manufacturer; the method of synthesis (or isolation) and purification of the drug substance; the process controls used during manufacture and packaging; and the specifications necessary to ensure the identity, strength, quality, and purity of the drug substance and the bioavailability of the drug products made from the substance, including, for example, tests, analytical procedures, and acceptance criteria relating to stability, sterility, particle size, and crystalline form. The application may provide additionally for the use of alternatives to meet any of these requirements, including alternative sources, process controls, and analytical procedures."

The FDA will use an upcoming final guidance entitled, *Drug Substance: Chemistry, Manufacturing, and Controls Information* to establish how NDA applicants can provide CMC information for the drug substance in the CTD format and meet the agency's expectations under the emerging risk-based CMC assessment model. The agency released a draft version of the guidance in January 2004. When finalized, the guidance will replace the 1987 guidance entitled, *Submitting Supporting Documentation in Drug Applications for the Manufacture of Drug Substances.*

In an NDA, the sponsor's description of the drug substance should include the following:

The Substance's Stability and Physical and Chemical Characteristics. Provide the substance's chemical name and related names (if available and appropriate), structural formula, physicochemical characteristics, the physical and chemical data necessary to elucidate and confirm the substance's chemical structure, and a description of the studies (including results) on the substance's stability. Regarding drug substance stability requirements for NDAs, applicants should refer to the ICH's December 2003 guideline entitled, *Q1A(R2) Stability Testing of New Drug Substances and Products* and, if applicable, to four annexes to this guideline, *Q1F Stability Data Package for Registration Applications in Climatic Zones III and IV, Q1B Guideline for the Photostability Testing of New Drug Substances and Products* (November 1996), *Q1C Stability Testing for New Dosage Forms* (May 1997), *and Q1E Evaluation of Stability Data* (June 2004). In January 2003, the ICH released a guidance entitled, *Q1D Bracketing and Matrixing Designs for Stability Testing in New Drug Substances and Products.* Applicants should also refer to the FDA's draft guidance entitled, *Stability Testing of Drug Substances and Drug Products* (June 1998), which is consistent with the ICH's Q1A guidance and which will, when published as a final guidance, supersede the FDA's *Guideline for Submitting Documentation for the Stability of Human Drugs and Biologics* (1987).

The Name and Address of the Manufacturer. Provide the name and address of each facility (i.e., besides those of the applicant) that participates in manufacturing the drug substance (e.g., performs the synthesis, isolation, purification, testing, packaging, or labeling), and describe the operation(s) that each facility performs.

Method(s) of Manufacture and Packaging. Provide a full description of the materials and method(s) used in the synthesis, isolation, and purification of the drug substance, including a list of starting materials, reagents, solvents, and auxiliary materials. Also, describe the process controls used at various stages of the manufacturing, processing, and packaging of the drug substance, and provide information on the characteristics of, and the test methods used for, the container-closure system. In addition, the original application should provide a full description of the preparation of any reference standard substance used, including a description of the purification steps. To recognize the role of emerging process validation technologies, CDER issued a March 2004 internal compliance policy document entitled, *Process Validation Requirements in Drug Products and Active Pharmaceutical Ingredients Subject to Pre-Market Approval* (formerly titled *Process Validation Requirements for Drug Products Subject to Pre-Market Approval*).

169

Specifications for the Drug Substance. Provide a full description of the acceptance specifications used to assure the identity, strength, quality, and purity of the drug substance and the bioavailability of drug products made from the drug substance, including tests, analytical procedures, and acceptance criteria relating to stability, sterility, particle size, and crystalline form. For additional guidance, applicants can refer to the following ICH final guidelines: Q3A *Impurities in New Drug Substances* (a draft revised guidance, Q3A(R), was issued in July 2000); Q2A *Text on Validation of Analytical Procedures: Definitions and Terminology* (1995); Q2B *Validation of Analytical Procedures: Methodology* (1997); and Q3C *Impurities: Residual Solvents* (1997). In January 2001, the ICH parties also released a final guidance entitled, Q6A *Specifications: Test Procedures and Acceptance Criteria for New Drug Substances and New Drug Products: Chemical Substances*, which provides recommendations on the selection and justification of acceptance criteria for new drug substances and the new drug products produced from these substances.

In December 1998, CDER issued a draft guidance for industry entitled, NDAs: *Impurities in Drug Substances*, in which the center recommends that applicants refer to the ICH's Q3A *Impurities in New Drug Substances* (1996) when seeking guidance on the identification, qualification, and reporting of impurities in drug substances that are not considered new drug substances. While CDER acknowledges that the Q3A document was developed to provide guidance on providing information on impurities in NDAs for new drug substances, the center emphasizes that applicants submitting NDAs for other products should refer to it as well. The applicants to which this recommendation applies would include firms submitting NDAs for new dosage forms for already approved drug products, for changes in drug substance synthesis or process, and for products containing two or more active moieties that are used individually in already approved drug products but that have not previously been approved or marketed together in a drug product. The FDA released a revised Q3A guidance in February 2003 entitled, Q3A *Impurities in New Drug Substances* to include new text on reporting, identification, and qualification thresholds, to provide a clear distinction in the listing of impurities and qualifications between ICH Q3A (listing impurities) and ICH Q6A (setting specifications), and to delete the exception to conventional rounding practices. In November 2003, the FDA released an ICH guidance entitled, Q3B(R) *Impurities in New Drug Products*, to provide modified and additional text on threshold limits, degradation products, and rounding.

As noted, the sponsor may provide for the use of alternatives in meeting any of the applicable requirements, including alternative sources, process controls, methods, and specifications. In some cases, reference to the current editions of the U.S. *Pharmacopeia* and the *National Formulary* may satisfy the content requirements outlined above.

Often, applicants utilize components (e.g., drug substances, nonstandard excipients, containers) manufactured by other firms. In such cases, the contract manufacturer may want to preserve the confidentiality of its manufacturing processes. Since an NDA must provide information on these processes, contract manufacturers will often submit this information directly to the FDA in a drug master file (DMF). This allows drug sponsors using the company's products to meet submission requirements by incorporating by reference information provided in the DMF. Because the drug sponsor never sees the information in the DMF, the confidentiality of the contract facility's manufacturing processes is maintained.

An incorporation by reference should be made in the section of the NDA in which the referenced information would normally appear. The reference must identify specifically where the agency can find the information in the DMF (or other referenced document), and must identify the file by name, reference number, volume, and page number (i.e., the FDA stores DMFs and reviews the information in the file only when referenced in a pending drug application). When the applicant cross-references a DMF submitted by another firm (e.g., a bulk drug man-ufacturer), the NDA must include a letter of authorization from the DMF's owner in addition to the information specified above. For more information on DMFs, sponsors should refer to CDER's *Guideline for Drug Master Files* (September 1989) or the FDA's website (www.fda.gov), which now has a DMF-specific information page.

In a January 2000 final rule, CDER eliminated Type I DMFs, which traditionally had been used to incorporate by reference information on manufacturing sites, facilities, operating procedures, and personnel in INDs, NDAs, and other applications. Under the final rule, which took effect in July 2000, information formerly pro-vided in Type I DMFs are to be provided in Type II, Type III, and Type V DMFs. CDER first proposed eliminat-ing Type I DMFs in July 1995 in response to the recommendations of an internal task force, which concluded that information in Type I DMFs was often outdated, that such DMFs were not always easily accessible to FDA investigators, and that facility-related information in Type I DMFs was typically available to agency investiga-tors at manufacturing facilities.

A *Description of the Drug Product.* Requirements for this subsection of the NDA were also revised slightly under an April 2004 final regulation. Under the revision, this subsection should provide the following:

> "A list of all components used in the manufacture of the drug product (regardless of whether they appear in the drug product) and a statement of the composition of the drug product; the specifica-tions for each component; the name and address of each manufacturer of the drug product; a description of the manufacturing and packaging procedures and in-process controls for the drug product; the specifications necessary to ensure the identity, strength, quality, purity, potency, and bioavailability of the drug product, including, for example, tests, analytical procedures, and accep-tance criteria relating to sterility, dissolution rate, and container closure systems; and stability data with proposed expiration dating. The application may provide additionally for the use of alterna-tives to meet any of these requirements, including alternative components, manufacturing and packaging procedures, in-process controls, and analytical procedures."

The FDA will use an upcoming final guidance entitled, *Drug Products: Chemistry, Manufacturing, and Controls Information* to establish how NDA applicants can provide CMC information for the drug product in the CTD for-mat and meet the agency's expectations under the emerging risk-based CMC assessment model. The agency released a draft version of the guidance in January 2003. When finalized, the guidance will replace the February 1987 guidance entitled, *Submitting Documentation for the Manufacture and Controls for Drug Products.*

In many ways similar to the drug substance section, this element of the NDA should include the following:

A List of Components. Provide a list of all components used in the manufacture of the drug product (regard-less of whether they appear in the final product).

A Statement of Drug Product Composition. Provide a statement of the product's quantitative composition, indicating the weight or measure for each substance used in the manufacture of the dosage form. Also, pro-vide the batch formula to be used in the product's manufacture.

Specifications and Analytical Methods for Inactive Components. Provide a full description of the acceptance specifications and test methods used to assure the identity, quality, and purity of each inactive ingredient.

Name and Address of Manufacturer(s). Provide the name and address of each facility involved in manufac-turing the drug product (e.g., the drug processing, packaging, labeling, or control applications), and describe the operations that each will perform.

Method(s) of Manufacture and Packaging and In-Process Controls. Provide a copy of the master/batch production and control records or a comparably detailed description of the production process (a schematic diagram of the production process is often helpful). Also, provide complete information on the characteristics of, and test methods used for, the container-closure system or other component parts of the drug product package to assure their suitability for packaging the drug product. To provide recommendations on meeting NDA submission requirements for information on drug product packaging materials, CDER released a final *Guidance for Industry: Container Closure Systems Used for the Packaging of Human Drugs and Biologics: Chemistry, Manufacturing, and Controls Documentation* (May 1999), and a May 2002 question-and-answer guidance entitled, *Container Closure Systems for Packaging Human Drugs and Biologics.* For further guidance on specific issues relevant to this subsection, applicants can refer to the ICH guideline entitled, *Q3C Impurities: Residual Solvents* (December 1997), as well as CDER's *Guidance for Industry for the Submission of Documentation for Sterilization Process Validation in Applications for Human and Veterinary Drug Products* (November 1994). To recognize the role of emerging process validation technologies, CDER issued a March 2004 internal compliance policy document entitled, *Process Validation Requirements in Drug Products and Active Pharmaceutical Ingredients Subject to Pre-Market Approval* (formerly titled *Process Validation Requirements for Drug Products Subject to Pre-Market Approval*).

Specifications for the Drug Product. Provide a full description of the specifications necessary to assure the product's identity, strength, quality, purity, potency, and bioavailability throughout its shelf life. The methods and standards of acceptance should be sufficiently detailed to permit FDA laboratories to duplicate them. Typically, applicants include data on the validation of the analytical methods in this section as well. For recommendations on impurities-related submission requirements, applicants can refer to the final ICH guidances entitled, *Q3B(R) Impurities in New Drug Products* (November 2003) and *Q3C Impurities: Residual Solvents* (December 1997). In January 2001, the ICH parties also released a final guidance entitled, *Q6A Specifications: Test Procedures and Acceptance Criteria for New Drug Substances and New Drug Products: Chemical Substances*, which provides recommendations on the selection and justification of acceptance criteria for new drug substances and new drug products produced from these substances.

Stability and Proposed Expiration Dating. Provide a complete description of, and data derived from, studies of product stability, including information establishing the suitability of the analytical method(s) used, and proposed expiration dating.

In this section as well, the sponsor may provide alternatives for meeting relevant requirements, including alternative components, manufacturing and packaging procedures, in-process controls, methods, and specifications. Reference to the current editions of the U.S. *Pharmacopeia* and the *National Formulary* may satisfy relevant requirements. Regarding drug product stability requirements for NDAs, applicants can refer to the ICH's revised 2003 guideline entitled, *Q1A(R2) Stability Testing of New Drug Substances and Products* and, if applicable, to four annexes to this guideline: *Q1B Guideline for the Photostability Testing of New Drug Substances and Products* (November 1996); *Q1C Stability Testing for New Dosage Forms* (May 1997); *Q1E Evaluation of Stability Data* (June 2004); and *Q1F Stability Data Package for Registration Applications in Climatic Zones III and IV* (December 2003). In January 2003, the ICH released a draft guidance entitled, *Q1D Bracketing and Matrixing Designs for Stability Testing of New Drug Substances and Products.* Applicants should also refer to the FDA's draft guidance entitled, *Stability Testing of Drug Substances and Drug Products* (June 1998), which is consistent with the ICH's Q1A guidance and which will, when published as a final guidance, supersede the FDA's *Guideline for Submitting Documentation for the Stability of Human Drugs and Biologics* (1987).

A 1993 final regulation modified content requirements for this portion of the chemistry, manufacturing, and controls section. The regulation mandated that applicants provide certain information about the batches o the drug product used to conduct the "pivotal" bioavailability and bioequivalence studies and the "primary" stability studies: (1) the batch production record; (2) the specifications and test procedures for each component and for the drug product itself; (3) the names and addresses of the sources of the active and noncompendial inactive components and of the container and closure system for the drug product; (4) the name and address of each contract facility involved in the manufacture, processing, packaging, or testing of the drug product, and identification of the operation performed by each contract facility; and (5) the results of tests performed on the drug product and on the components used in the product's manufacture. In addition, the 1993 regulation required that this section provide the "proposed or actual master production record, including a description of the equipment, to be used for the manufacture of a commercial lot of the drug product or a comparably detailed description of the production process for a representative batch of the drug product."

Although they increasingly will push for pharmaceutical development information going forward (see exhibit above), CDER chemists have often found it helpful when applicants submitted developmental pharmaceutics information beyond that called for in current FDA regulations and guidelines. Reviewers claim that the information can give CDER chemists a greater "comfort level" with the application because it describes the product's formulation development history and the company's rationale on formulation-related issues (e.g., methods, ranges, inactive ingredients). FDA officials strongly recommend, however, that sponsors ask CDER chemists about the utility of such information on a case-by-case basis, and about where the information should be located in the NDA if it is to be provided. It is interesting to note, however, that developmental pharmaceutics information is called for in the harmonized CTD format (see discussion above).

Environmental Impact Analysis Report. Like all applications and petitions requesting formal FDA action, an NDA must include either an environmental assessment (EA) or a claim for a categorical exclusion from the EA submission requirement. Fulfilling a promise made under a 1995 Clinton Administration regulatory reform initiative, the agency released a July 1997 final regulation to establish that EAs would be required only under "extraordinary circumstances" (e.g., when available data indicate that the expected level of exposure could seriously harm the environment).

Through this change, the FDA grants categorical exclusions, or exemptions, from EA requirements to all but a "fairly narrow category" of drugs and biologics. According to the July 1997 final regulation, an NDA will not "ordinarily" require the preparation of an EA in the following circumstances: (1) the application's approval will not increase the use of the active moiety; (2) the NDA's approval will increase the use of the active moiety, but the estimated concentration of the substance at the point of entry into the aquatic environment will be below 1 part per billion; or (3) the NDA is for a substance that occurs naturally in the environment and the application's approval does not alter significantly the concentration or distribution of the substance, its metabolites, or degradation products in the environment. A claim for categorical exclusion must include a statement of compliance with the categorical exclusion criteria, and must state that, to the applicant's knowledge, no "extraordinary circumstances" exist.

To provide further recommendations regarding the changes brought by the July 1997 regulation, CDER released a formal guidance entitled, *Environmental Assessment of Human Drug and Biologics Applications* (July 1998). In a March 2003 manual of policy and procedure (MaPP) entitled, *Environmental Assessments* (MaPP 5015.7), the agency noted that examples of extraordinary circumstances include:

- The drug substance intermediate or drug substance is derived from plants or animals taken from the wild.

- Available data establish that, at the expected level of exposure, there is the potential for serious harm to the environment.

- There is potential for action that adversely affects: (1) a species or the critical habitat of species determined under the Endangered Species Act or the Convention on International Trade in Endangered Species of Wild Fauna and Flora to be endangered or threatened; or (2) wild fauna or flora entitled to special protection under some other Federal law.

Field Copy Certification. U.S.-based applicants must include in this section a statement "certifying that the field copy of the application has been provided to the applicant's home district office." Since foreign applicants must provide the field copy with the archival and review copies, no such certification is needed in their applications. As noted, applicants that provide the chemistry, manufacturing and controls section in electronic form need no longer provide a field copy to the district office. Instead, CDER has asked companies making such electronic submissions to submit a letter to their home district offices certifying that the electronic chemistry, manufacturing and controls section has been forwarded to CDER.

Given the nature and detail of the chemistry, manufacturing, and control section, the FDA has, for many years allowed sponsors to submit the completed section 90 to 120 days before the anticipated filing of the entire NDA. In some cases, the agency claims, this may speed the NDA review process. FDA regulations note that the agency will review such "early submissions as resources permit." [*Editor's note*: Such pre-submissions are not part of the FDA's new Pilot 1-reviewable unit pilot program under PDUFA III (see discussion below)].

For such early submissions, both the archival and review copies of the section are required, while the field copy may be forwarded when the full NDA is submitted. The early submission should provide a cover letter the application form, an index to facilitate the location of the information within the section, and the identification of a sponsor contact person with whom the FDA may discuss the data. If any information required for the section is unavailable at the time of the advance submission, this should be noted in the cover letter.

B. *Samples*. Drug samples should not accompany the NDA submission, but should be submitted only in response to an FDA request. The FDA may request these samples to validate the adequacy of the analytical methods that the sponsor uses to identify the drug product and drug substance. Typically, the FDA requests that applicants submit samples directly to "two or more" agency laboratories that will perform the validation work.

Upon such a request, the applicant must submit "four representative samples of the following, with each sample in sufficient quantity to permit FDA to perform three times each test described in the application to determine whether the drug substance and the drug product meet the specifications given in the application:" the drug product proposed for marketing; the drug substance used in the drug product from which the samples of the drug product were taken; and reference standards and blanks (except that reference standards recognized in an official compendium need not be submitted).

Upon an FDA request, sponsors must also provide samples of the product's "finished market package." The FDA may ask for two copies of the package, although one generally suffices.

For FDA recommendations regarding samples, applicants should refer to an agency guidance entitled *Submitting Samples and Analytical Data for Methods Validation.* When issued as a final guidance, an August 2000 FDA draft guidance entitled, *Analytical Procedures and Methods Validation Chemistry, Manufacturing, and Control Documentation* will supersede that guidance.

C. *Methods Validation Package.* The archival copy of the NDA must include a methods validation package, which provides information that allows FDA laboratories to validate all of the analytical methods for both the drug substance and drug product. It should provide a listing of all samples to be submitted, including lot number, identity, package type and size, and quantity. In addition, the package usually includes descriptive information copied from pertinent sections of the NDA. FDA regulations state that "related descriptive information includes a description of each sample; the proposed regulatory specifications for the drug; a detailed description of the methods of analysis; supporting data for accuracy, specificity, precision and ruggedness; and complete results of the applicant's tests on each sample." To aid the reviewing chemist, these copies should retain the original pagination of the NDA sections from which they were copied.

The FDA provides specific advice on the development of this section in its *Guideline for Submitting Samples and Analytical Data for Methods Validation* (February 1987). In March 1995, the ICH published a final guideline entitled, Q2A *Text on Validation of Analytical Procedures*, which discusses "the characteristics that should be considered during the validation of the analytical procedures included as part of registration applications." More recently, the ICH parties published a final guideline entitled, Q2B *Validation of Analytical Procedures: Methodology* (May 1997), which provides recommendations on how manufacturers should consider the various validation characteristics for each analytical procedure, as well as guidance on the data that should be presented in a marketing application.

Four copies of the methods validation package should be included with the initial submission. Although FDA regulations state that three of the copies should be submitted in the archival copy, agency guidelines recommend submitting one copy with the archival copy and three additional copies with the chemistry, manufacturing, and controls section of the review copy. If the applicant does the latter, the submission should include a statement indicating that this option was selected.

Nonclinical Pharmacology and Toxicology Section Federal regulations state that this section should "describe, with the aid of graphs and tables, animal and in vitro studies with [the] drug." The section should provide all nonclinical animal and laboratory studies involving the drug, including data from preclinical studies originally submitted in the IND; data compiled and submitted during clinical investigations (e.g., long-term testing such as carcinogenicity and reproductive testing); and, in some cases, nonclinical studies not submitted previously.

The FDA reviews these studies to evaluate their adequacy and comprehensiveness, and to ensure that there are no inconsistent or inadequately characterized toxic effects. According to federal regulations, the principal content requirements for this section are:

1. Studies of the pharmacological actions of the drug in relation to its proposed therapeutic indication, and studies that otherwise define the pharmacologic properties of the drug or that are pertinent to possible adverse side effects.

2. Studies of the toxicological effects of the drug as they relate to the drug's intended clinical use(s), including, as appropriate, studies assessing the drug's acute, subacute, and chronic toxicity, carcinogenicity, and studies of toxicities related to the drug's particular mode of administration or conditions of use.

3. Studies, as appropriate, of the drug's effects on reproduction and on the developing fetus.

4. Any studies of the absorption, distribution, metabolism, and excretion of the drug in animals.

5. For each nonclinical laboratory study, a statement that it was conducted in compliance with good laboratory practice (GLP) regulations, or if the study was not conducted in compliance with those regulations, a brief statement of the reason for the noncompliance.

The FDA is sensitive to organizational problems regarding the presentation of toxicological, pharmacological and other data from nonclinical studies. Therefore, drug sponsors should refer to specific recommendations in the FDA's *Guideline for the Format and Content of the Nonclinical Pharmacology/Toxicology Section of an Application* (February 1987). Although it concedes that nonclinical data are collected over several years and are submitted in varying formats, the guideline recommends that the data be reorganized for the NDA submission. NDA applicants should also refer to a May 2001 FDA guidance entitled *Bioanalytical Method Validation*, which provides recommendations on developing validation information on bioanalytical methods for nonclinical pharmacology/toxicology studies as well as clinical studies.

As part of its continuing effort to standardize the NDA review process, CDER released a May 2001 reviewer guidance entitled, *Pharmacology/Toxicology Review Format*. By providing NDA applicants with what the FDA calls an "understanding of the standard format and content of primary pharmacology/toxicology [NDA] reviews," the guidance can provide some insights into this section of the application and how it will be evaluated and used. CDER is implementing such a standardized format for pharmacology/toxicology and other discipline reviews (e.g., clinical, clinical pharmacology) for several reasons, including that standardization provides for unified communication among multiple audiences and that it ensures that the most important information is captured in all IND and NDA reviews.

In 2003, CDER sought volunteer companies to participate in a pilot project under which firms provide sample animal toxicity datasets using a new electronic format called the Standard for Exchange of Nonclinical Data (SEND) format. The ongoing pilot provides industry with an opportunity to familiarize itself with the electronic dataset submission process at an early stage of product development. Under the pilot project, the agency accepts the submission of sample datasets from single- and repeat-dose toxicity studies, carcinogenicity studies, and reproductive toxicity studies. The agency will use experience from this pilot to test the SEND model and associated software tools that are being developed for the receipt, storage, viewing, and analysis of animal toxicity data. Once the agency completes the pilot phase, which is expected to last until year-end 2004, it plans to publish specific requirements for the submission of animal toxicity data in a SEND Implementation Guide.

Human Pharmacokinetics and Bioavailability Section The NDA must include a section providing data and analyses from all human pharmacokinetic and bioavailability studies (or information supporting a waiver of *in vivo* bioavailability data). The section should include data from and descriptions of any of the five general types of biopharmaceutic studies that were relevant for the investigational drug:

1. Pilot and background studies, which are conducted to provide a preliminary assessment of absorption, distribution, metabolism and/or elimination (ADME) of a drug as a guide in the design of early clinical trials and definitive kinetic studies.

2. Bioavailability/bioequivalence studies, including bioavailability, bioequivalence, and dosage form proportionality studies (this discussion should include a description of the analytical and statistical methods used in each study).

3. Pharmacokinetic studies, descriptions of which must include a discussion of the analytical and statistical methods used in each study.

4. Other *in vivo* studies using pharmacological or clinical endpoints.

5. *In vitro* studies designed to define the release rate of a drug substance from the dosage form (obviously, such dissolution tests are not relevant for drug forms such as injectables and some others).

According to FDA regulations, this section should comprise as many as three elements:

- "A description of each of the bioavailability and pharmacokinetic studies of the drug in humans performed by or on behalf of the applicant that includes a description of the analytical and statistical methods used in each study and a statement [that it was conducted according to relevant federal regulations]."

- "If the application describes in the chemistry, manufacturing, and controls section specifications or analytical methods needed to assure the bioavailability of the drug product or drug substance, or both, a statement in this section of the rationale for establishing the specification or analytical methods, including data and information supporting this rationale."

- "A summarizing discussion and analysis of the pharmacokinetics and metabolism of the active ingredients and the bioavailability or bioequivalence, or both, of the drug product."

The FDA provides its most detailed recommendations on the development and presentation of this section in its *Guideline for the Format and Content of the Human Pharmacokinetics and Bioavailability Section of an Application* (February 1987). In November 1994, the ICH published a final guideline entitled, *E4 Dose-Response Information to Support Drug Registration*, which describes the importance of dose-response information and the types of studies that sponsors can use to obtain such information (i.e., parallel-dose response, cross-over dose response, forced titration, and optional titration). Subsequently, the FDA released a May 2003 guidance entitled, *Exposure-Response Relationships-Study Design, Data Analysis, and Regulatory Applications*, which it said could be used along with the E4 guidance and other documents. In earlier years, the FDA published *Guidance for Industry-Drug Metabolism/Drug Interaction Studies in the Drug Development Process: Studies In Vitro* (April 1997), which provides recommendations on current approaches to *in vitro* studies of drug metabolism and interactions, and a variety of other final guidances, including *Population Pharmacokinetics* (February 1999) and *Pharmacokinetics in Patients with Impaired Renal Function* (May 1998). In the late 1990s, the center had released a spate of draft guidances relevant to this section of the NDA, including *In Vivo Drug Metabolism/Drug Interaction Studies-Study Design, Data Analysis, and Recommendations for Dosing and Labeling* (November 1998), *General Considerations for Pediatric Pharmacokinetic Studies for Drugs and Biological Products* (November 1998), *Draft Guidance on Food-Effect Bioavailability and Bioequivalence Studies* (October 1997), *Bioanalytical Methods Validation for Human Studies* (December 1998), *Bioavailability and Bioequivalence Studies for Nasal Aerosols and Nasal Sprays for Local Action* (June 1999), *Topical Dermatological Drug Product NDAs and ANDAs-In Vivo Bioavailability* (June 1998), and *Waiver of In Vivo Bioavailability and Bioequivalence Studies for Immediate Release Solid Oral Dosage Forms Containing Certain Active Moieties/Active Ingredients Based on a Biopharmaceutics Classification System* (January 1999). More recent guidance in this area includes *Bioavailability and Bioequivalence Studies for Orally Administered Drug Products-General Considerations* (March 2003), in which the agency revised its recommendations regarding study design and dissolution methods development, comparisons of BA measures, the definition of proportionality, and waivers for bioequivalence studies. Others include *Bioanalytical Method Validation* (May 2001), which provides recommendations on developing validation information on bioanalytical methods for pharmacokinetic evaluation of human clinical pharmacology, bioavailability, and bioequivalence studies, a February 2001 draft guidance entitled, *Statistical Approaches to Establishing Bioequivalence*, which discusses the use of average, population, and individual bioequivalence approaches and which replaces several earlier guidance documents in this area, and *Food-Effect Bioavailability and Fed Bioequivalence Studies: Study Design, Data Analysis, and Labeling* (December 2001).

Although designed for CDER drug reviewers, an April 2004 MaPP (4004.4) entitled, "Clinical Pharmacology and Biopharmaceutics Review Template" can provide some additional insights to NDA sponsors. Part of CDER's larger Good Review Practices (GRP) initiative, the reviewer template specifies how agency reviewers will document their evaluations of the NDA's clinical pharmacology and biopharmaceutics section.

Microbiology Section This section is required only in NDAs for anti-infective/antibiotic, antiviral, special pathogen, sterile and certain nonsterile drug products. Since anti-infective, antiviral, and special pathogen drugs affect microbial—rather than clinical—physiology, reports regarding the drug's *in vivo* and *in vitro* effects on the target microorganisms are critical for establishing product effectiveness.

For sterile and certain nonsterile drugs (e.g., aqueous dosage forms that can support microbiological growth), applicants must also provide information that permits CDER microbiologists to conduct a product quality assessment. However, such information should be provided in the chemistry, manufacturing and controls section of the NDA.

Current regulations require that an NDA's microbiology drug section include microbiology data describing: (1) the biochemical basis of the drug's action on microbial physiology; (2) the drug's antimicrobial spectra, including results of *in vitro* preclinical studies demonstrating concentrations of the drug required for effective use; (3) any known mechanisms of resistance to the drug, including results of any known epidemiologic studies demonstrating prevalence of resistance factors; and (4) clinical microbiology laboratory methods needed to evaluate the effective use of the drug. Full reports of the studies, summary tables, and a summary narrative should be included for each portion of this section.

Specific guidance on developing the microbiology component of the NDA is available in the FDA's *Guideline for the Format and Content of the Microbiology Section of an Application* (February 1987). While they are not directly applicable to the NDA's microbiology section, it is worth noting here that CDER released a spate of guidances as part of a series of documents to assist industry in conducting clinical trials on antimicrobial drugs for various infections. In 1998 alone, for example, the center released 20 such draft guidances for specific categories of antimicrobial drugs, including those for acute bacterial meningitis and sinusitis, acute otitis media, bacterial vaginosis, community-acquired pneumonia, Lyme disease, nosocomial pneumonia, uncomplicated gonorrhea, and uncomplicated urinary tract infections.

Clinical Data Section Since the FDA's conclusions regarding a new drug's safety and effectiveness are based largely on the data and analyses provided in the clinical data section, it is clearly the single most important element of the NDA. When taken together with the NDA's statistical component (see discussion below), the clinical section is also the application's most complex and voluminous.

Over the last several years, CDER's requirements for the NDA's clinical data section have been revised and clarified by several agency and ICH initiatives:

- Unwavering CDER interest in standardizing the NDA review process continues to have implications for several sections of the NDA, including the clinical data section. In late 1999, then-CDER Director Janet Woodcock, M.D., emphasized her desire to further standardize the review process, in part through the development and use of review "templates," which might ultimately reshape the presentation of clinical data. Woodcock also mentioned at the time that she had a plan for completing CDER's Good Review Practices (GRP) initiative, which passed a significant milestone in July 2003 when the agency released a draft of its long-awaited Good Review Management Principles (see Chapter 8) to identify best review practices in first-cycle NDA reviews. After implementing a standardized NDA review template for clinical reviewers on a pilot basis in 2001, CDER formally released its *Clinical Review Template* in the form of MaPP 6010.3 in July 2004 to provide "a structured outline" for the clinical review and to "promote consistency in the documentation of [review] elements and provide for the ready retrieval of information." A few months earlier, CDER had released a template for another aspect of the clinical review process—*Clinical Pharmacology and Biopharmaceutics Review Template* (April 2004).

- In July 2004, the FDA announced that it had adopted the Clinical Data Interchange Consortium's Study Data Tabulation Model (SDTM), which clinical trial sponsors can use to submit clinical data to the agency. Noting that the SDTM will lead to greater efficiencies in clinical research and NDA reviews, the agency was exploring "regulatory approaches" to require the SDTM standard for regulatory submissions. "The importance of a standard for the exchange of clinical trial data cannot be overstated," Acting FDA Commissioner Lester Crawford, Ph.D., stated at the time. "FDA reviewers spend far too much valuable time simply reorganizing large amounts of data submitted in varying formats. Having the data presented in a standard structure will improve FDA's ability to evaluate the data and help speed new discoveries to the public." In addition, the agency noted, the standard will help to "automate the largely paper-based clinical trials research process." The SDTM standard has been added to other specifications listed under the agency's draft guidance entitled, *Providing Regulatory Submissions in Electronic Format-Human Pharmaceutical Applications and Related Submissions.*

- In an August 1999 guidance entitled, *Submission of Abbreviated Reports and Synopses in Support of Marketing Applications*, CDER clarified that NDA sponsors may submit specific trial information in different "formats"—full study reports, abbreviated reports, and synopses—depending on the information's importance. According to the agency, the guidance was intended to address industry uncertainty that has prevented many companies from submitting "less-than-full" studies, an option that FDA officials claim has been available to firms under the agency's *Guideline for the Format and Content of the Clinical and Statistical Sections of New Drug Applications* (1988) and the ICH's E3 *Guideline for the Structure and Content of Clinical Study Reports* (1996). The August 1999 guidance emphasizes that abbreviated study reports and synopses are more applicable to the submission of efficacy data, and that full reports on safety will be required in most cases.

- In releasing two guidances under its so-called New Use Initiative—Primary and Supplemental Approvals, the FDA provided perhaps its most detailed discussion of the clinical efficacy data necessary to support drug approval (see Chapter 5). A May 1998 guidance entitled, *Providing Clinical Evidence of Effectiveness for Human Drug and Biological Products* offers the agency's latest and most detailed views regarding the "quantitative and qualitative standards" for establishing drug effectiveness, including situations in which a single pivotal trial can support drug approval." In an October 2001 guidance entitled, *Cancer Drug and Biological Products-Clinical Data in Marketing Applications*, CDER clarifies the clinical data necessary for oncology drugs, and notes that those requirements may be less demanding than those for less-serious diseases.

- Digital Electrocardiographic (ECG) Data Submissions. To improve the evaluation of specific drug-induced cardiac toxicity, CDER has expressed its interest in reviewing electronic submissions of ECG waveform data that are obtained during the course of "definitive" studies of drug effects on ventricular repolarization and that are annotated for interval measurements. After reviewing public comments regarding an April 2003 proposed model electronic format for the transport of digital ECG waveform data developed by the nonprofit group Health Level Seven, Inc. (HL7), the agency will release a draft guidance to recommend an electronic format for these data. In the meantime, CDER officials note that applicants have made regulatory filings with electronic ECG waveform data files, and that CDER reviewers have reviewed the files using a "freeware viewer" developed by a firm that has placed the viewer in the public domain (CDER provides a link to the viewer on its electronic submissions webpage). Ultimately, CDER wants to receive ECG waveform data in digital format from the full spectrum of ECG devices (i.e., standard 12-lead ECGs, Holter monitors, transtelephonic monitors, and implanted devices) along with annotations for events (e.g., standard ECG interval measurements, arrhythmic events).

Given the complexity and importance of the clinical and statistical sections, it is not surprising that the FDA's most detailed NDA-related guideline addresses these two sections of the NDA. The agency's 125-page *Guideline for the Format and Content of the Clinical and Statistical Sections of an Application* (July 1988) provides recommendations on formatting and organizing these sections and on presenting the clinical and statistical information and accompanying documentation. The guideline also describes a fully integrated clinical and statistical report for documenting the results of individual studies. An ICH final guideline entitled, E3 *Structure and Content of Clinical Study Reports* (July 1996) supersedes Section III of the FDA guideline, and provides format and content standards for "an integrated full report of an individual study."

As specified in the FDA's 1988 guideline, the first two elements in the clinical data section are: (1) a list of investigators supplied with the drug or known to have studied the drug, INDs under which the drug has been studied, and NDAs submitted for the same drug substance; and (2) a background/overview of the clinical investigations (i.e., the general approach and rationale used in developing clinical data). According to FDA regulations and the guideline referenced above, the NDA's clinical data section should comprise as many as 11 additional elements:

1. A description and analysis of each clinical pharmacology study of the drug, including a brief comparison of the results of the human studies with the animal pharmacology and toxicology data.

2. A description and analysis of each controlled clinical study pertinent to a proposed use of the drug, including the protocol and a description of the statistical analyses used to evaluate the study. If the study report is an interim analysis, this must be noted and a projected completion date provided. Controlled clinical studies that have not been analyzed in detail should be provided, along with a copy of the protocol and a brief description of the results and status of the study.

3. A description of each uncontrolled study, a summary of the results, and a brief statement explaining why the study is classified as uncontrolled.

4. A description and analysis of any other data or information relevant to an evaluation of the safety and effectiveness of the drug product obtained or otherwise received by the applicant from any foreign or domestic source. This might include information derived from commer-

cial marketing experience, reports in scientific literature, unpublished scientific papers, and controlled and uncontrolled studies of uses of the drug other than those proposed in the application.

5. An integrated summary of the data demonstrating substantial evidence of effectiveness for the claimed indications. Evidence is also required to support the dosage and administration section of the labeling, including support for the dosage and dose interval recommended, and modifications for specific subgroups of patients (e.g., pediatrics, geriatrics, patients with renal failure).

6. An integrated summary of all available information about the safety of the drug product, including pertinent animal data, demonstrated or potential adverse effects of the drug, clinically significant drug/drug interactions, and other safety considerations, such as data from epidemiological studies of related drugs. Unless provided under section 2 above, the integrated safety summary should also describe any statistical analyses used in analyzing the safety data.

7. For drugs that might be abused, a description and analysis of studies or information related to abuse of the drug, including a proposal for scheduling and a description of any studies related to overdosage.

8. An integrated summary of the benefits and risks of the drug, including a discussion of why the benefits exceed the risks under the conditions stated in the labeling.

9. A statement noting that each human clinical study was conducted in compliance with the IRB regulations and with the informed consent regulations. If the study was not subject to IRB regulations, the applicant must state this fact.

10. If the sponsor transferred any of its regulatory obligations regarding the conduct of a clinical study (e.g., monitoring) to a contract research organization (CRO), a statement providing the name and address of the CRO, the identity of the clinical study, and a listing of the responsibilities transferred. When a sponsor transfers all of its obligations, the NDA may provide a "general statement of this transfer" in lieu of an itemized listing.

11. If the sponsor reviewed or audited original subject records during the course of monitoring any clinical study to verify the accuracy of the case report forms submitted by the investigator, the NDA must provide a list identifying each clinical study audited or reviewed.

Because it is designed, in part, to assist companies in assessing clinical data and preparing clinical summaries for marketing applications, the ICH's September 1998 E9 *Statistical Principles for Clinical Trials* should also be consulted by applicants. Applicants might also review the ICH's E8 *General Considerations for Clinical Trials* (December 1997).

During the early 1990s, the FDA became increasingly concerned with gender-, age-, and race-related drug response differences, particularly following a study showing that many NDAs lacked this information. Such information was already requested in the agency's 1988 *Guideline for the Format and Content of the Clinical and Statistical Sections of New Drug Applications.* In 1993, then-CDER Director Carl Peck, M.D., wrote to industry to emphasize the importance of this information and to announce that NDAs would no longer be accepted for review without it.

The pressure on sponsors to test their drugs in, and provide clinical data on, special populations increased considerably during the mid- and late-1990s. Following the release of an ICH guidance entitled, *Guideline on*

Studies in Support of Special Populations: Geriatrics (August 1994), the FDA released a 1998 final regulation to explicitly require gender, age, and racial subgroup data in NDAs. Under the regulation, an NDA's integrated summaries of safety and effectiveness must each include demographic subset analyses by gender, age, and racial subgroups and, when appropriate, other relevant subgroups.

Consistent with the FDA's growing concern about the relationship between exposure (dose) and response (pharmacologic effect) in population subsets and the need for data characterizing this relationship in NDAs and other applications, CDER released a May 2003 guidance entitled, *Exposure-Response Relationships-Study Design, Data Analysis, and Regulatory Applications* (see discussion above in Human Pharmacokinetics and Bioavailabilty section). In working to characterize such relationships in human studies and submitting the resultant data, the agency advised applicants to use this guidance along with several others, including the ICH's E4 *Dose Response Information to Support Drug Registration* and E5 *Ethnic Factors in the Acceptability of Foreign Clinical Data*. The E5 document provides guidance on regulatory and development strategies to allow clinical data collected in one region to be used to satisfy data requirements in other regions, while permitting sponsors and regulatory bodies to adequately assess the impact of ethnic factors on a drug's safety, efficacy dosage, and dose regimen.

Safety Update Report Section As implied by its title, the safety update report is not filed with the original NDA, but is submitted in the form of updates at specific points in the application review process. Applicants must submit safety update reports four months after the NDA's submission, following the receipt of an approvable letter, and at other times requested by CDER.

In these reports, the applicant must update its pending NDA "with new safety information learned about the drug that may reasonably affect the statement of contraindications, warnings, precautions, and adverse reactions in the draft labeling." The updates must include the same types of information (from clinical studies animal studies, and other sources), and must be submitted in the same format, as the NDA's integrated safety summary. They must also include case report forms for each patient who died during a clinical study or who did not complete the study because of an adverse event (unless this requirement is waived). Federal regulations encourage applicants to consult with the FDA on the form and content of these reports prior to the submission of the first report.

Statistical Section As evidenced by the fact that the FDA addressed the NDA's clinical and statistical sections in a single guideline, the two components are closely related. In reality, the core of the statistical section comprises data and analyses taken directly from the application's clinical data section.

According to the agency's *Guideline for the Format and Content of the Clinical and Statistical Sections of New Drug Applications* (July 1988), the core of the statistical section should include the following sections taken verbatim from the NDA's clinical section: (1) a list of investigators supplied with the drug or known to have investigated the drug, INDs under which the drug has been studied, and NDAs submitted for the same drug substance (2) a background/overview of clinical investigations; (3) the controlled clinical studies section; (4) the integrated summary of effectiveness data; (5) the integrated summary of safety data; and (6) the integrated summary of benefits and risks.

The ICH guidance entitled, E9 *Statistical Principles for Clinical Trials* (September 1998) is the latest guidance addressing issues related to the statistical component of marketing applications. The guideline provides recommendations to sponsors regarding the design, conduct, analysis, and evaluation of clinical trials of an investigational product in the context of its overall clinical development. More germane to this discussion the guidance also provides recommendations on preparing application summaries and assessing efficacy and safety evidence, principally from late Phase 2 and Phase 3 clinical trials. For additional guidance, applicants should also consult the ICH guideline entitled, E3 *Structure and Content of Clinical Study Reports* (July 1996).

The FDA encourages applicants to meet with CDER—specifically, with the assigned biostatistical reviewer(s) within CDER's Office of Biostatistics—before an NDA's submission to discuss the section's format, tabulations, statistical analyses, and other important issues. In some cases, the agency permits applicants to submit, for review and comment, the preliminary tabulation of patient data and the materials on the statistical analyses of controlled clinical studies and/or safety data (see discussion of pre-NDA meetings below).

Pediatric Use Section From late 2002 to late 2003, the need for a "pediatric use" section in an NDA was clouded by court rulings and legislative initiatives. In late 2003, Congress passed and President Bush signed a new law that put to rest a several-year legal battle that challenged the FDA's authority to require that industry conduct pediatric studies of new drugs and submit the results of such studies in NDAs. In an October 2002 ruling, a U.S. district court had struck down the FDA's 1998 "pediatric rule," questioning the FDA's statutory authority to require pediatric studies. Instead of pursuing a time-consuming appeal of the ruling, the FDA worked with Congress to craft legislation that would provide the agency with the necessary authority. During this period, the agency was barred from enforcing pediatric testing and submission requirements, although it did encourage industry to continue with its pediatric programs. In November 2003, Congress passed the Pediatric Research Equity Act (PREA), which gave the FDA clear authority to require pediatric studies of drugs when other approaches are not sufficient to ensure that drugs are safe and effective in children.

Although the pediatric regulations (the "pediatric rule"), which first required a pediatric use section in the NDA, were struck down by the 2002 court ruling, they remain in the agency's regulations, essentially because the agency was unable to remove the regulation given the speed of the court decision and PREA's passage. Until it can release a draft guidance on PREA, the FDA is referring companies to the PREA language for establishing pediatric study and submission requirements. Meanwhile, the agency is expected to propose minor changes to the current pediatric regulations to make them consistent with the provisions of PREA.

Under PREA, all applications for new active ingredients, new indications, new dosage forms, new dosing regimens, and new routes of administration must contain a pediatric assessment unless the sponsor has obtained a waiver or deferral of pediatric studies. This assessment, PREA states, must "contain data, gathered using appropriate formulations for each age group for which the assessment is required, that are adequate (i) to assess the safety and effectiveness of the drug or the biological product for the claimed indications in all relevant pediatric subpopulations; and (ii) to support dosing and administration for each pediatric subpopulation for which the drug or the biological product is safe and effective." Under the original pediatric rule, applicants included in their NDAs a "pediatric use section" to provide a summary of the required pediatric assessment reports (submitted in full with the NDA), in addition to information "describing the investigation of the drug for use in pediatric populations, including an integrated summary of the information (the clinical pharmacology studies, controlled clinical studies, or uncontrolled clinical studies, or other data or information) that is relevant to the safety and effectiveness and benefits and risks of the drug in pediatric populations for the claimed indications, [and] a reference to the full descriptions of such studies provided in the [NDA's Human Pharmacokinetic and Bioavailability Section and Clinical Data Section]."

On its own initiative or at an applicant's request, the FDA can defer the submission or all or some of the pediatric assessment until after a drug has been approved in adults. The agency might grant such a deferral, for example, if the drug is ready for approval in adults before studies in pediatric patients are complete, or if pedi-

atric studies should be delayed until additional safety or effectiveness data have been collected. If an applicant decides to seek a deferral of the pediatric assessment, it must provide a certification of the grounds for
delaying pediatric studies, a description of the planned or ongoing studies, and evidence that the studies are
being or will be conducted with due diligence and at the earliest possible time.

Further, an NDA applicant can request a waiver from the pediatric assessment requirement if it certifies that

- The drug does not represent a meaningful therapeutic benefit over existing treatments for
  pediatric patients and is not likely to be used in a substantial number of pediatric patients;

- Necessary studies are impossible or highly impractical (e.g., because the number of such
  patients is too small or the patients are geographically dispersed); or

- There is evidence strongly suggesting that the drug product would be ineffective or unsafe
  in all pediatric age groups.

On certain grounds, applicants can also seek partial waivers that apply to specific pediatric age groups.

Case Report Tabulations Section During the FDA's most recent overhaul of its NDA regulations, the agency
declared that "an efficient agency review of individual patient data should be based primarily on well-organized
concise, data tabulations...." Reviews of the "more lengthy patient case report forms" should be reserved for
those instances in which a more detailed review is necessary, the agency stated (see discussion below).

In its *Guideline on Formatting, Assembling, and Submitting New Drug and Antibiotic Applications* (February 1987), however, the agency advises sponsors to "meet with FDA to discuss the extent to which tabulations of patient data
in clinical studies, data elements within tables, and case report forms are needed. Such discussions can also
cover alternative modes of data presentation and the need for special supporting information (for example
electrocardiograms, x-rays, or pathology slides)."

According to agency regulations and guidelines, the NDA must provide data tabulations on individua
patients from each of the following: (1) the initial clinical pharmacology studies (Phase 1 studies); (2) effec
tiveness data from each adequate and well-controlled study (Phase 2 and Phase 3 studies); and (3) safety data
from all studies.

Current regulations state that these tabulations should include "the data on each patient in each study, excep
that the applicant may delete those tabulations that the agency agrees, in advance, are not pertinent to a
review of the drug's safety or effectiveness." The FDA is willing to discuss appropriate deletions from these
tabulations at a "pre-NDA" conference.

Given that case report tabulation (CRT) and case report form submissions (see discussion below) can be volu
minous, it is not surprising that CRTs and CRFs were the first elements of the NDA to be accepted in elec
tronic form without their paper-based counterparts. As early as May 1996, CDER published a policy formall
establishing a waiver process through which applicants could obtain permission to do so. In reality, howevei
this waiver process was a stopgap measure to be used until the FDA could finalize its proposed rule on elec
tronic records and signatures, something that the agency did in March 1997. Under this regulation, all sec
tions of an NDA can be submitted electronically without accompanying paper-based submissions.

In subsequent actions, however, the agency indicated that it planned to ease into the era of electronic-onl
filings, and that some of its early steps would be taken with electronic CRT and CRF filings. In September 1997
the agency released a guidance document entitled, *Archiving Submissions in Electronic Format-NDAs*, which pro

vided guidance to applicants that wanted to make electronic submissions of CRFs and CRTs as part of the NDA's archival copy. A January 1999 guidance document entitled, *Providing Regulatory Submissions in Electronic Format-NDAs* then superseded the September 1997 guidance, and provided information on how applicants could submit the entire archival copy of the NDA in electronic format. This document was accompanied by another guidance, *Providing Regulatory Submissions in Electronic Format-General Considerations* (January 1999), which addressed some of the more technical aspects of electronic submissions for CRTs and other NDA elements.

In more recent guidances, the FDA has stated its preference that CRTs be submitted in electronic data sets. In an October 2001 guidance entitled, *Cancer Drug and Biological Products-Clinical Data in Marketing Applications*, for example, the agency notes that the electronic CRT "is the preferred form of data submission for most oncology submissions, because data submitted electronically can generally be reviewed more rapidly and thoroughly."

In 2001, the FDA began looking for volunteers to participate in pilot project involving a so-called "Patient Profile Viewer" (PPV), which is a program that allowed reviewers to display data collected from case report tabulations (CRT) submitted in electronic format. Ultimately, this pilot project became part of the joint FDA/industry effort undertaken by the Clinical Data Interchange Standards Consortium (CDISC). In July 2004, the FDA announced that it had adopted CDISC's "standard format, called the Study Data Tabulation Model (SDTM)... that sponsors of human drug clinical trials can use to submit data to the agency," and that it was "exploring regulatory approaches to require the use of the SDTM standard for regulatory submissions." CDER officials note that, once the agency begins to receive clinical datasets in the new study data tabulation model, agency reviewers will be better able to take full advantage of the PPV program.

Case Report Forms Section As stated above, the FDA does not require the routine submission of patient case report forms. Rather, an NDA must include CRFs for: (1) patients who died during a clinical study; and (2) patients who did not complete a study because of any adverse event, regardless of whether the adverse event is considered drug-related by the investigator or sponsor.

The FDA may request that the sponsor submit additional case report forms (and tabulations) that the agency views as important to the drug's review. Typically, the agency requests all case report forms for the pivotal studies. In doing so, the review division attempts to designate the critical studies for which case report forms are required approximately 30 days after the NDA's receipt. If a sponsor fails to submit the CRFs within 30 days of the FDA's request, the agency may view the eventual submission as a major amendment and extend the review period as appropriate.

Patent Information Applicants must provide information on any patent(s) on the drug for which approval is sought, or on a method of using the drug.

Patent Certification Applicants must provide a patent certification or statement regarding "any relevant patents that claim the listed drug or that claim any other drugs on which investigations relied on by the applicant for approval of the application were conducted, or that claim a use for the listed or other drug." According to the FDA's *Guideline on Formatting, Assembling, and Submitting New Drug and Antibiotic Applications* (February 1987), the patent certification and patent information sections should be attached to the application form (Form 356h) in the NDA submission.

Establishment Description The establishment description section is relevant for certain biological products only. Its incorporation in Form 356h is a function of the FDA's effort to develop a harmonized application form for both drugs and biologics.

Debarment Certification Since mid-1992, the FDA has required that all NDAs include a certification that the applicant did not and will not use the services of individuals or firms that have been debarred by the FDA. Under the Generic Drug Enforcement Act of 1992, the FDA is authorized to debar individuals convicted o crimes relating to the development, approval, or regulation of drugs or biologics from providing any service to applicants. The statute requires that applications for drug products include "a certification that the appli cant did not and will not use in any capacity the services of any person debarred...in connection with such application." To address some of industry's most frequently asked questions about debarment certification and information requirements, CDER released a September 1998 guidance for industry entitled, *Submitting Debarment Certification Statements*.

Field Copy Certification As noted, U.S.-based sponsors filing paper-based NDAs must submit a "field" copy o the application's chemistry, manufacturing, and controls section, application form, and summary directly to the relevant FDA district office for use during the pre-approval manufacturing inspection (see discussion above or chemistry, manufacturing and controls section). The applicant is also required to certify in its NDA that an exac copy of the application's chemistry, manufacturing, and controls section has been forwarded to the district office

User Fee Cover Sheet (Form FDA 3397) Since January 1994, the FDA has required that every new drug appli cation (unless exempted) include a copy of the User Fee Cover Sheet. This form provides information tha allows the FDA to determine whether the application is subject to user fees and, if so, whether the appropri ate fee for the application has been submitted (a check in the appropriate amount must be mailed to a spec ified FDA account at the same time that the NDA is forwarded to the agency). The agency issued the lates version of this form in December 2003. The User Fee Cover Sheet should be included with the NDA applica tion form in the first volume of the application.

Financial Information Section In 2000, the FDA revised its Form 356h to accommodate the new informatior required under its February 2, 1998, and December 31, 1998, final rules on investigator financial disclosure and certification. The agency issued these regulations for drug, biologic, and medical device applicants to ensure that investigator financial interests and sponsor/investigator financial arrangements that could affec the reliability of data submitted in premarketing applications are disclosed to the agency. Under these regu lations, an applicant must submit, in the NDA, a list of clinical investigators who conducted covered clinica studies and, for each clinical investigator, must provide one of the following:

1. A certification on Form 3454 that: (1) no financial arrangements with the investigator have been made under which study outcome could affect compensation; (2) the investigator has no proprietary interest in the tested product; (3) the investigator does not have a significant equity interest in the sponsor of the covered study; and (4) the investigator has not received "significant payments of other sorts" (see discussion below).

2. A disclosure on Form 3455 of specific financial arrangements between the investigator and sponsor and any steps that the sponsor has taken to minimize bias. Under the agency's reg ulations, disclosable financial arrangements include the following:

   A. Compensation made to the investigator in which the value of compensation could be affected by study outcome. This requirement applies to all covered studies that are ongoing or completed as of February 2, 1999, or later.

   B. A proprietary interest in the tested product, including, but not limited to, a patent, trademark, copyright, or licensing agreement. This requirement applies to all covered studies that are ongoing or completed as of February 2, 1999, or later.

C. Any equity interest in the sponsor of a covered study (i.e., any ownership interest, stock options, or other financial interest whose value cannot be readily determined through reference to public prices). This requirement applies to all covered studies that are ongoing or completed as of February 2, 1999, or later.

D. Any equity interest in a publicly held company that exceeds $50,000 in value must be disclosed only for covered clinical studies that are ongoing on or after February 2, 1999. The requirement applies to interests held during the time the clinical investigator is carrying out the study and for one year following the completion of the study.

E. Significant payments of other sorts, which are payments that have a cumulative monetary value of $25,000 or more made by the sponsor of a covered study to the investigator or the investigator's institution to support activities of the investigator exclusive of the costs of conducting the clinical study or other clinical studies (e.g., a grant to fund ongoing research, compensation in the form of equipment or retainers for ongoing consultation or honoraria) during the time the clinical investigator is carrying out the study and for one year following completion of the study. This requirement applies to payments made on or after February 2, 1999.

If, upon reviewing such information in the NDA, agency reviewers determine that the financial interests raise a serious question about the integrity of the data, the FDA may initiate an audit of the data provided by the clinical investigator in question, request that the applicant conduct further data analyses or that additional studies be conducted to confirm the results of the questioned study, decline to use the investigator's data as a basis for agency action, or take other appropriate action. According to CDER officials, when reviewers find that an investigator has a financial interest in a sponsor or the product under review, they will consider such information by more carefully scrutinizing the number of subjects the investigator enrolled and whether there were any outliers in terms of the adverse reactions reported by the investigator.

A disclosure or certification must be provided for each investigator of a "covered" clinical trial, FDA regulations state. Covered trials are defined as "any study of a drug, biological product, or device in humans submitted in a marketing application or reclassification petition that the applicant or FDA relies on to establish that the product is effective (including studies that show equivalence to an effective product) or any study in which a single investigator makes a significant contribution to the demonstration of safety. This would, in general, not include phase 1 tolerance studies or pharmacokinetic studies, most clinical pharmacology studies (unless they are critical to an efficacy determination), large open safety studies conducted at multiple sites, treatment protocols and parallel track protocols." In a March 2001 guidance document entitled, *Financial Disclosure by Clinical Investigators*, the FDA states that the sponsor must consider "the potential role of a particular study based on study size, design, and other considerations, and that studies other than controlled effectiveness studies could also be considered critical, such as a pharmacodynamic study in a population subset or a bioequivalence study supporting a new dosage form."

With regard to the lengths to which companies should go in collecting this information from investigators, the guidance states that, "sponsors and applicants should use reasonable judgment in deciding how much effort needs to be expended to collect this information. If sponsors/applicants find it impossible to obtain the financial information in question, applicants should explain why this information was not obtainable and document attempts made in an effort to collect the information."

Other Information If necessary, the sponsor may use this portion of the application to incorporate by reference any information submitted prior to the NDA filing. The sponsor must also provide an accurate and complete English translation of a foreign language document for any information originally written in a foreign language.

Other Possible Elements of the NDA: RiskMAPs and Pharmacogenomic Data

While not yet formal regulatory requirements, two types of information—"risk minimization action plans" and pharmacogenomic data—are likely to become routine elements of NDA submissions for some products in the near future.

The NDA and Risk Minimization Action Plans

As noted above, the FDA's focus on risk management under PDUFA III is likely to impact NDA submissions for certain drug products. In a May 2004 draft industry guidance entitled, *Development and Use of Risk Minimization Action Plans*, the FDA notes that, while routine risk minimization measures (e.g., FDA-approved professional labeling) will be sufficient for most products, "for a small number of products where a [risk minimization action plan (RiskMAP)] should be considered...sponsors are encouraged to consider developing a RiskMAP." The agency defines the RiskMAP as "a strategic safety program designed to meet specific goals and objectives in minimizing known risks of a product while preserving its benefits." In the draft guidance, the agency notes that a company can submit a RiskMAP before or after approval, and that the plan should be submitted in either the IND or NDA if it is filed in advance of marketing clearance.

At the same time, the FDA emphasizes that RiskMAPs should be "used judiciously to minimize risks without encumbering drug availability or otherwise interfering with the delivery of product benefits to patients." The agency also notes that, while the decision to develop, submit, or implement RiskMAPs will be made on a case-by-case basis, the following considerations will be common to most RiskMAP-related decisions:

- Nature and rate of known risks versus benefits: Comparing the characteristics of the product's adverse events with those of the product's benefits may help clarify whether a RiskMAP could improve the product's benefit-risk balance. The characteristics to be weighed might include the (1) types, magnitude, and frequency of risks and benefits; (2) populations at greatest risk and/or those likely to derive the most benefit; (3) existence of treatment alternatives; and (4) reversibility of adverse events observed.

- Preventability of the event: Serious and labeled adverse events that can be minimized or avoided by preventive measures are the preferred candidates for RiskMAPS.

- Probability of benefit: If factors that can predict effectiveness are identified, a RiskMAP could help encourage use accordingly to increase benefits relative to known risks.

In the draft guidance, the agency established that the tools used in risk minimization plans fall into three broad categories: (1) targeted education and outreach (health practitioner letters, training programs for health care practitioners or patients, continuing education, prominent professional or public notifications, patient labeling, and focused or limited promotional techniques such as product sampling); (2) reminder systems (i.e., systems that prompt, remind, double-check or otherwise guide health practitioners and/or patients in prescribing, dispensing, or receiving a product in ways that minimize risk); and (3) performance-linked access systems (e.g., systems that link product access to laboratory testing results or documentation), which the agency recommends be used when products have significant or otherwise unique benefits in a particular patient group or condition but unusual risks as well, and when routine risk minimization measures and reminder systems are insufficient to minimize those risks.

If the sponsor, likely after a discussion with the FDA, determines that a RiskMAP is necessary, the RiskMAP submission in the IND or NDA should include the following sections:

- Table of Contents

- Background: to explain why a RiskMAP is being considered and created.

- Goals and Objectives: to describe the goals and objectives of the RiskMAP.

- Strategy and Tools: to define the overall RiskMAP strategy and the tools to be employed to minimize the risk.

- Evaluation Plan: to describe the evaluation measurements or measures that will be used to periodically assess the effectiveness of the RiskMAP's goals, objectives, and tools.

When a sponsor makes a RiskMAP submission (i.e., as part of IND, NDA, or post-approval), the agency recommends that the company forward results from its evaluation of the risk minimization effort to the FDA as well. Such submissions should include data, analyses, the sponsor's conclusions regarding effectiveness, and any proposed modifications.

Under its PDUFA III commitments, the FDA had agreed to release a final version of the May 2004 guidance, as well as to other risk-management guidances, by September 30, 2004. Although the agency missed this goal, it was hoping to release a final RiskMAP guidance by late 2004 or early 2005.

Pharmacogenomic Data and the NDA

As noted, the FDA used a November 2003 draft guidance entitled, *Pharmacogenomic Data Submissions* to lay the groundwork for encouraging and, in some cases, requiring NDA applicants to submit pharmacogenomic data that they develop as part of the drug development process. Although the agency acknowledges that most pharmacogenomic data currently are exploratory or research-oriented and, therefore, need not be submitted in an NDA, sponsors should consider submitting the data voluntarily to help FDA reviewers and scientists understand the relevant scientific issues in this emerging field, the draft guidance states. While the agency prepared to release a final guidance document in late 2004, CDER officials claimed that center reviewers were actively reviewing and making decisions based on voluntarily submitted pharmacogenomic data.

When the submission of pharmacogenomic data is not otherwise required—and their submission will be required in some cases (see discussion below)—companies should submit what the agency calls "voluntary genomic data submissions," or VGDSs, which will be evaluated by a cross-center interdisciplinary pharmacogenomic review group (IPRG) to be formed within the agency. Although the agency pledges not to use VGDSs for "regulatory decision making," voluntary submissions will provide the FDA with access to emerging pharmacogenomic data "so that a foundation can be built for developing scientifically sound regulatory policies."

The FDA's draft guidance, the first of three pharmacogenomics guidances expected from the agency, came following a high-profile April 2002 public workshop and an April 2003 meeting at which the FDA Science Board encouraged the agency to move ahead with a guidance for industry. It also came in the wake of a pledge in the FDA's August 2003 Strategic Action Plan to "direct Agency research programs and develop standards to effectively handle emerging technologies, especially in the areas of pharmacogenomics...." to provide fo "more efficient and rapid translation of new scientific developments and breakthroughs into safe and effec tive medical products."

In the draft guidance, the agency acknowledged both industry's reluctance to undertake pharmacogenomic testing programs due to "uncertainties in how the data will be used by the FDA in the drug application review process," and the reality that "most experimental results may not be well enough established to be suitable for regulatory decision making." The agency did not use either as an excuse to surrender a role in pharma cogenomics, but instead used the guidance to clarify when and how it intends to use pharmacogenomic data in regulatory decision making—"that is, when the data will be considered sufficiently reliable to serve as the basis for regulatory decision making, when it will be considered only supportive to a decision, and when the data will not be used in regulatory decision making."

The draft guidance employs detailed "algorithms," or decision trees—one each for INDs, *new* NDAs/BLAs/sup plements, and approved NDAs/BLAs/supplements—as well as selected examples to help industry determine the regulatory status of pharmacogenomic data at the IND, NDA/BLA, and post-approval stages.

To comply with current regulations that require NDAs to include "reports of all investigations of the drug prod uct sponsored by the applicant," NDA sponsors "will need to provide reports of pharmacogenomic investiga tions in their NDAs," the draft guidance states. Although the agency does not outline specific requirements it notes that such reports may be necessary in the pharmacology/toxicology, human pharmacokinetics bioavailability, and clinical data sections.

The extent and format of pharmacogenomic investigation reports in NDAs will depend on the relevance and application of the information provided (see exhibit below).

Complete versus Partial NDA Submissions

The GRMPs and the Wisdom of Complete NDA Filings The user-fee program put a renewed focus on the need for an NDA to include all necessary sections, data, and information at the time of its submission. In fact senior FDA officials have directly credited the increasing quality of NDA submissions as one of the key driver behind improvements in NDA review timelines during the user-fee era.

While the PDUFA III agreements provide for a pilot program under which the agency will accept specific ele ments of NDAs before the complete application is submitted (see discussion below), the FDA's draft Good Review Management Practices (GRMP), a set of best practices for the NDA review process, otherwise dis courage such practices. Issued in July 2003, the draft GRMPs implore industry "to manage the drug develop ment pipeline" in a way that culminates in the submission of a complete application, even if that mean delaying an NDA/BLA's submission. Despite the fact that NDA refuse-to-file rates continue to hover at all-time lows, CDER officials have recently discussed the need for complete, well-organized applications, and have noted that the drug center may have been too willing to accept incomplete applications and rely on compa ny promises to remedy deficiencies during the review process.

"The applicant is strongly encouraged to manage the drug development timeline in a manner that leads to submission of a complete application, with the exception of safety updates, for FDA review," the GRMPs state "It has been FDA's experience that submission of a complete application leads to the most efficient review process and shortest approval time. In some cases, submitting a complete application may require a decision

An Algorithm for Pharmacogenomic Submissions to NDAs/BLAs/Supplements

NDA/NDA supplement sponsors that have generated or possess pharmacogenomic data related to a drug or biological product can comply with the regulations using the following algorithm, the May 2004 draft guidance states:

1. "Provide reports on pharmacogenomic investigations intended by the sponsor to be used in the drug label or as part of the scientific database being used to support approval as complete submissions (not in the form of an abbreviated report, synopsis, or VGDS), including information about test procedures and complete data, in the relevant sections of the NDA or BLA. If the pharmacogenomic test is already approved by the FDA or is the subject of an application filed with the Agency, information on the test itself can be provided by cross reference. The following examples would fit this category:

   • Pharmacogenomic test results that are being used to support scientific arguments made by the sponsor about drug dosing, safety, patient selection, or effectiveness.

   • Pharmacogenomic test results that the sponsor proposes to describe in the drug label.

   • Pharmacogenomic tests that are essential to achieving the dosing, safety, or effectiveness described in the drug label.

2. Submit reports of pharmacogenomic test results that constitute known valid biomarkers for physiologic, pathophysiologic, pharmacologic, toxicologic, or clinical states or outcomes in the relevant species, but that the sponsor is not relying on or mentioning in the label, to the Agency as an abbreviated report (not in the form of a synopsis or VGDS). (If a pharmacogenomic test of this type was conducted as part of a larger overall study, the reporting of the pharmacogenomic test results can be incorporated into the larger study report.)

3. Submit reports of pharmacogenomic tests that represent probable valid biomarkers for physiologic, pathophysiologic, pharmacologic, toxicologic, or clinical states or outcomes in the relevant species to the NDA or BLA as an abbreviated report. (If the pharmacogenomic testing of this type was conducted as part of a larger study, the abbreviated report can be appended to the report of the overall study.)

4. There is no need to submit detailed reports of general exploratory or research information, such as broad gene expression screening, collection of sera or tissue samples, or results of pharmacogenomic tests that are not known or probable valid biomarkers to the NDA or BLA. Because the Agency does not view these studies as germane in determining the safety or effectiveness of a drug, the submission requirements [for NDAs and BLAs] will be satisfied by the submission of a synopsis of the study. However, the Agency encourages the voluntary submission of the data from the study in a VGDS submitted to the NDA or BLA."

Upon the release of the pharmacogenomics draft guidance, FDA officials attempted to allay fears about the implications of pharmacogenomic data submissions. With the exception of cancer therapies, for which tumors can provide gene sequence expression data, experimental products are unlikely to face new FDA requirements in the near term under the guidance, then-CDER Director Janet Woodcock, M.D., claimed at a November 2003 workshop.

by the applicant to delay initial submission beyond a corporate target date. Such a delay in submission might ultimately result in an earlier approval date since a complete application might be approved at the end of th first review cycle and not require subsequent review cycles."

Although the GRMPs reluctantly acknowledge that the agency may begin an application review based on a com pany's agreement to complete the application, they encourage the reviewer to limit such situations. "Request for the FDA to accept for review *planned* amendments that complete an application during the first-cycle revie process should be minimized and should be discussed and agreed to in advance with the FDA (e.g., at the pre NDA/BLA meeting). Such requests and agreements should generally be limited to situations when the FD. agrees that there is a valid public health urgency to expedite the availability of an important new product."

Recently, top CDER officials have emphasized the importance of complete NDA submissions and the costs c incomplete applications. In mid-2004, CDER Office of New Drugs Director John Jenkins, M.D., noted that, whil firms continue to ask agency reviewers if they can submit data necessary for approval following the NDA's sut mission, "that's not the deal we made in PDUFA." Due to the high percentage of "incomplete applications" tha CDER continues to receive and accept, the drug center "is drowning in resubmissions," Jenkins stated.

PDUFA III and Pilot 1: The Reviewable Unit Although the agency touts the wisdom of complete NDA sut missions, it has a long history of accepting incomplete, or "rolling," NDAs in the interest of accelerating th review timeline in certain circumstances. While some CDER divisions have accepted incomplete, or "partial applications in an effort to expedite the review of selected high-priority products, FDAMA formally called o the agency to do so in some cases. Under the legislation's "fast track" review procedure, the FDA can agree t accept and begin the review of an incomplete NDA for a designated fast track product. In such cases, howev er, the partial NDA must provide the "letter date" of the FDA's agreement to accept the incomplete submis sion as well as the applicant's schedule for submitting all remaining sections of the NDA. The "fast track process applies only to drugs that have the potential to address unmet medical needs for serious and imme diately life-threatening conditions (see Chapters 8 and 15).

Building on CDER's experience in conducting rolling NDA reviews of presubmitted portions of certain dru applications, PDUFA III provides for the review of "a limited number" (only fast track products are eligible) c presubmitted portions of companies' marketing applications in the form of "reviewable units" (RU). Th agency provides for such submissions under the Pilot 1 (reviewable unit) continuous marketing applicatio program, under which the agency hopes to conduct a "comprehensive assessment of the added value, cost: and impact of...early reviews of parts of marketing applications."

Under an October 2003 guidance document entitled, *Continuous Marketing Applications: Pilot 1-Reviewable Units f Fast Track Products Under PDUFA,* the agency establishes that, to qualify for Pilot 1, a fast track product mu: have been the subject of an end-of-Phase 2 and/or pre-NDA meeting and will have demonstrated in clinic; trials significant promise as a therapeutic advance. Products not selected for Pilot 1 remain eligible for earl submission under the fast track program, the agency notes.

In the guidance, the FDA defines an RU as "a predefined portion of an applicant's NDA or BLA that, by agre ment between the applicant and the review division, can be submitted prior to submission of a complete ND or BLA. Ideally, an RU would be a complete technical section of the NDA or BLA." The agency notes, howe er, that "the experimental nature of Pilot 1 provides for flexibility in the definition of RUs such that a revie division and applicant may agree on submission of an RU that is less than a complete technical section (i.e a well-defined subsection of the complete technical section)."

A "plan" for RU content and submission should be documented in the end-of-Phase 2 or pre-NDA meeting minutes, or should be provided in a separate letter from the review division to the applicant. This documentation should describe the total number of RUs to be submitted, the specific content of each RU, and the projected date for each RU submission. Although the plan should "generally include no more than one RU submission for review under Pilot 1 per NDA technical review section," a review division may agree to a plan that provides for more than one presubmission for any technical review section. In addition, generally no more than four RUs would be accepted and reviewed for a single marketing application, the Pilot 1 guidance states.

The submission of RUs for an application should generally begin no earlier than one year before the date that the applicant anticipates submitting the complete NDA, the agency notes. Upon receipt of the RU, the review division will determine its acceptability within 60 days and will start the six-month review clock for the "complete review of the RU." Once an RU is accepted, the RU's review will proceed similar to a complete submission's assessment, including communication with the sponsor for minor clarifications and, if necessary, issuance of information request letters. The agency will adhere to the RU six-month review clock even when the complete application is submitted during that review.

By mid-2004, CDER officials announced that they had enrolled three NDAs and a BLA under Pilot 1, and that the applicants had submitted six reviewable units for these applications. In 2006, an independent consultant will provide a preliminary report on the value and demands of the Pilot 1 program.

Pre-NDA Meetings

Because of the NDA's complexity and because the FDA wants to avoid investing scarce resources reviewing deficient NDAs, the agency offers pre-submission conferences, called pre-NDA meetings, to all drug sponsors. Federal regulations state that the primary purpose of pre-NDA meetings "...is to uncover any major unresolved problems, to identify those studies that the sponsor is relying on as adequate and well-controlled to establish the drug's effectiveness, to acquaint FDA reviewers with the general information to be submitted in the marketing application (including technical information), to discuss appropriate methods for statistical analysis of the data, and to discuss the best approach to the presentation and formatting of data in the marketing application."

As it must for end-of-Phase 2 conferences, a sponsor must request a pre-NDA meeting with the division responsible for a drug's review. Although federal regulations establish that all drug sponsors have access to such conferences, the importance of the drug, the time constraints facing the relevant drug review division, and the significance of the scientific and regulatory issues at hand will do much to determine whether the FDA grants a pre-NDA meeting. CDER officials note that pre-NDA meeting requests are generally granted. In its PDUFA III commitments, the agency states that pre-NDA meetings and other Type B meetings (see Chapter 5 for a detailed discussion of the various types of meetings) "will be honored except in the most unusual circumstances." The pre-NDA meeting can take place any time before an NDA submission, but should not be held before Phase 3 studies near completion.

The FDA's most recent discussion of pre-NDA meetings and their significance appears in CDER's July 2003 draft guidance entitled, *Good Review Management Principles for PDUFA Products*, which focuses on good review principles and best practices to promote efficient first-cycle reviews of NDA submissions. "The pre-NDA/BLA meeting can be critical to creating a foundation for efficient review management," the draft guidance notes.

"The meeting should focus on the format of a proposed application and on creating a shared understanding between the FDA and the applicant of an acceptable content to support initial planning for efficient review management. The pre-NDA/BLA meeting generally should be scheduled 6 to 12 months prior to the anticipated date for application submission. This timing of the pre-NDA/BLA meeting ensures that the applicant has accumulated sufficient information regarding the product development program to hold a productive discussion and that adequate time is available for the applicant to incorporate any advice from the review division before submitting the application for review. In preparing for the pre-NDA/BLA meeting, the review division should attempt to address any specific questions raised by the applicant in the meeting background package. The review division should also provide feedback regarding any major deficiencies or omissions identified in the proposed application based on the summary information provided by the applicant in the meeting background package."

FDA commitments associated with PDUFA II and III have, in many cases, re-affirmed, and in other cases changed, CDER's standards for meetings as expressed in a 1996 policy entitled, *Formal Meetings Between CDER and CDER's External Constituents* (MaPP 4512.1). According to this MaPP, written requests for meetings should include at least six elements: a brief statement of the purpose of the meeting; a listing of the specific objectives/outcomes the requestor expects from the meeting; a proposed agenda, including the estimated time needed for each agenda item; a listing of planned external attendees; a listing of requested participants from CDER; and the approximate time at which supporting documentation (i.e., the "backgrounder") for the meeting will be sent to CDER (i.e., "x" weeks prior to the meeting, but should be received by CDER at least 2 weeks in advance of the scheduled meeting).

In a February 2000 guidance entitled, *Formal Meetings with Sponsors and Applicants for PDUFA Products*, the agency recommends a similar, but slightly more detailed, list of contents for meeting requests: (1) product name and application number; (2) chemical name and structure; (3) proposed indication(s); (4) the type of meeting being requested (in this case, a Type B meeting); (5) a brief statement of the purpose of the meeting, possibly including a discussion of the types of completed or planned studies or data that the sponsor or applicant intends to discuss at the meeting, the general nature of the critical questions to be asked, and where the meeting fits in the overall development plans; (6) a list of the specific objectives/outcomes expected from the meeting; (7) a preliminary proposed agenda, including estimated amounts of time needed for each agenda item and designated speaker(s); (8) a draft list of specific questions grouped by review discipline (e.g., clinical, chemistry); (9) a list of individuals (including titles) who will attend the proposed meeting from the sponsor's or applicant's organization and consultants; (10) a list of agency staff that the sponsor requests participate in the proposed meeting (if the applicant is uncertain as to what agency officials should attend, it does not need to include specific individuals in the request, but should include requested disciplines if known); (11) the approximate date on which the sponsor will forward supporting documentation (i.e., the information package) to the review division; and (12) suggested dates and times (i.e., morning or afternoon) for the meeting.

Within 14 days of receiving the request, the reviewing division must notify the requestor in writing (either by letter or fax) of the date, time, and location at which the meeting will be held, as well as the likely CDER participants. Under CDER's PDUFA III commitments, the pre-NDA meeting should occur within 60 calendar days of the agency's receipt of the meeting request. If such a meeting is immediately necessary for an otherwise "stalled" drug development program to proceed, a sponsor can request an earlier, "critical path meeting." Such meetings, FDA notes, generally will be reserved for dispute resolution, to discuss clinical holds, and to address special protocol assessments following the agency's initial evaluation. CDER must fulfill its meeting management system goals for at least 90% of meetings requests received from FY2003 through FY2007 (see Chapter 5 for a more detailed discussion of CDER's meetings management system).

The success of a pre-NDA meeting depends largely on sponsor preparation. To help FDA staffers prepare and to ensure that there will be a "meaningful discussion" at the meeting, sponsors should submit to the reviewing division an "information package" at least four weeks in advance of the formal pre-NDA meeting. This information package, which the agency's guidance recommends should be a fully paginated document with a table of contents, indices, appendices, cross references, and tabs, should generally include the following elements: (1) product name and application number; (2) chemical name and structure; (3) proposed indication(s); (4) dosage form, route of administration, and dosing regimen (frequency and duration); (5) a brief statement of the purpose of the meeting, possibly including a discussion of the types of completed or planned studies or data that the sponsor or applicant intends to discuss at the meeting, the general nature of the critical questions to be asked, and where the meeting fits in the overall development plans; (6) a list of the specific objectives/outcomes expected from the meeting; (7) a proposed agenda, including estimated amounts of time needed for each agenda item and designated speaker(s); (8) a list of specific questions grouped by review discipline (e.g., clinical, chemistry); (9) a clinical data summary (as appropriate); (10) a preclinical data summary (as appropriate); and (11) chemistry, manufacturing, and controls information (as appropriate). Although the applicant will have provided much of this information in the meetings request, it should be updated for the information package, the agency notes.

In recent years, CDER has begun to develop industry guidances for discipline-specific aspects of sponsor/applicant meetings. In a February 2000 draft guidance entitled, IND *Meetings for Human Drugs and Biologics: Chemistry, Manufacturing, and Controls Information*, for example, CDER outlined considerations relevant to the elements of pre-NDA meetings focused on CMC issues.

FDA staffers stress that a particularly important element of pre-NDA meetings is the portion devoted to the statistical review. To make optimal use of the meeting, the sponsor should send, or have present at the meeting, sample mock-ups or computer printouts of data to provide FDA statisticians the opportunity to offer advice on data organization and presentation.

Under CDER's PDUFA III commitments, final minutes of the formal meeting should be distributed to FDA and sponsor attendees within 30 days of the meeting. Applicants can submit their own draft minutes to the agency for consideration in developing the formal meeting minutes, provided that they are forwarded promptly. After reviewing the agency's formal minutes, the applicant can seek clarification or amendment of the minutes.

Assembling and Submitting the NDA

The FDA has extremely specific requirements for the NDA's assembly, many of which are provided in the agency's *Guideline on Formatting, Assembling, and Submitting New Drug and Antibiotic Applications* (February 1987). This 32-page document offers general guidance on such issues as content requirements, and more detailed specifications on such issues as paper size, maximum volume size, volume identification, and pagination. *Editor's note*: For the names of guidance documents that detail specifications relevant to eNDAs, see discussion above.

In mid-1997, CDER stopped supplying application binders to industry, and firms had to provide for the printing of their own binders. In November 1997, CDER issued a guidance entitled, *Required Specifications for FDA's IND, NDA, ANDA, and Drug Master File Binders* to provide companies with detailed specifications on application binders.

Due to difficulties that industry experienced in having commercial printers develop binders that met agency specifications as well as resources that CDER had to invest in rejacketing NDAs that included out-of-specification binders, the agency announced in April 1998 that industry could purchase official binders from the Government Printing Office. Applicants can obtain specific details on binder specifications and information on ordering binders through the FDA's website at www.fda.gov/cder/ddms/binders.html.

Amending the NDA

Either at its own initiative or in response to an FDA request, an applicant may seek to clarify or augment the information provided in the original NDA during the review process. For example, the applicant may submit a new analysis of previously submitted data, new data not available at the time of the NDA submission, or information necessary to address a deficiency in the drug application. As noted above, the FDA is now permitting NDA applicants to develop and submit NDA amendments in the common technical document (CTD) format (see discussion above). NDA applicants can provide amendments in the CTD format even when the conventional NDA format was used for the original application.

Regardless of the format in which it is submitted, any such information provided for an unapproved application is considered an NDA amendment. Depending on its timing, the submission of a significant amendment—a major reanalysis of clinical data, for example—may trigger an extension in the FDA's timeline for the application's review (see Chapter 8).

CHAPTER 8

The NDA Review Process

Over the last 15 years, no other aspect of the U.S. drug development and approval system has evolved as significantly as the FDA's new drug application (NDA) review and approval process. As the pendulum of public and political opinion has swung back and forth over this period, this closely watched process has been, at various times, buffeted by criticism from some who believe it is too slow and, at other times, from those who believe it has been accelerated to such a degree that Americans are now being exposed to potentially unsafe medications.

Today, the FDA's process for reviewing and approving new drugs and the applications that are submitted in support of them remains as controversial and as carefully watched as it has ever been. This is certainly not surprising, given the stakes involved—the constant need for therapeutic advances, the public health implications of regulatory decision-making, and the financial rewards of gaining access to the world's most lucrative pharmaceutical market.

The NDA Review Process: Post-PDUFA

The driving force behind the evolution that saw FDA drug review times virtually halved from the early to the late 1990s was, of course, the Prescription Drug User Fee Act (PDUFA), and the changes that CDER implemented to meet the increasingly aggressive review performance goals associated with the user-fee program. In the early and mid-1990s, CDER management instituted tight controls for managing and tracking drug reviews, and reorganized the center's drug review divisions into smaller, more therapeutically focused units (see Chapter 4). With such changes, an influx of new staffing funded by industry-paid user fees, and a new focus on meeting specific review performance goals, NDA review times improved markedly. In 1998 and 1999, for example, the median review time for new molecular entities (NME) was under a year, compared to 21 months in 1993.

But CDER's success in approving record numbers of new drugs in record time soon drew criticism in light of other developments during the late 1990s. After three approved drugs (Redux, Posicor, and Duract) were withdrawn within a nine-month span from late 1997 through mid-1998, agency critics quickly and openly charged that the focus on the speed of drug approvals had come at the expense of drug safety, which they claimed was contributing to the estimated 100,000 U.S. deaths each year related to adverse drug reactions. Subsequent safety-related drug withdrawals, including Rezulin, Lotronex, Raplon, and Baycol, continued to feed such perceptions as the FDA and industry headed into all-important discussions for the second reauthorization of PDUFA in late 2001.

True or not, these perceptions seemed to be supported, at the time, by public comments from CDER reviewers, including one medical reviewer who wrote in a *Washington Post* editorial that, "the program by which drug companies pay fees for review of their new drug applications has enabled FDA to hire new physician review ers (including myself) and to reduce the time needed for review. But an unfortunate consequence is a linkin of the productivity of FDA reviewers with the approval of new products. The more new drugs approved, th more productive the FDA appears, even if the new drugs are not as good as what is available today." I December 1998, the Public Citizen's Health Research Group (HRG) released the results of a survey of 52 CDEI medical officers in which some claimed that, under the prescription drug user fee program, certain drugs ha been approved too quickly, some approved drugs should never have been approved, "inappropriate pressure in the form of phone calls from Congress and senior FDA employees was being applied to encourage dru approvals, and reviewers were being pressured to alter their review opinions in some cases.

CDER officials responded to the resultant press, congressional, and public pressure by emphasizing that, dui ing the PDUFA years, its record of drug withdrawals "compared favorably" with its record in earlier years. Mor recent data suggest that drug withdrawal rates have even improved during the user-fee era: Just 1.6% (2/124 of the NMEs approved in the 1999-2003 period have been withdrawn (not including the September 2004 with drawal of Vioxx), compared with 2.9% (5/172) in the 1994-1999 period, 2.4% (3/127) in the 1989-1993 perioc and 4.4% (5/113) in the 1984-1988 period. (*Author's Note*: The FDA's initial response to Merck's September 200 voluntary safety-related withdrawal of Vioxx was a re-assessment of its postmarketing drug safety prograr (see Chapter 11) rather than a re-assessment of the drug approval process. The high-profile Vioxx withdraw al was the first following the several withdrawals in 2000 and 2001.)

While insisting at the time that drug withdrawal rates had not increased, FDA officials openly acknowledge the growing need for a particularly efficient and well-conceived post-marketing drug risk surveillance, assess ment, and management program to better address the demands created by speedier and greater numbers c new drug approvals. Therefore, CDER officials announced a reinvigorated postmarketing drug surveillanc program, and spoke about the need to apply "a new systems framework" to medical product risk managemen which would involve a better integration of the efforts of those involved in the prescribing and use of ne drugs (patients, practitioners) and better communication of the risks of drug use to both patients and phys cians. Further, under PDUFA III, increases in user fees would be used, in part, to fund new initiatives focuse on drug safety and risk management.

Despite such moves, many became convinced that the level of attention given to Redux, Rezulin, and othe drug withdrawals had begun to exact a price, largely in the form of more conservative FDA decision making i drug reviews. During 2000 and 2001, the perception of a full-blown "FDA slowdown" in drug reviews began t gain credibility, in part due to a downturn in new molecular entity (NME) approvals, which FDA official claimed was related to a downturn in industry submissions and not a slowdown in FDA reviews. Meanwhile average and median NME review times rose dramatically in 2000 and 2001, although agency officials claime the rise was due to a handful of drugs with exceedingly lengthy review times. Although the FDA continued t meet its PDUFA review goals, industry officials maintained that the agency was increasingly doing so by takin fewer positive actions (i.e., product approvals) on initial NDA submissions and by stretching the review per od by asking for more clarifications, data, and information through approvable and not-approvable actions.

While they initially rejected claims that CDER's NDA review performance was suffering, center officials di concede, in late 2001, that some application reviews might be suffering. In making their case for increase funding from either user fees or congressional appropriations, CDER officials claimed that the number c review cycles necessary to approve "standard" applications seemed to be growing, something that the believed "may be due to the fact that reviewers, pressed to meet the new PDUFA II goals for drug develor ment (e.g., meetings, special protocol assessments, and responses to clinical holds), have had less time to devote to resolving last-minute problems with these standard applications in time to meet the action goal date." Without additional funding under PDUFA III, FDA officials warned, the agency would be unable to "increase or even maintain" PDUFA performance levels.

While the PDUFA III era brought the FDA the increased user-fee funding it needed to add staff, to establish a $7 million "performance fund" to pursue initiatives for improving the drug review process, and to focus more intently on drug safety-related activities, it also brought a new FDA commissioner with an interest in improving the medical product review process and in having the agency play a more proactive role in the product development process. During his brief, but active, 17-month tenure (from October 2002 to March 2004), then-FDA Commissioner Mark McClellan, M.D., Ph.D., led several initiatives that will continue to reshape the NDA review process for some time:

- As part of a new agency-wide strategic plan spearheaded by McClellan, the agency introduced what it called the "Innovation Initiative," through which the agency is attempting to speed the development and approval of new drugs, biologics, and medical devices. Under the January 2003 Innovation Initiative, the FDA identified three key areas "for increased effort": (1) examining the root causes of multi-cycle NDA reviews and identifying and addressing "avoidable delays" and multiple review cycles; (2) instituting a continuous improvement/quality systems approach throughout the pre-market review process (e.g., enhanced reviewer training on good review management principles that are based on best practices (see discussion below), further development of standards for the review process); and (3) expanding collaborative clinical and pre-clinical guidance development (e.g., working with external experts, disease-specific guidance). Many of the Innovation Initiative's provisions dovetailed with elements of PDUFA III and other programs. Under PDUFA III, for example, the FDA will retain an independent expert consultant to conduct a comprehensive study of the first cycle review process (e.g., tracking all actions that take place during the first-cycle reviews and the identification of FDA and industry best practices that facilitated the review process). In mid-2003, CDER officials said that a preliminary, small-scale assessment of the causes of multiple-cycle application reviews suggested that many of the reviews were "unavoidable." Second-cycle reviews, some of which the agency acknowledged might have been avoided with early-stage FDA/industry communication, were triggered by, for example, emerging information late in the development process or unexpected study results needing further examination.

- In late June 2003, FDA officials announced that they had established a non-PDUFA-related benchmark through which the agency would attempt to further reduce NDA review times: The agency would seek a 10% reduction in the median review time for the first 50% of NDAs (and BLAs for biologics) for new molecular entities that are approved in the FY2005 through FY2007 cohorts. In announcing the new goal, McClellan conceded that, "while improving review cycle performance [under the PDUFA goals] is important, that's not the bottom line. The bottom line is reducing the overall time for development and approval of safe and effective new medicines... Reducing cycle time alone is unlikely to achieve this goal... We will do more than ever to help avoid multiple cycles of review and to increase the likelihood that an application to FDA gets it right the first time."

- In July 2003, the FDA released a long-awaited draft guidance entitled, *Good Review Management Principles for PDUFA Products* to identify current best review practices and discuss "future review management improvements" regarding the first-cycle of NDA reviews. Overall, the draft GRMPs encouraged CDER review divisions to "identify and resolve minor deficiencies in an application that otherwise meets the statutory standards for approval during the first-cycle review," and to avoid "unnecessary multiple-cycle reviews." Designed for both agency reviewers and industry, the draft GRMPs focus on each aspect of the all-important first-cycle review process for NDAs (e.g., presubmission, filing decision, review planning, review, communication, management of review timelines, advisory committee meetings, wrap-up labeling, and FDA action), and clarify the roles and responsibilities of FDA review staff at each stage. In part, the FDA's release of the draft GRMPs is the latest move in a several-year CDER effort to standardize the NDA review process, in part by releasing "review templates" for the NDA review disciplines. In April 2004, CDER released the *Clinical Pharmacology and Biopharmaceutics Review Template* to specify how agency reviewers should document clinical pharmacology and biopharmaceutics reviews. Then, in July 2004, CDER released a long-awaited *Clinical Review Template* in the form of MaPP 6010.3 to provide "a structured outline" for the clinical review and to "promote consistency in the documentation of [review] elements and provide for the ready retrieval of information."

Upon McClellan's sudden departure in 2004 to head the Centers for Medicare and Medicaid Services, Acting FDA Commissioner Lester Crawford emphasized that the agency would continue to pursue the many initiatives introduced during McClellan's tenure.

In addition to the agency initiatives outlined above, several other initiatives and factors seemed likely to influence the NDA review process going forward:

- *From Paper-based to Electronic NDAs.* CDER has spent the last several years laying the regulatory groundwork for computer-assisted new drug applications, or electronic NDAs (eNDA), to replace the traditional paper-based NDA (see Chapter 7). This process began with the release of a March 1997 final regulation, which established the agency's criteria for accepting electronic records, including eNDAs, and electronic signatures as equivalent to paper records and handwritten signatures (previously, electronic records and submissions could only supplement paper-based records and filings, which were required by regulation). With the March 1997 final regulation in place, CDER made various types of applications (e.g., INDs and NDAs) formally eligible for electronic submission by publishing guidances that address each type of submission. In recent years, the numbers of eNDAs submitted and the numbers of companies developing them have increased markedly. By late 2002, CDER officials reported that about 75% of all new NDA submissions were considered electronic filings and, of those, roughly 90% were entirely electronic. Under a December 2003 final rule (and a February 2004 draft guidance entitled, *Providing Regulatory Submissions in Electronic Format-Content of Labeling*), the agency required, for the first time, that a portion of the NDA—a new "content of labeling" section—be provided in electronic form in all cases (see discussion below).

- *From eNDAs to eCTDs.* CDER's flirtations with eNDAs and even paper-based CTDs were simply precursors to what regulators and industry saw as the true future for marketing dossiers: the eCTD. In April 2003, the FDA released an ICH guidance entitled, *M2 eCTD: Electronic Common Technical Document Specification* to "list the criteria that will make an electronic submission technically valid." Then, in an August 2003 draft guidance entitled, *Providing Regulatory Submissions in Electronic Format-Human Pharmaceutical Product Applications and Related Submissions*, the FDA recommended that companies begin submitting eCTD backbone files" because the agency believes that "having the information in the eCTD backbone files will result in greater efficiency in the future." CDER noted that, although the CTD and eCTD formats were developed for marketing dossiers, industry could unlock the true value of the eCTD by using the format for earlier submissions, particularly INDs. "We believe it is most beneficial to begin your eCTD-based submissions with the initial submission of the application," said the agency. "The maximum benefit will be derived once an application is in electronic format. This is particularly true for the IND, where submissions are provided over a long period of time." Further highlighting CDER's desire to accelerate the eCTD era was a simultaneously released web posting announcing that the center "would like to work closely with people who plan to provide a submission using the" new FDA-detailed eCTD specifications.

- *Adopting Standards for Clinical Data Submissions.* In July 2004, the FDA announced that it had adopted the Clinical Data Interchange Consortium's Study Data Tabulation Model (SDTM), which clinical trial sponsors can use to submit clinical data to the agency. Noting that the SDTM will lead to greater efficiencies in clinical research and NDA reviews, the agency was exploring "regulatory approaches" to require the SDTM standard for regulatory submissions. "The importance of a standard for the exchange of clinical trial data cannot be overstated," Acting FDA Commissioner Lester Crawford, Ph.D., stated at the time. "FDA reviewers spend far too much valuable time simply reorganizing large amounts of data submitted in varying formats. Having the data presented in a standard structure will improve FDA's ability to evaluate the data and help speed new discoveries to the public." In addition, the agency noted, the standard will help to "automate the largely paper-based clinical trials research process." The SDTM standard has been added to other specifications listed under the agency's draft guidance entitled, *Providing Regulatory Submissions in Electronic Format-Human Pharmaceutical Applications and Related Submissions.*

- In September 2004, CDER announced that it would, by mid-2005, transition to a new "risk-based pharmaceutical quality assessment system" under which it will encourage companies to submit different types of product chemistry-related information in NDAs and under which the center would reorganize its process for reviewing the chemistry section of NDAs (and INDs and sNDAs). As part of the new initiative, the FDA will ask NDA applicants to provide more pharmaceutical development information and to develop comprehensive quality summaries (similar to those provided in CTD-formatted applications) that will support a new review model for chemistry sections within new drug applications (see discussion below and Chapter 7). The new review model will involve what is called a pharmaceutical assessment lead (PAL), a high-level reviewer who will assess the NDA's chemistry section to identify the critical factors related to product quality and consider review-related needs before forwarding the application to a review chemist.

- *Pharmacogenomics and Other Advances in Scientific Understanding.* As they will other elements of the drug development and approval process, important scientific advances will continue to affect the NDA review process. In a November 2003 draft guidance entitled, *Pharmacogenomic Data Submissions,* for instance, the agency took its first step to encourage industry to submit pharmacogenomics information in NDAs and other applications to help FDA reviewers and scientists understand the relevant scientific issues in this emerging field (see discussion below). While the agency prepared to release a final guidance document in late 2004, CDER officials claimed that center reviewers were actively reviewing and making decisions based on voluntarily submitted pharmacogenomic data. Meanwhile, past drug withdrawals along with scientific advances in the understanding of specific drug effects and their implications for human health have sensitized drug developers and FDA reviewers to certain adverse drug effects—liver toxicities (the most common reason for drug withdrawals) and QTc prolongation, in particular—in assessing new drugs. In June 2003, for example, members of CDER's

Cardiovascular and Renal Drugs Advisory Committee encouraged the FDA to consider requiring that NDAs for all NMEs include clinical data characterizing effects on the QT interval.

- *Integration of Risk Management/Minimization into NDA Reviews.* As the result of the FDA's focus on risk management under PDUFA III, the reviews of certain NDAs are likely to involve an assessment of what are called "risk minimization action plans," or RiskMAPs. In a May 2004 draft industry guidance entitled, *Development and Use of Risk Minimization Action Plans*, the FDA notes that, while routine risk minimization measures (e.g., FDA-approved professional labeling) will be sufficient for most products, "for a small number of products where a [RiskMAP] should be considered...sponsors are encouraged to consider developing a RiskMAP," which the agency defines as "a strategic safety program designed to meet specific goals and objectives in minimizing known risks of a product while preserving its benefits" (see Chapter 7). In the draft guidance, the agency notes that a company can submit a RiskMAP before or after approval, and that the plan should be submitted in either the IND or NDA if it is to be filed in advance of marketing clearance. Under interim procedures adopted in late 2002, CDER began to involve reviewers from the center's Office of Drug Safety (ODS) in the NDA development (as early as the pre-NDA meeting) and review process to address risk management issues (e.g., the risk management plans). Under these procedures, ODS staff are involved in the reviews of all new molecular entities (NME) and any non-NME drugs thought to present a specific risk-management issue. The agency's PDUFA III commitments/procedures are even more explicit in reserving a role for ODS in the NDA review process: "Both the review division and the appropriate safety group will be involved in the review of the application...."

Although significant, such factors are unlikely to affect the basic nature of drug reviews. In several ways, the NDA review is similar to the IND review. The NDA is forwarded to the same division and, most likely, many of the same reviewers who evaluated the IND for the drug. And like the IND evaluation, the NDA review involves an assessment of key medical/clinical, nonclinical pharmacology/toxicology, and manufacturing issues. In several important ways, however, the NDA review process is unique:

- The NDA is a significantly larger and more complex document than the IND. Therefore, the NDA review absorbs far greater resources. Whereas INDs often comprise a few dozen volumes, NDAs for new molecular entities have averaged over 200 volumes in the past.

- The FDA's evaluation of the NDA involves a detailed assessment of the drug's clinical safety and effectiveness, while the IND review, in many cases, involves only an assessment of the drug's likely clinical effects based on preclinical animal data.

- The implications of the actions proposed in an NDA are much more substantial than those proposed in an IND. Under a newly activated IND, a drug is used in patient populations of limited size and under carefully controlled and monitored conditions. When an NDA is approved, however, a drug may be prescribed for thousands of patients who comprise a group much larger and less homogeneous than those that were involved in clinical trials. In addition, a marketed drug generally is used under significantly less carefully monitored conditions than during the clinical testing phase.

A Profile of the NDA Review Process

Several factors make efforts to profile the FDA's NDA review process particularly challenging. While CDER traditionally has maintained guidelines on various activities, the center has offered few analyses of the NDA review process in the past. Clearly, this is changing, however, as the agency continues to release various inter nal policy guidances (i.e., MaPPs) on specific aspects of the drug review process. CDER's July 2003 draft Good Review Management Principles provide perhaps the most detailed account of the initial NDA review cycle ever developed. As noted, CDER's related efforts to develop review "templates" for key review disciplines continue to provide important insights into the new drug review process. Meanwhile, the user-fee performance goals facing CDER have made some aspects of the review process more transparent and predictable.

Secondly, the various NDA review approaches by CDER's drug review divisions differ in some ways. While CDER reviewers function under the same umbrella of laws and regulations and while the drug center continues to look for ways to standardize the NDA review process, then-CDER Director Janet Woodcock, M.D., noted in 1999 that the drug review process remains very much a "cottage industry," and that reviewers are "artists" who have a certain license to approach and conduct NDA reviews as they choose within the general framework, policies, and review templates.

Continuing CDER reorganization and the adoption of new review models to increase review efficiencies also make profiling the NDA review process difficult (see discussions below). Still, the NDA review process is sufficiently uniform across CDER's new drug review divisions to permit a general analysis, such as the overview provided in the following sections.

Initial Processing of the NDA

As it does for INDs, CDER's Central Document Room (CDR) handles the initial processing of all NDAs, including electronic submissions. This processing is largely administrative in nature—staffers record information on the filing, including the name of the sponsor and the drug, and the application's identification number, which is assigned by the CDR. Staffers also stamp the application with a receipt date, which starts the review timeline applicable to the filing under the prescription drug user fee program (see discussion below). Any paper-based components of the NDA are then forwarded to the document room that supports the new drug review division that will evaluate the application. All electronic components of the NDA are forwarded to CDER's Electronic Document Room (EDR), where these documents are loaded onto servers and are archived. The EDR then notifies the NDA reviewers that the documents are available on the CDER network.

Processing Within the Drug Review Division

Following the initial processing of the NDA, CDER's Central Document Room forwards the submission to a similar document control room within the review division responsible for the application's review. After the NDA is logged in, a division staffer prepares an acknowledgement letter for the applicant. This letter informs the sponsor of the application's NDA number and date of receipt, and identifies the regulatory project manager who will serve as the company's contact person within the division—in many cases, the project manager assigned to a drug's IND will be assigned to the NDA as well. The project manager functions, in part, as a coordinator for the entire NDA review, ensuring that the application is distributed and is evaluated within milestones set for the NDA.

Upon receiving the NDA, the project manager performs an initial screening to ensure that the application is complete (and that all user fees have been paid). This screening is the first and less detailed of two such screenings that the application will face before gaining access to the formal review process. If the submission is found to be seriously incomplete, the division will refuse to file the NDA, and will return the submission to the applicant with a letter describing the deficiencies.

If the NDA passes this initial screening, the application's technical sections are distributed to members of th NDA review team. Specifically, the application will be forwarded to what are termed "core team members, which include, in addition to the RPM:

- the medical/clinical reviewer

- the pharmacology/toxicology reviewer

- the chemistry, manufacturing and controls reviewer

- the biometrics/statistical reviewer

- the clinical pharmacology and biopharmaceutics reviewer

- the clinical microbiology reviewer (e.g., for anti-infective drugs)

- the bioresearch monitoring reviewer (responsible for verifying clinical, nonclinical, or bio-pharmaceutic research data)

Although NDA review team assignments generally are based on reviewer assignments for the associated INI for the product, factors such as workload and competing priorities may influence these assignments. Whe necessary, these individuals will be supplemented by consultancy reviewers (e.g., staff to review environmen tal assessments, risk minimization plans, a drug's abuse potential, and tradename and labeling issues) fror other divisions.

Each reviewer then undertakes a more thorough, or technical, screening of the NDA, called a "completenes review" within some divisions and a "filing review" within others. This evaluation ensures that sufficient dat and information have been submitted in each area to justify "filing" the application—that is, initiating the foi mal review of the NDA. Reviewers can request, and NDA applicants can submit, additional information dui ing the filing review process.

Generally, the review team then convenes with division management in what is called a "45-Day Meeting" (s named because it takes place within 45 days of the NDA's submission) to determine whether the applicatio should be filed or refused (see section below). The formal filing decision is made by the review division direc tor based on the assessments and recommendations of the regulatory project manager, reviewers, team leac ers and, if necessary, consultants and the office director.

If, during the 45-day meeting, the team and division management agree that the application should be filec the meeting may then be used as a review-planning session. At this planning session, the review team assign a review priority to the application (i.e., standard or priority), a designation that reflects the therapeuti importance of the drug and that will define the agency's timeline for taking formal action on the applicatio (see discussion below). In addition, the review team will often set several internal review milestones that ar deemed necessary for the division to meet the review goal applicable to the NDA (see discussion below Although some divisions have shared these mid-review goals with the NDA's sponsor in the past, CDER's Jul 2003 GRMP draft guidance notes that, "the applicant should not expect to be apprised of all interim timeline for internal FDA processes..." and that "routine conveyance by the FDA of interim review process timelines an speculative action dates is discouraged."

The FDA's Refuse-to-File Authorities

NDAs that the review team and division management agree, prior to the start of the formal review, are incom plete or deficient become the subject of a formal refuse-to-file (RTF) action. In such cases, the review division prepares a letter advising the applicant of the RTF decision and the deficiencies upon which it is based. The division will attempt to forward this letter within 60 days after the NDA receipt date. According to CDER policy, all RTF decisions should involve consultations with the relevant office director (e.g., ODE I director).

For several reasons, the agency's RTF policies gained a significantly higher profile in the early 1990s. First, beginning in 1993, RTF decisions began to carry a direct financial penalty for NDA sponsors—for the first time under PDUFA I, companies had to surrender a portion of the full application fee when an NDA was refused. Moreover, with pressures to take action on NDAs within aggressive user-fee timelines, CDER officials warned industry that the application of the RTF policy would become more stringent. In a July 1993 RTF guidance document, CDER pointed out that, "in the past, decisions to refuse to file an application generally were based on extreme deficiencies, e.g., the total omission of a needed section or the absence of any study that was even arguably an adequate and well-controlled study. More recently, applications have been refused when less extreme deficiencies existed, but when it was clear that the deficiencies were severe enough to make the application not approvable without major modification."

Several years into the prescription drug user-fee program, the agency proclaimed that industry had responded to the clarion call for higher quality submissions, and that the increased quality of NDA filings was one of the program's most significant successes. More than a decade into the user-fee program, CDER's RTF rate dropped from 29% (1993) to 3% (2003). While some CDER divisions have not refused any NDAs in recent years, RTF rates can vary considerably between review units (see exhibit below).

CDER's July 1993 RTF guidance document states that the center will exercise RTF authority under three circumstances: (1) omission of a section of the NDA required under federal regulations, or presentation of a section in so haphazard a manner as to render it incomplete on its face; (2) clear failure to include evidence of effectiveness compatible with the statute and regulations; and (3) omission of critical data, information, or analyses needed to evaluate effectiveness and safety or provide adequate directions for use. Most importantly, the document instructs CDER to continue basing RTF decisions "on omissions or inadequacies so severe as to render the application incomplete on its face. To be a basis for RTF, the omissions or inadequacies should be obvious, at least once identified, and not a matter of interpretation or judgment about the meaning of data submitted. The RTF is not an appropriate vehicle for dealing with complex and close judgments on such matters as balancing risks and benefits, magnitude of drug effect, acceptability of a plausible surrogate marker, or nuances of study design (although designs that are obviously inadequate may lead to RTF...)." For a more recent discussion of RTF issues, applicants should refer to a May 2003 CDER MaPP entitled, NDAs: *Filing Review Issues* (see discussion below).

Despite the guidance quoted above, CDER's review divisions have considerable discretion regarding RTF decisions. For example, the document states that "minor defects or omissions that could be repaired after the review commenced and that would not materially interfere with or delay review of the remainder of the application should not lead to RTF." Further, the RTF policy provides review divisions with several discretionary powers (e.g., the right to not issue RTFs for NDAs for critically needed new drugs). In addition, even if the reviewers determine that the identified issues are "substantive and prohibit further review of the application," they can provide the applicant with an opportunity to address the deficiencies if those deficiencies are judged to be readily correctable in advance of the 60-day filing date.

Voluntarily withdrawing an NDA is an option available to applicants at any point following the NDA's submission, including the filing stage. According to CDER's July 2003 draft Good Review Management Principles

Divisional RTF Actions, 1993–2003
Percent of NDAs Refused

(# of RTF actions/# of NDA submissions)

	1993	1994	1995*	1996*	1997*	1998*	1999*	2000*	2001*	2002*	2003*
Cardio-Renal Drug Products	0% (0/11)	0% (0/8)	0% (0/11)	0% (0/9)	10% (1/10)	22% (2/9)	0% (0/9)	0% (0/7)	0% (0/8)	0% (0/9)	17% (1/6)
Neuropharmacological Drug Products	17% (1/6)	27% (3/11)	23% (3/13)	0% (0/16)	0% (0/15)	9% (2/22)	0% (0/10)	20% (3/15)	0% (0/10)	5% (1/19)	0% (0/13)
Oncologic Drug Products	–	–	0% (0/5)	10% (1/10)	0% (0/8)	9% (1/11)	8% (1/12)	0% (0/8)	0% (0/4)	0% (0/3)	0% (0/3)
Pulmonary Drug Products	–	–	20% (2/10)	14% (1/7)	0% (0/12)	0% (0/10)	0% (0/4)	0% (0/9)	8% (1/12)	0% (0/3)	0% (0/8)
Medical Imaging and Radiopharm. Drug Products	–	–	0% (0/8)	0% (0/5)	0% (0/4)	0% (0/6)	0% (0/2)	0% (0/4)	0% (0/4)	0% (0/1)	25% (1/4)
Gastrointestinal and Coagulation Drug Products	57% (4/7)	15% (2/13)	0% (0/13)	0% (0/11)	0% (0/7)	0% (0/6)	0% (0/6)	8% (1/12)	25% (1/4)	0% (0/9)	0% (0/4)
Metabolism and Endocrine Drug Products	50% (6/12)	11% (2/19)	0% (0/12)	0% (0/12)	0% (0/9)	8% (1/12)	8% (2/24)	11% (2/19)	13% (2/15)	14% (1/7)	0% (0/14)
Anti-Infective Drug Products	27% (4/15)	0% (0/8)	0% (0/12)	33% (1/3)	0% (0/11)	0% (0/6)	0% (0/5)	0% (0/6)	0% (0/4)	25% (1/4)	0% (0/4)
Antiviral Drug Products	0% (0/7)	0% (0/15)	0% (0/11)	0% (0/8)	0% (0/6)	0% (0/6)	13% (1/8)	0% (0/7)	0% (0/3)	0% (0/8)	0% (0/4)
Dermatological and Dental Drug Products	–	–	0% (0/13)	0% (0/7)	0% (0/11)	10% (1/10)	0% (0/13)	0% (0/10)	0% (0/5)	0% (0/3)	0% (0/4)
Anesthetic, Critical Care and Addiction Drug Products	–	–	0% (0/12)	0% (0/3)	0% (0/2)	0% (0/7)	0% (0/3)	0% (0/3)	0% (0/3)	0% (0/6)	0% (0/4)
Anti-Inflammatory, Analgesic and Ophthalmic Drug Products	–	–	0% (0/12)	11% (1/9)	0% (0/8)	0% (0/7)	0% (0/14)	0% (0/12)	0% (0/7)	0% (0/10)	6% (1/17)
Special Pathogens and Immunologic Drug Products+	–	–	–	0% (0/9)	0% (0/12)	0% (0/8)	0% (0/9)	0% (0/5)	0% (0/9)	0% (0/7)	0% (0/10)
Reproductive and Urologic Drug Products	–	–	0% (0/6)	7% (1/14)	0% (0/13)	0% (0/8)	0% (0/15)	0% (0/16)	0% (0/12)	7% (1/15)	0% (0/10)
Over-the-Counter Drug Products	–	–	0% (0/2)	0% (0/0)	0% (0/0)	0% (0/4)	0% (0/2)	0% (0/2)	0% (0/1)	0% (0/0)	0% (0/0)
Total**	29% (25/86)	13% (17/133)	4% (5/140)	4% (5/123)	0.8% (1/128)	5% (7/131)	3% (4/136)	4% (6/135)	4% (4/101)	4% (4/104)	3% (3/108)

* 1995–2003 data are fiscal year data. Data as of 4/30/98 for FY97 and 1/31/99 for FY98.

** Divisional statistics may not add to totals because of several reorganizations.

+ Division created in 1997. FY95 and FY96 figures adjusted to include drugs under this division as if it had existed as c FY95.

Source: FDA; U.S. Regulatory Reporter

guidance, however, "officials at the FDA should not request or suggest to an applicant that the applicant withdraw a pending marketing application except in the most unusual circumstances (e.g., the marketing application was submitted to the wrong FDA center)." Although some firms may prefer to withdraw an NDA rather than face an "adverse regulatory action" (an RTF action or a not-approvable action later in the process), the GRMP draft guidance establishes that a review division should leave this decision to the applicant. The draft GRMPs also discourage applicants from withdrawing an NDA, noting that "it is generally preferable for the Agency to issue an official written regulatory action documenting its review...."

Under a July 2004 proposed regulation, the FDA would implement another change that might further discourage companies from withdrawing applications to avoid an "adverse regulatory action." According to the proposed rule, "if, by the time it receives such notice [of a sponsor's intent to withdraw an application], the agency has identified any deficiencies in the application, we will list such deficiencies in the letter we send the applicant acknowledging the withdrawal." Such an FDA communication of deficiencies, some believe, could expose NDA sponsors to increased investor pressure to publicly disclose the specific application deficiencies identified in such agency letters.

In recent years, some have recommended that the agency toughen its criteria at the filing stage. A March 2003 Department of Health and Human Services report, for example, suggested that the agency can and should use its RTF authorities more aggressively. Meanwhile, the FDA's July 2003 draft Good Review Management Principles implore industry "to manage the drug development pipeline" in a way that culminates in the submission of a complete application, even if that means delaying an NDA submission. And while certain CDER officials have even mentioned that the center may be too lenient in accepting some "fileable but incomplete" NDA submissions, CDER's RTF rates continue to hover near all-time lows.

Although certain CDER divisions had accepted incomplete applications, sometimes called "rolling NDAs," in the past as part of an effort to expedite the review of high-priority products, legislative and regulatory initiatives have attempted to formalize this practice over the last several years. First, the FDA Modernization Act of 1997 formally called on the agency to accept rolling NDAs in specific cases. Under the legislation's "fast track" review procedure, which is applicable to drugs that have the potential to address unmet medical needs for serious and life-threatening conditions, the FDA can accept for filing and begin the review of an incomplete NDA for a designated fast track product, provided that the applicant provides a schedule for the submission of information necessary to make the application complete and that the company pays the required user fees. In most cases under this program, the agency will accept only "complete sections" of the NDA (e.g., a complete chemistry, manufacturing and controls section) before the remaining sections are submitted (see Chapter 15).

More recently, under PDUFA III, the agency agreed to establish a pilot program under which it would accept specific elements of NDAs—termed "reviewable units"—before the complete application is submitted (see Chapters 7 and 15). Ultimately, the agency will have an expert formally assess the costs and benefits of this pilot program to, for the first time, gain a true indication of whether this long-standing practice actually leads to faster and more efficient reviews.

Outside these programs, however, the agency is openly discouraging—although not entirely prohibiting—the submission of incomplete NDAs (see Chapter 7). In its July 2003 GRMP draft guidance, the agency states that "requests for the FDA to accept for review planned amendments that complete an application during the first-cycle review process should be minimized and should be discussed and agreed to in advance with the FDA.

Such requests and agreements should generally be limited to situations when the FDA agrees that there is a valid public health urgency to expedite the availability of an important new product." Then, in mid-2004, CDER Office of New Drugs Director John Jenkins, M.D., noted that, while firms continue to ask agency reviewers if they can submit data necessary for approval following the NDA's submission, "that's not the deal we made in PDUFA." Due to the high percentage of "incomplete applications" that CDER continues to receive and accept the drug center "is drowning in resubmissions," Jenkins stated.

PDUFA III and Early Notification of NDA Issues

Given their focus on improving the first-cycle reviews of NDAs, both PDUFA III and CDER's GRMP initiative include provisions that address the filing review process, what could be seen as the first significant step in that cycle. To notify applicants as early as possible regarding potential "substantive deficiencies" in the NDA, the FDA agreed to communicate deficiencies identified in the filing review process directly to applicants via letter, conference, fax, secure e-mail, or other "expedient means" within 14 days after the 60-day application filing date for 90% of the FY2005-FY2007 NDAs. Subsequently, the agency disclosed that it planned to issue these communications, called "74-day letters," even in those cases in which the initial filing review detected no deficiencies.

While acknowledging the value of such early alerts to applicants, CDER officials quickly relayed their concerns that industry might place more-than-the-appropriate significance on 74-day letters. In particular, CDER officials emphasized that the identification of what are called "filing review issues" in 74-day letters is based on the initial, preliminary review at the filing stage. Also, in response to some industry uncertainty regarding 74-day letters that do not identify specific issues, CDER officials have pointed out that such "no issue" letters may, in some cases, reflect the fact that a reviewer, although he or she determines that an NDA is fileable, may lack the time to provide more detailed feedback.

Despite characterizing filing review issues as important deficiencies, the FDA notes in MaPP 6010.5-NDAs Filing Review Issues (May 2003) that such issues are "distinct from application deficiencies that serve as the basis for a Refuse to File action. Filing review issues pertain only to applications that have been filed." While this passage implies that filing review issues are less serious than deficiencies that serve as the basis for refuse to file actions, it adds that filing review issues comprise "substantive deficiencies or concerns...that appear to have been inadequately addressed in the application and merit particular attention during the review process. These issues may have significant impact on the Agency's ability to complete the review of the application or approve the application or parts of the application."

MaPP 6010.5 adds that 74-day letters should include the agency's expectations in terms of an applicant's response to the identified issues. In this way, the letters provide applicants with not only an early indication of review issues, but what the agency expects the applicant to do to address these issues as the review process proceeds.

In mid-2003, CDER officials released selected statistics on the center's early experiences with 74-day letters. Over a six-month period, CDER issued 38 74-day letters, 18 of which were characterized as "issue letters" because a division identified filing review issues. During this period, the center also issued 20 "no issue" letters, which informed the sponsors that the review divisions did not identify substantive issues during the preliminary filing reviews. Among the issues that CDER cited as filing review issues over this period included: (1) uncertainty regarding the trade name sought by the sponsor; (2) preliminary indications that a primary efficacy analysis cited in an NDA had failed; and (3) a question regarding the adequacy of data relating the clinical trial product to the product that would be marketed.

According to CDER data, CDER was able to issue 74-day letters within the established user-fee review timeline for 80% of the FY2003 NDAs. Under its PDUFA III performance goals, the agency had committed to issuing such letters within 74 days of receipt for 50% of the FY2003 submissions, 70% of the FY2004 submissions, and 90% of the FY2005-FY2007 filings.

The Preapproval Inspection

Traditionally, a division's decision to file an NDA has triggered a few actions, including the beginning of the primary review process (see discussion below). It has also triggered a division request for a preapproval inspection of the sponsor's manufacturing facilities. Under CDER's emerging *Good Review Management Principles*, however, CDER advises that requests for manufacturing facility inspections and research site inspections (see discussion below) "be made early in the review cycle and, optimally, prior to the filing date."

During preapproval inspections, FDA field investigators audit manufacturing-related statements and commitments made in the NDA against the sponsor's actual manufacturing practices. Specifically, the FDA has several goals in conducting these inspections:

1. To verify the accuracy and completeness of the manufacturing-related information submitted in the NDA.

2. To evaluate the manufacturing controls for the preapproval batches upon which information provided in the NDA is based.

3. To evaluate the manufacturer's capabilities to comply with cGMPs and manufacturing-related commitments made in the NDA. In doing so, the FDA investigator will determine whether the necessary facilities, equipment, systems, and controls are functioning.

4. To collect a variety of drug samples for analysis by FDA field and CDER laboratories. These samples may be subjected to several analyses, including methods validation, methods verification, and profile sampling (i.e., taking a "fingerprint" of the actual product).

Under CDER's traditional policy, product-specific preapproval inspections generally were conducted for products: (1) that were new chemical or molecular entities; (2) that had narrow therapeutic ranges; (3) that represented the first approval for the applicant; or (4) that were sponsored by a company with a history of cGMP problems or that were manufactured in a facility that has not been the subject of a cGMP inspection over a considerable period. Under its *Pharmaceutical cGMPs for the 21st Century* initiative (see Chapter 11), however, CDER revised its preapproval inspection compliance program to allow its field inspectors to employ a risk-based approach, which provides agency inspectors with greater flexibility in determining whether a preapproval inspection is warranted in specific cases. In September 2003, CDER revised its compliance policy program guidance manual 7346.832-Preapproval Inspections to no longer mandate that manufacturers of the top 200 prescription drugs or companies manufacturing narrow therapeutic range products be automatically targeted for preapproval inspections as part of the NDA review process. These changes, said the agency, were designed to "help reduce the number of preapproval inspections and leverage preapproval resources, where practical, for post approval and/or cGMP coverage."

Under the revisions to program guidance manual 7346.832, CDER's new "strategy for assigning inspection requests for preapproval inspections has been divided into two categories, (1) categories [of products and applications] that will regularly prompt an inspection request, and (2) categories when the district office may elect to perform an inspection." Although the following categories will regularly prompt a preapproval inspection request, the field offices can recommend that the inspection not be conducted, consistent with th agency's emerging risk-based approach: (1) new molecular entities (including finished drug products an active ingredients); (2) priority NDAs; (3) a first application filed by an applicant; (4) for-cause inspections; (5 original NDA applications submitted by firms with an unacceptable cGMP status or that have not bee inspected within the past two years; (4) certain pre-approval supplemental applications (e.g., for site chang or major construction) if the applicant's cGMP status is unacceptable; (5) treatment INDs; and (6) wheneve CDER has information indicating that an inspection of a clinical supplies manufacturer is warranted to pro tect patient health.

In September 2004, the FDA announced that it planned to spend the next year revamping the entire preap proval inspection program "to further reflect the thinking that has been derived from the cGMP for the 21s Century Initiative, including means for better Agency communication from review to inspection on produc design, identifying process issues that are most relevant to product design, and the use of center specialist on inspections."

During September 2003, CDER and the Office of Regulatory Affairs announced the formation of a nev Pharmaceutical Inspectorate, a specialized group that will conduct certain highly complex drug manufac turing quality inspections, including relevant preapproval inspections (see Chapter 11). According to CDEF the Pharmaceutical Inspectorate comprises a special group of field inspectors within the agency's large field inspectional force who have "specialized experience and specific training in evaluating pharmaceuti cal manufacturing" and who will be trained in and dedicated to assessing high-risk drug manufacturin operations. CDER estimated that the Pharmaceutical Inspectorate would grow to 50 "highly trained indi viduals" by FY2007.

By fall 2004, CDER reported that 26 candidate inspectors were selected for the Pharmaceutical Inspectorate and that training had begun. Because one of the agency's goals is to foster a closer working relationshi between field inspectors and CDER's review chemists, the new candidates were scheduled to go on tempc rary details within CDER and other centers (CBER) to learn about the centers' work.

It is CDER's goal to have the preapproval inspection assigned and conducted two months before the actio due date applicable to an NDA. More specific guidance on CDER's preapproval inspection program is avail able from the center's Compliance Program Guide 7346.832.

Under a pilot cGMP-related program initiated in early 1999, CDER had been contacting drug-manufacturin facilities routinely to inform them of when agency investigators would arrive for preapproval inspection: Although the pilot program was discontinued in early 2001, FDA investigators in many district offices still hav the option of providing manufacturing sites with advance notice of upcoming preapproval inspections. If a inspection involves a new manufacturing site or a site that received a past warning letter, no such advanc notice is provided.

At the conclusion of the preapproval inspection, the field office that conducted the inspection will recorr mend that the application be approved or that approval be withheld because of the inspection results (c because the facility was not ready). According to CDER data, the center conducted preapproval inspection on 589 manufacturing plants in support of NDAs during FY2003.

Under the FDA Modernization Act of 1997, no action of a review division (e.g., NDA review) may be delaye based on the results of a preapproval inspection or other information from field personnel, or the lack of infoi mation from the field investigators (such as delays in conducting such an inspection), "unless the reviewing division determines that a delay is necessary to assure the marketing of a safe and effective product." In MaPP 6020.8 entitled, *Action Packages for NDAs and Efficacy Supplements*, however, CDER notes that, before an action on an NDA can be taken, all requested facility inspections must have "progressed sufficiently that a recommendation from the Division of Manufacturing and Product Quality can be documented."

It is important to note that other types of FDA inspections that are conducted on a preapproval basis can affect the progress, or even the outcome, of the NDA review process. Under CDER's Bioresearch Monitoring (BIMO) Program, agency investigators inspect clinical investigators, drug sponsors, nonclinical facilities, IRBs, and others to ensure the accuracy and validity of data submitted in an NDA, and to ensure that the rights and welfare of clinical subjects were protected during clinical trials (for a complete discussion of CDER's Bioresearch Monitoring Program, see Chapter 14). MaPP 6020.8 notes that, before CDER can take a formal action on an NDA, the BIMO inspection(s) relevant to the application must have progressed sufficiently that the BIMO reviewer can provide an assessment of the "usability" of the data in the NDA.

The Primary Review Process

Once the review team determines that an NDA is "fileable," the "primary" review begins. During this process, each member of the review team sifts through volumes of research data, analyses, and information applicable to his or her reviewing expertise:

Clinical Reviewer: Evaluates the clinical data to determine if the drug is safe and effective in its proposed use(s). In determining the product's risk/benefit ratio, the clinical reviewer(s) assesses the clinical significance of the drug's therapeutic effects in relation to its possible adverse effects. Under its Good Review Practices initiative, CDER continues its efforts to standardize NDA reviews in all review disciplines and to outline both the safety and efficacy components of the clinical review. The first product of this effort was a November 1996 draft reviewer guidance entitled, *Conducting a Clinical Safety Review of a New Product Application and Preparing a Report on the Review*, which stated that "the goals of a safety review are (1) to identify important adverse events that are causally related to the use of the drug, (2) to estimate incidence for those events, and (3) to identify factors that predict the occurrence of those events. If there is one principle that underlies this guidance it would be the inadequacy of an approach involving only the review of individual studies in an NDA without any attempt to integrate the findings. Consequently, this guidance focuses on approaches to organizing and integrating the findings across studies in a manner that facilitates the regulatory tasks." After implementing a standardized NDA review template for clinical reviewers on a pilot basis in 2001, CDER formally released a long-awaited *Clinical Review Template* (July 2004) in the form of MaPP 6010.3 to provide "a structured outline" for the clinical review and to "promote consistency in the documentation of [review] elements and provide for the ready retrieval of information." A few months earlier, CDER had released the *Clinical Pharmacology and Biopharmaceutics Review Template* (see discussion below) to specify how agency reviewers should document clinical pharmacology and biopharmaceutics reviews. Also, under a component of the Good Review Practices initiative called the Reviewer Diagram Project (GRP Track II), several CDER clinical reviewers have attempted to document and outline their individual NDA review processes to allow reviewers and managers to record and visualize the steps in the process (as of mid-2004, five medical reviewers from four divisions had developed and released clinical review diagrams).

Pharmacology/Toxicology Reviewer: Evaluates the entire body of nonclinical data and analyses, with a focus on the newly submitted long-term test data, to identify relevant implications for the drug's clinical safety. In May 2001 as part of the good review practices initiative, CDER implemented and released an internal review guidance entitled, *Pharmacology/Toxicology Review Format*, which provides a standardized review format for IND/NDA pharmacology/toxicology reviews. Upon the release of the guidance, CDER stated that is employs a standardized format for such reviews for several reasons, including that standardization provides for unified communication among multiple audiences and that it ensures that the most important information is captured in all reviews.

Chemistry Reviewer: Evaluates commercial-stage manufacturing procedures (e.g., method of synthesis or isolation, purification process, and process controls), and the specifications and analytical methods used to assure the identity, strength, purity, and bioavailability of the drug product. Under the FDA's *Pharmaceutical cGMPs for the 21st Century* initiative, CDER will be adopting, in mid-2005, a new "pharmaceutical quality assessment system" that will include a new model for the center's review of the NDA's chemistry section (see exhibit below).

Statistical Reviewer: Evaluates the pivotal clinical data to determine if there exists statistically significant evidence of the drug's safety and effectiveness, the appropriateness of the sponsor's clinical data analyses and the assumptions under which these analyses were performed, the statistical significance of newly submitted nonclinical data, and the implications of stability data for establishing appropriate expiration dating for the product.

Biopharmaceutics Reviewer: Evaluates pharmacokinetic and bioavailability data used to establish appropriate drug dosing. In April 2004, CDER released the *Clinical Pharmacology and Biopharmaceutics Review Template* to specify how agency reviewers should document clinical pharmacology and biopharmaceutics reviews.

Microbiology Reviewer: For certain drug products (anti-infectives, antivirals, and special pathogen drugs), a CDER microbiologist will evaluate the drug's effects on target viruses or other microorganisms. For sterile drugs and certain non-sterile drug products (e.g., aqueous dosage forms that can support microbial growth), a microbiologist will conduct a product quality assessment.

Bioresearch Monitoring Reviewer: As noted, a reviewer from CDER's Division of Scientific Investigations (DSI) provides an assessment of the "usability" of the clinical, nonclinical, and biopharmaceutics data in the NDA.

Based on an NDA's content, the review team may "issue consults" to review other elements of the application including, as necessary, the environmental assessment, a drug's abuse potential (consulted to CDER's Controlled Substances Staff), and the tradename/package insert/patient package insert, MedGuide or other consumer information (consulted to CDER's Division of Drug Marketing, Advertising and Communications). Also included as consult reviewers for the NDA will be postmarketing drug safety staff from CDER's Office of Drug Safety, who will work with the review division to assess "risk minimization action plans" and advise both applicants and the review division staff on appropriate post-approval risk management tools (see exhibit below).

Much of the primary review process involves reviewers' attempts to confirm and validate the sponsor's conclusion that a drug is safe and effective in its proposed use. However, it is also likely to involve a reanalysis or an extension of the analyses conducted and presented by the sponsor in the NDA. For example, the medical reviewer may seek to reanalyze a drug's effectiveness in a particular patient subpopulation not analyzed in the original submission. Similarly, the reviewer may disagree with the sponsor's assessment of evaluable patients, and seek to retest effectiveness claims based on the reviewer-defined patient populations.

There is also likely to be considerable communication between review team members during the primary review process. If a medical reviewer's reanalysis of clinical data produces results different than the sponsor's for example, the reviewer is likely to forward this information to the statistical reviewer with a request for

CDER's New Quality Assessment System and the Review of the NDA's Chemistry Section

Under the *Pharmaceutical cGMPs for the 21st Century Initiative*, CDER's Office of New Drug Chemistry (ONDC) is establishing "a modern, risk-based pharmaceutical quality assessment system to replace the current CMC review system." Scheduled for full implementation in spring 2005,* the new quality assessment system "is intended to address the multiple challenges and difficulties facing ONDC and to establish a framework to facilitate continuous CMC improvement and innovation in the pharmaceutical industry."

According to an FDA document entitled, ONDC's *New Risk-Based Pharmaceutical Quality System* (September 2004), the challenges and difficulties facing ONDC include the following:

- Inconsistencies in application quality combined with a lack of adequate pharmaceutical development information in NDA submissions is preventing the agency from taking full advantage of risk-based assessments, and is leading to multiple CMC review cycles and an increase in the number of postmarketing manufacturing supplements submitted.

- A lack of process understanding on the part of the applicant and the submission of insufficient product knowledge information in NDAs could be leading to tight product specifications at the time of approval.

- Due to heavy FDA workload and lack of resources, insufficient scientific dialogue between CMC reviewers and applicants is taking place during drug development and prior to the submission of NDAs.

- The reliance on a single chemistry reviewer to evaluate the entire CMC section of a drug application throughout the entire product life cycle is not facilitating the optimal use of ONDC's limited resources or available expertise.

- Valuable FDA resources are being used to generate comprehensive CMC summaries and analyze raw data in CMC submissions, which are tasks that could be accomplished efficiently by NDA applicants.

The new quality assessment system encompasses several initiatives, whose objectives are to allow the rapid integration of new technologies into pharmaceutical manufacturing and to expedite the reviews of NDAs and supplemental NDAs (see Chapter 7). According to the FDA, the new system will focus on critical pharmaceutical quality attributes (chemistry, pharmaceutical formulation, manufacturing process, product performance), and will rely "more on the information provided by the applicant (e.g., the comprehensive quality overall summary (QOS) and the pharmaceutical development report) and less on the voluminous raw data current being submitted (e.g., the executed batch records, raw stability data, methods validation package)" (see Chapter 7).

ONDC Restructuring and the NDA Review

To make ONDC more efficient, effective and flexible in managing CMC-related issues and workload, CDER will reorganize ONDC and revise its CMC review process for NDAs and sNDAs. Although CDER's traditional review process has relied on a single chemistry reviewer to evaluate the entire CMC section of a drug application throughout the entire product lifecycle—IND through NDA through postapproval supplements—the nature and complexity of modern pharmaceutical manufacturing dictates a new system, the agency argues.

—continued—

213

–continued–

Under the restructured ONDC, the NDA and NDA supplement review functions will be separated to address the critical CMC issues more expeditiously in both the pre-approval and post-approval areas. The reorganization, whose implementation is expected to be simultaneous with CDER's larger reorganization upon its move to consolidated offices in spring 2005, is expected to involve the following:

- The formation, within ONDC, of separate and dedicated premarketing and postmarketing chemistry divisions that will be responsible for IND/NDA and supplemental review functions, respectively, and for improving the efficiency and effectiveness in each area. Chemists in the three planned premarketing divisions may consult, when necessary, with chemists in the postmarketing division.

- Each of the three premarketing divisions will feature a pharmaceutical assessment lead (PAL), a high-level reviewer who will serve as "a dedicated scientific liaison" to the relevant new drug review division and who will perform an initial assessment of each NDA before the application is assigned to a primary chemistry reviewer within the "pool" of reviewers available within that therapeutic area. In conducting an initial assessment of the NDA, the PAL will identify critical pharmaceutical quality attributes (chemistry, pharmaceutical formulation, manufacturing process, product performance) and develop a "Big-Picture" assessment protocol and timeline for completing the review. In essence, this will comprise a high-level review to determine the most important factors or quality attributes related to the product's safety/effectiveness, whether the relevant issues will require that the CMC review involve a review by an interdisciplinary team of reviewers or a particular reviewer, and whether there are any issues that must be addressed immediately (e.g., through a refuse to file action). Each new drug review division will have at least one PAL and group of "pool" chemistry reviewers dedicated to the division and IND/NDA submissions in that therapeutic area.

- As part of the reorganization, the review chemists that will support the new drug review divisions will no longer be located within these groups, but will be housed within ONDC's new premarketing and postmarketing divisions. According to ONDC officials, however, the lead chemists and review chemists will continue to specialize in and be dedicated to specific therapeutic areas and divisions.

- The postmarketing division will also feature a PAL, who will perform an initial assessment of each CMC supplement to determine if it needs further evaluation. The PAL will perform a brief review for minor CMC changes or, if necessary, develop an assessment protocol for major CMC changes before assigning the supplement to a reviewer.

- To optimize the use of its limited resources and available expertise, ONDC will assemble, when necessary, a small team of interdisciplinary scientists (i.e., chemists, pharmaceutical scientists, engineers, and/or others as needed) and assign the team to the submission. This will likely be used for combination products and other complex cases.

- Further, ONDC will establish a branch that will provide expert assessment and advice on manufacturing science, which will become an integral part of the new quality assessment system.

*At this writing, CDER had not yet formally implemented organizational changes to the Office of New Drug Chemistry, but had announced the basic framework of its new risk-based pharmaceutical quality assessment system.

reanalysis of the data. Likewise, the pharmacology reviewer may work closely with the statistical reviewer in evaluating the statistical significance of adverse drug effects in long-term animal studies (e.g., tumor rates).

In recent years, FDA officials have also disclosed cases in which CDER drug reviewers have consulted with outside experts (i.e., other than those on agency advisory committees) to supplement internal reviewer expertise for certain NDAs. During a May 2003 public meeting, for example, then FDA Commissioner Mark McClellan, M.D., Ph.D., disclosed that CDER oncology reviewers consulted with four outside experts during the review and accelerated approval of Millennium's myeloma therapy Velcade (bortezomib) in 2003.

Mid-Review CDER/Sponsor Communications Invariably, the primary review creates a need for agency communication with, and the clarification of some issues or data by, the NDA sponsor. With the shortening of drug reviews, it is likely that all FDA/sponsor communication, including mid-review dialogue, has increased over the past decade. Such communications may take many forms, ranging from informal telephone communications to face-to-face meetings (see discussion below on applicant's right to meetings) to videoconferences.

In large part due to fallout from CBER's review of the Imclone cancer therapy Erbitux, the FDA's July 2003 Good Review Management Principles draft guidance implies a greater degree of management control over certain forms of review division/applicant communications at key points in the NDA review process (e.g., filing decision, formal action). While not necessarily discouraging "informal communication methods" (e.g., telephone calls, facsimile) for timely communication, the draft guidance emphasizes that the agency should not request or suggest that an applicant take a certain action (e.g., withdraw an application) and that all communications must be documented in the application file.

In the interest of expediting the review process, CDER first pledged, under the user-fee program, to alert sponsors to NDA deficiencies earlier in the review process. Through what are called discipline review letters, the agency "submits deficiencies to sponsors in the form of mid-review letters when each discipline has completed its initial review of the pending application," the agency's user-fee commitments state. Some firms believe that such notifications allow them to address NDA deficiencies earlier in the review process.

The agency outlined its use of these mid-review communications in a November 2001 guidance entitled, *Information Request and Discipline Review Letters Under the Prescription Drug User Fee Act.* The guidance outlines two forms of mid-review communications:

Discipline Review (DR) Letter. A concept first introduced under PDUFA II, the DR letter is "a letter used to convey early thoughts on possible deficiencies found by a discipline review team [e.g., clinical, chemistry, pharmacology/toxicology] for its portion of the pending [NDA] at the conclusion of the discipline review. DR letters are not considered to be action letters because they do not represent a complete review of the submission and, therefore, do not stop the user fee review clock... A single DR letter may contain comments from multiple discipline reviews if it is more efficient to do so." In the guidance, the agency cautions industry about the limitations of the discipline review letters: (1) because a DR letter may be issued without input from upper supervisory levels (i.e., division or office director), the identified deficiencies ultimately may be resolved at these levels without additional applicant input or additional deficiencies may arise as a result of management input (i.e., it does not represent final agency decisions on the application); and (2) the agency is not obligated to review an applicant's response to DR letters in the review cycle in which the letter was issued, although the division may review such information if it can do so without adversely affecting its ability to meet its user-fee performance goal. Given these two limitations, applicants may want to consider the value in developing a rapid response to a DR letter rather than waiting for a formal action letter. In other words, the ultimate action letter issued on the application "may contain additional or fewer deficiencies than were provided in the previously issued discipline review letters, depending on the final review of the application and supervisor evaluation by division and/or office directors," the guidance points out.

Although the agency's guidance is not entirely clear on this point, it appears that all review disciplines involved in the NDA evaluation are responsible for issuing discipline review letters in most cases. The guidance points out, however, that a DR letter will not be sent "if its issuance would delay or coincide with the issuance of an action letter. The absence of a DR letter for a particular discipline should not be construed to mean that the action letter will not contain any deficiencies for that discipline."

In practice, DR letters have not been widely used in CDER according to many review divisions, largely because most discipline reviews are completed so close to the due dates for formal action letters. FDA officials believe that DR letters will become far more common under PDUFA III, however, in part because the communications will be a formal element of the continuous marketing application program (Pilot 1-reviewable units), and because the agency will be tracking DR letter-related performance more closely going forward.

Information Request (IR) *Letters.* The information request letter, which has been used by CDER for some time, is a letter sent to an applicant during the NDA review to request further information or clarification that is needed or would be helpful to allow completion of the discipline review. Because an IR letter, unlike a DR letter, is issued during the discipline review and because it requests information that assists in the completion of that review, applicant responses to such a letter are usually reviewed during the review cycle in which the IR letter was issued. Applicants are expected to respond to IR letters "as quickly as possible," the guidance notes.

FDA regulations also require other forms of sponsor communications. Specifically, sponsors must continue forwarding new safety information during the entire NDA review to ensure that reviewers have the most up-to-date information for the decision-making process. Through "safety update reports," sponsors must provide periodic updates on any new safety-related information obtained from clinical studies, animal studies, or other sources (see Chapter 7). Sponsors must submit these reports four months after the original NDA submission, following the receipt of an "approvable" letter, and after an FDA request. Usually, the agency will request a safety update within 90 to 120 days of an approval action.

Technological advances will continue to influence the nature of mid-NDA review sponsor/FDA communications in coming years. In 1999, for example, CDER rolled out a secure e-mail system through which NDA sponsors and NDA reviewers can exchange encrypted regulatory communications electronically. CDER has been using e-mail systems on a pilot basis for several years. CDER officials have even claimed that, without secure email systems, they would have been unable to meet their review goals for certain drugs. They add that the secure e-mail system has proven particularly useful for exchanging, reviewing, and implementing revisions to proposed drug labeling during the final negotiation process that immediately precedes the formal approval

Today, an estimated 70 pharmaceutical companies—compared to just a handful in 2000—are actively forwarding regulatory documents and are communicating with the project managers and reviewers responsible for their pending NDAs through secure e-mail systems. Typical e-mail messages can range from communication necessary to schedule sponsor/division meetings to regulatory documents such as pharmacology/toxicology reports, draft clinical protocols, draft product labeling, and statistical reports, according to CDER staffers.

While e-mail communications are proving to be an increasingly popular means of supplementing or replacing telephone conversations, meetings, and faxes, they are not yet considered "formal communications." I

Emerging Elements of the NDA Review Process: RiskMAPs and Pharmacogenomic Data

While not yet formal regulatory requirements, two types of information—"risk minimization action plans" and pharmacogenomic data—are likely to become routine elements of NDA submissions and factors in the NDA review process for some products in the near future.

The NDA and Risk Minimization Action Plans

As stated, the FDA's focus on risk management under PDUFA III is likely to impact NDA submissions and reviews for certain drug products. In a May 2004 draft industry guidance entitled, *Development and Use of Risk Minimization Action Plans*, the FDA establishes that, while routine risk-minimization measures (e.g., FDA-approved professional labeling) will be sufficient for most products, "for a small number of products where a [risk minimization action plan (RiskMAP)] should be considered...sponsors are encouraged to consider developing a RiskMAP," which the agency defines as "a strategic safety program designed to meet specific goals and objectives in minimizing known risks of a product while preserving its benefits." In the draft guidance, the agency notes that a company can submit a RiskMAP before or after approval, and that the plan should be submitted in either the IND or NDA if it is filed in advance of marketing clearance (see Chapter 11).

When a sponsor makes a RiskMAP submission as part of the NDA, postmarketing drug safety staff from CDER's Office of Drug Safety (ODS) will serve as consult reviewers for the NDA. ODS staffers will assess the RiskMAP and advise both applicants and the review division staff on appropriate post-approval risk management tools.

Although the FDA agreed to release a final version of this guidance, as well as other risk-management guidances, by September 2004 under its PDUFA III commitments, the agency did not meet this goal. At this writing, the agency was hoping to release a final guidance by late 2004 or early 2005.

Pharmacogenomic Data and the NDA

The FDA used a November 2003 draft guidance entitled, *Pharmacogenomic Data Submissions* to lay the groundwork for encouraging and, in some cases, requiring NDA applicants to submit pharmacogenomic data that they develop as part of the drug development process. Although the agency acknowledges that most pharmacogenomic data currently are exploratory or research-oriented and, therefore, need not be submitted in an NDA, sponsors should consider submitting the data voluntarily to help FDA reviewers and scientists understand the relevant scientific issues in this emerging field, the FDA states. While the agency prepared to release a final guidance document in late 2004, CDER officials claimed that center reviewers were actively reviewing voluntarily submitted pharmacogenomic data.

When the submission of pharmacogenomic data is not otherwise required—and their submission will be required in some cases (see Chapter 7)—companies should submit what the agency calls "voluntary genomic data submissions," or VGDSs, which will be evaluated by a cross-center interdisciplinary pharmacogenomic review group (IPRG) to be formed within the agency. Although the agency pledges not to use VGDSs for "regulatory decision making," voluntary submissions will provide the FDA with access to emerging pharmacogenomic data "so that a foundation can be built for developing scientifically sound

—continued—

217

–continued–

regulatory policies." The draft guidance emphasizes that "the FDA will not use information submitted through the voluntary process for regulatory decision making on INDs or NDAs." Rather, the document notes, VGDS filings will be analyzed by the IPRG and the relevant review division staff for "scientific and informational purposes."

In the November 2003 draft guidance, the agency acknowledged both industry's reluctance to undertake pharmacogenomic testing programs due to "uncertainties in how the data will be used by the FDA in the drug application review process," and the reality that "most experimental results may not be well enough established to be suitable for regulatory decision making." The agency did not use either as an excuse to surrender a role in pharmacogenomics, but instead used the guidance to clarify when and how it intends to use pharmacogenomic data—"that is, when the data will be considered sufficiently reliable to serve as the basis for regulatory decision making, when it will be considered only supportive to a decision, and when the data will not be used in regulatory decision making."

Upon the release of the pharmacogenomics draft guidance, FDA officials attempted to allay fears about the implications of pharmacogenomic data submissions. With the exception of cancer therapies, for which tumors can provide gene sequence expression data, experimental products are unlikely to face new FDA requirements in the near term under the guidance, then-CDER Director Janet Woodcock, M.D., claimed at a November 2003 workshop.

---

other words, although a company may forward materials via secure e-mails, those materials cannot yet substitute for the official hardcopy submissions that are necessary for agency archiving. CDER, however, continues to work on initiatives under which sponsors ultimately will be able to submit applications and communications through secure e-mail and/or electronic gateway facilities that will allow for formal archiving and that will eliminate the need for companies to follow-up with an official archival copy.

Reaching an Institutional Decision on the NDA

When the technical reviews are completed, each reviewer must develop a written evaluation that presents his or her conclusions on, and recommendations regarding, the NDA. In most cases, the medical reviewer i responsible for evaluating and reconciling the conclusions of reviewers in all other scientific disciplines. The result is an action letter (see discussion below), which provides an approval or disapproval decision and the basis for that recommendation.

In reality, the reconciling of all reviewer conclusions and the development of what CDER calls an "institutiona decision" on an NDA's approvability is likely to involve considerable dialogue between the medical reviewe and reviewers in the other disciplines, as well as each primary reviewer's supervisor, the division director and if necessary, the office director. Since the ultimate decision hinges most directly on clinical safety, effective ness, and risk/benefit issues, however, the medical reviewer and his or her supervisor are generally assume to have the most influence in this process.

To address those cases in which a review team is not able to reach a consensus, CDER developed MaPP 4151. entitled, *Resolution of Disputes: Roles of Reviewers, Supervisors, and Management: Documenting Views and Findings an Resolving Differences* (August 1996). This policy states that, "the review teams' recommendations are...reviewe by discipline-specific supervisors or team leaders, the division directors, and, if necessary, the office directors

(In the case of a reviewing medical officer, a division director or deputy director reviews the primary findings.) The review process ensures that each application is considered from an array of different perspectives and concerns. The process also requires that reviewers, supervisors or team leaders, and management work together. In most cases, consensus on a drug application is usually achieved through discussion as the reviews proceed. If consensus does not occur during the review process, management ultimately must resolve the differences. In all cases, it is essential that the views of all persons involved in the review process be respected and that the official administrative record of the review reflect differences of opinion if they exist... If disagreement arises at any level of the review process and remains unresolved, the reviewing official who disagrees with the drafted conclusions or recommendations must prepare a separate document explaining: (1) the nature of the difference of opinion; (2) the reasons for the differing opinion; and (3) the recommended changes in the findings or recommendations. This document must remain in the file with the reviewer's documentation." If the division supervisors and division director are unable to resolve the scientific or regulatory dispute, it may be brought to the director of CDER's Office of New Drugs.

Despite this policy, internal reviewer disputes in NDA reviews received considerable public attention during the past several years. In a December 1998 HRG reviewer survey, for example, several CDER medical officers claimed that there had been instances in which "inappropriate pressure" was applied by center management and even Congress to encourage drug approvals and that, in other cases, the opinions of NDA reviewers were suppressed or reviewers were pressured to alter their review opinions.

Perhaps in response to persistent concerns in this area, CDER included the following passage in a November 2002 MaPP entitled, *Action Packages for NDAs and Efficacy Supplements* to emphasize the independence of reviewers and to specify how disagreements are to be documented:

"A scientific review of an application is considered a reviewer's own work and cannot be altered by division management or the review once it is final. Disagreements by team leaders, division directors, or office directors with any or all of a reviewer's major conclusions must be documented in a separate review or in an addendum to the review."

In November 2004, shortly following the high-profile safety-related withdrawal of Vioxx, CDER announced a new "pilot procedure" to provide drug reviewers with an additional outlet to air their "differing professional opinions" regarding regulatory actions or policy decisions. Under MaPP 4151.2 (Documenting Differing Professional Opinions and Dispute Resolution—Pilot Program), any CDER employee who believes that the agency "is failing to act in a situation that will have a significant negative impact on the public health" can prepare a written statement that will be reviewed by CDER's director and ombudsman. If the center director and ombudsman agree that the contested decision/action could have a significant impact on public health, the CDER director will then appoint an ad hoc review panel to assess the issue. To comprise individuals who have not been directly involved in the original decision-making process, the ad hoc panel will have 30 calendar days to evaluate the disputed issue and make a formal recommendation to the CDER director, who will then have another five business days to reach a decision.

If there are important scientific or medical issues on which CDER reviewers would like to obtain independent advice before reaching their decision, they also may be able to bring the issues before one or more independent prescription drug advisory committees that support the drug center. A review division may decide to seek advisory committee input on a pending NDA for the following or other reasons: the application is for an NME or a new class of drug; the clinical study design used novel clinical or surrogate endpoints; the application raises significant issues regarding safety and/or effectiveness of the drug; or the application raises significant public health questions regarding the drug's role in a disease's treatment or prevention. For a more detailed discussion of CDER's advisory committee process, see Chapter 10.

In 2000, CDER introduced a pilot program under which CDER's new drug review divisions could request an internal meeting of senior center officials to consider particularly difficult or complex regulatory decisions. Initially called "pre-decision" meetings under the pilot program, such meetings are now called "regulatory briefings," which a review division may request to gain the input of senior center officials on an IND- or NDA-related issue, or an issue related to general CDER policy or a particular class of drugs. During these meetings, division reviewers present an issue to CDER senior officials (e.g., ODE directors, CDER director) and perhaps others for comment and possible recommendations. These "internal advisory committee meetings," as CDER staffers sometimes characterize them, provide drug reviewers with an informal mechanism through which they can obtain additional insights and perspectives on the drug approval-related issues before them. Unlike advisory committee meetings, regulatory briefings involve discussions of issues only, and do not culminate in a formal vote on an issue. While NDA applicants are not invited to the meetings, CDER officials claim that they are often informed when their applications are to be considered at such meetings.

The Formal Action on an NDA

The final channels through which an NDA must pass to obtain FDA approval will depend on issues such as the drug's novelty and importance. Generally, NDAs for NMEs and prescription-to-OTC switches, for example, need the approval of higher levels of FDA management than do marketing applications for less-innovative products. Although federal regulations specify authority delegations for NDA "sign-off," or signatory, power (i.e., final approval authority), the regulations do give CDER some flexibility to delegate these powers (see discussion below).

Once an approval, approvable, or not-approvable recommendation is reached by the reviewers (primary reviewers) and their supervisors/team leaders/branch chiefs (secondary review), the decision must then be evaluated and approved by the director of the applicable drug review division. In most cases, the division director is expected to author a "brief summary review" of the application after examining the various discipline primary and secondary reviews and discussing those assessments with the review team. For the division director's review (and subsequent office- or center-level reviews, if necessary), the regulatory project manager assembles what is termed an "action package," which is a concept designed to facilitate the agency's final review of and decisions regarding NDAs and NDA supplements. In a November 2002 MaPP entitled, *Action Packages for NDAs and Efficacy Supplements* (MaPP 6020.8), CDER defines the action package as, "a compilation of (1) FDA-generated documents related to review of an NDA or efficacy supplement (i.e., from submission to final action), (2) documents (e.g., meeting minutes, pharmacology reviews) pertaining to the format and content of the application generated during drug development (investigational new drug IND)), and (3) labeling submitted by the applicant." All action packages, says the policy, must include what is called a summary review "that documents conclusions from all reviewing disciplines about the drug product, noting any critical issues and disagreements with the applicant and how they were resolved, recommendation for action, and a explanation of any nonconcurrence with review conclusions."

MaPP 6020.8 actually provides some interesting detail on how the final review documents—most importantly, the action package's summary review—are developed within CDER, and about how internal disagreements are to be addressed in these documents. "The summary review will generally be done by the medical team leader for applications where the division director is the signatory authority and by the medical team leader or the division director where the office director is the signatory authority. Where the division director or office director has not written a separate review, he or she should write a brief statement of concurrence with the summary review or signify concurrence with signature comments if the review is routed through [CDER's Document File System] for signature. If the signatory authority disagrees with the conclusions or the recommendations made by the summary reviewer or wants to add further analysis of particular points, a separate review must be written to document this."

CDER offers its most recent discussion of NDA sign-off procedures in its draft GRMP guidance. "A decision regarding the signatory authority for an application should be made as soon as possible following receipt of the application," the document states. "Generally, the signatory authority for actions on an application for new molecular entities (NME) is delegated to the office level above the review division [for what is sometimes called the 'tertiary review']. This level of signatory authority for NMEs allows in-depth review by the Agency's more senior managers, often warranted by the novel issues presented in these submissions. This level of expertise comprises a significant knowledge base and promotes consistency in decision making with respect to NMEs. For a non-NME submission, the signatory authority for the action is generally delegated to the review division director. However, in certain situations, the signatory authority may be retained at the office level above the division (e.g., first-in-class switch from prescription to over-the-counter marketing)."

For those NDAs (e.g., NMEs) for which the office director (e.g., ODE I, II, III) has signatory authority, the relevant office director generally develops a "written summary review" as part of the final action on the application. This review summary should identify any disagreements noted at lower review levels and document final determinations regarding these issues.

FDA Action Letters

The FDA communicates its official decision on an NDA through what is called an "action letter." The action letter represents an important element in the agency's efforts to meet its review performance goals under the user-fee program—that is, the agency must "act on" NDAs within specific time frames. CDER fulfills this requirement by issuing an action letter, which constitutes a complete action on the application and which stops the review clock for the filing.

Currently, there are three types of action letters—approval, approvable, and not-approvable—that detail CDER's decisions on NDAs at the end of a review cycle. Under PDUFA II, however, the FDA had agreed to simplify this three-letter scheme by replacing approvable and not-approvable letters with "complete response" letters, which will detail all the application's deficiencies. After several years, the FDA finally issued a July 2004 notice under which it proposed shifting to the complete response letters.

Acknowledging that its current system of approvable and not approvable letters often sends unclear and misleading messages regarding a drug application's current status and ultimate approvability, the FDA said that the complete response letter will represent "a consistent and more neutral mechanism to convey that we cannot approve a drug marketing application in its current form... Issuance of complete response letters will ensure a consistent approach to informing sponsors of needed changes before we can approve an application, with no implication as to the ultimate approvability of the application."

Simply due to their name alone, complete response letters, in effect, will provide fewer insights on an NDA's deficiencies than did the more descriptively titled approvable and not-approval letters. According to the proposed rule, "in the past, some drug manufacturers have expressed concern that a not approvable letter sends an unintended message that a marketing application will never be approved, which could adversely affect a company's ability to raise capital."

In the proposed rule, the agency defines the complete response letter as "a written communication to an applicant from FDA usually identifying all of the deficiencies in an application or abbreviated application that must be satisfactorily addressed before it can be approved." The only case in which the complete response letter will not identify *all* deficiencies will be when the agency decides to issue a complete response letter before it conducts relevant inspections or the labeling review because data in the application are found to be inadequate to support approval.

Until the FDA finalizes the July 2004 proposal on complete response letters, the agency will continue to employ the long-standing three-letter scheme for NDA reviews.

Approval Letter When CDER sends an approval letter, the subject drug is considered approved as of the date of the letter. Generally, an applicant must submit final printed labeling before a drug is approved. If CDER finds that the draft labeling is acceptable or if the agency requires only minor editorial changes, however, the NDA may be approved based on the draft labeling. In such cases, the agency reminds the firm that marketing of the product with labeling other than that agreed to by the agency would cause the product to be viewed as misbranded (i.e., an unapproved product).

First-Cycle Review Outcomes by NDA Submission Cohort, FY1997-FY2003

First-Cycle Review Outcomes

	Approval	Approvable	Not Approvable	Withdrawal
FY1997	43%	30%	19%	6%
FY1998	35%	34%	27%	3%
FY1999	45.2%	34%	14%	6%
FY2000	38%	40%	14%	8%
FY2001	19.8%	48%	24%	8%
FY2002*	40.0%	47%	12%	1%
FY2003**	27%	57%	11%	5%

* as of January 31, 2004, when 95 of 96 FY2002 NDAs had received first actions. **as of January 31, 2004, when 62 of 104 NDAs had received first actions.

Source: FDA

When the signatory authority (i.e., the individual with final "sign off" authority) signs the approval letter (or any action letter), the regulatory project manager will fax it to the applicant. The project manager should then call the applicant to document the receipt of the action letter, after which the applicant may wish to hold or schedule a brief telephone conference to gain a full understanding of the final agency decision.

Rarely, if ever, do drug sponsors receive an approval letter for an original NDA without first receiving a request for more data (e.g., in an information request letter), a clarification of existing data or analyses, or modification of the application in its originally submitted form (e.g., product labeling). In many cases, however, such requests are made through mid-review communications that do not comprise a formal agency action on the NDAs (see discussion above).

Although greater numbers of NDAs are being approved (i.e., receiving approval letters) in CDER's first actions during the user-fee era, the rate of first-cycle approvals has varied in recent years. After approving about 45% of NDAs from the FY1999 cohort in the first review cycle, the agency was able to approve just 38% and 19.8% of FY2000 and FY2001 NDAs, respectively, after the first review cycle. The review patterns for the FY2001 cohort were particularly worrisome for industry, since the agency was able to clear just 20% of both priority and standard NDAs in this cohort (generally the agency's first-cycle performance for priority drugs is far better). While CDER's first-cycle approval rate bounced back in FY2002 (to 40% of NDAs), an early-indicator analysis of review outcomes for the FY2003 cohort suggests that it will decline again.

Percent of Standard/Priority Original NDAs Approved in First Review Cycle by Submission Cohort, FY1997-FY2003

Percent of NDAs Approved in First Review Cycle

	Priority NDAs	Standard NDAs
FY1998	50%	31%
FY1999	61%	40%
FY2000	52%	34%
FY2001	20%	20%
FY2002*	58%	37%
FY2003**	43%	23%

* as of January 31, 2004, when 95 of 96 FY2002 NDAs had received first actions. **as of January 31, 2004, when 62 of 104 NDAs had received first actions.

Source: FDA

As noted, CDER's draft GRMPs and other initiatives are focusing, in part, on creating an environment in which first-cycle approvals can be granted whenever possible and appropriate. As part of its "Innovation Initiative," through which the agency is attempting to speed the development and approval of new drugs, biologics, and medical devices, CDER will be examining the root causes of multi-cycle NDA reviews and identifying and addressing "avoidable delays" and multiple review cycles. In mid-2003, CDER officials said that a preliminary, small-scale assessment of the causes of multiple-cycle application reviews suggested that many of the reviews were "unavoidable." Second-cycle reviews, some of which the agency acknowledged might have been avoided with early-stage FDA/industry communication, were triggered by, for example, emerging information late in the development process or unexpected study results needing further examination.

Reasons for Lengthy NDA Reviews: A CDER Analysis

In response to criticism regarding lengthening drug review times, CDER undertook a study of 29 NDAs that were approved in 2000 and 2001 and whose review times surpassed the 12-month mark. The analysis found that the NDA reviews were longer due to the following concerns:

Reason	Percentage of 29 NDAs in Sample
Safety	38%
Efficacy	21%
Manufacturing	14%
Labeling	14%
Chemistry	10%

Source: CDER

Prior to granting approval, the review division may also ask for an applicant's commitment to conduct certain drug studies following approval. Although the agency states that such postmarketing studies are not considered essential for a drug's approval, the studies provide "additional information or data that could, for example, change the prescribing information or use of the drug or provide additional assurance or verification of product quality and consistency." Under a policy guide on such "Phase 4 commitments," the FDA and drug sponsor must agree to the specific commitments and a schedule for fulfilling these commitments prior to approval (see Chapter 11). Either prior to, or at the time of, drug approval, the applicant must submit a letter describing the Phase 4 commitments and a schedule for initiating and completing the Phase 4 studies. The approval letter should list all Phase 4 commitments and the schedule for their completion.

Approvable Letter According to federal regulations, the FDA will send the applicant "an approvable letter if the application...substantially meets the requirements [for marketing approval] and the agency believes that it can approve the application...if specific additional information or material is submitted or specific conditions (for example, certain changes in labeling) are agreed to by the applicant." Often, the FDA will use an approvable letter to request changes to the product's proposed labeling and to require the submission of safety update reports and the product's final printed labeling.

Unless otherwise specified by the FDA, the sponsor has ten days after the date of the approvable letter to do one of the following:

- Submit a resubmission (i.e., a formal response to the action letter), or acknowledge its intent to file a resubmission, to the NDA (see discussion below).

- Withdraw the application. The FDA will consider the applicant's failure to respond to an approvable letter within ten days to represent the applicant's request to withdraw the application.

- For applications involving new drugs (not including antibiotics), ask the FDA to provide the applicant an opportunity for a hearing on whether grounds exist for denying the application's approval. Sponsors would make such a request when the FDA issues an approvable letter, but specifies in the letter marketing conditions (e.g., restrictive labeling) that are unacceptable to the applicant.

- For an antibiotic, file a petition or notify the FDA of an intent to file a petition proposing the issuance, amendment, or repeal of a regulation.

- Notify the FDA that the applicant agrees to a review period extension of a specified length so the applicant may give further consideration as to which of the previous four options it will pursue. The FDA will grant any reasonable request for an extension, and will consider the applicant's failure to respond during the extended review period to represent a request to withdraw the application.

Over the last several years, the percentage of NDAs that triggered approvable letters in the first review cycle has risen consistently (see table above). And over the last four fiscal years, the plurality of NDAs has received approvable letters at the end of the first review cycle. Although the percentage of NDAs receiving approvable letters hovered just under the 50 percent mark for the FY2001 and FY2002 NDA cohorts, an early-indicator analysis suggests that it could be well more than half for the FY2003 NDA cohort.

Keep in mind that an approvable letter—as well as an approval or not-approvable letter—is also a possible outcome at the conclusion of second- and subsequent-cycle reviews.

The FDA used its July 2004 proposed regulation on complete response letters to propose other changes, including revisions to the current requirements relevant to an applicant's response to an action letter other than an approval letter (i.e., under the proposed regulation, this would be a response to a complete response letter rather than either an approvable or not approvable letter). As noted above, current regulations require that an applicant take one of several specific actions, or alert FDA of its intent to take one of several specific actions, within ten days of the approvable/not approvable letter's date (otherwise, the agency will consider the applicant's failure to respond to represent a request to withdraw the application). The agency has proposed to eliminate the ten-day requirement that applicants act (or declare their intention to act), and to streamline the number of options available to applicants once they receive a complete response letter. Under the proposed regulation, NDA applicants would have three options after receiving a complete response letter:

- *File a Resubmission*. The applicant can, of course, resubmit the application, addressing all deficiencies identified in the complete response letter.

- *Withdraw the* NDA. The applicant can withdraw the application, an action that will be without prejudice to a subsequent submission.

- *Request an Opportunity for Hearing*. The applicant can ask the agency for an opportunity for a hearing on whether there are grounds for denying the application's approval.

Under the proposed rule, the applicant would have one year to take one of the three actions. If the applicant does not take one of these actions within this timeframe, the agency will consider the applicant's failure to act as a request to withdraw the NDA.

Not-Approvable Letter A not-approvable letter is forwarded to the applicant if the FDA believes that the drug application is insufficient to justify approval. The letter describes the NDA deficiencies that were the basis for the not-approvable action. Unless the FDA indicates otherwise, the sponsor must take one of the five actions specified above for approvable letters within ten days.

Fewer NDAs than ever are receiving not-approvable letters at the conclusion of the initial review cycle. Only 12% of FY2002's original NDA submissions triggered not-approvable actions, what was at least a several-year low (see table above).

CDER officials acknowledge that, in the past, drug review divisions and sponsors have openly discussed whether it was preferable for the agency to issue an approvable or not-approvable letter in certain cases. Except in terms of perception, the two letters are similar with regard to regulatory implications—that is, each requires a "resubmission" (see discussion below) and an additional review cycle. While NDA sponsors have had some input into whether they would receive approvable or not-approvable letters in the past, CDER officials announced in late 2002 that they would be attempting to discourage such division/sponsor dialogues due to concern that there might be undue influence on the drug center's review staff.

Applicant Responses to Approvable or Not-Approvable Letters Once the applicant has developed a complete response to all of the deficiencies and issues specified in an approvable or not-approvable letter, it should include this response in what is termed a "resubmission." Under the FDA's user-fee commitments, such resubmissions are now classified, and are assigned review goals, based on the information contained within them. A resubmission should include a cover letter that provides a statement indicating that the applicant considers the resubmission to represent a complete response to the action letter. In addition, the applicant has the option of offering an opinion on how the resubmission should be classified.

Under the user-fee program, all resubmissions are classified into either Class 1 or Class 2. Class 1 resubmissions are more straightforward submissions that can include the following items or any combination of these items: (1) final printed labeling; (2) draft labeling; (3) safety updates submitted in the same format, including tabulations, as the original safety submissions with new data and changes highlighted (when large amounts of new information, including important new adverse experiences not previously reported with the product are presented in the resubmission, however, it will be considered a Class 2 resubmission); (4) stability updates to support provisional or final dating periods; (5) commitments to perform Phase 4 studies, including proposals for such studies; (6) assay validation data; (7) final release testing on the last 1 or 2 lots used to support approval; (8) a minor re-analysis of data previously submitted by the applicant (determined by the agency as fitting the Class 1 category); or (9) other minor clarifying information (determined by the agency as fitting the Class 1 category). Under its PDUFA III performance goals, the agency has committed to acting on 90 percent of Class 1 NDA resubmissions within two months.

At this writing, CDER was exceeding its Class 1 resubmission goals. The center had reviewed and acted on 44 of 45 FY2002 and FY2003 Class 1 resubmissions within two months, easily surpassing the 90% goal.

A Class 2 resubmission is a resubmission that includes any item not identified above for Class 1 resubmissions, including any item that would warrant presentation to an advisory committee or any issue that would warrant a re-inspection of a manufacturing facility. For all years covered by PDUFA III (FY2003-FY2007), CDER committed to reviewing 90 percent of Class 2 resubmissions within six months.

Of the 80 FY2002 and FY2003 Class 2 resubmissions acted on at this writing, CDER had reviewed all 80 within its six-month goal.

According to an April 1998 guidance entitled, *Classifying Resubmissions in Response to Action Letters*, the agency will forward an acknowledgement letter to the applicant within 14 days of a resubmission's receipt. Assuming that the agency finds the resubmission to be complete, the acknowledgement letter will reveal the classification of the resubmission and specify the review performance goal for the application.

Final Printed Labeling

Generally, labeling is the final major consideration in a drug's approval. Not until an NDA is virtually approved, or is judged to be "approvable," does labeling become the primary focus of the drug approval process.

There are several practical reasons why labeling concerns are left until late in the drug review process. First, it is impossible to develop labeling with accurate accounts of indications, warnings, contraindications, and specific use instructions without conclusions drawn from pivotal clinical study data. Also, FDA reviewers will not invest significant time in evaluating proposed labeling until they are reasonably convinced that a drug is safe and effective for its proposed use, and that the drug's NDA is nearing approval.

Labeling often becomes a principal concern once the review division advances toward an approval or issues an approvable letter, which, among other things, requests that the applicant forward its final printed labeling (i.e., all the labeling to appear on or to accompany a drug's package or container). At this point, it is likely that only the labeling and possibly some minor deficiencies in an NDA stand between a drug and its approval. And as CDER states in MaPP 6020.8, "with the exception of minor editorial changes, there must be agreement on the labeling text between the Agency and applicant at the time of application approval. Minor editorial changes are those that could appropriately be included in an annual report" [to an NDA]. Although a review team and review division may reach preliminary agreements with the NDA applicant regarding the labeling, additional labeling negotiations may be necessary following the signatory authority's review of the action package (see discussion below).

The NDA Review and the New "Content of Labeling" Section. It is important to note that the FDA's labeling review will also now include an assessment of a new labeling-related section within the NDA. Under a December 11, 2003, final regulation, the FDA is requiring companies submitting NDAs (and NDA supplements and annual reports) to provide what it calls a "content of labeling" section, and that the new section be provided in electronic form. Specifically, this new section of the NDA will comprise the contents of the package insert, and will include all text, tables, and figures.

Interestingly, the new "e-labeling" requirement will not affect any existing components of the NDA—applicants, for instance, will still be required to submit copies of the formatted label and all labeling. In addition, firms will continue to have the option of submitting these existing marketing application components in an electronic or paper-based format. In February 2004, the agency issued a draft guidance entitled, *Providing Regulatory Submissions in Electronic Format-Content of Labeling* (see Chapter 7).

Draft Package Labeling Drug sponsors first propose labeling for a new pharmaceutical through what is called draft package labeling. Generally, draft labeling is submitted as part of the original NDA.

The specific labeling requirements facing a drug in its finished package form will depend on whether it is proposed for use as a prescription or as an over-the-counter (OTC) medicine. Principally because of dispensing differences, FDA labeling requirements for OTC and prescription drugs differ significantly.

Prescription Drug Labeling According to federal regulations, prescription drug labeling must be "informative and accurate..., contain a summary of the essential scientific information needed for the safe and effective use of the drug...," and "be based, whenever possible, on data derived from human experience." In enforcing these and other requirements, the FDA has authority over the format and types of information that appear: (1) on the immediate drug container (i.e., manufacturer name, general brand name, lot number, etc.); and (2) on the outer carton in which the drug is shipped to physicians, hospitals, pharmacies, and other prescription drug dispensers.

A primary element in prescription drug labeling is the package insert. Drug manufacturers use prescription drug package inserts to meet the requirement that the physician or pharmacist be provided with the essential information needed to ensure the safe and effective use of the drug. Since the large body of information needed to satisfy this requirement cannot reasonably be placed on a prescription product's immediate container or package, manufacturers include it on a package insert. Such inserts generally comprise several sections, including the following:

- a product description section describing the drug's dosage form, route of administration, ingredients, and therapeutic/pharmacologic effect;
- a clinical pharmacology section describing the action of the drug in humans and, if pertinent, its activity and effectiveness in animal and *in vitro* tests;
- an indications and usage section describing specific safety conditions and identifying indications supported by evidence of clinical effectiveness;
- a contraindications section;

- a warnings section describing potential safety hazards and steps to be taken if reactions occur;

- a precautions section discussing drug interactions and possible side effects in specific population groups such as pregnant women;

- an adverse reactions section;

- a drug abuse and dependence section, including a discussion of possible abuses and physical or psychological dependencies;

- an overdose section identifying specific signs, symptoms, complications, and laboratory findings that are associated with overdosage (this section might also specify the amount of the drug in a single dosage likely to cause overdosage symptoms and/or a life-threatening situation);

- a dosage and administration section identifying the recommended usual dose, safe upper dosage limit, and dosage modifications for children and the elderly; and

- a section describing how the drug is supplied (i.e., the drug's dosage form, strength, and unit availability).

Based on its perceptions of the package insert's limited effectiveness in conveying important risk-related information to physicians and patients, the FDA issued a long-awaited proposed regulation that would require a new and simplified format for the package insert. In August 2004, senior FDA officials noted that finalizing this proposed rule was one of their top priorities, and that they hoped to release the final rule b year-end 2004. The proposed rule called for the package inserts of new and recently approved drugs to includ a new introductory "Highlights of Prescribing Information" section featuring the most important and mos commonly referred-to prescribing information in bulleted format, as well as an index to prescribing informa tion. The agency also proposed that the labeling of all new molecular entities approved for less than thre years contain an inverted black triangle "to serve as a signal for increased vigilance and reporting of suspect ed adverse reactions...and to help ensure that drugs are used with particular care during their initial years c marketing." The proposed regulation is designed to streamline what are now viewed as requirements tha have led to an overly complicated drug label, and to upgrade the useability of the package insert by requirin companies to place the most important drug- and risk-related information at the beginning of the label.

A June 2000 draft guidance also sought to focus labeling-development efforts on key risk-related informatior Entitled *Content and Format of the Adverse Reactions Section of Labeling for Human Prescription Drugs and Biologics*, th draft guidance emphasized the need for sponsors to focus the label's adverse reactions section on drug safe ty information that is important to prescribing decisions and to observing, monitoring, and advising patient The common format recommended in the guidance divides the adverse reactions section into two subsec tions: (1) a new "overview" subsection that highlights the adverse reactions that are most serious and mos commonly occurring, and those that most frequently result in clinical interventions; and (2) a "discussior subsection that addresses in greater detail the significance of adverse reaction data obtained from the clin cal trials. The guidance also recommends that subjective and nonspecific terms, such as "well tolerated "rare," "infrequent," and "frequent," should be avoided, since they have no precise meaning and can, therefore be misleading.

A July 2001 draft guidance entitled, *Guidance for Industry: Clinical Studies Section of Labeling for Prescription Drugs an Biologics*, attempts to better focus a drug's labeling on key clinical studies. In focusing on a drug's effectivenes for its approved indication, the clinical studies section of drug labeling should include information on clinical studies that provide primary support for effectiveness or important information on the limitations of effectiveness, or other clinical studies that contribute important efficacy data not provided by these primary support studies, the draft guidance states. Generally, studies that imply effectiveness for unapproved indications, active control studies that imply comparative efficacy or safety claims not supported by substantial evidence, and studies that are not adequate and well controlled should not be included in the labeling's clinical studies section, the FDA states.

These efforts to revise the package insert are just the latest in a series of recent regulatory and legislative initiatives to upgrade drug labeling. Under an August 1997 final rule, the FDA required that prescription drug labeling provide information on product use in elderly patients (i.e., patients aged 65 and older). A "Geriatric use" subsection within a label's "Precautions" section must describe what is known about the effects of a drug in the elderly and list any limitations, hazards, or monitoring needs associated with geriatric use. While the agency "encourages further study of drug effects in the elderly" through this regulation, the agency makes clear that the labeling requirements are designed to specify a place and format for available information and not to require additional clinical studies on geriatric uses. In October 2001, the FDA released an industry guidance document entitled, *Content and Format for Geriatric Labeling*.

Under the FDA Modernization Act of 1997 (FDAMA), Congress made some modifications to prescription drug labeling requirements. Most importantly, the legislation required that the "Rx only" symbol replace the previous mandatory statement—"Caution: Federal law prohibits dispensing without a prescription." The agency formally implemented this and other labeling changes mandated by FDAMA through a February 2002 final regulation.

Under a February 2004 final regulation, the FDA also began requiring that the product labels for most prescription and OTC drugs feature bar codes that must provide the National Drug Code (NDC) number. The requirement is designed to help reduce the number of medication errors in hospitals and other health care settings.

OTC Drug Labeling OTC labeling requirements are, with regard to content at least, similar to those for prescription pharmaceuticals. The labeling for nonprescription products must provide information regarding active ingredients, dosage and administration, indication, drug action, warnings, precautions, drug interaction, and overdosage.

Because OTC products are self-prescribed and because their use often does not involve the guidance of a physician or pharmacist, however, OTC drug labeling must be structured differently. Much of the essential information provided to a pharmacist or physician through the package insert of a prescription drug must be detailed on the outer package of the OTC product's container. In fact, all of the information that will allow the consumer to select and use the OTC product safely and effectively must appear on the outer package. This information must be presented in a manner suitable for the comprehension of the lay public.

Due to what it perceived as consumer difficulties in understanding OTC product labeling information, the FDA implemented a March 1999 regulation to establish consumer-friendly format and content requirements for OTC drug labels. The regulation requires that the information provided in OTC drug labeling include standardized headings, be presented in a specified order, and meet minimum type size, type style, and graphics requirements.

The FDA's Review of Draft Labeling When it becomes apparent that an NDA will be approved, agency reviewers evaluate the draft package labeling on at least two levels. First, the draft labeling is reviewed for it consistency with the regulatory requirements for prescription or OTC drugs. Each important element of th proposed labeling (i.e., indications, use instructions, warnings, etc.) is then evaluated in view of conclusion drawn from nonclinical and clinical testing. All claims, instructions, and precautions must be based upon, an accurately reflect, the findings of the key test results, preferably from clinical studies.

If the FDA has major reservations about the draft labeling, the agency will usually forward to the sponsor letter detailing its suggestions for revised labeling. In some cases, FDA reviewers themselves may revise a por tion of the labeling, and instruct the sponsor to include the revision in the final printed labeling. Agency com ments can relate to virtually any aspect of the proposed drug labeling, including the drug indications, genera wording, the labeling format, and the warnings/precautions.

The labeling "negotiation process," through which a drug's final approved labeling is agreed upon, can con sume several weeks or several months. The length and complexity of the process will depend upon severa factors, including the nature and number of the FDA's comments and the degree to which the applicant i agreeable to making recommended revisions. It might also be affected by CDER's increasing focus on "gettin; labeling right" when a product is first introduced (i.e., because prescribers tend not to pay as much attentio to postapproval label modifications).

In some cases, the sponsor will have to submit several revisions of its labeling before the FDA finds an accept able version. Disagreements over labeling content, wording, and design are generally resolvable throug either mail and telephone correspondence or through FDA-sponsor meetings.

In the FDA's July 2003 GRMP draft guidance, the agency notes that labeling negations should be "implement ed well in advance of [an NDA's] final action goal date and should not impede timely completion of the first cycle review." The draft guidance adds that the CDER review division should not only communicate requeste changes in the applicant's proposed label language, but the reasons for the requested changes as well in a effort to decrease the number of back-and-forth negotiations. In October 2003 comments in response t CDER's proposed GRMPs, the Biotechnology Industry Organization (BIO) encouraged the center to go eve further, by instituting the practice of defining a target date (at least 30 days in advance of the application du date) for the initiation of labeling negotiation discussions.

In recent years, both the FDA and industry have shown an interest in expediting what can be a lengthy labe ing negotiation process. Given that CDER's internal labeling review process can involve many parties (i.e., nc only primary reviewers, but consultants from its Office of Drug Safety and Division of Drug Marketin; Advertising, and Labeling), it can also be a complex process as well.

To expedite the labeling review process, CDER officials began moving toward the electronic submission of th complete package insert during 2000. Ultimately, the center hopes to permit labeling submissions to be made and related negotiations to be conducted, electronically. To this end, the FDA issued a December 2003 fina regulation to require that companies submitting NDAs file a new section, called the "content of labeling" sec tion, in electronic form (see discussion above and Chapter 7). The agency is requiring this new section of th NDA, which comprises the package insert and all text, tables and figures, to streamline the drug labelin review process and to expedite the approval of post-approval labeling changes.

Sponsor Rights During the NDA Review Process

Over the past decade, legislative and regulatory initiatives affected several aspects of NDA sponsors' rights during the review of their applications. Companies should be aware of these rights and the courses of action available to them should these rights be violated. Sponsor rights during the NDA review process fall into roughly four categories: (1) the right to a timely review; (2) the right to request meetings or conferences with the FDA; (3) the right to protest if the sponsor believes its rights are violated; and (4) the right to confidentiality.

The Right to a Timely Review Under the Prescription Drug User Fee Act of 1992, PDUFA reauthorizing legislation passed in 1997 and 2002, and FDA/industry agreements associated with PDUFA II and PDUFA III, the federal government has redefined the timeframes applicable to drug application reviews. For years prior to the user-fee program, CDER had operated under legal requirements mandating that the agency review and act on NDAs within 180 days of their submission. Most often, however, the 180-day time frame had been called a "phantom" requirement that CDER used as a goal or target, but seldom as a strictly enforced rule.

Agreements associated with PDUFA I, II, and III established a new series of drug review targets for the FDA, while the user-fee laws themselves provided the means—specifically, revenues derived from user fees—through which the agency could restaff and retool itself to meet these deadlines. Under PDUFA I and II, the FDA implemented a series of NDA review-related performance goals that became more aggressive with each year. Under PDUFA III, however, the agency simply adopted the user-fee review goals in effect for the last year of PDUFA II:

- For priority NDAs: to review and act on within six months for 90% of original NDAs submitted from FY2003 to FY2007.

- For standard NDAs: to review and act on within 10 months for 90% of original NDAs submitted from FY2003 to FY2007.

It is important to note that the FDA's user-fee review commitments establish timeframes within which the agency is to take formal action on drug applications—in other words, there are no user-fee timelines within which the FDA is expected to *approve* an application, since such goals would be impractical for a variety of reasons. Acknowledging that meeting user-fee review goals is a hollow achievement unless new medicines also reach patients (i.e., gain approval), FDA officials announced in June 2003 that they had established a non-PDUFA-related benchmark through which the agency would attempt to further reduce NDA review times: The agency would seek a 10% reduction in the median review time for the first 50% of NDAs (and BLAs for biologics) for new molecular entities that are approved in the FY2005 through FY2007 cohorts. In announcing the new goal, then-FDA Commissioner Mark McClellan, M.D., conceded that, "while improving review cycle performance [under the PDUFA goals] is important, that's not the bottom line. The bottom line is reducing the overall time for development and approval of safe and effective new medicines... Reducing cycle time alone is unlikely to achieve this goal... We will do more than ever to help avoid multiple cycles of review and to increase the likelihood that an application to FDA gets it right the first time."

In a March 2003 report entitled, FDA's *Review Process for New Drug Applications*: A *Management Review*, however, the HHS Inspector General recommended that the FDA consider lengthening its 10-month goal for standard NDAs by one or two months. The report cited FDA reviewer concerns about the amount of time available for product reviews under the user-fee goals, which the HHS characterized as "an important management issue warranting attention."

Some in the pharmaceutical industry have expressed concern that the FDA's overly intense focus on meeting user-fee review timelines may, as an unintended consequence, undermine what might otherwise be first-cycle

NDA approvals, and that the agency may not be making the most of flexibility provided by the user-fee per formance goals to promote more rapid drug approvals. In October 2003 comments issued in response to CDER's July 2003 GRMP draft guidance, the Pharmaceutical Research and Manufacturers of America (PhRMA encouraged the agency to "include language that, at least, provides for the possibility of a review division opt ing to miss a first-cycle goal date for an important product intended to treat a serious or life-threatening dis ease when the division director, perhaps with authorization from the office of center level, determines that the product can be approved and made available more quickly than if it undergoes a second-cycle review." PhRMA notes that the draft GRMPs make "no mention of mitigating circumstances under which FDA would choose to miss a goal date to promote earlier access, even though the PDUFA goals have never held FDA to completing 100% of application reviews within the specified time frames."

Because of different review performance goals applicable to standard and priority applications (six month versus ten months under PDUFA III), the agency introduced detailed criteria for classifying priority origina and supplemental submissions (see Chapter 9):

Priority Application. A priority application is for a product that, if approved, "would be a significant improvemen compared to marketed products [approved (if such is required), including non-'drug' products/therapies] in the treatment, diagnosis, or prevention of a disease. Improvement can be demonstrated by, for example: (1 evidence of increased effectiveness in the treatment, prevention, or diagnosis of disease; (2) elimination o substantial reduction of a treatment-limiting drug reaction; (3) documented enhancement of patient compli ance; or (4) evidence of safety and effectiveness of a new subpopulation."

Standard Application. All applications not qualifying as priority are classified as standard submissions.

Editor's Note: Although it has no significance in a drug's review priority, each drug also receives a chemica rating, which represents the product's chemical novelty. These ratings may be one of the following: Type 1 new molecular entity; Type 2-new ester, new salt, or other noncovalent derivative; Type 3-new formulatior Type 4-new combination; Type 5-new manufacturer; Type 6-new indication; or Type 7-drug already markete but without an approved NDA. CDER is currently revising its policy on assigning chemical ratings. Also, i cases in which a drug's conventional therapeutic rating is considered inadequate to identify a product's defin ing characteristics, the agency may assign a "special situation" rating, such as Type AA for AIDS drugs or Typ V for designated orphan drugs. Like the chemical rating, these ratings have no direct effect on a product' review priority.

In reviewing data on new drug approvals over the past decade, it remains difficult to see lasting trends in th FDA's assignment of priority status to new drugs. After granting priority status to just under a third of NME that were cleared in 2000 and 2001, CDER granted the prized status to 41% and 43% of NMEs approved in 200 and 2003, respectively. Priority designations seemed to reach their peak for those NMEs cleared in 1993 an 1994, when more than half of the new drugs obtained priority status. For NDAs overall (i.e., for NMEs and nor NMEs), priority designations were granted to 19 percent, 14 percent, and 15 percent of applications approve in 2003, 2002, and 2001, respectively.

The review timelines applicable to an NDA can be extended if the sponsor submits a "major" amendment t the original application during the review process. A major amendment involves the submission of a larg amount of new, previously unreviewed data (e.g., new clinical or animal studies) or any submission that sig nificantly affects the review process (e.g., a reanalysis involving multiple reviewing disciplines). When majc amendments are submitted within three months of an application's action due date, the FDA can extend th review time frames by three months. The FDA's July 2003 Good Review Management Principles draft guidance emphasizes that a review division should consider reviewing a major amendment in the current review cycle:

"The review division retains the authority to determine whether to extend the review clock in response to such [major] amendment. In making this decision, the review division should consider the contents of the amendment, the status of each discipline's review for the application, the division's workload and staffing, and the likelihood that review of the major amendment could lead to approval of the application during the first-cycle review. For example, the review division should generally not extend the review clock if a major amendment addressing issues identified in a [discipline review] letter is submitted during the last three months of the review cycle when the application is not approvable due to another discipline's identification of major deficiencies that cannot reasonably be corrected by the applicant within the new extended review timeline. In this scenario, the review division should take a timely action, deferring review of the major amendment to the next review cycle."

Throughout the PDUFA II years and in the first year of PDUFA III, the FDA reported that it exceeded its review performance goals for original NDA reviews. In a December 2003 performance report to Congress, for example, the agency declared that it had exceeded its review goals for the FY2002 NDA cohort, and that it was poised to exceed its goals for the FY2003 submissions.

In fulfilling its user-fee goals over more than a decade, CDER has produced significant reductions in average and median NDA review times, even if these measures have risen somewhat more recently (see exhibit below). In 2003, for example, CDER's median review time was 15.4 months for standard NDAs and 7.7 months for priority applications. The center's mean review time for NMEs cleared in 2003 was 16.9 months, an improvement over the 17.8-month average in 2002 but still up considerably from the 11.7-month mean in 1998.

What is also striking about the transformation of CDER's drug approval process under the user-fee program is the number of drugs obtaining rapid drug reviews. For example, 57% of the NMEs approved in 2003 were reviewed in 12 months or less, compared to just over a third in the early years of the user-fee program.

The Right to Meetings Given their importance in the drug development and review process, agency/sponsor meetings were the subject of several industry and CDER initiatives over the past decade. In 1996, for example, CDER released a policy document outlining the center's procedures for scheduling and conducting formal meetings with sponsors. Under FDA/industry agreements associated with PDUFA's reauthorization, the agency implemented a meetings-management system under which CDER has adopted new standards for scheduling and holding sponsor meetings. And, not surprisingly, close "interactions between the applicant and the Agency's therapeutic review divisions" is one of the core principles outlined in CDER's July 2003 Good Review Management Principles (GRMP) draft guidance (see discussion above).

CDER communicates openly with sponsors about scientific, medical, and procedural issues that arise during the NDA review process. These exchanges may take the form of telephone or videoconferences, letters, or face-to-face meetings, whichever is the most appropriate to discuss and resolve the relevant issue.

All sponsors have the right to at least one, and possibly several, conferences with the FDA during and after the NDA review. While other forms of correspondence will occur routinely throughout the NDA review, the sponsor must make a formal written request before CDER will grant and schedule a conference.

Key Drug Submission and Approval Statistics, 1993–2003

	1993	1994	1995	1996	1997	1998	1999	2000	2001	2002	2003
NDA Submissions	86	114	121	120	128	121	139	115	98	109	119
NDA Approvals	70	62	82	131	121	90	83	98	66	78	72
Avg. Review Time for All Original NDAs (in months)	24.1	26	22.7	21.6	17.6	12.8	13.5	15.0	17.2 (s)[+] 7.7 (p)[+]	21.8 (s)[+] 19.7 (p)[+]	NA
Avg. FDA Review Time for Original NDAs*	–	21.5	18.8	17.1	14.9	11.6	11.7	12.7	14.5 (s)[+] 6.9 (p)[+]	14.2 (s)[+] 11.5 (p)[+]	NA
Median Review Time for All Original NDAs (in months)	20.8	19	16.5	15.4	14.4	12.0	12.0	11.2	14.0 (s)[+] 6.0 (p)[+]	15.3 (s)[+] 19.1 (p)[+]	15.4 (s)[+] 7.7 (p)[+]
Median FDA Review Time for Original NDAs*	–	15.8	15.3	14.8	12.2	12.0	11.8	10.9	12.0 (s)[+] 6.0 (p)[+]	12.7 (s)[+] 13.8 (p)[+]	11.9 (s)[+] 7.7 (p)[+]
NME Approvals	25	22	28	53	39	30	35	27	24	17	21
Avg. Review Time for NMEs (in months)	26.5	19.7	19.2	17.8	16.2	11.7	12.6	17.6	16.4	17.8	16.9
Avg. FDA Review Time for NMEs*	–	21.2	17.4	15.8	14.3	10.7	10.9	13.4	16.0 (s)[+] 7.3 (p)[+]	14.0 (s)[+] 11.0 (p)[+]	20.5 (s)[+] 12.0 (p)[+]
Median Review Time for NMEs (in Months)	21.0	17.5	15.9	14.3	13.4	12.0	11.6	15.6	14.4	16.3	9.9
Median FDA Review Time for NMEs*	–	15.3	15.2	12.0	12.8	11.9	10.0	13.9	15.7 (s)[+] 6.0 (p)[+]	12.5 (s)[+] 13.8 (p)[+]	13.8 (s)[+] 6.7 (p)[+]
IND Submissions	2,323	2,156	1,566	1,419	1,996	2,419	1,763	1,815	1,872	2,374	2,120
Commercial IND Submissions	382	345	358	412	437	498	440	424	425	428	426

*excludes sponsor time. [+] s=standard; p=priority (in 2001, CDER began reporting exclusively by standard and priority applications rather than by all NDAs and NME-NDAs, as in previous years).

Source: PAREXEL's Pharmaceutical R&D Statistical Sourcebook 2004/2005

The number of meetings to which a sponsor is entitled may depend upon the subject drug and the priorit given to it by the FDA. Under regulations implemented in 1985, the agency claimed to have made FDA-spor sor conferences more accessible to all applicants. Conferences relevant to the NDA review process include th following:

The 90-Day Conference. Approximately 90 days after it receives an NDA, CDER provides sponsors of certain drug an opportunity to meet with officials and drug reviewers. Generally, such meetings are available only to spor sors of either NMEs or major new indications of currently marketed drugs. The purpose of the conference i to inform an applicant about the general progress and status of its NDA, and to advise the company of def ciencies that have been identified but not yet communicated. However, the 90-day conference is not manda tory, and sponsors may choose not to request such a meeting. Also, the conference may be either a telephon or face-to-face meeting. The fact that CDER is, under PDUFA III, issuing 74-day letters (see discussion above to alert applicants to NDA deficiencies early in the review process may affect the frequency with which appl cants request 90-day conferences.

The End-of-Review Conference. The end-of-review conference is offered to all applicants after CDER has issue either an approvable or not-approvable letter for an NDA. During this meeting, FDA officials discuss what fu ther steps the sponsor must take before the application can be approved.

Other Meetings. Sponsors may request additional meetings to discuss scientific, medical, and other issues that arise during the review process. Because of already heavy demands on its time, however, CDER is likely to grant conferences only for more important issues. For resolving less significant issues, the agency will probably suggest communication by telephone or letter.

While it advocates close NDA applicant/FDA interaction during the review process, CDER's July 2003 GRMP draft guidance cautions that not all meetings requests will be granted. "Under 21 CFR 314.102 and PDUFA meeting management policy, applicants can request meetings during the review process as an opportunity to receive feedback regarding the application review status and deficiencies," the draft GRMP guidance states. "The FDA will evaluate meeting requests based on whether the meeting is likely to serve a useful purpose warranting the time and resources required to prepare for and conduct the meeting (e.g., whether the meeting has the potential to resolve significant application deficiencies or issues and further review of the application). Requests for meetings primarily focused on *status updates* generally are not an efficient use of the review division's limited time and resources and may actually slow the review process because of the need for preparation. Such meeting requests ordinarily will be denied."

Under the FDA's new meetings-management system, a review division should notify the sponsor of a meeting date within 14 calendar days of receiving the formal meeting request. The agency will be called upon to meet this goal for 90% of meetings requests during the PDUFA III years (FY2003-FY2007).

Agreements under PDUFA III classify FDA/sponsor meetings during NDA reviews as Type C meetings, meaning that the FDA should ensure that the meetings take place within 75 calendar days of the agency's receipt of formal meeting requests. The agency must meet this goal for 90% of meetings requests received from FY2003-FY2007.

Applicants seeking to schedule a meeting with CDER should consult at least two documents: a 1996 CDER policy document entitled, *Formal Meetings Between CDER and CDER's External Constituents* (MaPP 4512.1), and a February 2000 industry guidance entitled, *Formal Meetings with Sponsors and Applicants for PDUFA Products.*

The Right to Protest and Appeal FDA Actions/Decisions Although recent regulatory initiatives have done much to make the FDA and sponsors "partners" in drug development, the NDA review process can, in some cases, result in disputes based on scientific or other issues. Agency regulations permit any "interested person"—which includes a sponsor or applicant—to obtain a formal review of any agency decision by raising the matter with the supervisor of the employee who made the decision at issue.

Dispute resolution has become a fairly visible issue over the past several years. In fact, CDER has undertaken several related initiatives on the subject:

- Under the user-fee program, the FDA has established a two-tier appeals process for resolving scientific agency/sponsor disputes (see discussion below).

- In February 2000, CDER released an industry guidance entitled, *Formal Dispute Resolution: Appeals Above the Division Level* to provide guidance for resolving scientific and procedural disputes that cannot be resolved at the division level, and to describe procedures for formally appealing decisions that cause such disputes.

- In a November 18, 1998, revised regulation, the FDA explicitly stated that a sponsor, applicant, or manufacturer of a drug may request a review of a scientific controversy by an appropriate advisory committee. Since the agency still retains the discretion as to whether advisory committee input will be sought on such issues, the amended regulation calls for the agency to inform the requestor, in writing, of the reasons for a denial of a request for advisory committee review (see Chapter 10).

- In 1995, CDER established the CDER ombudsman function, which is designed to provide a mechanism through which sponsors and others can "seek solutions to problematic interactions and suggest better ways for [the center] to do its work." In virtually all cases, however, interactions with the CDER ombudsman are considered informal and, therefore, are not subject to the dispute resolution policies and goals established for formal dispute resolution efforts.

- Under a draft guidance outlining a special dispute-resolution process for good manufacturing practices (GMP) inspections, CDER initiated a 12-month pilot under which applicants could challenge cGMP inspection results regarding scientific and technical issues. Based on its experience with the pilot program, CDER hopes to issue a final guidance in early 2005.

Despite CDER's implementation of formal dispute resolution mechanisms, it is important to note that, fo many firms, resolving issues through informal means remains the preferred route. Many center officials expec most firms, particularly larger and more experienced firms, to attempt to address and resolve dispute through less formal means, in part because formalizing the process can lengthen and complicate it. Accordin to CDER officials, one of the more common informal ways that companies seek to address disputes is t request a meeting with a review division and to request that the relevant office director (e.g., ODE I, II, III) b present at the meeting to offer senior management input on the issue.

Traditionally, CDER has had a fairly sophisticated process for helping sponsors settle disputes. The proces through which a particular dispute is resolved may depend upon whether the problem is procedural/admin istrative or scientific/medical in nature.

Administrative and Procedural Disputes. Administrative and procedural disputes may involve problems such a sponsor difficulties in scheduling FDA meetings and obtaining timely agency responses to inquiries. Th sponsor may also believe that the agency is not following procedures consistent with current laws or regula tions. When such problems arise, the FDA recommends that a sponsor first contact the project manager wh is handling its application. Project managers are experts in the NDA review process, and are likely to have th most complete information about the status of a pending application. Because of this and because projec managers work very closely with NDA reviewers, they can resolve many procedural or administrative problem if the agency is at fault.

Scientific and Medical Disputes. The FDA believes that the 90-day and end-of-review conferences as well as var ous other FDA-sponsor communications provide adequate vehicles for addressing and resolving scientific an medical disputes. The agency recognizes that there are exceptions, however. When the sponsor believes tha conferences have proven inadequate, it may request a meeting with the management of the appropriat reviewing division. At that time, the applicant may suggest that the FDA seek the advice of outside expert such as consultants and other agency advisors. The sponsor may also invite its own consultant when such meeting is granted.

If a specially scheduled meeting fails to resolve a dispute, the applicant or the agency may propose that th scientific/medical issue be referred to one of the FDA's standing advisory committees, which consist largely c non-FDA medical experts (see Chapter 10). The committee will review the issue and make recommendation The FDA can then follow these recommendations or take its own course of action.

Formal Dispute Resolution Under FDA regulations and policies, a sponsor should first attempt to address an NDA- or supplemental NDA-related scientific or procedural issue at the review division level. If division-level formal or informal mechanisms fail to resolve the issue, the sponsor can request that the division reconsider the issue after the company provides the division an opportunity to review any materials on which the sponsor intends to rely in an appeal to the next level.

Issues that are not resolvable at the review-division level (i.e., after a formal request for reconsideration) should then be appealed at the office level (i.e., ODE I, II, etc.). If necessary, the sponsor can then appeal to the director of the Office of New Drugs and then to the center director.

According to CDER's February 2000 guidance, the applicant should request formal dispute resolution at the office or center level by submitting a written request and supporting documentation to the center's formal dispute resolution project manager (DRPM). The DRPM will forward the request to the appropriate CDER official, who will provide a response after reviewing the materials and the administrative record. That response may represent any one of several outcomes, including a decision on the matter, a decision to seek input from an advisory committee or other internal or external experts, or a request for more information from the sponsor. If the agency denies the appeal, its written response should identify the reasons for the denial and any actions that the sponsor might take to address the specific issue.

The agency's response (i.e., via letter or telephone) to a sponsor appeal regarding a user-fee product should occur within 30 calendar days of the DRPM's receipt of the formal request. According to its user-fee goals, CDER is expected to provide such responses within this timeframe for at least 90% of the written appeals received from FY2003-FY2007.

The Right To Confidentiality Given the quantity of competitively sensitive data and information submitted in NDAs, confidentiality issues are of great importance to drug sponsors. Both the FDA and the federal government have policies and procedures designed to protect from public disclosure certain types of information submitted in NDAs.

The degree of protection (from public disclosure) afforded to information and data submitted in an NDA depends on a few factors, including the nature of the information or data and the application's status (i.e., under review, approvable, or approved).

Under current laws and regulations, the agency may not, at any time either during the NDA review or after approval, publicly disclose or release any information or test data that qualify as trade secret or commercial or financial information. According to FDA regulations, a trade secret "may consist of any commercially valuable plan, formula, process, or device that is used for the making, preparing, compounding, or processing of trade commodities and that can be said to be the end product of either innovation or substantial effort." The regulations also emphasize that "there must be a direct relationship between the trade secret and the productive process."

Commercial or financial information considered privileged or confidential means "valuable data or information which is used in one's business and is of a type customarily held in strict confidence or regarded as privileged and not disclosed to any member of the public" by the company to which it belongs.

Under certain circumstances, the FDA does have the authority to disclose confidential commercial information to foreign regulatory agencies and to certain international organizations. It is important to note, however, that the regulations that authorize such exchanges also include several safeguards to prevent unauthorized disclosures, and that virtually all disclosures of confidential commercial information have occurred with th sponsor's consent. The situations under which the agency would consider disclosing confidential commerci⟨ information without the sponsor's consent generally involve cases in which obtaining the sponsor's conser might adversely affect or compromise an enforcement action (see discussion below).

Confidentiality Prior to Approval In general, the FDA will not publicly disclose the existence of an NDA before ⟨ issues an approvable letter for the application, unless the NDA's existence has been previously publicly di⟨ closed or acknowledged (e.g., by the sponsor or other lawful manner). Once an approvable letter has bee issued, the FDA can disclose the NDA's existence, which the agency traditionally has done in a periodic lisɪ ing of applications that have reached the approvable stage. Given that the agency has proposed to eliminaɪ approvable letters, however, it has had to develop and propose new standards for such disclosures (see di⟨ cussion below).

If an unapproved NDA's existence has not been publicly disclosed or acknowledged, no data or informatio contained within it is available for public disclosure until an approval letter is issued (see discussion below If, however, the pending NDA's existence has been publicly disclosed or acknowledged, the FDA commissior er may, at his or her discretion, "disclose a summary of selected portions of the safety and effectiveness daɪ that are appropriate for public consideration of a specific pending issue" (e.g., for consideration at an ope session of an advisory committee meeting).

Confidentiality Following Approval Once the agency issues an approvable letter, the NDA's existence and certai non-confidential data within it can be publicly disclosed by the agency. Unless an applicant can show th⟨ "extraordinary circumstances" exist, the following information will become immediately available for publi disclosure:

- a "disclosable review package," sometimes called an "approval package" and previously termed a "summary basis of approval" document, that provides information on the results of each aspect of the NDA review (e.g., medical, pharmacology, and chemistry review);

- a protocol for a test or study, unless it is shown to fall within the definition of trade secret or confidential commercial information;

- adverse reaction reports, product experience reports, consumer complaints, and other similar data and information after certain confidential information is deleted (information that would identify the subject or any physician or institution);

- a list of all active ingredients and any inactive ingredients previously disclosed to the public; and

- an assay method or other analytical method, unless it serves no regulatory or compliance purpose and is shown to fall within the definition of trade secret or confidential commercial information.

Proposed Changes to NDA Confidentiality Standards

Although current regulations prohibit the agency from publicly acknowledging the existence of an NDA ⟨ related application until the agency issues an approvable letter for the application (unless the application existence has been previously publicly disclosed or acknowledged), these regulations must be revised giv⟨ that the FDA is proposing to eliminate approvable letters themselves (see discussion above). In its July 20C proposed regulation, the agency proposes to delay allowable FDA disclosures of the existence of an NDA unɪ after an approval letter is issued for the application, unless the application's existence has been previously publicly disclosed or acknowledged.

"The changes that we are proposing to the disclosure provisions would mean that FDA disclosure of the existence of an NDA...might result in later disclosure than sometimes occurs under the current regulation (i.e., with respect to those applications for which FDA now issues approvable letters)," the agency notes. "However, we believe that this effect would be limited because most applicants (at least for NDAs) publicly reveal the existence of their applications before agency issuance of an approval letter. Moreover, the proposed change would be consistent with the agency's long-standing presumption that, before approval (and absent evidence to the contrary), the existence of an application is confidential commercial information...."

The agency, however, is seeking comments on whether it should reconsider the appropriateness of disclosing an NDA's existence when a complete response letter is issued and, if so, what conditions if any should be placed on such a disclosure. "For example, one alternative to the proposed approach would be that FDA would publicly disclose the existence of an NDA...following issuance of a complete response letter unless the applicant notified the agency (by some specified deadline) that the applicant had not publicly disclosed or acknowledged the existence of the application...," the agency states. "This approach would allow applicants to prevent agency disclosures of the existence of an application despite the issuance of a complete response letter. However, it also would create the potential for inadvertent disclosure and necessitate the establishment of a system to record and track applicants' positions regarding disclosure. This could be burdensome to applicants and the agency."

CHAPTER 9

The FDA's Priority Review Policy

Given the workload-to-staffing disparity that has often characterized the FDA during its history and the corresponding disparity in the therapeutic significance of new medicines under review, it is not surprising that the agency has evolved a system under which marketing applications for new drugs could be prioritized based on their implications for the public health. Traditionally, CDER has employed a relatively straightforward drug classification system to assist its reviewers in prioritizing NDA reviews. Although the system has been revamped to some degree under the FDA's user-fee program, it continues to permit the agency to allocate its resources to what are perceived to be the most important NDAs, independent of such factors as the chronological order of the submissions.

Essentially, the FDA's priority review policy is important because it puts public health before something that is also critical to any government regulatory agency: the absolute need to act impartially and to adopt procedures, policies, and practices that reinforce its impartiality to those who it serves and to whom it answers. Without such a policy, the practical realities of reviewing and approving applications based on any criterion other than their dates of submission would be far more difficult for an agency whose every move can be scrutinized by Congress, industry, the media, and the public.

While some have argued that CDER's drug classification system was not significant in the past, the prescription drug user fee program has placed greater emphasis on a drug's "therapeutic rating," which CDER generally assigns upon the filing of an NDA. Under CDER commitments made as part of the user-fee program, a drug's therapeutic rating—either priority or standard—determines the center's review goal for the product's NDA. Throughout the life of PDUFA III (October 1, 2003 through September 30, 2007), the center must review and take action on 90 percent of priority NDAs within 6 months and 90 percent of standard NDAs within 10 months.

Although the review performance goals for drug applications have comprised the centerpiece of the FDA's user-fee program, agency officials have attempted to establish informal goals that move beyond the current targets. It is important to note that the FDA's user-fee review commitments establish timeframes within which the agency is to take formal action on priority and standard drug applications—in other words, there are no user-fee timelines within which the FDA is expected to *approve* an application, since such goals would be impractical for a variety of reasons. Acknowledging that meeting user-fee review goals is a hollow achievement unless new medicines also reach patients (i.e., gain approval), FDA officials announced in June 2003 that they had established a non-PDUFA-related benchmark through which the agency would attempt to further reduce NDA review times: The agency would seek a 10% reduction in the median review time for the first 50% of NDAs (and BLAs for biologics) for new molecular entities that are approved in the FY2005 through FY2007 cohorts. In announcing the new goal, then-FDA Commissioner Mark McClellan, M.D., conceded that, "while improving review cycle performance [under the PDUFA goals] is important, that's not the bottom line. The bottom line is reducing the overall time for development and approval of safe and effective new medicines.. Reducing cycle time alone is unlikely to achieve this goal... We will do more than ever to help avoid multiple cycles of review and to increase the likelihood that an application to FDA gets it right the first time."

This is not to say that the agency's priority designation system has been unsuccessful in promoting faster review times for new drugs, in particular significant new drugs. Over the last several years, the implications that a priority designation had for a drug's review time were unmistakable. On average, priority new molecular entities (NME) cleared in 2003 gained FDA approval 7.5 months faster than their standard counterparts (see discussion below). There were other benefits for products with the prized priority designation: In recent years, priority NDAs were far more likely to be approved in CDER's first review cycle than were standard NDAs

Such realities raised the stakes for industry, which craved the priority designation even more than it had in the past. Some company officials reported pursuing fast track designation, which offers benefits for certain drugs that fulfill unmet medical needs, not necessarily because of the benefits flowing directly from the designation, but because they believed that such designations could help them obtain for their drugs a review status that is more likely to lead to rapid product approval—priority review status.

The great rewards (i.e., earlier approval) associated with priority designation also raised the profile of the designation system under user-fee program. Critics have charged that the FDA's criteria for priority designation were too broad, and that they should be revised to ensure that only genuinely innovative therapies gain the highest review status. Others went further, calling for the criteria to be revised to include only drugs for severe and life-threatening illnesses and conditions for which no current treatments are available.

More recently, some have called for a revision in the review timelines themselves rather than the criteria used to categorize drugs as either standard or priority. In a March 2003 report entitled, FDA's *Review Process for New Drug Applications: A Management Review*, the HHS Inspector General recommended that the FDA consider lengthening its 10-month goal for standard NDAs by one or two months. The report cited FDA reviewer concern about the amount of time available for product reviews under the user-fee goals, which the HHS characterized as "an important management issue warranting attention."

Despite such criticisms and calls for revision, the FDA's priority review system remains a central element in the user-fee program.

Therapeutic Rating

While the FDA's existing alphanumeric classification system for drugs generally comprises two primary elements—a chemical rating and a therapeutic rating (e.g., 1P)—it is the therapeutic rating that determines drug's review priority. According to a 1996 CDER standard operating procedure document entitled, *Priority Review Policy* (MaPP 6020.3), all original NDAs and effectiveness supplements are to be given a therapeutic rating "based on an estimate of [the drug's] therapeutic, preventative or diagnostic value." The document adds that "the priority determination does not take into consideration any information or estimate of price and is based on conditions and information available at the time the application is filed. It is not intended to predict a drug's ultimate value or its eventual place in the market."

This estimate of therapeutic, preventative or diagnostic value must be considered in the context of CDER' definition of a "priority" product.

Priority Drugs Under CDER policy, a priority drug is one that "if approved, would be a significant improvement compared to marketed products [approved (if such is required), including non-'drug' products/therapies] in the treatment, diagnosis, or prevention of a disease. Improvement can be demonstrated by, for example: (1) evidence of increased effectiveness in treatment, prevention, or diagnosis of disease; (2) elimination or substantial reduction of a treatment-limiting drug reaction; (3) documented enhancement of patient compliance; or (4) evidence of safety and effectiveness of a new subpopulation."

Standard Drugs Under the FDA's user-fee program, drugs that do not qualify as priority products (P) are classified as standard therapies (S).

Since its criteria for determining a product's eligibility for priority designation (as well as for the fast track, treatment IND, Subpart H, and Subpart E programs) hinges, in large part, on a drug's therapeutic potential compared to available products, the agency issued a July 2004 industry guidance to address uncertainty regarding the definition of "available therapy." Under the guidance entitled, *Available Therapy*, the agency acknowledges that it has never formally defined the term. "Some confusion has arisen regarding whether *available therapy* refers only to products approved by FDA for the use in question, or whether the term could also refer to products used off-label or to treatments not regulated by FDA, such as surgery." In view of this, the agency uses the July 2004 guidance to establish that:

"*Available therapy* (and the terms *existing treatments* and *existing therapy*) should be interpreted as therapy that is specified in the approved labeling of regulated products, with only rare exceptions... Only in exceptional cases will a treatment that is not FDA-regulated (e.g., surgery) or that is not labeled for use but is supported by compelling literature evidence (e.g., certain established oncologic treatments) be considered *available therapy.*"

Special Situation Drugs The FDA may consider the conventional priority or standard rating code to be inadequate to properly identify a product's defining characteristics. In such cases, a review division may assign a drug one or more "special situation" ratings in addition to the "P" or "S" rating:

Type AA-AIDS Drug: "The drug is indicated for the treatment of AIDS or HIV-related disease."

Type E-Subpart E Drug: "The drug was developed and/or evaluated under the special procedures for drugs intended to treat life-threatening and severely debilitating illnesses" (see Chapter 15).

Type F-Fraud Policy Applies: "Substantive review of the application is deferred pending the outcome of a validity assessment of the submitted data as provided for by Compliance Policy Guide 7150.09. This code remains in the system throughout the audit and after when (a) the data are found to be not valid and a not approvable letter is issued or (b) the applicant withdraws the application before the audit is completed or after the audit is completed (data found to be not valid) but before a not approvable letter is issued."

Type G-Data Validated: "A validity assessment was performed on the application as provided for by CPG 7150.09, and the questions regarding the reliability of the data were satisfactorily resolved."

Type N-Non-Prescription Drug: "The drug has product labeling that provides for non-prescription (over-the-counter [OTC]) marketing. Applications will be labeled with an N designator whether all indications, or only some, are non-prescription."

Type V-Designated Orphan Drug: "The drug has officially received orphan designation...at the request of its sponsor/applicant" (see Chapter 13).

Assigning the Therapeutic Rating Because of a priority classification's significance, drug sponsors will ofter engage review division staff in classification-related discussions well before the NDA is submitted. Dependin on clinical trial results, some sponsors may attempt to explore with a division its chances of obtaining a pri ority classification as early as the IND phase, while others may wait until later in the process (e.g., the pre NDA meeting). Given that there is no formal process through which sponsors seek priority designation different companies are likely to employ various practices in proposing such designations for their products

The most recent discussion of the FDA's process for assigning review priority appears in the agency's July 200 Good Review Management Principles (GRMP) draft guidance. "A decision regarding the review priority (i.e. *priority or standard*) for NDAs, BLAs, and efficacy supplements should be made as soon as possible followin receipt of the application," the document states. "The review division director, in consultation with the offic director as appropriate, makes the review priority decision. The criteria for this decision are based on the ther apeutic advantage potentially offered by a new drug or biologic product relative to marketed products. A deci sion regarding review priority should be made for every application submitted, regardless of whether th applicant has explicitly requested priority status. The decision should be based on the merits of the produc and the application data and should not be contingent on internal FDA considerations such as competin workload or currently available resources in the review division or on whether the subject product was desig nated fast track during the development phase."

Although CDER's draft GRMP document notes that a "preliminary designation" of review priority may be mad prior to an NDA's submission in some cases, "an official decision about review priority can be made only afte the application is received for review." At that point, the agency notes, the presubmission assessment of a application's review priority may be changed. "This can occur for several reasons, including, but not limite to, failure of the clinical studies to demonstrate the expected advantage over existing therapy, or approval c the subject application."

Since the priority classification determines the review timeline applicable to an NDA, MaPP 6020.3 states tha "the review priority should be determined and assigned at the 45-day meeting if the application is to be filed Both MaPP 6020.3 and CDER's draft GRMPs establish that, although a drug may be classified down from a pri ority to a standard product during the NDA review, the initial classification is locked in during the applica tion's initial review cycle.

"The final review classification of a new drug may change from [priority] to [standard] during the course of th review of a marketing application (NDA), either because of the approval of other agents or because of avai ability of new data; however, the review priority classification assigned at the time of filing will not change dur ing the first review cycle and the user fee time frame of the original review cycle will be that based on th original priority," MaPP 6020.3 states. If the reviewing medical officer or team leader wishes to change a drug classification following the first review cycle, he or she must recommend the change "justified on the basis o for example, new information in an IND or NDA, medical literature, advisory committee opinions or approv of a pharmacologically similar drug." The division director is responsible for approving the recommende change. MaPP 6020.3 makes no reference to the possibility of applications being upgraded from standard t priority during the initial review cycle.

Chemical Novelty Rating

The numeric element in CDER's priority classification code represents the chemical novelty of a drug proc uct's active ingredient. In essence, this rating indicates to FDA chemistry reviewers whether the active ingredient is new or is related to compounds already on the market.

Although the chemical novelty rating does not have any practical implications for a drug's review priority, that may change in subtle ways. CDER will now track and report its performance regarding new molecular entities (drugs with a Type 1 chemical rating, see below) separately under PDUFA III, for example. Further, as mentioned above, agency officials have announced that they have established a non-PDUFA-related benchmark through which the agency would seek a 10% reduction in the median review time for the first 50% of NMEs that are approved in the FY2005 through FY2007 cohorts.

Until CDER releases a new MaPP for assigning chemical novelty ratings, which it has promised to do for the last several years, policy guide 4820.3 will remain in effect. According to this document, a drug is to be assigned one of the following seven chemical ratings:

Type 1-New Molecular Entity: "A drug for which the active moiety (present as the unmodified base [parent] compound, or an ester or a salt, clathrate, or other noncovalent derivative of the base [parent] compound) has not been previously approved or marketed in the United States for use in a drug product, either as a single ingredient or as part of a combination product or as part of a mixture of stereoisomers.

"The active moiety in a drug is the molecule or ion, excluding those appended portions of the molecule that cause the drug to be an ester, salt (including a salt with hydrogen or coordination bonds) or other noncovalent derivative (such as a complex, chelate, or clathrate) of the molecule, responsible for the physiological or [pharmacological] action of the drug substance. The active moiety is the entire molecule or ion, not the 'active site.'

"Ordinarily, an ester is not considered an active moiety as most ester linkages are rapidly broken, with the de-esterified molecule circulating in the blood. However, there can be exceptions to this where a stable ester is the active moiety, the de-esterified molecule being inert; an example of this is organic nitrates, where the nitrate esters are the active moieties. The organic base molecules (glycerol, isosorbide) are inert."

Type 2-New Ester, New Salt, or Other Noncovalent Derivative: "A drug for which the active moiety has been previously approved or marketed in the United States but for which the particular ester, or salt, clathrate, or other noncovalent derivative, [of] the unmodified base (parent) compound has not yet been approved or marketed in the United States, either as a single ingredient, part of a combination product, or part of a mixture of stereoisomers."

Type 3-New Formulation: "A new dosage form or formulation, including a new strength, where the drug has already been approved or marketed in the United States by the same or another manufacturer. The indication may be the same as that of the already marketed drug product or may be new.

"A drug with changes in its inactive ingredients such that clinical studies (as opposed to bioequivalence studies) are required is considered to be a Type 3 drug. A drug previously approved or marketed only as a part of a combination (either a manufactured combination or a naturally occurring mixture) or a mixture of stereoisomers will also be considered a Type 3 drug. A combination product all of whose components have previously been approved or marketed together in combination with another drug will also be considered to be a Type 3 drug.

"A change in the strength of one or more drugs in a previously approved or marketed combination is considered to be a new formulation, not a new combination."

Type 4-New Combination: "A drug product containing two or more active moieties that have not been previous ly approved or marketed together in a drug product by any manufacturer in the United States. The new prod uct may be a physical or a chemical (ester or non-covalent) combination of two or more active moieties. / new physical combination containing one or more active moieties that have not been previously approved o marketed is considered to be a Type 1,4 drug.

"A chemical combination of two or more active moieties previously approved or marketed as a physical com bination is considered to be a Type 1 drug if the chemical bond is a non-ester covalent bond. If the two moi eties are linked by an ester bond, the drug is considered a Type 4 drug if the moieties have not been previousl marketed or approved as a physical combination, and a Type 2 drug if the combination has been previousl marketed or approved."

Type 5-New Manufacturer: "A drug product that duplicates a drug product (same active moiety, same salt, sam formulation [i.e., differences not sufficient to cause the product to be a Type 3; may require bioequivalenc testing, including bioequivalence tests with clinical endpoints, but not clinical studies], or same combination already approved or marketed in the United States by another firm. This category also includes NDAs fo duplicate products where clinical studies were needed because of marketing exclusivity held by the origina applicant."

Type 6-New Indication: "A drug product that duplicates a drug product (same active moiety, same salt, same for mulation, or same combination) already approved or marketed in the U.S. by the same or another firm excep that it provides for a new indication."

Type 7-Drug Already Marketed But Without An Approved NDA: "The application is the first NDA for a drug produc containing one or more drugs marketed at the time of application or in the past without an approved NDA Includes (a) first post-1962 application for products marketed prior to 1938, and (b) first application for DESI related products first marketed between 1938 and 1962 without an NDA. The indication may be the same as or different from, the already marketed drug product."

CDER's Prioritization Policy At Work

It is difficult to know precisely how CDER's drug review divisions implement the drug classification system o a day-to-day basis. According to MaPP 6020.3, "a 'priority' designation is intended to direct overall attentio and resources to the evaluation of applications for products that have the potential for providing significan preventative or diagnostic therapeutic advance as compared to 'standard' applications.

"The review priority classification determines the overall approach to setting review priorities and user fe review time frames but is not intended to preclude work on all other projects. It does not imply that staff work ing on a priority application cannot work on other projects, such as 30-day safety reviews of a newly submit ted investigational new drug application (IND), preparation for end-of-phase 2 conferences, etc. Certain a hoc special assignments may also take precedence. The supervisor is to advise the reviewer and team leade when an ad hoc assignment is to take precedence."

Although CDER's priority review policy and the user-fee review goals are designed to focus resources o important new drugs, the user fee timelines also offer important assurances for non-priority products. Whil CDER must concentrate reviewing resources on priority products, for example, it cannot do so to the poir that it is unable to meet the 10-month review goal for standard applications. In addition, since priority clas sifications are made independently by each CDER review division, drugs are prioritized within each therapeutic area, providing at least some assurance that products in high-priority and high-profile areas such as AIDS and cancer do not compete for resources against drugs in lower-profile therapeutic areas. This policy does not prevent the agency, however, from giving more staffing resources to certain divisions (e.g., AIDS) based on workload and the significance of the therapeutic area, something that has come under scrutiny in the past.

The Impact of CDER's Priority Review Policy

Assessing the true impact of CDER's priority review policy—and its ability to promote faster approvals for high-priority products—is difficult because there are numerous factors that affect the speed with which drugs are reviewed. While it is true that the agency's review goal for high-priority products is shorter compared to that for other products, it might also be true, for example, that sponsors and reviewers may tend to invest more time early on in an important product's development and pre-NDA period, and that these investments may ultimately result in speedier reviews.

Whatever the factors, however, it is clear that CDER is reviewing and approving priority drugs more quickly than standard products. CDER's average review times for priority and standard new molecular entities (NME) approved in 2003 were 12.0 months and 20.5 months, respectively (see exhibit below). Over the past six years, the priority-versus-standard product review gap has varied considerably, from as little as 4.8 months in 1998 to as much as 15.3 months in 2000. Given that CDER's review performance goal for standard NDAs is now 10 months (i.e., rather than the 12-month goal that was phased out during the last year of PDUFA II), it is conceivable that the review-time gap will shrink at least somewhat going forward.

Priority/Standard NME Review Gap, 1995-2003 (in months)			
	Mean Approval Time for Priority NMEs	Mean Approval Time for Standard NMEs	Gap
2003	12.0	20.5	7.5
2002	14.2	20.3	6.1
2001	8.3	19.7	11.4
2000	7.4	22.7	15.3
1999	8.8	16.9	8.1
1998	9.5	14.3	4.8
1997	9.5	18.2	8.8
1996	13.7	19.7	6
1995	10.1	23.6	13.5

Source: PAREXEL's Pharmaceutical R&D Statistical Sourcebook 2004/2005

Not surprisingly given their shorter approval times, priority products are significantly more likely to be approved in CDER's first review cycle (i.e., an approval rather than an approvable or not-approvable action). While CDER approved 58% of the priority NDAs submitted during FY2002 (October 2001-September 2002) in the first review cycle, for example, it approved just 37% of the standard NDAs in the FY2002 cohort (see exhibit below).

Percent of Standard/Priority Original NDAs Approved in First Review Cycle by Submission Cohort, FY1997-FY2003

	Percent of NDAs Approved in First Review Cycle	
	Priority NDAs	Standard NDAs
FY1998	50%	31%
FY1999	61%	40%
FY2000	52%	34%
FY2001	20%	20%
FY2002*	58%	37%
FY2003**	43%	23%

* as of January 31, 2004, when 95 of 96 FY2002 NDAs had received first actions. **as of January 31, 2004, when 62 of 104 NDAs had received first actions.

Source: PAREXEL's Pharmaceutical R&D Statistical Sourcebook 2004/2005

Patterns in Priority/Standard Designations for New Drugs

Given the value of priority review status, it is not surprising that industry has watched trends in the FDA assignment of priority designations quite closely. There have been no lasting trends in priority/standard designations since the user-fee era began, however.

During the 1980s and early 1990s, roughly half of all NMEs approved by CDER were priority products. As the user-fee era matured, however, the prevalence of priority designations for new product approvals declined markedly. After rising during the first years of the user-fee program (from 42% in 1992 to 52% in 1993 and 59% in 1994), the percentage of approved NMEs with priority designations began a several-year decline. After priority designations declined to less than 25% of NMEs approved in 1997, the lowest mark in at least 15 years, priority designations for approved NMEs have returned to more typical levels. In 2002 and 2003, just over 40% of approved NMEs were priority drugs.

NMEs Approved Based on Therapeutic Potential, 1985–2003

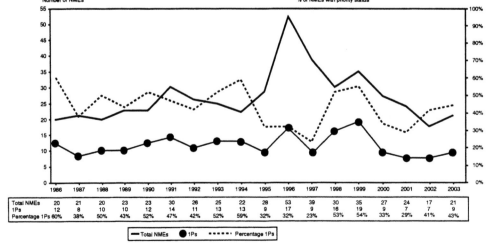

	1986	1987	1988	1989	1990	1991	1992	1993	1994	1995	1996	1997	1998	1999	2000	2001	2002	2003
Total NMEs	20	21	20	23	23	30	26	25	22	28	53	39	30	35	27	24	17	21
1Ps	12	8	10	10	12	14	11	13	13	9	17	9	16	19	9	7	7	9
Percentage 1Ps	60%	38%	50%	43%	52%	47%	42%	52%	59%	32%	32%	23%	53%	54%	33%	29%	41%	43%

Source: PAREXEL's Pharmaceutical R&D Statistical Sourcebook 2004/2005

Meanwhile, after peaking in 1999, priority designations for original NDAs overall have been in decline over the last several years. While 34% of NDAs cleared in 1999 had priority designations, only 15% and 14% of those NDAs approved in 2001 and 2002, respectively, earned such designations. Priority designations rebounded slightly in 2003 (see exhibit below).

Percent of All Approved NDAs Receiving Priority Review Status, 1994-2003

After declining from 1994 through 1997, the percentage of approved NDAs with priority review status increased in the late 1990s. The percentage of approved NDAs that received priority status doubled from 1997 to 1999, but dropped again in 2000, 2001, and 2002, and rose slightly in 2003.

Year	Total NDA Approvals	NDAs w/ Priority Review Status	% NDAs w/ Priority Review Status
1994	62	17	27
1995	82	15	18
1996	131	29	22
1997	121	20	17
1998	90	25	28
1999	83	28	34
2000	98	20	20
2001	66	10	15
2002	78	11	14
2003	72	14	19

Source: CDER

CHAPTER 10

Advisory Committees and the Drug Approval Process

While it employs a larger contingent of medical, scientific, and drug development specialists than any drug regulatory agency in the world, the FDA does not necessarily conduct its new drug reviews in a vacuum free from all outside input. Throughout the review process, CDER's new drug review divisions have access to independent prescription drug advisory committees whose purpose is to provide advice and added perspective on technical and medical issues related to the safety, effectiveness, testing, labeling, and use of new and approved drugs.

Today, CDER has access to more than a dozen prescription drug advisory committees (see listing below) that are focused on specific therapeutic areas and that are comprised largely of leading scientists, most of whom are active researchers with academic appointments. In addition, CDER has several other advisory panels—including the Drug Safety and Risk Management Advisory Committee (and its Drug Abuse Subcommittee), the Nonprescription Drugs Advisory Committee, and the Advisory Committee for Pharmaceutical Science—that can also become involved in prescription drug issues. CDER manages and coordinates the advisory committee process largely through its Advisors and Consultants Staff, which today resides within CDER's Office of Executive Programs.

CDER's advisory committees, which are regulated under the Federal Advisory Committee Act of 1972, convene periodically to discuss issues that the center believes to be of major importance to public health. Since 1964, CDER's new drug review divisions have looked to the advisory committees for recommendations on issues such as the approvability of specific drugs, the adequacy of drug development approaches (e.g., evaluating new guidelines or study design issues), and the status of certain marketed drugs. According to the agency, committee discussions of such issues bring more diverse input to the decision-making process, provide access to technical expertise that may not be available within the agency, and open FDA decision-making procedures to broader scrutiny.

Perhaps surprisingly for a program that is generally perceived to work so successfully and that provides the FDA with access to leading clinicians and experts so inexpensively, CDER's advisory committee program has been subject to various reform initiatives through the years. During the early 1990s, for example, CDER faced growing pressure to standardize committee processes. In response to a series of Institute of Medicine (IOM) recommendations in 1991, CDER revised its existing advisory committee procedures and detailed them in a document entitled, *Policy and Guidance Handbook for FDA Advisory Committees* (1994). The handbook represented the agency's first real attempt to establish criteria for identifying intellectual bias and for granting conflict-of-interest waivers for committee members (see discussion below). The agency has adopted many of the IOM recommendations, including a system for advance scheduling of committee meetings and a policy that spon sors will "generally" receive questions to be posed to advisory committees prior to the meeting.

More recently, the advisory committee process has evolved due to such factors as budgetary limitations, leg islative initiatives, legal proceedings and regulatory developments:

- A 30% budget cut for CDER's Advisors and Consultants Staff, which manages and coordinates the advisory committee process, appeared to be affecting the number and length of committee meetings in early 2004. While the agency held that it was not refusing to hold any meetings sought by CDER's review divisions, the number of days on which CDER advisory committees held meetings in early 2004 was down by over half compared to 2003. In recent years, CDER's review divisions have been seeking advisory committee input for fewer drugs prior to approval, although many believe that is due to tight review deadlines under the user-fee program.

- In late 2002, CDER disbanded two of its advisory committees—the Medical Imaging Drugs Advisory Committee and the Pharmacy Compounding Advisory Committee. At the time, the agency determined that an advisory committee specific to medical imaging drugs was not necessary, and that an existing committee or subcommittee could handle the panel's responsibilities. Today, medical imaging drugs are likely to be reviewed by other committees responsible for the therapeutic areas (e.g., oncology) in which the drugs are being applied. The Pharmacy Compounding Advisory Committee was disbanded due to court decisions that invalidated section 503A of the Food, Drug, and Cosmetic Act, under which this committee was established. Every two years, the agency must assess and renew each advisory committee or the committee's charter will expire automatically.

- In response to growing government interest in potential conflicts of interest in the research and regulation of medical products, CDER released a 2002 draft guidance entitled, *Disclosure of Conflicts of Interest for Special Government Employees Participating in FDA Product Specific Advisory Committees*. Under the draft guidance, the FDA proposes that more information regarding the nature and magnitude of an advisory committee member's (otherwise called a "special government employee") conflict of interest be made publicly available whenever that member is granted a waiver for those conflicts of interest and is, therefore, permitted to participate in committee deliberations on particular products (see discussion below). Specifically, the draft guidance calls for the public disclosure of information relating to the nature and magnitude of a member's conflict of interest prior to a committee meeting. In a September 2004 FDA study of public perceptions regarding conflicts of interest and FDA advisory committees, 70.6% of those attending committee meetings from March 2003 to July 2003 said they trusted the FDA to monitor conflicts of interest among committee members. Only 16.2% of the surveyed attendees held that the agency should not allow members with conflicts of interest to participate in any capacity at advisory committee meetings.

- In a May 2004 report, the U.S. General Accounting Office urged the FDA and other agencies to examine the viewpoints of potential candidates before appointing them to advisory committees. Congress requested the report in response to concern that HHS and FDA were appointing committee members who reflected the views held by the agencies or the Bush Administration. "Assessing the points of view of individual members is fundamental to ensuring that committees as a whole are, and are perceived as being, fairly balanced in terms of points of view because agencies must first know whether the members have particular viewpoints or whether they may have—or may reasonably be perceived as having—certain biases."

- The Food and Drug Administration Modernization Act of 1997 (FDAMA) introduced several important reforms to the advisory committee process, including a handful of reforms that affect the drug review process directly. Under FDAMA, CDER must either take action within 90 days of a committee recommendation (e.g., on a drug's approval) or specify why such an action has not been taken. To date, CDER officials report that the center has not had any problem meeting this new requirement. In addition, a committee must now meet within 60 days of the date on which a subject is ready for its review. FDAMA also includes provisions on committee membership, conflict-of-interest issues, and training (see discussions below). To provide guidance on FDAMA's impact on the advisory committee process, CDER has released a guidance for industry entitled, *Advisory Committees: Implementing Section 120 of the Food and Drug Administration Modernization Act of 1997* (October 1998).

- Under a legal settlement associated with a Public Citizen's Health Research Group (HRG) lawsuit against the FDA, CDER agreed to provide the public, in advance or at the time of certain committee meetings, with access to materials provided to advisory committee members. This settlement applies directly to meetings at which pending product approval issues will be discussed (e.g., NDAs for new drugs, prescription-to-OTC switches, ANDAs for generic drugs), but not to "post-approval and non-approval issue-oriented advisory committee meetings," including those that will involve the discussion of guidance documents, product classification/re-classification, post-approval adverse drug events, product withdrawal, and post-approval monitoring programs." To minimize the time involved in complying with these disclosure requirements, CDER used a December 1999 draft guidance to "strongly encourage" sponsors to submit advisory committee background packages (i.e., background information packages that sponsors provide in advance of committee meetings) that may be disclosed in their entirety (i.e., that do not contain any information that the sponsor asserts is exempt from disclosure because it is trade secret or confidential or because it would constitute an unwarranted invasion of personal privacy) and to submit an electronic version of the packages. Under the draft guidance, a sponsor can submit a fully releasable submission 22 business days prior to the committee meeting, but must submit a partially releasable package (i.e., a package that must be redacted by CDER) 48 days before a meeting. Submitting a partially releasable package for a priority review product has other significant implications for the sponsor: "Such a submission will be considered an agreement by the sponsor to extend by 2 months the review time for the review cycle in which the advisory committee will be held," the agency states in its draft guidance. The December 1999 draft guidance establishes that several types of information in such packages will be considered disclosable in most cases, including summary tables of safety and effectiveness data, summaries of adverse drug reaction data, and clinical and preclinical protocols.

- In a July 1998 direct final rule that ultimately would be withdrawn, CDER amended its regulations governing the review of agency decisions by inserting a statement to establish that drug sponsors may request the review of a "scientific controversy" by an appropriate scientific advisory committee. The FDA was required to make this change under the provisions of FDAMA. Several weeks after releasing this final rule, the agency was forced to withdraw the rule when the Pharmaceutical Research and Manufacturers of America (PhRMA) responded that the final rule did not "fulfill the mandate" of FDAMA because it relied largely on existing mechanisms and that it did not establish new procedures for dispute resolution (the agency is required to withdraw direct final rules automatically when they trigger significant adverse comments within the comment period). In response to an earlier FDA draft guidance on dispute resolution, PhRMA held that the FDA should not be able to deny sponsors' requests for advisory committee review of scientific disputes unless it can present "compelling" reasons for such a denial. At the time, CDER officials speculated that the role of advisory committees in the dispute resolution process is likely to be minor, pointing out that disputed issues are likely to have been addressed by the time that the agency can coordinate and convene a committee meeting to address them. Still, in a February 2000 guidance document entitled, *Formal Dispute Resolution: Appeals Above the Division Level*, CDER does provide a mechanism through which sponsors can seek committee review of a disputed issue.

Largely because advisory committee recommendations often have major medical and financial implications the public profile of the committees and their actions remains quite high. Although committee recommen dations are not binding on the FDA, these recommendations are seen by the financial community and th pharmaceutical industry as forerunners of agency decisions on products. As a result, committee meeting receive considerable attention not just from the companies whose products are being considered, but fror financial analysts and the trade press as well.

So rarely does a CDER action directly contradict a committee recommendation that it makes significant new when one does. In August 1999, CDER's Division of Antiviral Drug Products approved Glaxo Wellcome's influen za treatment Relenza despite an earlier committee recommendation against approval. Specifically to addres this seeming contradiction, Division of Antiviral Drug Products Director Heidi Jolson, M.D., authored a mem pointing out that Glaxo Wellcome had addressed the advisory committee's concerns regarding post-treatmen symptom fluctuation by submitting new analyses, adequate labeling, and Phase 4 study commitments.

More recently, CDER issued a May 2004 not approvable letter for the Rx-to-OTC switch of the emergency cor traceptive Plan B, despite a strong recommendation from the Reproductive Health Drugs Advisory Committe that the switch be approved. Concerned that the agency's action was based on the Bush Administration' political agenda rather than scientific concerns, members of Congress pledged to introduce a bill instructin the agency to conduct a formal review of its decision-making process in this case. Congress also asked th General Accounting Office to investigate the not approvable decision, which the FDA said was based on th lack of information showing that Plan B could be used safely by consumers under the age of 16 years withou medical supervision.

As noted, the advisory committee system and its role in the drug approval process have been the targets c criticism over the years. CDER received some criticism in the late 1990s for approving a few drugs (later witł drawn) when certain advisory committee members disagreed on the drugs' approvability. In a December 199 issue of the *Journal of the American Medical Association*, FDA officials defended the agency's actions by stating tha critics who complain that certain advisory committee members disagreed with FDA's decision to approv products that were later withdrawn are, in effect, arguing "for approving a product only when there is una nimity or...for the suppression of dissent."

A November 2000 FDA "lessons learned" report on CDER's experience with Rezulin, an approved diabete therapy whose 1997 approval and March 2000 withdrawal due to liver toxicity created considerable contro versy, cited several problems with the center's pre-approval and postmarketing processes, including the adv sory committee process. The clinical biases of advisory committee members and the committee's lack c expertise in risk management were factors in the pre- and post-marketing assessment of Rezulin, CDE staffers interviewed for the report stated. The "ability [of the advisory committee evaluating Rezulin] to ful

---

CDER Advisory Committees

Anesthetic and Life Support Drugs Advisory Committee

Anti-Infective Drugs Advisory Committee
- Pediatric Subcommittee

Antiviral Drugs Advisory Committee

Arthritis Advisory Committee

Cardiovascular and Renal Drugs Advisory Committee

Dermatologic and Ophthalmic Drugs Advisory Committee

Drug Safety and Risk Management Advisory Committee
- Drug Abuse Subcommittee

Endocrinologic and Metabolic Drugs Advisory Committee

Gastrointestinal Drugs Advisory Committee

Nonprescription Drugs Advisory Committee

Oncologic Drugs Advisory Committee

Peripheral and Central Nervous System Drugs Advisory Committee

Advisory Committee for Pharmaceutical Science

Psychopharmacologic Drugs Advisory Committee

Pulmonary-Allergy Drugs Advisory Committee

Advisory Committee for Reproductive Health

---

grasp the many highly complex scientific and regulatory issues surrounding the approval and eventual withdrawal" of Rezulin could have been improved by the addition of experts in epidemiology and hepatology, or by the formation of a "safety advisory committee," the report noted. One CDER interviewee even claimed that the advisory committee's composition and the selection of public speakers were intentionally biased in Rezulin's favor.

Although CDER's advisory committee program is over four decades old, the significant evolution in the center's drug review process has had several implications for the program. For a number of reasons, for example, the environment for committee use is now more complex. Tight drug review timelines under the agency's user-fee program, for instance, have made it difficult to schedule and hold advisory committee meetings in many cases.

User-fee deadlines and other factors have prompted some review divisions to dramatically shift their policies on referring drugs and issues for advisory committee consideration. One division, the Division of Neuropharmacological Drug Products, even announced in the mid-1990s its intention to forego, whenever possible, bringing new drugs to an advisory committee. More recently, groups such as the Division of Oncologic Drug Products, which have in earlier years brought nearly all new molecular entities (NME) before a committee prior to approval, are now seeking advisory committee input on fewer new drugs on a pre approval basis.

More recent CDER disclosures provide detailed and telling statistics on trends in advisory committee use Although CDER's review divisions routinely brought more than half of all NMEs before committees in th early years of the user-fee program, far more are being approved without committee input today. Of the NME cleared in 2000 and 2001, for example, less than 20% were considered by an advisory committee prior t approval. While about 40% of NMEs cleared in 2002 and 2003 were subject to committee review, budgetar limitations (see discussion above) and other factors seem to ensure that this rate will decline once again.

A Look at Committee Membership

The nature of an advisory committee's membership is a function of several factors, including the panel's chai ter and the technical expertise necessary to evaluate the issues likely to come before the panel. Membershi comprises primarily physicians, although qualified experts in such disciplines as epidemiology, nursing, bic statistics, pharmacology, toxicology, and psychology are also included. A technically qualified, consume nominated member may be designated as a voting member of a committee as well. The FDA hires all "voting committee members as "special government employees." As of 2004, each CDER committee also includes non-voting representative who is nominated by industry groups and who represents general industry inte ests (e.g., provides industry views on the costs of proposed studies, the need for certain studies).

Nominated by professional or consumer organizations, other committee members, private individuals, c FDA staffers, advisors must be judged to be broadly trained and experienced, of established professional rep utation and personal integrity, and committed to the public interest. While the agency seeks balance in term of gender, race, and geographic location, technical competence is the overriding consideration in selectin members. Because members serve terms that last up to four years and are likely to address a wide variety c issues during these periods, perhaps the ideal committee members are those who have recognized accom plishments and leadership within their fields and demonstrated abilities and interests in issues outside the specialties.

Although FDAMA included provisions regarding membership requirements for newly formed advisory com mittees (i.e., new panels formed under FDAMA), it did not require existing committees to comply with th new provisions. In its October 1998 guidance document entitled, *Advisory Committees: Implementing Section* 120 *the Food and Drug Administration Modernization Act of* 1997, however, the FDA established that, to further the goal of the statutory amendments, it intended to modify current advisory committee membership on a meeting by-meeting basis and to recharter committees when necessary to reflect the FDAMA provisions (see discus sion below).

Under FDAMA, an advisory committee comprises two types of members: (1) core members, who are appoin ed by the FDA commissioner or his or her designee based on their scientific or technical expertise and wh serve for the duration of the committee or until the terms of appointment expire, they resign, or they ai removed by the commissioner or the designee; and (2) ad hoc members, who are called upon to supplemer the core membership on an ad hoc basis so that the committee considering an issue includes consumer/patient representative, an industry representative, and at least two representatives who are spe cialists with expertise in the particular disease or condition for which the drug is proposed. Provided that the participation is not blocked by conflict-of-interest laws or regulations (see discussion below), core membei will be voting members at committee meetings.

Today, there are fundamental differences between consumer and patient representatives. Consumer representatives are considered "core" voting members of the committee and serve terms of up to four years. On the other hand, patient representatives are chosen for their experience with a particular serious or life-threatening disease under discussion by the committee, and are ad hoc voting members only for that issue.

The FDA has several standards for ensuring the independence and objectivity of its advisory committees. First, no FDA employees may serve as committee members—under FDAMA, no person who is a full-time government employee and who is engaged in the administration of the Food, Drug and Cosmetic Act may be a voting member. The FDA does, however, appoint an employee as an executive secretary for each committee. Although not a panel member, the executive secretary is the agency's liaison to the committee, and is responsible for all administrative planning and preparation for meetings. Within CDER, this executive secretary is a staffer within the center's Advisors and Consultants Staff.

The agency's dialogue with advisors is an aspect of the committee process that has remained controversial over the years. Some critics argue that agency staffers influence the views of advisors during such exchanges, an argument that top agency staffers openly reject. According to an internal CDER guide on policies and practices for center discussions with committee members, "it is never appropriate for either applicants or agency staff to lobby or negotiate with committee members about positions or conclusions the advisory committee should adopt on issues about to come before them. It is, however, appropriate for agency staff and corporate sponsors to provide members with background information on the issues at hand, and during meetings, to discuss the data and their own interpretation of the data with the whole committee."

Conflict of Interest Standards for Committee Members The agency also has fairly detailed financial conflict-of-interest standards for its members. As mentioned, FDAMA introduced several administrative conflict of interest provisions, and the agency updated its *Policy and Guidance Handbook for FDA Advisory Committees* in 2000 to more fully address conflict-of-interest criteria. Committee members are screened for such conflicts when they are nominated. Unless a waiver is obtained, a committee member may not vote on any matter relevant to a clinical investigation or drug approval if the member or his or her immediate family (i.e., spouse and minor children) stands to gain financially from the ultimate recommendation. In addition, appointed members must file a statement disclosing their financial interests prior to each meeting.

Since many leading clinicians and scientists in academia work closely with product sponsors and since at least two members of an advisory committee must be knowledgeable about the disease that a product under committee review is intended to treat, conflict-of-interest concerns can be a severely limiting factor for the agency in maintaining the committee program. Individuals who have affiliations or investments that might present conflict-of-interest problems may be appointed to committees based on their qualifications, however. On a case-by-case basis, the agency will consider waivers to allow the participation of such advisors in committee deliberations.

Under FDAMA provisions, waivers may be granted if the member's participation is necessary to afford the committee essential expertise. A waiver may not be granted if a committee is to consider the member's own scientific work, however (i.e., the committee member's work as a principal investigator or as a major participant in the studies to be considered). In less clear-cut situations, the decision on whether to exclude, or seek a waiver for, a committee member will involve the weighing of the extent of the financial interest against the agency's need for the member's expertise.

As they have for the FDA and other government agencies themselves, conflict of interest concerns have arisen for advisory committee members in recent years. In June 2000 hearings, the FDA's waiver process came under fire from certain members of Congress. The agency, for example, was questioned why a committee member had obtained a waiver to vote on, and participate in discussions of, a vaccine product when that member had received an annual $75,000 grant from the sponsor and had served as a principal investigator in studies for a directly competitive product. FDA officials countered that the member's involvement in the product's development was not relevant to the issue being discussed at the committee meeting, and that she was an expert in the areas in which the agency most needed expertise. The officials also emphasized that vaccine expertise is rare, and that committee members are permitted to participate when their expertise is considered more critical than the relevant conflict of interest. Members of Congress also criticized the FDA and other agencies for permitting committee members who are not allowed to vote on an issue due to conflict of interest issues to participate in committee discussions and, therefore, to influence the votes of other panel members.

As noted, the FDA released a 2002 draft guidance under which it proposed that more information regarding the nature and magnitude of an advisory committee member's conflict of interest be disclosed whenever that member is granted a waiver for those conflicts of interest and is, therefore, permitted to participate in committee deliberations on particular products (see discussion below). Under the draft guidance, information relating to the nature and magnitude of a member's conflict of interest would be disclosed to the public prior to a committee meeting.

In September 2004, the FDA released the results of a survey that studied the attitudes and opinions of a sampling of individuals who attended FDA advisory committee meetings in the spring of 2003. Specifically, the study attempted to examine the "perceived fairness and credibility of FDA advisory committee meetings related to FDA's management of real or potential conflicts of interest among advisory committee members." The survey's findings included the following:

- 70.6% of meeting attendees said they trusted the FDA in monitoring conflicts of interest among its advisory committee members, and only 11.5% said they did not trust such efforts.

- Only 7.3% of meeting attendees said that an advisory committee decision cannot be trusted if any of its members have conflicts of interest. Fully 86.8% of respondents felt such decisions can be trusted. Only 20.2% stated that they are concerned about advisory committee members' conflicts of interest.

- 75.1% of audience members felt that the FDA should permit members with conflicts of interest to participate in any capacity at committee meetings, while only 16.2% disagreed.

- Fully 87.6% of the meeting attendees felt that, as a practical matter, the agency should accept that advisory committee members may have some conflicts of interest to gain access to the best expertise in a particular field.

Committee members are paid for their time, and are reimbursed at the standard federal rate for travel, food and lodging costs. Because of this cost structure, the advisory committee program is seen as a cost-efficient vehicle for obtaining input from many of the country's most knowledgeable, talented, and experienced scientists and clinicians.

When CDER Uses Advisory Committees

As stated, the advent of the prescription drug user fee program has complicated CDER's use of advisory com mittees in some ways. Further, given the limited number of advisory committee meetings, CDER must be careful to select for panel consideration issues with major implications for the public health.

As an internal FDA policy document points out, "advisory committees are composed of committed but busy leading scientists, most of whom are active researchers with academic appointments. Participation in FDA deliberations does not free them of their other obligations. As meetings are usually 2 days long, occur 2 to 5 times per year, and involve substantial pre-meeting preparation, it is clear that, for many committee members, current meeting schedules represent a substantial commitment. Therefore, we must select issues for discussion in ways that maximize the valuable contribution of our advisors as a public health resource, as well as make efficient use of the agency's staff's time preparing for and participating in such meetings."

Various FDA and CDER documents have attempted to identify the broad range of issues that may be considered by the committees, and general rules for selecting the most significant issues. Although this range includes general drug development issues (e.g., guidelines, study designs), emerging issues regarding marketed drugs (e.g., adverse reactions, labeling), and CDER's management of the drug evaluation process, the most important in the context of this discussion is committee deliberation on the approvability of specific drugs.

The FDA's 1994 advisory committee handbook made no important changes to the criteria that the agency uses in selecting drugs and issues. According to the handbook, CDER attempts to select topics for advisory committee presentations as follows:

- "Applications for approval of the first entity in a pharmacological class will routinely be presented as well as any other new chemical entity whose evaluation poses special problems or raises issues of broader interest."

- "New drugs that are expected to have a major therapeutic impact, whether or not they are [new chemical entities] will ordinarily be presented. Similarly, major new uses of marketed drugs will ordinarily be presented to advisory committees."

- "Applications for initial Rx to OTC switches of a drug will routinely be presented to an advisory committee...."

- Major safety concerns involving marketed drugs will "usually be presented" to advisory committees.

- Clinical guidelines "will routinely be presented" to the relevant committee for consideration before being adopted.

- At least once annually, a new drug review division will be selected to present a "program review on important and controversial drugs under development and applications for NCEs that are pending."

The most recent discussion of reasons that may prompt a review division to seek advisory committee input appears in CDER's draft Good Review Management Principles guidance (July 2003). According to the draft document, the reasons include, but are not limited to: "(1) the application is for an NME or a new class of drug; (2) the clinical study design used novel clinical or surrogate endpoints; (3) the application raises significant issues regarding safety and/or effectiveness of the drug or biologic; or (4) the application raises significant public health questions regarding the role of the drug or biologic in the treatment or prevention of a disease."

The process for selecting issues often involves several steps. To identify potential topics for committee meetings, the executive secretary for each advisory committee periodically meets with the director of the drug review division that the committee serves. These topics may be discussed during internal staff meetings. Generally, the review division consults with the office director regarding decisions to bring a drug or issue before an advisory committee.

It is important to note that CDER is not the only body that has input on committee agendas. A drug sponsor may request that a pending issue involving its product be brought before a committee, for example. Likewise, committee members themselves may request that certain issues of interest be considered.

Agenda items agreed to within CDER are then discussed with the committee chairperson to obtain his or her advice on the ones that should be selected and how best to present the issues. Meeting agendas agreed to during this process are then published in the *Federal Register*.

In considering the data on a new drug or a significant new use of an already approved drug, the committee might evaluate any of several issues, depending on the nature of the questions posed to it. These issues can include:

- the adequacy of the design and conduct of studies intended to provide substantial evidence of effectiveness;
- the data supporting the proposed dose and dosing schedule;
- critical studies;
- the appropriateness of surrogate endpoints for particular situations;
- the safety data base;
- the need for additional studies or special surveillance after marketing;
- the need to limit indications to a particular subset of the overall potential treatment population;
- the overall risk/benefit relationship of the new agent;
- the need for special labeling features, such as boxed warnings, limitations on use, monitoring requirements, or patient package inserts;
- the appropriateness of proposed prescription-to-OTC switches; and
- the primary review of selected portions of NDAs.

How Advisory Committees Function

CDER officials are quick to point out that each advisory committee has its own personality and unique relationship with the review division that it serves. The committee chairperson has a significant influence over the committee's personality and method of functioning. As noted above, the chairperson has input on which issues are selected for committee deliberation and on the presentation of these issues.

Although the product of the advisory committee process is generally a recommendation discussed and issued during a committee meeting, the process is considerably more involved. In many respects, periodic committee meetings represent the final stage of a lengthier and more complex process.

One of the fundamental principles of this process is that advisors be given sufficient information to allow them to provide informed recommendations during meetings (see discussion below). According to CDER policy guide on committee discussions, "it is essential that the advisory committee collectively receive input from the agency regarding the staff's review of the data that will be presented to the committee. This provides committee members with the agency's expert analysis of the validity and organization of the data offered by sponsors, an analysis to which the agency usually brings more resources, expertise and experience than are available to the committee. It is also important that the committee have access to the agency's evaluation of the sponsor's data analyses, including the agency's evaluation of statistical techniques used, analysis of design issues, and assessment of the results of studies. Without such information, the committee may fail to address issues that will be critical to the agency's reasoning when it formulates a final decision on the issue." Sponsors often provide "additional data, sometimes with additional documentation to focus discussion or assist an identified committee member serving as a primary or secondary reviewer of the drug."

Because they often play important roles during committee meetings, sponsors must also be informed of meeting agendas. "Every effort should be made to be sure the sponsor understands the issues that will be raised for discussion by agency reviewers," the agency states. "There are many ways to do this, including deficiency letters to sponsors, pre-meetings between the sponsor and agency in anticipation of any advisory committee discussions (it is useful to offer the sponsor an opportunity for such a meeting), and communicating to the sponsor any questions to be posed to the committee in advance of the meeting."

Committee Meeting Scheduling and Practices FDAMA introduced several requirements for CDER's scheduling of advisory committee meetings. Specifically, FDAMA establishes that CDER must schedule advisory committee meetings so that a matter can be presented to a committee within 60 calendar days of its being considered "ready for review"—that is, when the center and sponsor have completed all preparatory work for its presentation at such a meeting. Because of the busy schedules of committee members, the law encourages CDER to schedule committee meetings on an annual basis based on anticipated and pending drug applications. According to CDER's draft Good Review Management Principles (July 2003), a committee meeting generally should be scheduled no later than two months before the user-fee review goal date for a standard application, and no later than one month before the target date for a priority application.

So committee members can appropriately prepare for a meeting, a review division assembles an information package and forwards it (through the CDER executive secretary for the committee) to the committee members before the scheduled meeting. Under practices adopted as a result of the HRG settlement, the agency now forwards this CDER background package to the committee members at least 18 business days before the meeting (the agency must send a redacted version of this package to the sponsor at least 14 business days before the meeting). Under these same practices, the agency must also send a sponsor-prepared background package (assuming the sponsor has submitted one in time) to the committee members at least 21 business days prior to the meeting. Advisory committee members have responded positively to the new practices, claiming that such information is now provided on a much more predictable basis (i.e., previously, it might have been forwarded a month to a day in advance of a meeting, according to FDA staffers). Committee members also report that the pre-meeting information packages are now smaller and more focused.

Among the unfortunate outcomes of the HRG settlement are restrictions that, in certain cases, will be placed on sponsor and advisory committee member access to the questions that CDER will pose at committee meetings. This is a complicated—and seemingly unintended—outcome of the detailed post-settlement timelines that have been established for the processing and release of committee materials. As noted, the timetable requires CDER to get its background package to the advisory committee members at least 18 business days in advance of a committee meeting. In most cases, however, one of the important items that comprise th CDER background package—CDER's list of final questions to the committee—is not ready by this time. Whe a CDER review division is unable to finalize its questions by this deadline and to send the questions as par of the CDER background package, the highly structured timetable does not permit the agency to forward it questions to the committee—and therefore make them available to the sponsor—until the morning of th day before the committee meeting (i.e., when all the releasable meeting-related materials are provided to th public). To the degree that the drug sponsor is unable to glean the precise wording and focus of the division' questions from informal discussions with CDER staff and from reviewing other elements of CDER's back ground package (i.e., CDER must send a copy of its background package at least 14 business days in advanc of a meeting), this can be a significant hurdle for a sponsor's efforts to prepare for a committee meeting Requesting a meeting with a review division close to a committee's meeting date may be one way for an appli cant to address this challenge.

FDA officials note that most background packages today include a reasonable representation of the fina questions. They add that the final questions can be forwarded to committee members a few days before meeting as long as there are sufficient copies for the public at the meeting itself. Questions are often revise during the meeting.

In its draft Good Review Management Principles (July 2003), CDER notes that the applicant and review div sion generally share their draft committee presentations prior to the committee meeting. So the division ca avoid redundancy in its presentation, the draft principles encourage applicants to share their planned pre sentations with the division "as far in advance of the meeting as feasible."

According to recent FDA documents, CDER is now developing a standard operating procedure that will ider tify the roles and responsibilities of agency staff in preparing for committee meetings. This document i expected to provide further details regarding the timing and content of background packages for committe members and procedures for the public release of redacted background packages in advance of a committe meeting.

In some cases, the FDA will post "issues for discussion" (not the final questions) on its web site 24 hour before a meeting. Further, CDER has established an FDA Advisory Committee Information Line (800-741 8138) to provide information on upcoming meetings.

Rarely, if ever, do committee members review an entire NDA or IND, although some review divisions appoir a "committee reviewer"—a committee member who would either become involved in the evaluation of a application or would receive more detailed information on an application and make a separate report to th full committee. While a few divisions—the Division of Oncologic Drug Products, in particular—like to involv a single advisory committee member early in the development and review process, the considerable wor involved in coordinating such activities is likely to prevent more divisions from adopting such practices.

Generally, a majority of voting committee members comprises a quorum (i.e., the minimum number of men bers that must be present to hold a meeting). Under existing regulations, however, CDER may specify in a pa ticular advisory committee charter that a quorum is less than the majority of total current voting member In some cases, such as when a committee comprises two diverse groups of experts (e.g., the Dermatolog and Ophthalmic Drugs Advisory Committee), the subgroup of committee members with expertise relevant t the issue under discussion is sufficient to represent a quorum.

Committee meetings, during which issues are discussed and recommendations are voted upon, are attended by committee members, key personnel from the relevant drug review division(s), and often representatives from the drug firm whose product is under discussion. A meeting will generally consist of two or more of the following segments:

- *Open Public Hearing.* Every advisory committee meeting includes an open public hearing (at least an hour in duration), during which any interested person may present data, information, or oral or written views that are relevant to the advisory committee's agenda or other work.

- *Open Committee Discussion.* With limited exceptions, advisory committees are required to conduct their discussions of pending matters in open sessions. Although access to open discussions is not restricted, no public participation is permitted during this segment without the consent of the committee chairperson. External consultants and the drug sponsor may be asked, or may request the opportunity, to present data to the committee. Typically, sponsor and FDA presentations consume much of the time allocated to open committee discussions.

- *Closed Presentation of Data.* Data and information that are prohibited from public disclosure are presented to the advisory committee in a closed portion of the meeting. This policy applies to discussions involving information considered to be trade secrets by the sponsor, and the disclosure of personal information about clinical subjects. Only key FDA staffers, advisory committee members, agency consultants, and drug sponsors attend this segment of a meeting. This allows the sponsor to present and discuss sensitive information, such as manufacturing processes, without concern that competitors will gain access to the information.

- *Closed Committee Deliberations.* Committees may also choose to discuss issues in a closed session, in which attendance is limited to agency staff, committee members, and individuals invited by the committee chairperson. Such sessions are generally reserved for the discussion of existing internal documents whose premature disclosure might significantly impede proposed agency action.

Advisory committees are asked to make their recommendations as specific as possible, and to address key questions posed by the FDA. Today, all committee votes are taken in a manner that permits the meeting transcript to reflect the vote of each committee member (e.g., committee votes are no longer conducted through a show of hands).

Further, FDAMA introduced a provision under which CDER is required, within 90 calendar days of a committee's recommendation, to notify the sponsor or applicant of the "status of FDA's decision on the matter." If CDER has not reached a decision by this point, it should provide an indication of the reasons that a determination has not been reached.

How Influential Are CDER's Advisory Committees?

There is no real measure of advisory committee influence in the drug review process. Although committee recommendations are not binding on the FDA, there are few instances in which agency decisions directly contradict these recommendations.

Still, it remains difficult to gauge whether committee decisions direct or simply support FDA decisions. As stated above, some critics of the process have even suggested that FDA officials direct committee recommendations during pre-meeting communications. Others claim that, all too often, the agency convenes com mittees to simply confirm conclusions that agency reviewers have already made.

It is also difficult to determine whether the agency would have reached the identical decision had the divi sion not consulted an advisory committee. In fact, CDER's advisory committee policy guide acknowledge that a division may seek committee recommendations on a drug for which the division has already reache "a strong conclusion as to approvability."

In all likelihood, the influence of committee recommendations differs from case to case. Some FDA official claim that the degrees of committee influence are best portrayed through several scenarios:

Scenario #1: The review division is faced with a particularly complex technical issue on which it has not reache a decision. This might also include situations in which the advisory committee has expertise not availabl within the agency, or situations in which a drug's approval represents a "close call" given the risk/benefit pro file of the product. In such situations, advisory committees are likely to have the most influence on FDA deci sion making.

Scenario #2: The review division has reached a preliminary decision, but wants advice on specific issues. Fo example, the division may have decided to approve a certain drug, but wants committee input on issues suc as appropriate dosing, labeling, or the need for follow-up studies.

Scenario #3: The review division has made a decision, but would be more comfortable if an independent revie supported the initial determination. For example, the FDA may have reached a not-approvable decision o an NDA, but may decide to bring the decision before an advisory committee to permit the sponsor to preser its case to an outside review body. Although the division is open to reconsider its decision if so advised b the committee, recommendations offered in this context may be less likely to affect agency decision makin§

What Sponsors Should Know About Advisory Committees

Given the importance of advisory committee meetings, drug sponsors have much to gain by studying a com mittee before making a presentation to it. This is particularly important given the dynamic nature of the adv sory committee process and the fundamental differences between the panels themselves.

Today, researching advisory committees is much easier than it has been in the past. Another outgrowth of th HRG settlement is that the agency is making considerably more committee-related information available, pa ticularly through its website. Meeting background materials, transcripts, agendas, and agency questions ar now accessible, as are the presentation materials prepared and submitted by other sponsors for committe meetings. Today, CDER has largely completed its goal of posting the curriculum vitae of each advisory com mittee member on its website as well.

The advisory committee meeting process, sponsor approaches to and preparations for committee meeting and commercial services designed to support sponsors in preparing for such meetings are all far more sophi: ticated than they were even a decade ago. Although detailed discussions on the technical and content-rela ed issues important in preparing for committee meetings cannot be presented here, several essenti: principles remain as relevant as they have been in the past:

- Learn as much as possible about the committee members, particularly the chairperson. Each member's particular areas of expertise and interest are also extremely important.

Some experts advise obtaining each member's curriculum vitae and research papers to gain insights about his or her interests, and to help anticipate possible concerns and questions.

- Gain a full understanding of the relevant issues as the review division views them. Division reviewers set the committee's agenda, and frame and phrase the specific questions to which the committee must respond.

- Learn how the committee functions, how meetings are conducted, how the committee reaches its decisions, and how much it values solicited and unsolicited input from the sponsor, clinical investigators, statisticians, outside consultants, and others.

- Research what topics are on the committee's agenda. This will affect the amount of time a drug sponsor will be given to present its case. For example, the Oncologic Drugs Advisory Committee is known to move quickly through agenda topics, and to address two or more products at a single meeting. CDER provides agenda-related materials to all companies scheduled to participate in an upcoming meeting (i.e., those relevant to the sponsor).

CHAPTER 11

Beyond Approval: Drug Manufacturer Regulatory Responsibilities

When a new drug obtains FDA approval, it enters another stage of the product life cycle to which different regulatory standards apply. Considering the fundamental differences between general marketing and comparatively tightly controlled clinical testing, however, the premarketing and postapproval responsibilities facing drug companies are remarkably similar in many respects.

Just as the sponsor must ensure that its drug is produced according to accepted manufacturing standards during clinical testing, the company must provide similar assurances when the product is marketed to the general public. Similarly, as the FDA calls upon sponsors to submit important test data during a drug's development, the agency also requires sponsors to report any postmarketing data or information that might cause the FDA to reassess a drug's safety and effectiveness.

In addition to abiding by the conditions of use (e.g., labeling, manufacturing commitments) detailed in its approved application and any subsequent supplements, an NDA holder must fulfill several postapproval responsibilities in both product reporting and manufacturing. Traditionally, most postmarketing requirements have fallen into one of four broad areas:

- General Reporting Requirements;

- Adverse Drug Experience (AE) Reporting Requirements;

- Current Good Manufacturing Practice (cGMP); and

- Phase 4 Clinical Study Commitments.

PDUFA III and several agency initiatives have brought a renewed regulatory focus on the postapproval phase of a product's life cycle. Although PDUFA I and PDUFA II focused largely on the clinical testing and FDA review stages of product development, PDUFA III also focuses on the postapproval phase and drug safety. In negotiating PDUFA III, both the FDA and critics of the user-fee program were able, with the help of emerging data on drug withdrawal rates, to argue that the user-fee program had focused too much attention on drug approval, and not enough on drug safety and risks. Since hundreds of millions of dollars had been invested in shortening the drug development and approval process, they argued that the user-fee program should provide funds to upgrade processes to ensure that the products that are being developed and approved through these speedier processes are safe and that their risks are properly managed once they reach the market. In total, an estimated $80 million in user fees is to be allocated to support such activities during the PDUFA III years (FY2003-FY2007).

PDUFA III's so-called pre- and peri-NDA risk management plans embody several different elements and con cepts that can affect the postapproval phase, including: (1) FDA/sponsor pre-NDA/BLA consideration of an dialogue regarding the need for risk management tools and post-approval risk management studies; (2) th introduction of a so-called "peri-approval period" (two years postapproval for most products and up to thre years for products requiring risk management beyond standard labeling, such as a black box warning), durin which the FDA may employ user fees to assess an applicant's implementation of a risk management plan; (3 the FDA may employ user fees to independently evaluate product utilization for drugs with important safet concerns for the first three years post approval. See section below on postapproval risk management.

General Reporting Requirements

According to federal regulations, sponsors of approved NDAs must develop and submit to the FDA several di ferent types of reports and materials—field alert reports, annual reports, advertising/promotional labelin specimens, and "special" reports. Taken together with AE reports, these submissions allow the FDA to mon tor a drug's distribution and effects. The reports also alert the FDA to information that might represer grounds for regulatory action (e.g., product recall).

Field Alert Reports Federal regulations require NDA holders to report, within three working days of receip any information:

- "...concerning any incident that causes the drug product or its labeling to be mistaken for, or applied to, another article."

- "...concerning any bacteriological contamination, or any significant chemical, physical, or other change or deterioration in the distributed drug product, or any failure of one or more distributed batches of the drug product to meet the specifications established for it in the application."

Companies may provide this information by telephone or other rapid means to the FDA district office respor sible for the reporting manufacturing facility, assuming that the initial notification is followed by a promp written follow-up report. Applicants must submit two copies of the written report, which should be plainl marked, "NDA-Field Alert Report."

Annual Reports The annual report plays several important roles in the FDA's monitoring of a markete drug's safety and quality. First, the report provides the FDA with a convenient summary of new researc data, distribution information, and labeling changes. Also, the annual submission is the vehicle throug which manufacturers must report certain types of information that need not be provided in any othe mandatory filing.

The applicant must file two copies of the annual report with the FDA drug review division responsible for eva uating and approving a subject drug's NDA. The report must be submitted each year within 60 days of th anniversary date of the drug's U.S. approval, and must be accompanied by a completed *Transmittal of Perioa Reports for Drugs for Human Use* form (Form FDA-2252). CDER released an August 2003 draft guidance entitle *Providing Regulatory Submissions in Electronic Format-Annual Reports for NDAs and ANDAs* to recommend how firm can submit annual reports electronically.

Annual reports must include the following types of information "that the applicant received or otherwis obtained during the annual reporting interval that ends on the anniversary date [of the drug's U.S. approval]

Summary of New Information. A brief summary of "significant" new information obtained during the previous year that might affect the safety, effectiveness, or labeling of the drug product. Also, the sponsor must detail any action that it has taken or is planning to take in response to this new information (e.g., submitting a labeling supplement, adding a warning to the labeling, or initiating a new study). Under regulations (the "Pediatric Rule") that went into effect in April 1999 and that were later struck down by an October 2002 court ruling, the agency had also required that this summary "briefly state" whether labeling supplements for pediatric use have been submitted, and whether new studies have been initiated in the pediatric population to support appropriate labeling for the pediatric population (see Chapter 16). The regulation also said that, when possible, the applicant should provide an estimate of patient exposure to the drug product, with special reference to the pediatric population (neonates, infants, children, and adolescents), including dosage form. Although these regulations were struck down by an October 2002 court ruling that questioned the FDA's statutory authority to require pediatric studies under the Pediatric Rule, Congress passed and President Bush quickly signed, in late 2003, the Pediatric Research Equity Act of 2003 (PREA), which established clear FDA authority to require pediatric studies in appropriate circumstances. At this writing, the FDA was developing both a new regulation and a new draft guidance to address pediatric testing and submission requirements (including those relevant to NDA annual reports) under PREA.

Distribution Data. Information on the quantity of the product distributed, and the amounts forwarded to drug distributors. This section must provide the National Drug Code (NDC) number, the total number of dosage units of each strength or potency distributed (e.g., 100,000/5 milligram tablets, 50,000/10 milliliter vials), and the quantities distributed for domestic and foreign use.

Labeling. Labeling information and samples, including currently used professional labeling, patient brochures or package inserts (if any), a representative sample of the package labels, and a summary of product labeling changes implemented since the last report (or a statement that no changes were implemented). Under a December 2003 final rule, the FDA revised its regulations to require that a new "content of labeling" section be provided in electronic format in NDAs, supplements, and annual reports. The new regulation, which revised FDA requirements for the labeling component of the NDA annual report, established that the content of labeling section must comprise the package insert or professional labeling, and must include all text, tables, and figures (see Chapter 7). To provide guidance to firms submitting a content of labeling section in original NDAs, supplements, and annual reports, CDER issued a February 2004 draft industry guidance entitled, *Providing Regulatory Submissions in Electronic Format-Content of Labeling.*

Chemistry, Manufacturing, and Controls Changes. Information on chemistry, manufacturing, and controls (CMC) changes, including reports of any new experiences, investigations, studies, or tests involving chemical, physical, or other properties of the drug, that may affect the FDA's previous conclusions on the product. The report should also provide a full description of all implemented manufacturing and controls changes that did not require a supplemental application (see Chapter 12). Under its *Pharmaceutical cGMPs for the 21st Century* initiative, the FDA issued a 2004 final regulation and guidance document (entitled *Changes to an Approved NDA and ANDA*) to establish when and how (e.g., through a supplemental NDA or annual report) certain changes—mostly CMC changes—should be reported to the agency. These actions represented the next steps toward the agency's emerging risk-based approach, under which the FDA plans to streamline supplemental filing and annual report requirements for approved products for which reduced post-marketing reporting requirements would be unlikely to result in product quality problems (see discussion below and Chapter 12). Due to what the FDA viewed as the "wide variability" of CMC sections submitted in annual reports, the agency had published a 1994 guidance entitled, *Guidance for Industry: Format and Content for the CMC Section of an Annual Report.*

Nonclinical Laboratory Studies. Information from nonclinical laboratory studies, including copies of unpublishe reports, summaries of published reports of new toxicological findings in animal studies, and *in vitro* studie (e.g., mutagenicity) conducted, or otherwise obtained, by the sponsor relating to the product's ingredient: The agency may also request copies of published reports.

Clinical Data. Published clinical trials on the drug (or abstracts of them), including: trials on safety and effec tiveness; studies on new uses; biopharmaceutic, pharmacokinetic, and clinical pharmacology studies; an reports of clinical experiences pertinent to safety (e.g., epidemiologic studies) conducted or obtained by th sponsor. Also needed are summaries of completed unpublished clinical trials—a study is considered com pleted one year after its conclusion—or pre-publication manuscripts (if available) developed or obtained b the applicant. Supporting information should not be reported. Review articles, papers describing the use o the drug product in medical practice, papers and abstracts in which the drug is used as a research tool, pro motional articles, press clippings, and papers that do not contain tabulations or summaries of original dat should not be reported. Consistent with its pediatric initiative, the FDA required, under the Pediatric Rule that this section of the annual report also include an analysis of available safety and efficacy data in the ped atric population, changes proposed in the labeling based on this information, and an assessment of dat needed to ensure appropriate labeling for the pediatric population. Although the FDA's Pediatric Rule wa struck down in a 2002 court ruling, Congress quickly passed (and President Bush signed into law) the Pediatri Research Equity Act of 2003 (PREA), which established clear FDA authority to require pediatric studies an information in appropriate circumstances. Since PREA's passage, the FDA has been developing both a ne regulation and a new draft guidance to address pediatric testing and submission requirements (includin those relevant to NDA annual reports) under PREA.

Postmarketing Study Commitment Status Report. A statement on the current status of any postmarketing studie performed by, or on behalf of, the applicant, including those that the sponsor agreed to conduct as part of th drug's approval (see section below on Phase 4 commitments). Under the FDA's Pediatric Rule, this statemer also had to indicate whether postmarketing clinical studies in pediatric populations were required or agree to, and if so, the status of these studies (see discussion on Pediatric Rule above and in Chapter 16).

Under FDAMA and an October 2000 implementing regulation, CDER revised its requirements for the postma keting study status report in the NDA annual report. According to current requirements, each annual report t an approved NDA must include "a status report of each postmarketing study of the drug product concernir clinical safety, clinical efficacy, clinical pharmacology, and nonclinical toxicology that is required by FDA (e.g accelerated approval clinical benefit studies, pediatric studies) or that the applicant has committed, in writin to conduct either at the time of approval of an application for the drug product or a supplement to an appl cation, or after approval of the application or a supplement." An applicant must report on the status of suc postmarketing studies each year until the FDA notifies the company, in writing, that the agency concurs wit the company's determination that the study commitment has been fulfilled or that the study is either no long feasible or would no longer provide useful information (see discussion on Phase 4 clinical studies below).

According to the FDA's April 2001 draft guidance entitled, *Reports on the Status of Postmarketing Studie Implementation of Section 130 of the Food and Drug Administration Modernization Act of 1997*, postmarketing statu reports submitted in annual reports should be accompanied by Form FDA-2252 (Transmittal of Annu Reports for Drugs for Human Use). The cover letter should clearly identify the submission as an "Annu Report on Postmarketing Studies." It is important to note that, although sponsors must continue to report o other types of postmarketing studies in the annual report (e.g., product stability studies, product dissolutic studies, the development of an improved potency assay), these reports are not subject to the same FDAMA provisions as those identified above (i.e., required or agreed to).

According to the draft guidance, a sponsor may characterize the status of its Phase 4 study in any one of five ways: pending (study has not begun, but the projected date for patient accrual has not passed), ongoing (the study is proceeding, but is behind the original schedule); terminated (the study was ended before completion, the company does not intend to complete the study as originally designed, and the company has not yet submitted a final study report to the FDA); or submitted (the study has been concluded or terminated and the company has submitted a study report to the FDA and is awaiting the agency's advice as to whether the study commitment has been met).

Other Reports Federal regulations state that sponsors must be prepared to file other reports, including:

Advertisements and Promotional Labeling. NDA holders must "submit specimens of mailing pieces and any other labeling or advertising devised for promotion of the drug product at the time of initial dissemination of the labeling and at the time of initial publication of the advertisement for a prescription drug product. Mailing pieces and labeling that are designed to contain samples of a drug product are required to be complete, except that the sample of the drug product may be omitted. Each submission is required to be accompanied by a completed transmittal Form FDA-2253 (Transmittal of Advertisements and Promotional Labeling for Drugs for Human Use) and is required to include a copy of the product's current professional labeling."

The agency has different standards for the submission of advertisements and promotional labeling approved under its accelerated approval program (see Chapter 15). Under this program, a sponsor must submit these materials (i.e., for evaluation during the NDA review process) for any advertising and labeling that the company plans to disseminate within 120 days of a drug's approval. For advertising and promotional labeling that the firm hopes to disseminate after this 120-day period, the sponsor must submit the materials at least 30 days prior to the intended date of initial dissemination or publication. To describe the process for reviewing promotional materials for drugs approved under the accelerated review program, CDER released a March 1999 draft industry guidance entitled, *Accelerated Approval Products-Submission of Promotional Materials.*

Advertising and promotional labeling are among the submissions that CDER has included in its electronic submissions initiative. In a January 2001 draft guidance entitled, *Providing Regulatory Submissions in Electronic Format-Prescription Drug Advertising and Promotional Labeling,* CDER states that applicants that decide to submit advertisements and promotional labeling in electronic format should file the entire submission electronically.

Special Reports. The FDA may require that the applicant submit any of the reports profiled above at times different than those required under federal regulations.

Report on Withdrawal of Approved Drug Product From Sale. Within 15 working days of withdrawing an approved drug product from the market, the applicant must submit, on Form FDA 2657 (Drug Product Listing), the following information: (1) the National Drug Code number; (2) the identity of the drug product by established name and proprietary name; (3) the NDA number; and (4) the date of the drug's withdrawal. The agency requests, but does not require, that applicants also indicate the reasons for the withdrawal.

Adverse Drug Experience Reporting Requirements

Following a drug's approval, NDA holders must continue to collect, analyze, and submit data on adverse drug experiences (AE) so that the company and the FDA can continually reassess the product's risk/benefit relationship and the conditions under which it should be used. Perhaps more than any other aspect of FDA regulation, the agency's AE reporting standards have been in transition throughout the past 15 years. This transition has been driven by several factors, including international harmonization efforts, continuing FDA effort to encourage the electronic submission of regulatory filings, and an increased focus on drug safety.

At this writing, CDER's postmarketing AE reporting program and requirements continued to evolve based o several developments and factors, including the following:

- Shortly after the high-profile withdrawal of Merck's Vioxx due to safety concerns, the FDA announced, in November 2004, several actions designed to strengthen CDER's program for monitoring postmarketing drug safety. The FDA announced that it would be sponsoring an Institute of Medicine (IOM) study of the agency's postmarketing drug safety system. From the study, the agency will seek recommendations on additional steps that it could take "to learn more about the side effects of drugs as they are actually used." Also as part of this initiative, CDER planned to conduct workshops and advisory committee meetings to discuss complex safety and risk management issues for marketed and investigational drugs.

- In the late 1990s, CDER began to take steps toward what some in the center called a "revitalized pharmacovigilance program," an effort that has continued along with an increasing focus on risk management in recent years. As noted, PDUFA III is providing the FDA with close to $80 million for risk-management and pharmacovigilance programs to help ensure the safe use of drug and biological products. At the center of CDER's focus on postmarketing drug safety is its Office of Drug Safety (ODS), which was established in early 2002 and which houses the divisions and staff that evaluate drug adverse experience reports and other postmarketing data, and that provide key consultations to CDER's drug review divisions regarding drug safety and risk management tools and programs. With an influx in new funding and staffing, ODS was expected to grow as much as 150% during the course of PDUFA III (from a pre-PDUFA III staffing level of 80 to 90 employees), according to some estimates. In its five-year history, ODS has experienced some turbulence, including a succession of directors. Further, during a 2004 controversy involving antidepressant drugs and their association with pediatric suicidality, some members of Congress claimed, based on interviews with FDA staff, that CDER had relegated ODS to "a subservient role" to the Office of New Drugs (OND) in evaluating drug safety issues.

- In March 2003, the FDA published a lengthy and much-anticipated proposed rule that would amend the agency's safety information reporting requirements for human drug and biological products. Nicknamed "The Tome," the proposed rule is designed to harmonize the U.S. adverse experience reporting requirements with international standards, to expand the agency's ability to monitor and improve the safe use of both investigational and marketed human drug and biological products, and to improve the quality and usefulness of industry's pre- and post-marketing safety reporting. When finalized, the proposed rule will have implications for virtually all aspects of FDA's AE reporting requirements, including the critical definitions associated with AE reporting and content and reporting standards for periodic postmarketing AE reports (see discussion below).

- Over the last several years, CDER has continued to migrate toward a system for the electronic submission of adverse experiences. During 1997, a system called the Adverse Event Reporting System (AERS) replaced the FDA's Spontaneous Reporting System (SRS) database for adverse event reports. According to the agency, AERS enables the agency to receive adverse experience reports from pharmaceutical companies through electronic submissions, "transmitted data base to data base through standardized pathways." Under the AERS system, most of the content (e.g., narratives and fields other than medical history and laboratory data) from paper-based reports are full-text entered and are scanned by the agency upon their receipt. In addition, the AERS system utilizes MedDRA (the Medical Dictionary for Regulatory Activities), which was developed by ICH. AERS is designed to provide a "paperless" means for FDA postmarketing safety evaluators to screen individual reports, and to provide new tools for the enhanced surveillance of drug safety. Today, CDER accepts electronic individual case safety reports from many drug firms under a pilot program that began in 1998 (see discussion below). When CDER released a May 2001 draft industry guidance entitled, *Providing Regulatory Submissions in Electronic Format-Postmarketing Expedited Safety Reports*, CDER brought this pilot program into its "production phase," under which these reports are accepted in a completely electronic format. CDER estimates that 21 percent of the total expedited AE reports it received in 2003 were in electronic form, and that electronic reports cut costs by at least 30 percent. CDER officials have announced that they hoped to be receiving 80% of all adverse event reports in electronic form by year-end 2004. In a November 1999 advanced notice of proposed rulemaking, however, CDER announced its plans to issue a proposed rule that would require industry to submit electronic versions of all postmarketing expedited individual case safety reports and individual case safety reports contained in periodic AE reports. The agency claims that such requirements, which will apply only to postmarketing AE reports and will provide a waiver process for small companies, will help to harmonize the reporting of postmarketing safety information worldwide and expedite the detection of safety problems. To provide recommendations for electronic submissions of periodic AE reports, CDER released a June 2003 draft guidance entitled, *Providing Regulatory Submissions in Electronic Format-Postmarketing Periodic Adverse Drug Experience Reports*. Companies can make such electronic submissions through either the FDA's electronic data interchange (EDI) gateway or on physical media.

- Under PDUFA III, the FDA agreed to develop industry guidances on risk-management activities for the three phases of a product's lifecycle—during development, during the product application and review process, and during the postmarketing period. In May 2004, the agency released a draft industry guidance entitled, *Good Pharmacovigilance Practices and Pharmacoepidemiologic Assessment* to address postapproval risk assessment issues. Although the agency notes in the draft guidance that routine pharmacovigilance will be sufficient for most products, "in certain limited circumstances, unusual safety signals may become evident before approval or after a product is marketed that could suggest that consideration by the sponsor of enhanced pharmacovigilance efforts or a pharmacovigilance plan may be appropriate." The draft guidance defines a pharmacovigilance plan as "a plan developed by a sponsor that is focused on detecting new safety signals and/or evaluating already identified safety signals. Specifically, a pharmacovigilance plan describes pharmacovigilance efforts above and beyond routine postmarketing spontaneous reporting, and is designed to enhance and expedite the sponsor's acquisition of safety information." The agency recommends that a sponsor's decision to develop a pharmacovigilance plan be based on "scientific and logistical factors," including the likelihood that the signal represents a potential safety risk, the event's frequency and severity, and the nature of the at-risk population(s). In April 2004, the FDA also released a draft ICH guidance entitled, E2E *Pharmacovigilance Planning* to describe a method for summarizing the identified risks of a drug, the potential of important unidentified risks, and the potentially at-risk populations and situations that were not studied before the drug was approved.

- In recent years, CDER has gained access to a variety of commercial databases that provide non-patient-identifiable information on the actual use of marketed prescription drugs in adults and children. This information assists the center in determining the public health significance of the postmarketing adverse experience reports that it receives. In fact, under PDUFA III, the FDA may employ user fees to access drug utilization databases in an effort to independently evaluate product utilization for drugs with important safety concerns for the first three years post approval.

Key Definitions Relevant to Adverse Drug Experience Reporting The adverse drug experience (AE) report-ing area has very much its own language. In fact, reporting requirements are directly linked to criteria outline in the definitions of several terms that appear in federal regulations: "adverse drug experience," "unexpecte adverse drug experience," "life-threatening," "serious adverse drug experience," and "disability."

Adverse Drug Experience. An adverse experience is defined as "any adverse event associated with the use of drug in humans, whether or not considered drug related, including the following: an adverse event occurrin in the course of the use of a drug product in professional practice; an adverse event occurring from drug ove dose whether accidental or intentional; an adverse event occurring from drug abuse; an adverse event occur ring from drug withdrawal; and any failure of expected pharmacological action."

Unexpected Adverse Drug Experience. An "unexpected" event is any adverse drug experience "that is not listed i the current labeling for the drug product. This includes events that may be symptomatically and pathophys ologically related to an event listed in the labeling, but differ from the event because of greater severity c specificity. For example, under this definition, hepatic necrosis would be unexpected (by virtue of greate severity) if the labeling only referred to elevated hepatic enzymes or hepatitis. Similarly, cerebral thron boembolism and cerebral vasculitis would be unexpected (by virtue of greater specificity) if the labeling onl listed cerebral vascular accidents. 'Unexpected,' as used in this definition, refers to an adverse drug exper ence that has not been previously observed (i.e., included in the labeling) rather than from the perspective c such experience not being anticipated from the pharmacological properties of the pharmaceutical product.'

Serious Adverse Drug Experience. A "serious adverse drug experience" is "any adverse drug experience occurring ä any dose that results in any of the following outcomes: Death, a life-threatening adverse drug experienci inpatient hospitalization or prolongation of existing hospitalization, a persistent or significant disability/incä pacity, or a congenital anomaly/birth defect. Important medical events that may not result in death, be life threatening, or require hospitalization may be considered a serious adverse drug experience when, base upon appropriate medical judgment, they may jeopardize the patient or subject and may require medical c surgical intervention to prevent one of the outcomes listed in this definition. Examples of such medical even include allergic bronchospasm requiring intensive treatment in an emergency room or at home, bloo dyscrasias or convulsions that do not result in inpatient hospitalization, or the development of drug depei dency or drug abuse."

Life-Threatening Adverse Drug Experience. A "life-threatening" AE is "any adverse drug experience that places th patient, in the view of the initial reporter, at immediate risk of death from the adverse drug experience as occurred, i.e., it does not include an adverse drug experience that, had it occurred in a more severe forn might have caused death."

Disability. The term "disability," which is important because it is used in the definition of serious AE, is define as "a substantial disruption of a person's ability to conduct normal life functions." For clarification, the FD adds that "only a persistent or significant disability or incapacity is intended... Thus, disability is not intended to include experiences of relatively minor medical significance such as headache, nausea, vomiting, diarrhea, influenza, and accidental trauma (e.g., sprained ankle)."

Adverse Drug Experience Reporting Requirements NDA holders and certain "nonapplicants" (any person whose name appears on the drug product's label as a manufacturer, packer, or distributor) have AE reporting responsibilities. To avoid unnecessary duplication of reporting, however, federal regulations permit "nonapplicants" to meet their reporting requirements by submitting all serious AE reports directly to the applicant rather than to the FDA.

Under federal regulations, NDA holders and relevant nonapplicants must develop and implement written procedures for the surveillance, receipt, evaluation, and reporting of postmarketing adverse drug experiences. Further, NDA holders must promptly review all adverse drug experience information obtained or otherwise received by the applicant from any source, foreign or domestic, including information derived from commercial marketing experience, postmarketing clinical investigations, postmarketing epidemiological/surveillance studies, reports in the scientific literature, and unpublished scientific papers.

Given the degree of recent and continuing evolution in the postmarketing safety reporting area, none of CDER's existing guidance documents fully captures current requirements. In March 2001, however, CDER released a draft guidance entitled, *Postmarketing Safety Reporting for Human Drugs and Biological Products, Including Vaccines*. When finalized, this guidance will replace CDER's two existing guidances: *Postmarketing Reporting of Adverse Drug Experiences* (March 1992) and *Postmarketing Adverse Experience Reporting for Human Drug and Licensed Biological Products: Clarification of What to Report* (August 1997). CDER concedes, however, that even the draft guidance will have to be revised to reflect all of the pending changes in the safety reporting area.

The agency requires NDA holders to make two types of postmarketing AE reports when necessary: 15-day alert reports, sometimes called postmarketing expedited safety reports, and periodic adverse experience reports. In June 1997, the FDA eliminated the requirement that companies also make "expedited 15-day increased frequency reports" to alert the FDA to any significant increases in the frequency of reports on AEs that are both serious and expected and reports of therapeutic failures.

15-Day Alert Reports. NDA holders and relevant nonapplicants must report each postmarketing AE "that is both serious and unexpected, whether foreign or domestic, as soon as possible, but in no case later than 15 calendar days of initial receipt of the information by the applicant" or nonapplicant. These reports are sometimes called "expedited postmarketing reports."

FDA Form 3500A (MedWatch Form) must be completed and submitted for each report of an adverse drug experience. Foreign events may be submitted either on an FDA Form 3500A, or, if preferred, on a CIOMS I form. Applicants and relevant nonapplicants may use the CIOMS I form without prior FDA approval. They can also use an alternative reporting format, such as a computer-generated FDA Form 3500A or computer-generated tape or tabular listing, provided that the content is equivalent to that found in the FDA Form 3500A and that CDER's MedWatch office agrees to the alternative in advance. Each completed FDA Form 3500A should refer only to an individual patient or a single attached publication.

Consistent with CDER's August 1997 guidance entitled, *Postmarketing Adverse Experience Reporting for Human Drugs and Licensed Biological Products: Clarification of What to Report*, applicants and relevant nonapplicants are expected to have access to certain information before forwarding postmarketing AE reports. To reduce or eliminate incomplete reports, CDER recommends that, at a minimum, an AE report, including both 15-day alert and periodic reports (see discussion below), provide the following "four basic elements:" an identifiable patien (even if not precisely identified by name and date of birth); an identifiable reporter; a suspect drug product and an adverse event or fatal outcome.

15-day alert reports that are based on information in the scientific literature must be accompanied by a cop of the published article. The alert reporting requirements for serious, unexpected AEs "apply only to report found in scientific and medical journals either as case reports or as the result of a formal clinical trial."

Unless the applicant or nonapplicant concludes that there is a reasonable possibility that the drug caused th adverse experience, the firm is not required to submit a 15-day alert report for an AE obtained from a post marketing study (whether or not conducted under an IND). Applicants and relevant nonapplicants must sep arate and clearly mark alert reports for AEs that are derived from postmarketing studies and those that ar being reported spontaneously.

One of the FDA's goals in the October 1997 final rule was to more clearly delineate relevant requirements fo lowing the submission of an initial 15-day alert report. Applicants and relevant nonapplicants must "prompt ly" investigate each AE that is the subject of a 15-day alert report, and submit follow-up reports within 1 calendar days of receipt of the new information or as requested by the FDA. If additional information is nc obtainable, a company should maintain records of its unsuccessful attempts to obtain the information. A before, the 15-day alert reports and follow-ups to them must be submitted under separate cover and may nc be included, except for summary or tabular purposes, in a periodic report (see discussion below).

In September 2003, CDER released a draft ICH guidance entitled, E2D *Postapproval Safety Data Managemen Definitions and Standards for Expedited Reporting* to provide definitions associated with postapproval product safe ty information and standards for the collection and expedited reporting of safety information to regulatoi authorities. While the draft guidance notes that many companies have applied the concepts of the pre approval phase-focused ICH guidance E2A *Clinical Safety Data Management: Definitions and Standards for Expedite Reporting* to the postapproval phase, it adds that "there is a need to provide further guidance on the defin tions and standards for postapproval expedited reporting."

CDER and the Electronic Submission of Expedited AE Reports After its eNDA efforts, CDER's electronic submissior program for postmarketing adverse experiences (AE)—at least in terms of 15-day expedited reports—is eas ly its second most advanced. Following the release of the ICH's subsequently modified guidance entitled, E2 *Data Elements for Transmission of Individual Case Safety Reports* in early 1998 (revised again in April 2002), CDER/Pharmaceutical Research and Manufacturers of America (PhRMA) working group agreed to initiate pilot program for the electronic submission of postmarketing expedited AE reports. While there was some in tial discussion regarding whether CDER's pilot program should focus on postmarketing expedited or perioc ic reports, expedited reports won out largely because these documents provide the center with th all-important first "signals" of potential health problems. An estimated 15 to 20 pharmaceutical companie were members of the working group and participated in the pilot program at various times.

Other advances within the center—largely AERS—had set the stage for the pilot program. For the pilot prc gram, CDER developed a three-step process relevant for any company seeking to submit electronic postma keting expedited AE reports to AERS:

Pilot Phase: In the pilot phase, the manufacturer forwards a proposed AE report in SGML format to CDER, whic runs the report against its "test" database. This process continues iteratively until both CDER and the mani facturer are satisfied that the report meets all the edit criteria of the SGML specification.

Pilot Production Phase: Once the pilot phase is complete, the manufacturer then begins to submit electronic expedited reports on a routine basis, but also forwards an identical paper-based version of each electronic report in parallel.

Production Phase: The formal availability of the so-called production phase began in May 2001, when CDER added postmarketing AE reports to the e-submissions public docket and then published a draft guidance entitled, *Postmarketing Expedited Safety Reports*. In this phase, CDER accepts the reports electronically without any accompanying paper version. According to the draft guidance, the individual case safety report (ICSR) component of the expedited report can be forwarded on either physical media (i.e., floppy disk, CD-ROM, or digital tape), or through the agency's electronic data interchange (EDI) gateway. CDER prefers that companies use the EDI gateway "because this allows the most efficient processing of the reports." According to CDER officials, there were 13 companies in the full production phase at this writing. Many other companies are advancing in the two earlier phases.

CDER has already revealed its intentions to require electronic reporting of expedited AE reports. In a November 1999 advanced notice of proposed rulemaking, CDER announced its plans to issue a proposed rule that would require industry to submit electronic versions of postmarketing expedited ICSRs and ICSRs contained in periodic AE reports using ICH-recommended standardized medical terminology, data elements, and electronic submission standards (see discussion below). The agency claims that such requirements, for which there would be a waiver available to smaller companies, would help to harmonize the reporting of postmarketing safety information internationally, and would expedite the detection of drug safety problems.

Periodic Adverse Drug Experience Reports. Periodic reports must be submitted, in duplicate, quarterly for the first three years following a drug's approval in the United States, and annually thereafter. The quarterly reports must be submitted within 30 days of the close of each quarter (i.e., the first quarter beginning on an application's U.S. approval date). Annual reports must be filed within 60 days of the anniversary date of the application's U.S. approval.

A periodic report must contain each of the following components:

- A copy of FDA Form 3500A for each AE not reported as a 15-day alert report, with an index consisting of a line listing of the applicant's patient identification number and adverse reaction terms.

- A narrative summary and analysis of the information in the periodic report, and an analysis of the 15-day alert reports submitted during the reporting period.

- A narrative discussion of actions taken since the last report because of adverse drug experiences (e.g., labeling changes or studies initiated).

In its August 1997 clarification of postmarketing AE reporting requirements, the FDA encouraged manufacturers to request waivers from the requirement that an FDA Form 3500A be submitted for postmarketing AEs that are both nonserious and labeled. In making waiver requests, companies are asked to certify that complete (i.e., including the four basic informational elements) individual case safety reports of nonserious and labeled AEs will be maintained in corporate safety files. The companies should also agree, following an FDA request, that they will submit one or more of these AE reports to the agency within five calendar days of receiving the request. The FDA reminds companies that it will continue to expect, in periodic reports, a history by body system of all AE terms and counts of occurrences for nonserious and labeled AEs. This waiver process, which the agency is planning to incorporate into its postmarketing reporting regulations, is covered

---

An Analysis of AE Reports to CDER in 2003

In 2003, CDER said it received 370,887 reports of "suspected drug-related adverse events," including:

- 22,955 "MedWatch reports" from individuals (this is a report from an individual, generally a health care practitioner, notifying the FDA directly of a suspected serious adverse event).

- 144,310 15-day expedited reports from drug manufacturers.

- 58,998 periodic reports for serious AEs from drug manufacturers.

- 144,624 periodic reports for nonserious AEs from drug manufacturers.

Source: FDA

---

in a November 1999 MaPP entitled, *Granting Waivers Under 21 CFR 314.90 for Postmarketing Safety Reportin Requirements Under 21 CFR 314.80* (MaPP 6004.1).

FDA regulations point out that, unlike 15-day reporting standards, periodic reporting requirements are nc applicable to adverse drug experiences encountered in postmarketing studies (whether or not conducte under an IND), reports in the scientific literature, or foreign marketing experience, for which only seriou unexpected adverse event reports must be submitted as 15-day reports. Periodic reporting requirements als do not apply to manufacturers of human use prescription drugs without approved NDAs, which are covere under FDA regulations at 21 CFR 310.305.

Under a waiver process implemented following the release of the ICH guidance entitled, E2C *Clinical Safety Dat Management: Periodic Safety Update Reports*, CDER first permitted companies to file their period reports in a format— the periodic safety update report (PSUR)—that was advocated in the E2C guidance. Although few companie opted to submit periodic reports in the PSUR format initially, more are now pursuing waivers in response t CDER's encouragement.

At its discretion, the FDA may require an applicant to submit periodic reports at intervals different than thos specified above. Upon its approval of a supplement supporting a major new indication for an alread approved drug, for instance, the agency may re-establish a quarterly reporting interval for the product.

Federal regulations state that follow-up information on AEs reported in a periodic report may be provided i the subsequent periodic report.

e-Submissions for Periodic Postmarketing AE Reports As noted above, CDER had discussed undertaking a pilot prograr for the electronic submission of periodic postmarketing AE reports, but until late 2001, had not taken form steps to permit or encourage such filings. In November 2001, CDER announced that postmarketing periodic ind vidual case safety reports may be submitted electronically without accompanying paper-based copies.

To provide recommendations for electronic submissions of periodic AE reports, CDER released a June 200 draft guidance entitled, *Providing Regulatory Submissions in Electronic Format-Postmarketing Periodic Adverse Dru Experience Reports*. Companies can make such electronic submissions through either the FDA's electronic dat interchange (EDI) gateway or on physical media. CDER officials claim that, as of late 2004, the center ha received at least some period reports electronically.

Center officials point out, in fact, that transitioning periodic AE reports to the electronic reporting system will be helped by the fact that they are similar to expedited reports in so many respects. The periodic reports comprise the individual case reports that are submitted with, and are formatted exactly as they are in, the expedited reports, as well as an analysis component that will appear, to the AERS system, much like the attachments now submitted with the expedited reports.

Pending Revisions to the FDA's Postmarketing AE Reporting Requirements In March 2003, the FDA published a lengthy and much-anticipated proposed rule that would amend the agency's safety information reporting requirements for human drug and biological products. The proposed rule, nicknamed "The Tome," is designed to harmonize the U.S. adverse experience reporting requirements with international standards, to expand the agency's ability to monitor and improve the safe use of both investigational and marketed human drug and biological products, and to improve the quality and usefulness of industry's pre- and post-marketing safety reporting.

When finalized, the proposed rule will have implications for virtually all aspects of the FDA's AE reporting requirements. Although a complete discussion of the Tome is beyond the scope of this chapter, the following sections highlight several of the proposed rule's key provisions and their possible implications.

Expedited Reporting of Safety Information The FDA has proposed to define and incorporate the term "suspected adverse drug reaction" (SADR) in its pre- and post-marketing safety reporting regulations. Specifically, the FDA has proposed that SADR replace the terms "associated with the use of the drug" (for pre-marketing AE reporting) and "adverse drug experience" (for post-marketing reporting) in applicable regulations (i.e., 21 CFR §310.305, 312.32, 314.80, and 600.80).

A SADR is defined as "a noxious and unintended response to any dose of a drug [or biological] product for which there is a reasonable possibility that the product caused the response. In this definition, the phrase 'a reasonable possibility' means that a relationship cannot be ruled out." The FDA says that the SADR definition, which does not make reference to an assessment of actual evidence or arguments to support causality, "has the effect of requiring [expedited] reporting of a reaction unless the company is sure that the product did not cause the reaction."

If the SADR definition remains in the final published rule as proposed, many analysts believe that it would likely lead to an increase in the number of expedited safety reports submitted from clinical trials. Reports are likely to increase because any adverse event for which a causal/contributory relationship cannot be conclusively ruled out would qualify as a reportable SADR. The implementation of the SADR definition would not likely affect the submission of spontaneously reported adverse events, since these reports must already be submitted to the FDA, regardless of whether they are considered drug-related.

Another industry concern is that the proposed SADR definition may have an impact on product labeling, since the definition implies that adverse events for which a causal/contributory relationship cannot be ruled out are possibly drug-related. The implementation of the SADR definition without further clarification could encourage the inclusion of long laundry lists of irrelevant adverse events in product labels, even though the likelihood of a true causal relationship is minimal, industry officials claim. This could compromise the quality and usefulness of safety information in product labeling, they argue. It is worth noting that previously published FDA and CIOMS V safety labeling guidance documents encourage the inclusion of adverse events in product labeling *only when* a causal or contributory relationship is suspected, reasonably established, or inferred based on facts (evidence) or plausible arguments that support such a relationship.

The proposed rule would also require the expedited reporting of:

- Actual and potential medication errors that occur in the United States, even if no adverse reaction results from the error, or the potential medication error is averted before the product's administration;

- Unexpected reactions for which a determination of seriousness cannot be made;

- Certain designated medical events that historically have been associated with drug toxicity (e.g., liver failure, aplastic anemia, seizures), regardless of whether they are expected or unexpected and serious or non-serious;

- Safety findings from animal or human studies or other information that is considered sufficient to warrant changes in product administration; and

- All serious adverse reactions for blood and blood products, in addition to currently required reports for fatalities.

Quality of Safety Reports Several provisions in the proposed rule are designed to improve the quality of safety information submitted to the FDA. The proposed rule, for instance, would require that a company health care professional speak directly to the initial reporter of a SADR (active query) when additional information is needed to appropriately evaluate an individual case safety report, and that this professional pursue direct verbal contact repeatedly until the necessary information is obtained. In addition, the actual narrative summary of the individual case safety report would be required to document unsuccessful attempts to obtain complete case details for serious SADRs through active queries.

Currently, many companies elect to solicit additional information from reporters of adverse events via written inquiries and means other than direct telephone contact. A requirement that direct active queries be used in addition to traditional methods in obtaining follow-up information from reporters could impose an additional resource burden on industry.

The proposed rule would codify a requirement that all individual case safety reports contain a minimum data set in accordance with ICH recommendations (i.e., identifiable patient, identifiable reporter, suspect product and a SADR). In addition to the minimum data set, the proposed rule would require that serious SADR reports, designated medical event reports, and medication error reports contain a "full data set," a requirement that the firm must fulfill by completing all applicable elements in the FDA Form 3500A, including a concise medical narrative of the case. When an initial report does not contain a full data set, there will be a 30-day follow-up period during which the manufacturer will be required to pursue complete information (30-day follow-up report requirement does not apply to reports of serious, expected SADRs). All attempts to obtain additional information during the 30-day follow-up period, including unsuccessful efforts, should be documented. Under the proposal, companies would be required to obtain only a minimum data set for non-serious SADRs (except non-serious SADRs resulting from a medication error).

Another provision in the proposed rule would require that a licensed physician at the company be made responsible for the content and medical interpretation of post-marketing safety reports submitted to the FDA. Depending on how it is interpreted, this provision could have an impact on companies that effectively utilize a variety of non-physician clinical specialists/experts to review and manage acquired safety data.

Lastly, the proposed rule would require that post-marketing individual case safety reports be coded using the MedDRA terminology that was developed through the ICH process. This requirement is intended to facilitate the comparison of global safety information.

Periodic Safety Reports The Tome proposes requirements that would, over time, transition periodic postmarketing reports to internationally harmonized formats and reporting timeframes. Specifically, it proposes that companies submit traditional U.S. periodic safety reports (TPSRs) as described above, periodic safety update reports (PSURs), or interim periodic safety reports (IPSRs). The type of periodic report that a company should submit will depend on the drug product's approval date.

The proposed rule would also reconfigure the FDA's current reporting timeframes for periodic postmarketing reports from the current scheme, which calls for quarterly reports for the first three years following approval and then annual reports thereafter. For products approved prior to January 1, 1998, companies would be required to submit either a TPSR or a PSUR initially at six-month intervals and then at longer intervals as the product ages (e.g., every six months in the first two years after approval, annually for the next three years, and then every five years). For products approved on or after January 1, 1998, companies would be required to submit a PSUR in accordance with the ICH's E2C guidance. In addition, the FDA has proposed that a number of U.S.-only appendices be submitted with the PSUR.

The proposed rule would also require that companies submit an abbreviated IPSR at 7.5 and 12.5 years after a product's approval. The IPSR is designed to provide an overview of the product's safety profile without some of the detail and summary tabulations required in a PSUR.

In public comments, industry has expressed concern that the proposed rule would impose certain periodic safety report requirements that are inconsistent with the original ICH guideline entitled, E2C *Clinical Safety Data Management: Periodic Safety Update Reports for Marketed Drugs* (November 1996) and a subsequent addendum to the ICH's E2C guideline. The February 2004 addendum provides additional information on issues regarding the submission of PSURs, including when separate reports should be filed and the appropriate synchronization of national product birthdates with international birthdates for reporting purposes.

Additional Provisions Other provisions of the FDA's March 2003 proposed rule include the following:

- Clarification of what information must be reviewed on the Internet for safety reporting.

- Required submissions for spontaneously reported individual cases of serious, expected SADRs that occur abroad. Current regulations require the reporting of such cases only if they occur in the United States.

- Mandatory submission of an autopsy report, hospital discharge summary, or death certificate for reports of death and hospitalization.

- Requiring PSURs to provide information on resistance to antimicrobial drug products.

- Eliminating the requirement that safety-related information be submitted in post-marketing approved drug and biological product annual reports if the information is also provided in the proposed post-marketing expedited and periodic safety reports.

Current Good Manufacturing Practice (cGMP)

Since 1962, federal drug law has mandated that firms producing drugs for administration to humans operate under regulatory and quality control standards called current good manufacturing practice (cGMP). The statutory requirement calls for all drugs—including drug products (i.e., finished dosage forms) and drug components (i.e., bulk ingredients)—to be made in conformance with cGMP to ensure that the substances meet legal requirements of safety, and that they have the identity, strength, quality, and purity that they purport or are represented to possess. In the late 1970s, the FDA had envisioned several different sets of cGMPs, wit separate standards for finished dosage forms, bulk ingredients, and other classes of products. To date, how ever, the FDA has published only one broadly applicable cGMP regulation, which is relevant to finishe dosage forms. Since establishing cGMP requirements, the FDA has exhibited a preference for a "general reg ulatory approach," and for supplementing this approach with additional specificity when necessary. In it most recent effort to add specificity to its cGMP requirements, the agency proposed to clarify certain manu facturing, quality control and documentation requirements and to update requirements for process and meth ods validation (see discussion below).

The agency has stated that its cGMP regulations are based on "fundamental concepts of quality assurance: (1 Quality, safety, and effectiveness must be designed and built into a product; (2) quality cannot be inspecte or tested into a finished product; and (3) each step of the manufacturing process must be controlled to max imize the likelihood that the finished product will be acceptable." Even as the FDA moved in late 2004 to adop a comprehensive new approach in the cGMP oversight area (see discussion below), it emphasized that th "overarching philosophy articulated in both cGMP regulations and in robust modern quality systems is 'Quality should be built into the product, and testing alone cannot be relied on to ensure product quality.'"

It is worth noting that the applicability of cGMP requirements is not restricted to approved drug products. A the FDA establishes in its *Guideline on the Preparation of Investigational New Drug Products (Human and Animal)* (Marc 1991), experimental drugs used in clinical testing are subject to certain cGMP requirements as well. In lat 2004, CDER was developing additional guidance on cGMP requirements for drugs used in Phase 1 clinical tr als. The goal of the new guidance will be "to ease the progress of new drugs through the early stages of deve opment," FDA officials stated.

The Pharmaceutical cGMPs for the 21st Century Initiative In August 2002, the FDA announced that it woul be undertaking a comprehensive assessment of its existing cGMP programs with an eye toward enhancing an modernizing the regulation of product manufacturing and product quality. The two-year initiative was th product of several factors, including the FDA's acknowledgment that the last comprehensive revision to it cGMP regulations occurred almost 25 years earlier. The center also claimed that the process efficiency an effectiveness of pharmaceutical manufacturing had not advanced sufficiently over the years due to the pha maceutical industry's reluctance to employ continuous process improvements in the manufacturing are Industry countered that the lack of advancement in drug manufacturing was due to concern regarding the reg ulatory implications of manufacturing changes.

Under its *Pharmaceutical cGMPs for the 21st Century* initiative, the FDA established several key objectives, includ ing the following:

- Implementing risk-based approaches that allow the FDA and industry to focus on critical areas for improving product safety and quality.

- Ensuring that regulatory review, compliance, and inspection policies are based on state-of-the-art pharmaceutical science.

- Encouraging the "early adoption of new technological advances by the pharmaceutical industry."

- Facilitating industry's application of modern quality management techniques, including the implementation of quality systems approaches, to all aspects of pharmaceutical production and quality assurance.

- Enhancing the consistency and coordination of the FDA's drug quality regulatory programs, in part by further integrating enhanced quality systems approaches into the agency's business processes and regulatory policies concerning review and inspection activities.

To promote industry's "rapid adoption of modern manufacturing practices" as its comprehensive, two-year reassessment proceeded, the FDA released several cGMP guidance documents under the cGMP initiative in August 2003, including: (1) a final Part 11 guidance on the use of electronic records and signatures to remove barriers to scientific and technological advances and encourage the use of risk-based approaches; (2) a draft guidance on aseptic processes used in sterile drug manufacturing; (3) a draft guidance on a pilot process for resolving disputes over scientific and technical issues related to pharmaceutical cGMP; (4) a draft guidance on the preparation and use of a comparability protocol for assessing chemistry, manufacturing, and control (CMC) changes to protein drugs products and biological products (CDER officials have announced that they will re-assess this draft guidance with an eye toward reducing regulatory burdens and providing greater flexibility); and (5) a draft guidance on process analytical technology (PAT), which is a framework for allowing regulatory processes to adopt more readily state-of-the-art technological advances in drug development, production, and quality assurance (Note: a final version of the PAT guidance was released in September 2004). In addition, the agency entered into several cGMP-related collaborations with universities and such groups as the National Science Foundation's Center for Pharmaceutical Processing Research to identify the factors that predict drug manufacturing performance and to upgrade the agency's foundation in the area of innovative pharmaceutical manufacturing technologies.

Further, in September 2003, CDER and the FDA's Office of Regulatory Affairs announced the formation of a new Pharmaceutical Inspectorate, which will conduct drug manufacturing quality inspections on prescription drug manufacturers and other "complex or high risk pharmaceutical operations" as well as pre-approval inspections. According to CDER, the Pharmaceutical Inspectorate comprises a group of field inspectors who function within the agency's field inspectional force and who have "specialized experience and specific training in evaluating pharmaceutical manufacturing" (see discussion below).

In September 2004, the FDA released a final report on its cGMPs for the 21st Century initiative to highlight the specific steps the agency had taken and plans to take to "develop and implement quality systems management and a risk-based product quality regulatory system," including the following:

- The formation of an internal FDA Council on Pharmaceutical Quality to oversee the implementation of the FDA's new system. The new council, which was scheduled to begin operations in late 2004, has been charged with policy development, coordination, and continuing change management, including the ongoing implementation of certain quality management systems within the agency relating to pharmaceutical quality regulation.

- The issuance of a September 2004 industry draft guidance entitled, *Quality Systems Approach to Pharmaceutical Current Good Manufacturing Practice Regulations*. When finalized, this guidance will provide recommendations on how industry can meet the FDA's cGMP regulations by employing "a comprehensive quality systems approach, which encourages continuous improvement and risk management in the manufacturing of human and veterinary drugs, including human biological products." The guidance, which is intended to serve as a "bridge" between the 1978 cGMP regulations and the agency's current understanding of quality systems, describes a model that, if implemented, "will allow manufacturers to operate robust, modern quality systems that are fully compliant with cGMP regulations."

- The FDA's adoption of a more systematic risk-based approach to the inspectional oversight of pharmaceutical manufacturing. This new approach will begin, in the fall of 2004, with the pilot implementation of a risk-based model for prioritizing domestic manufacturing sites for routine human drug cGMP inspections. The new approach, which recognizes that the FDA no longer has the resources to meet the statutory requirement that domestic drug manufacturing establishments be inspected at least once every two years, is based on a risk-ranking and filtering method that will help the agency best exploit its limited surveillance and enforcement resources while maximizing the impact of those resources on the public health. The agency outlined the new approach in a September 2004 white paper entitled, *Risk-Based Method for Prioritizing CGMP Inspections of Pharmaceutical Manufacturing Sites-A Pilot Risk Ranking Model*.

- The replacement of the CMC review system currently operated by CDER's Office of New Drug Chemistry (ONDC) with a new "risk-based pharmaceutical quality assessment system." Under the new system, ONDC's review functions for reviewing INDs/NDAs and CMC supplements will be separated to address the critical CMC issues more expeditiously in both the pre-approval and postapproval areas (see Chapters 4, 8, and 12).

- The FDA's decision to seek membership in the Pharmaceutical Inspection Cooperation (PIC) Scheme, a cooperative arrangement among health authorities to lead the international development, implementation, and maintenance of harmonized cGMP standards and quality systems of worldwide pharmaceutical inspectorates. This decision is seen as the latest in the agency's efforts to harmonize pharmaceutical quality standards and requirements wherever possible. Similar to other key regulatory standards, cGMP standards in the United States, Japan, and the European Union have been a topic area under the ICH harmonization initiative. During the ICH era, the FDA has released several cGMP- and drug manufacturing-related guidance documents developed through the harmonization initiative, including Q7A *Good Manufacturing Practice for Active Pharmaceutical Ingredients* (October 2001). Intended to ensure the manufacturing of APIs "under an appropriate system for managing quality," the guideline provides cGMP-related recommendations in several areas, including quality management, production and in-process controls, validation, change control, and clinical trial APIs. In March 1998, the FDA released its own related draft guidance entitled, *Manufacturing, Processing, or Holding Active Pharmaceutical Ingredients*.

Upon the September 2004 final report's release and the FDA's announcement that the Pharmaceutical cGMP for the 21st Century initiative would be entering its next phase (implementation and continuous improvement), the agency released several related guidance documents. Among these were draft guidances entitled *Current Good Manufacturing Practice for Combination Products* (September 2004) and PAT-A *Framework for Innovative Pharmaceutical Development, Manufacturing, and Quality Assurance* (September 2004). At the time, the agency also announced that it intends to withdraw a 1996 proposed rule designed to clarify and amend certain cGMP requirements (e.g., validation and methods validation requirements, required dedicated production processes for certain drugs, testing and investigation of discrepancies/failures) and to re-examine comments received on the proposed rule in the context of "more recent scientific and technical advances and quality systems and risk management concepts."

The recent initiatives outlined above will supplement other, ongoing manufacturing- and product quality-related initiatives within CDER's Office of Pharmaceutical Sciences. In development since January 1996, the Product Quality Research Institute (PQRI), for example, is a collaboration between CDER, industry and academia, and is focused on conducting research to generate scientific information to support emerging regulatory policy. In part, the initiative is helping to identify the types of product quality information that should b submitted in regulatory filings to CDER and to promote efficiency and consistency in the center's regulatory requirements and processes. Further, under its CMC "risk-based review proposal," OPS is attempting to identify those drugs that present little/no product quality risks, and to develop a list of quality attributes and acceptance criteria that will permit the agency to reduce submission requirements for such drugs and focus, instead, on more complex drugs that are more likely to present CMC-related problems.

The FDA's cGMP Standards

The FDA's cGMP regulations seek to ensure the quality of drugs by setting minimum standards for all drug manufacturing facilities. The regulations establish standards in ten separate areas:

- organization and personnel;
- buildings and facilities;
- equipment;
- control of components and drug product containers and closures;
- production and process controls;
- packaging and labeling controls;
- holding and distribution;
- laboratory controls;
- records and reports; and
- returned and salvaged drug products.

Organization and Personnel One of the most important cGMP requirements addresses a facility's quality control unit, which each manufacturing facility must have to ensure compliance with cGMP. According to federal regulations, the quality control unit assumes "the responsibility and authority to approve or reject all components, drug product containers, closures, in-process materials, packaging materials, labeling, and drug products and the authority to review production records to ensure that no errors have occurred or, if errors have occurred, that they have been fully investigated." In addition, the one-or-more-person quality control unit is responsible for approving or rejecting all procedures or specifications affecting the identity, strength, quality, and purity of the drug product.

Included in this category of requirements are provisions to ensure that the professionals responsible for performing, supervising, or consulting on the manufacture, processing, packing, or holding of a drug are adequate in number, free from any illness that may endanger the product, and sufficiently qualified by education, training, and experience to carry out their respective tasks. Facility staff must be trained not only in their specific tasks, but in cGMP as well. The facility must document this training.

Buildings and Facilities cGMP building and facility requirements are designed to ensure that any structures used to manufacture, process, pack, or hold a drug are of a suitable size, construction, and location to allow proper cleaning, maintenance, and operation. These requirements call for the separation of areas or other control systems to reduce the possibility of product-to-product cross-contamination and other mishaps. Specific requirements for lighting, ventilation, heating and cooling systems, plumbing, sanitation, and maintenance are also provided.

Equipment In general, cGMP equipment requirements address equipment design, size, location, and main tenance. To ensure that drug product attributes are not adversely affected, surfaces that contact component: in-process materials, or drug products must not be reactive, additive, or absorptive. Lubricants and other sub stances required for equipment operations must not cause product contamination.

At predetermined intervals, all utensils and equipment must be cleaned, maintained, and sanitized accorc ing to specific written procedures. cGMP establishes special requirements for demonstrating and verifyin the proper performance of filters and automatic, mechanical, and electronic equipment (including con puters).

Components and Drug Product Container and Closure Controls A facility must maintain detailed writte procedures for the receipt, identification, storage, handling, sampling, testing, and approval/rejection of con ponents and drug product containers and closures. Upon receipt, these materials must be inspected visuall for appropriate labeling and contents, container damage, broken seals, and contamination. Before use, sam ples from each lot of components must be drawn, and the components tested for identity and conformity wit purity, strength, and quality specifications. Drug product containers and closures must be tested for confoi mance to applicable written requirements.

Production and Process Controls Manufacturing facilities must maintain written procedures for productio and process controls designed to ensure that the drug products have the identity, strength, quality, and pur ty they claim or are represented to possess. Special cGMP requirements exist for the charge-in of component: yield calculations, the identification of compounding and storage containers, processing lines, and the majc equipment used in the production of drug batches, the sampling and testing of in-process materials and dru products, and the limiting of the time necessary to complete each phase of production.

Packaging and Labeling Controls All packaging and labeling materials must be sampled, examined, or tes ed before their use. Documented procedures must be established for the receipt, identification, storage, har dling, sampling, examination, and testing of labeling and packaging materials. cGMP regulations also speci requirements for labeling issuances and accountability, packaging and labeling operations control an inspection, tamper-resistant packaging for OTC drugs, drug product inspection, and expiration dating.

To reduce the frequency of drug product mislabeling, the FDA revised the cGMP labeling control regulatior in 1993. Specifically, the revision defined the term "gang-printed labeling," specified conditions for the use gang-printed or cut labeling, and exempted manufacturers that employ certain automated inspection systen from labeling reconciliation requirements. The agency has delayed the implementation of some elements this regulation (i.e., those provisions applicable to labeling other than immediate container labels) until can finalize a related regulation proposed in July 1997. At this writing, a draft regulation had been develope and was being reviewed internally within the agency. Under the original proposal, the FDA sought to amen cGMP packaging and labeling control provisions by limiting the application of special control procedures fi the use of cut labeling to immediate container labels, individual unit cartons, or multiunit cartons containir immediate containers that are not packaged in individual unit cartons. The FDA also proposed to permit th use of any automated technique that physically prevents incorrect labeling from being processed by labelir and packaging equipment when cut labeling is used.

Holding and Distribution Requirements Facilities must maintain detailed written procedures describing th warehousing operations (including quarantine and special storage procedures) and distribution methoc used for a drug product. To expedite the process of locating products in case of a recall, facilities must mai tain records relating to the distribution of products. In most cases, facilities should implement the "first in, first out" (FIFO) principle in storing and distributing the product.

Laboratory Controls Each organizational unit within a firm is required to maintain procedures for control mechanisms. These procedures and mechanisms, such as specifications, standards, sampling plans, and test procedures, are designed to ensure that components, drug product containers, closures, in-process materials, labeling, and drug products conform to appropriate standards of identity, strength, quality, and purity. Laboratory controls, which must be reviewed and approved by the quality control unit, include: (1) the determination, through documented sampling and testing procedures, that each shipment lot of components, drug product containers, closures, and labeling conforms to relevant specifications; (2) the determination, through sampling and testing procedures, that in-process materials conform to written specifications; (3) the determination that the laboratory is complying with written descriptions of drug product sampling procedures and specifications; and (4) the determination that instruments, apparatus, gauges, and recording devices have been calibrated at suitable intervals according to written procedures that provide specific directions, schedules, limits for accuracy and precision, and provisions for remedial action in the event accuracy and/or precision limits are not met.

A written program must be designed for stability testing studies. The results of these tests are used to determine appropriate storage conditions and expiration dates for each drug. Reserve samples of drug substances and drug products must be retained for specific intervals.

Also included in the laboratory controls subpart of the cGMP regulations are requirements for: (1) the sampling, testing, and release for distribution of drug product batches; (2) special testing for sterile, pyrogen-free, ophthalmic, and controlled-release drugs, reserve sample retention, laboratory test animals; and (3) testing for penicillin contamination.

In September 1998, CDER released a draft industry guidance entitled, *Investigating Out of Specification* (OOS) *Test Results for Pharmaceutical Production*. The draft guidance, which defines OOS results as "all suspect results that fall outside the specifications or acceptance criteria established in NDAs, official compendia, or by the manufacturer," provides CDER's thinking on how manufacturers should evaluate suspect, or out of specification, test results in the manufacture and laboratory testing of active pharmaceutical ingredients, excipients, and other components. The draft guidance applies to laboratory testing during the manufacture of active pharmaceutical ingredients, excipients, and other components as well as the testing of the finished product to the extent that cGMP requirements apply.

Records and Reports Appropriately approved and checked master records must be maintained to assure uniformity between product batches. The facility must prepare batch records for each batch of product. Facilities must retain records for all drug components, drug product containers, closures, and labeling for at least one year after the expiration date of the drug product for which they were used. Certain OTC drugs do not require expiration dating because they meet specific exemption criteria. For these drugs, records must be kept for three years after distribution of the last lot of drug product incorporating the component or using the container, closure, or labeling. CGMP regulations also specify requirements for master and batch production records, laboratory records, distribution records, and complaint files.

The agency's March 1997 electronic signatures and electronic records rule (21 CFR Part 11) had significant implications for production, standard operating procedure, laboratory, quality, and all other cGMP and non-cGMP records and documents that CDER regulations require industry to maintain or submit. Provided that certain standards were met, Part 11 provided the necessary regulatory and structure to allow the use of electronic records and electronic signatures in lieu of paper-based records and signatures, respectively. The agency's goal in Part 11 was to permit the use of electronic records and signatures while establishing standards that would minimize opportunities for readily falsifying electronic records and to maximize the chance for detecting such falsifications.

The FDA's implementation and enforcement of Part 11 standards have undergone a major transformation since the agency released its first draft Part 11 Scope and Application guidance document in February 2003. Concerned that its interpretation of Part 11 standards was actually discouraging innovation, the agency ultimately withdrew this and several related guidances and released a final Part 11 Scope and Application guidance (August 2003) that considerably liberalized its interpretation of and approach to Part 11. At this writing, the agency was still considering whether to overhaul its Part 11 regulations.

It is important to note that, although the earliest push for electronic records and signatures was in the cGMP area (i.e., full handwritten signatures for master and batch production records), Part 11 is applicable to every FDA recordkeeping requirement across all of the agency's program areas. Further, it is equally important to note that Part 11, which took effect in August 1997, simply permits, rather than requires, companies to employ electronic records and signatures in lieu of paper-based records and signatures, respectively.

Returned and Salvaged Drug Products Any returned drug products must be identified and held. A manufacturer must destroy such products if there is any doubt about their safety, identity, strength, quality, or purity, but may reprocess the products if the resultant drug can meet applicable standards, specifications, and characteristics. Reprocessing must be conducted according to written and company-approved procedures. Drugs subjected to improper storage, including extremes in temperature, humidity, smoke, fumes, pressure, age, radiation due to natural disasters, fires, accidents, or equipment failures may not be salvaged and returned to the marketplace.

The Enforcement of cGMP While some critics have claimed that cGMP provisions are too general and difficult to enforce, the FDA has an active program designed to ensure manufacturer compliance. Traditionally enforcement responsibilities have fallen mainly on the FDA's district offices located throughout the United States, which have monitored the industry by inspecting each drug manufacturing facility within their region at least once every two years.

When a foreign or domestic inspection is completed, the manufacturer is alerted to any detected cGMP violations. Minor violations are generally handled by the FDA's district offices, which provide the manufacturer a period of time within which to address the detected violations. For major violations, the district office files a report with FDA headquarters, which reviews the case and decides on the appropriate regulatory action.

Consistent with the larger *Pharmaceutical cGMPs for the 21st Century Initiative* (see discussion above), CDER's cGMP compliance program has adopted a risk-based approach. In its FY2004 Annual Performance Plan, for example, the agency notes that it "has changed the performance target for manufacturing inspections from 20% of all drug establishments to 55% of high-risk establishments in support of a risk-based approach that focuses scarce inspectional resources on drug establishments where FDA intervention is likely to achieve the greatest public health impact." During FY2004, the agency hoped to inspect roughly half of all prescription drug facilities, since prescription drugs "are more potent and susceptible to cross contamination and variability concerns." In addition, the agency hoped to inspect all facilities at what it calls "new registrants," and about half of the estimated 130 sterile product manufacturers.

As noted above, the FDA plans to adopt a more systematic risk-based approach to the inspectional oversight of pharmaceutical manufacturing as part of its *Pharmaceutical cGMPs for the 21st Century Initiative.* This new approach will begin in the fall of 2004 with the pilot implementation of a risk-based model for prioritizing domestic manufacturing sites for routine human drug cGMP inspections. The new approach, which recognizes that the FDA no longer has the resources to meet the statutory requirement that domestic drug manufacturing establishments be inspected at least once every two years, is based on a risk-ranking and filtering method that will help the agency best exploit its limited surveillance and enforcement resources while maximizing the impact of those resources on the public health. To be reassessed in September 2006, the new approach will employ over 70 potential factors in the areas of process, product, and facility to characterize a manufacturing site's risk potential. The agency outlined the new approach in a September 2004 white paper entitled, *Risk-Based Method for Prioritizing CGMP Inspections of Pharmaceutical Manufacturing Sites-A Pilot Risk Ranking Model.*

The new cGMP initiative is expected to reinforce the principles employed in a systems-based cGMP inspectional approach that the agency fully implemented in early 2002 (following its pilot use in several districts). While the earlier inspection approach focused on products, the systems-based approach focuses on the assessment of six manufacturer systems: quality; production; laboratory controls; facilities and equipment; materials; and packaging and labeling. Based on specific criteria and assessments, CDER inspectors can choose to assess specific combinations of these systems, although an assessment of the quality systems is mandatory. In analyzing data from the pilot program, CDER officials found that the systems-based approach improved inspectional efficiency and reduced mean inspection time by 12 hours.

In September 2003, CDER and the Office of Regulatory Affairs announced the formation of a new Pharmaceutical Inspectorate (see discussion above), which will conduct drug manufacturing quality inspections on prescription drug manufacturers and other "complex or high risk pharmaceutical operations" as well as pre-approval inspections. According to CDER, the Pharmaceutical Inspectorate comprises a special group of field inspectors who work within the agency's larger field inspectional force, who have "specialized experience and specific training in evaluating pharmaceutical manufacturing" and who will be trained in and dedicated to assessing high-risk drug manufacturing operations. CDER estimated that the Pharmaceutical Inspectorate would grow to 50 "highly trained individuals" by FY2007. At this writing, the drug center had established a process to identify and train these inspectors.

cGMP Inspections Traditionally, cGMP inspections have been conducted on an unannounced basis—that is, the facility to be inspected generally was not given advance notice by the FDA field office. The cGMP inspector arrived at the plant and, after the presentation of credentials and a notice of inspection, was given immediate access to the building.

In early 2001, the Office of Regulatory Affairs (ORA) announced that it would not extend a pilot program under which the agency was conducting pre-announced manufacturing inspections. Under the program, ORA provided, for the first time, notification of an upcoming inspection (at least five days before the scheduled inspection), formal notification to drug manufacturers of positive inspection results, and annotated FDA-483 forms—the forms on which problems discovered during inspections are noted. ORA decided to implement the pilot program after pre-announced inspections in the medical device area produced a 70 percent time savings over unannounced inspections.

Although ORA decided not to extend the pilot program, it allowed FDA district offices to continue to conduct pre-announced inspections at their own discretion. In addition, the agency left to the districts' discretion whether they would continue the practice of annotating FDA-483s.

The use of announced inspections has long been the modus operandi for inspections of non-U.S. drug man ufacturers. For foreign manufacturing facilities, the FDA makes only cGMP inspections that are pre-arrange with the manufacturers a few months in advance. The most frequent subjects of foreign cGMP inspections al bulk active pharmaceutical ingredient manufacturers.

In recent years, the FDA's international surveillance activities have increased considerably. With greater func ing for foreign inspections, the FDA significantly increased its inspectional activities targeted at foreign man ufacturing facilities during the mid-1990s. In mid-1997, the FDA and European Union (EU) regulatoi established a mutual recognition agreement (MRA) under which they planned to exchange and general accept each other's drug and medical device cGMP inspections without necessitating re-inspections. Th MRA, which was ratified in the United States and Europe, began with a three-year transitional peric (December 1999-December 2002), during which the regulators were to establish the equivalence of their pr approval and postapproval cGMP inspections and determine the essential information that must be preser in cGMP inspection reports to facilitate their mutual acceptance by the participating regulatory agencies.

Due to resource issues and competing priorities on both sides, no work has been done on the implementi tion of the MRA for some time. Also impeding the MRA's implementation is at least one significant impass Although the EU authorities want the FDA to provide an EU-wide inspectional equivalency determination, th FDA insists on undertaking country-by-country equivalency assessments.

Recent Data on cGMP Inspection Outcomes In FY2003, CDER conducted 1,512 cGMP inspections, according to FD data. The center reviewed 51 field recommendations for regulatory action, and approved 34 of them, incluc ing 27 warning letters, four injunctions, and three seizures. In addition, CDER reviewed 184 foreign establisl ment inspection reports, resulting in one warning letter and one import alert.

The most recent internal FDA analyses of cGMP inspection reports show that procedural issues are the mo commonly cited compliance problems. CDER found that a failure to document or follow production/proces control procedures was cited on 52% of inspection reports from 2001 to 2003. Other common findings incluc ed issues with the quality control unit's (QAU) responsibilities/procedures (42%), the absence of written pr duction/process control procedures (31%), and the failure to maintain complete and accurate bate production records.

The FDA's issuance of cGMP-related warning letters has declined markedly in recent years. During 2003, th agency issued only 29 cGMP warning letters, down from 70 in FY2001 and 58 in FY2002.

Phase 4 Commitments

Sponsor commitments made at the time of a drug's approval may also become, in effect, postmarketir requirements. For example, a sponsor may agree or be required, at the time of approval, to conduct addition testing on a drug to further characterize the product's safety, effectiveness, or optimal use, or to assess i effects in specific subpopulations. Often called "Phase 4 commitments," these commitments—and sponsoi progress in fulfilling them—are actively tracked by the FDA following approval (see discussion below).

Although the agency can seek Phase 4 commitments for any drug prior to or following licensing, the FD/ 1993 regulations on accelerated approval (Subpart H) codified its authority to require postapproval studic under the Subpart H program. These regulations established that the FDA can require Phase 4 studies whe it approves an application on the basis of a surrogate endpoint or on the basis of an effect on a clinical en point other than survival or irreversible morbidity. Since this time, the Phase 4 study requirement has been extended to other products, including those approved under the FDA's "fast track" product approval system (see Chapter 15).

Product approval trends—including the fact that many new drugs were being approved so quickly in the mid-1990s—led to an increasing focus on postmarketing studies and surveillance, and on whether industry was fulfilling its Phase 4 study commitments. Under the FDA Modernization Act of 1997 (FDAMA), for example, sponsors that agree to conduct Phase 4 studies as part of an NDA approval are required to provide annual updates on the status of postmarketing studies within their annual reports (see discussion above). In addition, FDAMA provides the FDA with greater authority to monitor the progress of postmarketing studies that drug applicants have agreed to conduct, and requires the agency to keep the public and medical community informed about these postmarketing "obligations" and the related activities of applicants. Further, CDER's Office of Drug Safety now has a unit responsible for tracking all Phase 4 study commitments.

For required or agreed-to studies, FDAMA and an October 2000 implementing regulation also require sponsors to submit postmarketing study protocols. Typically, protocols for required studies (e.g., accelerated approval clinical benefit studies) should be submitted prior to an NDA's approval, while it is general FDA practice to ask sponsors to submit protocols for other postmarketing studies (e.g., agreed-to studies) within three months of the date of the postmarketing study commitment. All study protocols should include the sponsor's proposed schedule for the completion of patient enrollment (or initiation of an animal study, if applicable), completion of the study, and the submission of a final report to the FDA.

When a postmarketing study is completed, the sponsor should submit the final report as a separate submission to the NDA with a Form FDA 356h and a cover letter. The final study report should describe the study and its results, and should explain how the study fulfills the Phase 4 requirement or commitment. Otherwise, the report should explain why the study was unable to fulfill the requirement or commitment. After reviewing the final report, the FDA will determine whether or not the sponsor has fulfilled the requirement/commitment. If the agency concludes that the study commitment has been met or that the study is either no longer feasible or would no longer provide useful information, the commitment will be considered satisfied and the sponsor will no longer be required to report on the study's status in the annual report. In other cases, the agency could determine that a new study and study commitment are necessary.

Under FDAMA, CDER is also required to make publicly available certain information that sponsors submit in their annual Phase 4 status reports for required and agreed-to studies. FDAMA establishes that information in these reports should be made available to the extent necessary "to identify the applicant or to establish the status of the study including the reasons, if any, for failure to conduct, complete, and report the study." In its final rule implementing this aspect of FDAMA, CDER states that such information would include the Phase 4 study protocol, patient accrual rates, reports of unexpected suspected adverse drug reactions, and study results, but would not include trade secrets or information considered important to preserve personal privacy. FDAMA also requires the FDA to publish an annual report in the *Federal Register* on the status of Phase 4 studies (see discussion below).

Under PDUFA III, the FDA is called upon to disclose to the public—and in other cases, require companies to inform prescribers—if an applicant fails to meet its Phase 4 commitments. "If a sponsor fails to complete an agreed upon study required by this section by its original or otherwise negotiated deadline, the Secretary shall publish a statement on the Internet site of the Food and Drug Administration stating that the study was not completed and, if the reasons for such failure to complete the study were not satisfactory to the Secretary, statement that such reasons were not satisfactory to the Secretary." If a sponsor fails to complete certai required Phase 4 studies (e.g., under accelerated approval for serious or life-threatening diseases) for reasor unsatisfactory to the FDA, the agency may also require that the company "notify practitioners who prescrib such drug or biological product of the failure to complete such study and the questions of clinical benefi and, where appropriate, questions of safety, that remain unanswered as a result of the failure to complet such study."

In mid-2003, the agency established a website to provide the public with information on the status of pos marketing study commitments. Further, the agency also began, in May 2003, to issue annual reports on firm performance in conducting postmarketing commitment studies. A total of 122 NDA and ANDA applicants ha 1,338 open postmarketing commitments as of September 2003, according to CDER data. About two-thirds the open commitments (65%) were pending (study had not been initiated, but did not meet the criteria fc delayed), 20% were ongoing (study was proceeding according to or ahead of schedule), 2% were delayed, 13 were submitted, and .4% were terminated. Of the 79 postmarketing NDA/ANDA commitments that the FD defined as "concluded," 94% met the commitment, while the study was no longer necessary or feasible for th remaining 6%.

Because differing policies within CDER's review divisions made tracking Phase 4 commitments unmanageab in the past, CDER used an October 1996 MaPP entitled, *Procedures for Tracking and Reviewing Phase 4 Commitmen* (MaPP 6010.2) to standardize the manner in which these commitments are sought, implemented, and tracke MaPP 6010.2 states that CDER's policy regarding Phase 4 commitments will be based on the following requir ments:

- Phase 4 commitments and a schedule for fulfillment of those commitments should be agreed upon with the applicant prior to the approval of an application.
- The agency's approval letter should list all Phase 4 commitments and the schedule for completing each commitment.
- Relevant information regarding Phase 4 study commitments also should be documented in the administrative record. These might include, for example, study objectives, research designs, reporting frequency, and study report formats for clinical studies or test methodology, frequency of testing, and method of data analysis for chemistry commitments. If these details are not determined at the time of approval, this should be noted and a schedule for resolving the issues should be described in the approval letter.
- A Phase 4 tracking system linked to the Centerwide Oracle-based Management Information System (COMIS) will be used to monitor the status of Phase 4 commitments.

Just prior to, or at the time of, NDA approval, a division's project manager (i.e., consumer safety officer) w be responsible for assuring "that the applicant of the pending NDA submits a letter of commitment descri ing any Phase 4 studies they agree to conduct after approval of the application and the schedule for initiatic and completion of those studies and submission of the study results," MaPP 6010.2 states.

For applications that receive accelerated reviews (Subpart H), the division must assure at this time that th Phase 4 study protocols are evaluated for their ability to meet the stated objectives and commitments. Pha 4 protocols for other applications may be submitted following approval, after which CDER must review th protocols "promptly (usually within 30 days)."

At least annually, a division's project manager must evaluate the status of outstanding voluntary Phase 4 commitments and, at least twice annually, must evaluate the status of outstanding Subpart H Phase 4 commitments. "For overdue outstanding commitments (some studies may be time-sensitive and need closer scrutiny), [the project manager must] generate what is called a 'Dunner Letter,'" which is a notification to the sponsor that it has failed to respond to a Phase 4 commitment. Editor's note: "dunner" is a generic term used to refer to a letter that is not an action letter (i.e., approval, approvable, or not-approvable). MaPP 6010.2 does not address compliance actions beyond the issuance of dunner letters.

Various aspects of CDER's postmarketing study commitment effort have been criticized over the years, including what some perceive to be industry's low rate of fulfilling these commitments. Certain industry officials have maintained that some Phase 4 study commitments—as much as a quarter according to one estimate—are unnecessary. Since premarketing studies are growing in size and duration, some within industry believe that the need for Phase 4 studies should be declining.

In August 2004, both the Pharmaceutical Research and Manufacturers of America (PhRMA) and the Biotechnology Industry Organization (BIO) asked the FDA to reassess the necessity of Phase 4 postmarketing testing requirements in many cases. With the increase in Phase 4 studies required by the FDA as part of new drug approvals (see discussion below), the organizations claim that firms will initiate fewer development projects. PhRMA asked the agency to consider establishing "a process for ongoing review by therapeutic area to distinguish necessary Phase IV studies from those that are informative but not required for the safe use of a drug... Absent this process, sponsors can be faced with escalating Phase IV programs with little or no offsetting reduction in the Phase III testing program."

Trends in Postmarketing Commitments for New Drugs Today, only a small handful of new molecular entities (NME) are obtaining FDA approval without a significant postmarketing study commitment by the sponsor, according to a variety of recent studies. A Tufts Center for the Study of Drug Development analysis showed that the FDA requested postmarketing studies for 73% of new molecular entities (NME) approved from 1998 through 2003. Further, a U.S. *Regulatory Reporter* study of the approval letters for the 50 NMEs approved from 2001 through 2003 showed that the prevalence of postmarketing commitments has risen from 75% to almost 90% over this period (see exhibit below).

Percent of NMEs Approved with
Postmarketing Commitments, 2001-2003

	% of NMEs with Postmarketing Commitment
2003	86% (18/21)
2002	82% (14/17)
2001	75%* (18/24)

*drops to 67% if two extremely minor postmarketing commitments not included, one to revise a method to improve specificity and another to provide histopathological exams for animals in a rat carcinogenicity study.

Source: U.S. Regulatory Reporter

The 18 postmarketing commitments agreed to for the 2003-approved NMEs ran the gamut, from agreement to conduct randomized, placebo-controlled studies for further assessing a drug's safety and efficacy to a sir gle nonclinical toxicology study. Not surprisingly, the more demanding postmarketing commitments wer often associated with drugs approved under the FDA's accelerated approval program (Subpart H).

The vast majority of the postmarketing commitments associated with the 2003-approved new drugs called fc significant studies of some sort. In fact, of the 18 NMEs with postmarketing commitments, only three did nc call for the conduct of clinical studies (i.e., Zavesca, Somavert, and Ertaczo).

The Tufts Center for the Study of Drug Development analysis showed that the need for Phase 4 studies ha varied considerably between therapeutic classes. All anti-infective NMEs cleared in 1998-2003, for example required Phase 4 studies, compared to just 36% of the analgesic, anti-inflammatory, and ophthalmic drug approved in the same period.

Post-Approval Risk Management

As noted above, PDUFA III and several agency initiatives have brought a renewed regulatory focus on th postapproval phase of a product's life cycle. While PDUFA I and PDUFA II focused largely on the clinical tes ing and FDA review stages of product development, a primary focus of PDUFA III is on the postapproval phas and drug safety. Pointing out that hundreds of millions of dollars had been targeted at shortening the dru development and approval process under PDUFA I and II, the FDA was able to convince Congress and indus try that the user-fee program should provide funds to upgrade processes to ensure that the products that ai being developed and approved through the agency's speedier review processes are safe and that their risk are properly managed once they reach the market. In total, an estimated $80 million in user fees is to be allc cated to support such activities during the PDUFA III years (FY2003-FY2007).

PDUFA III provides for pre-NDA discussions of risk minimization action plans (RiskMAP, see Chapter 7) an the inclusion of proposed risk management tools (i.e., beyond the package insert). More importantly to th context of this discussion, it introduced the concept of a "peri-approval" period for specific products, an established new FDA authorities and specific sponsor requirements during this period. For drugs submitte on or after October 1, 2002, PDUFA III allows the FDA to tap user fees to review an applicant's implementi tion of a risk management plan "for a period of up to two years post-approval for most products and for a per od of up to three years for products that require risk management beyond standard labeling (e.g., a black bc or bolded warning, medication guide, restricted distribution)."

According to the FDA's user-fee goals and procedures, sponsors must report "issues that arise during impl mentation of the risk management plan (e.g., whether the plan is effective) ...to FDA" in the form of either periodic AE report or NDA annual report (see discussion above).

In a July 2004 response to the FDA's draft guidance entitled, *Development and Use of Risk Minimization Actic Plans*, PhRMA claimed that, under the agency's proposed criteria, "virtually any product on the market coul be determined to need a [risk minimization action plan] of one form or another." PhRMA requested that th FDA revise the guidance to emphasize that RiskMAP's should be considered for "only a limited number products."

CHAPTER 12

The Supplemental NDA and Postapproval Changes to Marketed Drugs

Following a drug's approval, the NDA holder can access and "supplement" the application's data to seek FDA authorization to market variations of the drug beyond those provided for in the approved NDA. Supplemental NDAs (sNDA) are submitted to the FDA when a firm wants to implement certain changes to an approved drug (e.g., dosage form, strength), its specifications, its manufacturing processes, its indication, or its labeling. Federal regulations require that "the applicant...notify the Food and Drug Administration about each change in each condition established in an approved application beyond the variations already provided for in the application."

In practice, sNDAs are submitted to obtain regulatory authorization for a wide variety of modifications to approved drugs. These include proposed changes to an approved drug's manufacturing and control methods (manufacturing supplement), dosage form or route of administration, indication (efficacy supplement), ingredients or strength, dosage schedule, labeling, and container and closure system.

Perhaps more than any other aspect of FDA drug regulation, requirements for sNDAs have been modified almost continually by regulatory reform initiatives beginning in the mid-1990s. These agency-adopted reforms did not affect the nature or function of the supplemental NDA, but rather the situations in which such submissions are needed and the data and information that such filings must include. Today, a new wave of reform initiatives continues to affect sNDA requirements, particularly those relevant to postmarketing manufacturing-related changes (see discussion below).

Recent History of Regulatory Reform and sNDAs Over the past decade, the most significant regulatory reforms affecting sNDAs have addressed the review and approval of manufacturing changes. In early 1995, the FDA promised to issue a guidance document that would "reduce the number of manufacturing changes that require preapproval by FDA." The agency fulfilled this commitment by publishing a November 1995 guideline that established submission requirements for a variety of postapproval manufacturing and drug composition changes to immediate release solid oral dosage form drugs (see discussion below). Specifically, the guideline exempted more types of manufacturing process, site, equipment, and formulation changes from the requirement for FDA approval prior to implementation. This guideline has since been followed by other guidances applicable to other dosage forms.

In March 1997, following months of industry/FDA negotiations and agency efforts to find ways to encourage drug companies to develop and submit sNDAs for new uses of approved drugs, the agency unveiled what it called the

New Use Initiative. The goal of this initiative was "to speed up the development of new and supplemental uses of medications by using all available data to determine the effectiveness of drugs and biological products."

Essentially, the agency's *New Use Initiative* comprised two guidances that clarified efficacy data requirements for new and supplemental uses. The guidances establish that the FDA is willing to accept efficacy data from variety of different sources (i.e., not just from two pivotal trials) as the basis for approving supplemental use (see discussion below).

These initiatives were followed, in November 1997, by a series of reforms brought by the FDA Modernization Act of 1997 (FDAMA). The reforms, which did not formally take effect until late 1999 and which in many ways mirrored the initiatives discussed above, were intended to streamline sNDAs for manufacturing changes, new indications, and other types of postapproval modifications.

With regard to manufacturing changes, the FDA reform legislation provided that a company must submit, and obtain FDA approval for, a supplemental NDA before implementing a "major" manufacturing change. Other changes may be implemented either after an sNDA has been filed (i.e., a changes-being-effected supplement or a changes-being-effected-in-30-days supplement) or immediately without an sNDA submission (i.e., minor changes to be reported in an NDA annual report). FDAMA also called on the agency to issue new sNDA standards and guidances, and to take steps to provide a higher profile for and facilitate the review of supplemental applications. Although these and related FDAMA provisions for manufacturing-related sNDAs became effective in November 1999, the FDA did not revise its regulations to reflect these changes until April 2000 (see discussion below).

Pharmaceutical cGMPs for the 21st Century Initiative and Implications for sNDAs In September 2004, the FDA announced the results of a two-year review of its pharmaceutical, current Good Manufacturing Practice (cGMP), and chemistry, manufacturing and controls (CMC) regulatory review programs. The review was undertaken with numerous objectives, including to encourage the early adoption of new technological advances in pharmaceutical manufacturing, to facilitate industry's implementation of quality systems approaches to all aspects of pharmaceutical production and quality assurance, and to encourage the implementation of risk based approaches that focus both industry and FDA attention on critical areas.

After completing the wide-ranging assessment of current practices and newly available tools to enhance manufacturing science, the agency unveiled, in September 2004, "a new framework for the regulatory oversight of manufacturing quality that is based on quality systems and risk management approaches." The agency's new framework will have several important implications for postapproval manufacturing changes, including sNDA submission requirements and the FDA's process for reviewing postapproval manufacturing changes. In its September 2004 final report entitled, *Pharmaceutical CGMPs for the 21st Century-A Risk-Based Approach*, the FDA stated that:

> "The Office of New Drug Chemistry (ONDC) within CDER has developed and is implementing a new risk-based pharmaceutical quality assessment system to replace its current CMC review process. This new system should reduce the need to submit manufacturing supplements and increase first-cycle approval of new drug applications, thereby making drug products available to patients in a timelier manner. The system should also encourage manufacturers to implement new technologies, such as process analytical technology, and facilitate continuous manufacturing improvements."

In implementing this new system, ONDC will be reorganizing and revising its approach to CMC reviews of both IND/NDAs and sNDAs. While CDER's traditional review process has relied on a single chemistry reviewer evaluate the entire CMC section of a drug application throughout the entire product lifecycle—IND through NDA through postapproval supplements—the nature and complexity of modern pharmaceutical manufacturing point up the need for a new system, the agency stated. In the restructured ONDC, the IND/NDA and CMC supplement review functions will be separated to address the critical CMC issues more expeditiously in both the preapproval and postapproval areas. The restructuring, whose implementation is expected to be simultaneous with CDER's larger reorganization and its move to consolidated offices in spring 2005, will involve the following:

- The formation, within ONDC, of separate, dedicated premarketing and postmarketing chemistry divisions that will be responsible for IND/NDA and sNDA review functions, respectively, to improve efficiency and effectiveness in each area. Chemists in the premarketing division may consult, when necessary, with the postmarketing divisions.

- As part of the reorganization, the review chemists that will support the respective new drug review divisions will no longer be located in the drug review groups that they support, but will be housed within ONDC's new premarketing and postmarketing divisions. According to ONDC officials, however, the review chemists will continue to specialize in and be dedicated to specific therapeutic areas and divisions.

- Like the premarketing division, the postmarketing chemistry division will feature a pharmaceutical assessment lead (PAL), who will perform an initial assessment of each CMC supplement to determine if it needs further evaluation. The PAL will perform a brief review for minor CMC changes or, if necessary, develop an assessment protocol and review timeline for major CMC changes before assigning the sNDA to a reviewer. As a first step in the transition to the new PAL-led model, ONDC is having their lead chemists "triage" incoming sNDAs to determine the filability of the application, the degree of review needed for the specific manufacturing change proposed, and the likely review process and resources needed for the review.

In NDAs, the FDA will also be seeking more information in certain areas—pharmaceutical development information and descriptions of design considerations—that might ultimately reduce the need for manufacturing-related sNDAs later in the process. To facilitate continuous improvement and manufacturing process optimization, the FDA says that its new pharmaceutical quality assessment system will focus on risk-based assessments relying on available knowledge about the product and manufacturing process.

ONDC's new postmarketing division expects to be able to streamline the sNDA review process "based on the degree of process understanding exhibited in the application and the extent of controls and quality systems that have been implemented throughout the applicant's manufacturing process." The FDA believes that the approach can reduce the frequency and extent of the prior review of manufacturing changes by the agency.

A central element in the agency's shift to a risk-based approach to postapproval manufacturing changes, and a reduction in the need for sNDAs to support such changes, will be a forthcoming guidance on comparability protocols. In a September 2003 draft guidance entitled, *Comparability Protocols— Protein Drug Products and Biological Products-Chemistry, Manufacturing, and Control Information*, the agency provided recommendations for preparing and using comparability protocols, which are "predefined change evaluation plans" through which firms can justify reduced reporting categories for specific manufacturing changes. The FDA is now finalizing the guidance "to incorporate the tenets of the risk-based approach to ensuring reductions in postapproval manufacturing changes and to ensure that appropriate manufacturing science is incorporated in the decision-making processes."

When to Submit Supplemental versus Original NDAs

In earlier years, sponsors often had the option of submitting either full or supplemental NDAs for drug changes that required FDA approval before their formal implementation. Some companies maintained that sNDAs had certain advantages over full submissions, while others held that original NDAs should have been submitted whenever possible.

Under policies instituted as part of the FDA's user-fee program, however, such options no longer exist in most cases. Because different fees apply to certain original and supplemental NDAs, the agency now specifies when each type of application should be used. In a guidance document entitled, *Separate Marketing Applications and Clinical Data for Purposes of Assessing User Fees Under the Prescription Drug User Fee Act of* 1992, the FDA specifies when original and supplemental NDAs are appropriate for changes to approved products:

1. Changes in the composition of an approved product to support a change in the dosage form or route of administration should be submitted in separate original NDAs. Route of administration changes in which the new product remains quantitatively and qualitatively identical to the approved product in composition (e.g., an injectable liquid dosage form intended for use by the intravenous and intraperitoneal routes) can be submitted in sNDAs, however. Also eligible for sNDAs are dosage form changes in which the new product is identical to the approved product in quantitative and qualitative composition (e.g., a sterile liquid in a single dose vial that is intended for use as either an injectable or an inhalation solution).

2. Modifications to an approved product that are based on chemistry, manufacturing, or controls data and bioequivalence or other studies (e.g., safety and immunogenicity) and that change the strength or concentration, change the manufacturing process, equipment or facility, or change the formulation (e.g., different excipients) should be submitted as supplements to an approved application. Ordinarily, such modifications do not warrant a new original application unless they involve a change in the dosage form or route of administration.

3. Requests for approval of a new indication, or a modification of a previously approved indication, should each be submitted individually in a separate supplement to an approved NDA. According to the FDA, "each indication is considered a separate change for which a separate supplement should be submitted. The policy allows FDA to approve each indication when it is ready for approval rather than delaying approval until the last of a group of indications is ready to be approved."

The FDA's user-fee policies have had several other implications for sNDAs. Sponsors of supplements that require clinical data to support approval must pay user fees for such applications, for example.

On the other hand, the FDA's user-fee program also provides many sNDAs with a significantly higher level of review priority. Under PDUFA III, for example, the agency has the following goals for sNDAs submitted from FY2003-FY2007: to review 90% of priority efficacy supplements within 6 months; to review 90% of standard efficacy supplements within 10 months; and to review 90% of all manufacturing supplements within 6 month and those requiring prior approval within 4 months. In addition, the agency also faces review performance goals for resubmitted efficacy supplements and for early-stage communications of deficiencies discovered in efficacy supplements (i.e., 74-day letters, see Chapter 8).

Supplemental NDA Submission Requirements

No universal sNDA data submission requirements exist. The nature of the change proposed in an sNDA directly determines the testing and submission requirements applicable to the change. Federal regulations state that "the information required in the supplement is limited to that needed to support the change."

Obviously, changes to a drug's indication, ingredients, or route of administration are likely to require clinical data to prove the product's safety and effectiveness. In contrast, some modifications to a drug's manufacturing or control methods may require only that the change be described and supported by stability and bioequivalence data (Note: No drug produced through a manufacturing change, whether significant or otherwise, may be distributed before the NDA holder validates the change's effects on the product's identity, strength, quality, purity, and potency). Therefore, sNDAs can range from minor filings to documents longer and more complex than some NDAs. All sNDAs, however, must provide an archival copy and a review copy that include an application form, appropriate technical sections, samples, and labeling.

The nature of the change proposed in an sNDA also determines when the application must be submitted and whether the sponsor must await FDA approval prior to implementing the change. In its regulations and relevant guidance documents, the FDA has categorized postapproval changes into various classes. Those changes that are most likely to affect the FDA's conclusions about the approved drug's safety and effectiveness require the submission, and FDA approval, of an sNDA prior to implementation. Less significant changes do not require FDA approval, but may require either the submission of an sNDA at the time of implementation or a description in the sponsor's annual report.

Postmarketing Manufacturing Changes

Although they attempted to ease regulatory burdens associated with postapproval manufacturing changes, a variety of legal and regulatory initiatives undertaken in the mid- and late 1990s have done much to complicate any attempt to characterize the regulatory requirements associated with such modifications. For several years stretching from 1997 through 2004, regulatory requirements for postmarketing manufacturing changes were dictated primarily by FDAMA provisions, by a November 1999 guidance document that provides agency recommendations on the FDAMA provisions, and by a series of guidances on postapproval manufacturing changes to drugs with certain types of dosage forms (see discussion below on scale-up and postapproval changes (SUPAC) below). In April 2004, however, the FDA released a comprehensive final regulation to implement FDAMA's provisions regarding postmarketing manufacturing changes. At the same time, the agency released a final guidance document entitled, *Changes to an Approved* NDA *or* ANDA, which replaced an identically titled November 1999 guidance.

As noted above, industry will have to monitor the FDA's progress in implementing its new "framework for the regulatory oversight of manufacturing quality" and its effects on reporting requirements for postapproval manufacturing changes. The agency's new framework will have several important implications for postapproval manufacturing changes, including requirements for sNDA submissions and the FDA's process for reviewing postapproval manufacturing changes.

FDAMA and Postmarketing Manufacturing Changes FDAMA's Section 116 first became the basis for sNDA submission requirements facing postapproval manufacturing changes in November 1999, the established effective date for this section of the law. Because the agency was unable to issue final regulations to implement Section 116 by this date, this FDAMA section replaced the existing regulations (CFR 314.70-Supplements and other changes to an approved application), and the agency stated that the section would serve as "the sole basis for FDA's regulation of postapproval manufacturing changes for products approved in" NDAs and ANDAs until implementing regulations are published.

This was largely the case until April 2004, when the agency released regulations implementing FDAMA' Section 116. Along with several initiatives under the agency's *Pharmaceutical cGMPs for the 21st Century Initiati* (see Chapter 11) and the agency's SUPAC guidances (see discussion below), Section 116 was seen as the ne> step in the agency's so-called risk-based approach, which seeks to reduce regulatory burdens for minor mar ufacturing changes and to focus industry and FDA resources on those changes that are likely to have the mos important public health implications.

The April 2004 FDA regulation and the *Changes to an Approved* NDA *and* ANDA guidance establish reporting cat egories (e.g., different types of sNDAs, annual report) for various postapproval changes, most of which ar manufacturing-related: components and composition; manufacturing sites; manufacturing process; specifica tions; container closure systems; miscellaneous changes; and multiple related changes. The regulation an guidance also address postmarketing labeling changes as well (see discussion below).

The April 2004 FDA regulations and accompanying guidance establish reporting categories that are, in mos respects, similar to those defined in earlier SUPAC guidances (see discussion below). In implementin FDAMA, however, the regulation and guidance provide for two categories of "changes being effected" sNDA for manufacturing changes. Further, the agency notes that, whenever the regulation and guidance's reportin categories are inconsistent with those in the SUPAC guidances, the regulation/guidance supersedes th SUPAC guidances. Because neither the regulation nor guidance provides extensive recommendations o reporting categories for components and composition changes, however, the agency recommends that spor sors refer to recommendations in previous guidances, particularly the SUPAC guidances, for such changes.

FDAMA and the April 2004 guidance establish four types of changes (and reporting categories) based on the potential to adversely affect the identity, strength, quality, or potency of a product as they may relate to th drug's safety or effectiveness:

Major Change-Prior Approval Supplement. A change that has a substantial potential to adversely affect a produ is considered a "major change," and requires the submission, and FDA approval, of a "prior approval supple ment" before the distribution of a product manufactured using the specified change. A sponsor can reque: that the FDA expedite the review of a prior approval supplement due to public health reasons (e.g., drug shor age) or if a delay in implementing the change would impose an "extraordinary hardship" on the applican Examples of manufacturing changes that would be considered major changes include modifications that ma affect the controlled (or modified) release, metering or other characteristics (e.g., particle size) of the dos delivered to the patient, any fundamental modification in the manufacturing process or technology (e.g., fo drug products, changing from a dry to wet granulation or a change from one type of drying process to anotl er), and establishing a new procedure for reprocessing a batch of drug substance or drug product that fails t meet the approved specification.

Moderate Change-Changes Being Effected in 30 Days Supplement. A change that has a "moderate potential" t adversely affect a product will, unless identified by the FDA as being eligible for a "changes being effecte supplement (see discussion below), require a "changes being effected in 30 days supplemental NDA." Th type of moderate change requires the submission of an sNDA at least 30 days before the distribution of th product made using the change. If the agency does not contact the applicant within this 30-day period, th company is free to distribute the product. However, the FDA may contact the sponsor within the 30-day pei od to inform the company that a prior approval supplement is required for the change or that the suppleme is incomplete. The company would then have to delay distribution until a prior approval supplement is sul mitted and approved (i.e., if one is required) or, if the supplement is deemed incomplete, delay distribution until the supplement is amended with the missing information. After its review, the agency may also order that the manufacturer cease distribution if the FDA disapproves the supplemental application. Examples of changes in specifications that would require a changes being effected in 30 days supplement include a change in the regulatory analytical procedure (other than those identified as major changes or editorial changes) or any relaxation in an acceptance criterion or deletion of a test to comply with an official compendium that is consistent with FDA statutory and regulatory requirements.

Moderate Change-Changes Being Effected Supplement. If the agency identifies a change that has a moderate potential to adversely affect a product as a change that can be implemented upon an sNDA's submission, the sponsor can implement the modification after the agency receives the supplement supporting the change. This type of supplement is called a "changes being effected" supplement. If the agency disapproves a change under a changes being effected supplement, it can then order the firm to cease distribution of the drugs made using the disapproved change. Examples of moderate changes in the container closure system that can be submitted in a changes being effected supplement include a change in the size and/or shape of a container for a nonsterile drug product (except for solid dosage forms) without a change from one container closure system to another, and a change in or the addition or deletion of a desiccant.

Minor Change-Annual Report. A change that has a minimal potential to adversely affect a drug product does not require an sNDA. Rather, the applicant need only describe minor changes in its subsequent annual report to the approved NDA. Examples of manufacturing changes that would be considered minor changes include minor modifications in an existing code imprint for a dosage form (e.g., changing from a numeric to an alphanumeric code) and a change in the order of addition of ingredients for solution dosage forms or solutions used in unit operations (e.g., granulation solutions).

In discussing these reporting categories, the agency notes that sponsors can use what are called "comparability protocols" to reduce the reporting category for specific changes. Proposed comparability protocols, which describe the tests, validation studies, and acceptable limits to be achieved in demonstrating the absence of an adverse effect caused by a manufacturing-related change, can be submitted either in an original NDA or as a prior approval sNDA. In 2003, the FDA released a pair of draft guidances regarding comparability protocols: *Comparability Protocols-Chemistry, Manufacturing, and Controls Information* (February 2003) and *Comparability Protocols-Protein Drug Products and Biological Products-Chemistry, Manufacturing, and Controls Information* (September 2003). As noted above, the FDA plans to finalize the September 2003 guidance to incorporate the tenets of CDER's emerging "risk-based approach to ensuring reductions in postapproval manufacturing changes and to ensure that appropriate manufacturing science is incorporated in the decision-making processes."

Neither FDAMA nor the April 2004 regulation (or accompanying guidance document) addresses either sNDA submission requirements or agency review targets for such applications. sNDA submission requirements are addressed more fully in existing agency guidances, the SUPAC guidances in particular (see discussion below), the FDA notes, while review goals are specified in the agency's PDUFA III commitments and in the agency's May 1998 guidance entitled, *Standards for the Prompt Review of Efficacy Supplements, Including Priority Efficacy Supplements.*

SUPAC and SNDAs for Manufacturing Changes Before FDAMA's Section 116 regulations took effect in November 1999, a series of guidances on scale-up and postapproval changes—called SUPAC guidances—had been the key regulatory documents defining requirements associated with postapproval manufacturing changes for several types of products (i.e., other than the regulations for such changes). From November 199 through 1999, CDER published SUPAC guidances applicable to several different types of drug dosage forms

Although the provisions of FDAMA and its April 2004 implementing regulations now represent the basis fc reporting requirements for all postapproval manufacturing changes, the SUPAC guidances remain relevant i several respects. As noted above, they continue to provide the most detailed guidance on reporting categorie for postapproval changes in drug components and composition. In addition, unlike FDA regulations and exis ing guidance documents, the various SUPAC guidances provide recommendations on the data and informa tion that must be developed and submitted to support various postmarketing manufacturing changes.

While agency officials have claimed in the past that they would continue to update the existing SUPAC guidance and develop and publish new SUPAC documents, the FDA is now busy re-evaluating all relevant guidance doc uments in view of the April 2004 regulations and ongoing cGMP initiative. At a minimum, the FDA plans to revis the SUPAC guidances to harmonize them with the April 2004 guidance. CDER officials caution, however, tha their re-evaluation could result in more significant steps, such as the merging of various agency guidances.

The FDA's first SUPAC guidance, a 1995 guidance document entitled, *Immediate Release Solid Oral Dosage Form Scale-Up and Post Approval Changes* (SUPAC-IR): *Chemistry, Manufacturing and Controls; In Vitro Dissolution Testing; I Vivo Bioequivalence Documentation*, revised the sNDA requirements applicable to postapproval manufacturin changes for relevant drug products. The November 1995 document was only the first in a series of SUPA guidances for drugs in a variety of dosage forms. CDER has since released SUPAC guidances for modifie release solid oral dosage forms (October 1997) and nonsterile semisolid dosage forms (June 1997), and January 1999 guidance that addresses immediate release and modified release solid oral dosage form equir ment changes. In addition, CDER released an April 1998 SUPAC guidance for postapproval changes to ana lytical testing laboratories (PAC-ATLS). In late 1998, CDER released a pair of draft SUPAC guidances: November 1998 draft guidance on chemistry, manufacturing and controls documentation needed in submis sions to support postapproval changes in the manufacturing or specifications of intermediates used in th synthesis of bulk drug ingredients (BACPAC I); and a December 1998 draft manufacturing equipment adder dum to the June 1997 nonsterile semisolid dosage form SUPAC guidance.

The published SUPAC-IR guidance—and the subsequent SUPAC guidances—classified postapproval manu facturing changes into as many as three levels—Levels 1, 2, and 3—and established postmarketing reportir requirements for changes within each of these levels (i.e., sNDA, annual report). The agency has defined thes levels broadly for each type of change. The following levels apply to SUPAC-IR component, composition, ar process changes, for example:

> *Level* 1: changes that are unlikely to have any detectable impact on formulation, quality, or performance.
>
> *Level* 2: changes that could have a significant impact on formulation, quality, or performance.
>
> *Level* 3: changes that are likely to have a significant impact on formulation, quality, or per formance.

It is worth noting that some types of changes, such as manufacturing changes, have only two levels in th SUPAC guidances.

For each type of postapproval manufacturing change addressed by the SUPAC-IR document—components ar composition changes, manufacturing site changes, scale up/scale down of manufacture, and manufacturir process/equipment changes—the level of the change and the testing and reporting requirements (e.g., sNDA, annual report) associated with the change are established. Generally, the less significant SUPAC-IR changes—most Level 1 changes, for example—require only a description in an annual report. The more important changes—most Level 3 changes, for instance—call for the submission and FDA approval of an sNDA prior to implementation (i.e., a "prior approval" supplement). Many Level 2 changes can be implemented simultaneously with an applicant's submission of a "changes being effected" supplement.

As noted above, however, the reporting categories in the SUPAC guidances are superseded by those within the April 2004 *Changes to an Approved* NDA *or* ANDA guidance whenever they differ.

Expedited Review for NDA Chemistry Supplements Under agency regulations, NDA holders have the right to request that the agency expedite its review of any supplemental NDA requiring prior approval "for public health reasons or if a delay in making the change described in it would impose an extraordinary hardship on the applicant." In an internal policy manual entitled, *Requests for Expedited Review of* NDA *Chemistry Supplements* (MaPP 5310.3, June 1999), CDER provided guidance on the submission and review of expedited review requests for NDA chemistry supplements.

Under MaPP 5310.3, expedited review for chemistry sNDAs may be granted when an application is relevant to a public health need (e.g., drug availability), extraordinary hardship on the applicant (e.g., catastrophic event such as a fire) or unforeseeable events (e.g., the abrupt discontinuation of active ingredient supply), or agency need (e.g., government drug purchase program). According to CDER's internal policy, expedited review will be considered "only when there is sufficient documentation to support a need for review in less than four months." The document also notes that "granting of an expedited review does not change the information that should be submitted in the supplement to support the change." In such cases, the applicant must mark its supplement and mailing cover with the following statement: "Supplement-Expedited Review Requested."

"Bundled" CMC Supplements In early 2000, CDER established a "bundling coordinator" to coordinate the center's processes for handling so-called "bundled supplements," which are groups or clusters of NDA or ANDA supplements for chemistry, manufacturing, and controls changes that affect more than one original submission and that will be reviewed in multiple review divisions. The center laid out its plans for processing bundled supplements in a January 2000 MaPP entitled, *Review of the Same Supplemental Change to More than One* NDA *or* ANDA *in More than One Review Division* (MaPP 5015.6).

After an applicant notifies CDER that it plans to submit a supplement for a change that will affect applications in multiple review teams, divisions, or offices, the bundling coordinator and Office of New Drug Chemistry (ONDC) managers will determine if the change can be submitted in a bundled supplement. If the center decides to accept a bundled submission, it will identify a "lead ONDC chemistry team" for the review based on the team that has the most supplements (within that set, the oldest NDA will be designated the "lead NDA"). After the team assigns a chemistry team leader, a lead reviewer will be assigned. The bundling coordinator will distribute a memo to all chemistry team leaders, project managers, and document room staffers who will be involved in the reviews of the various supplements, and will track the progress of the reviews of the bundled supplements. While the various supplement review teams will work together through the lead reviewer, each team is responsible for issuing its own action letter.

At this writing, it was not yet clear how the existing sNDA bundling process would be affected by the ONDC restructuring and chemistry sNDA-related reforms associated with the Pharmaceutical cGMPs for the 21st Century Initiative (see discussion above).

Labeling Changes

Although the FDA's April 2004 *Changes to an Approved* NDA *or* ANDA guidance focuses primarily upon postmarketing manufacturing changes, it also addresses postapproval changes in other areas, such as labeling changes. Labeling changes cover a wide array of modifications, ranging from changes in a container label layout to the addition of new indications.

All significant, or "major," postmarketing drug labeling changes must be approved by the FDA before implementation. Although some labeling changes of lesser importance can be made prior to approval (see discussion below), changes such as the addition of new indications, changes in dosage strengths, changes in dosage form, and changes in recommended dosage schedules require the submission, and FDA approval, of an sNDA before implementation.

As it does for postmarketing manufacturing changes, the *Changes to an Approved* NDA *or* ANDA guidance specifies three different reporting categories for labeling changes:

Major Labeling Changes. As noted, all major changes require the submission and approval of an sNDA before being implemented. The guidance specifies that any change in the labeling, except those designated as moderate or minor change by regulation or guidance, be submitted as a prior approval supplement. Major changes include labeling changes based on postmarketing study results, the addition of pharmacoeconomic claims based on clinical studies, the addition of superiority claims over another product, and the expansion or contraction of the target patient population based on data. Although the addition of new indications (see discussion below), dosage strengths, and dosage forms, among other labeling changes, are not specifically listed in the guidance, it is assumed that such changes will always require a prior approval sNDA given the nature and given that they are not specifically listed as moderate or minor changes.

Moderate Labeling Changes. The April 2004 guidance provides examples only of moderate labeling changes for which a changes being effected supplement must be submitted (i.e., there are no references to moderate changes for which a changes being effected in 30 days sNDA must be filed). Moderate changes for which changes being effected supplements are required include: (1) the addition or strengthening of a contraindication, warning, precaution, or adverse reaction; (2) the addition or strengthening of a statement regarding drug abuse, dependence, psychological effect, or overdosage; (3) the addition or strengthening of an instruction regarding dosage and administration intended to further promote the safe use of the product; or (4) the deletion of false, misleading, or unsupported indications for use or claims for effectiveness.

Minor Labeling Changes. Labeling modifications that involve editorial or similar minor changes, or changes in the information concerning the description of the drug product or information on how the drug is supplied (i.e., not involving a change in dosage strength or dosage form) do not require the submission of an sNDA and need only be described in an annual report to the NDA. Examples of such modifications include the addition of a distributor's name, foreign language versions of the labeling (assuming no change is made to the content of the approved labeling and that a certified translation is included), and changes in the layout of the package or container label that are consistent with FDA regulations and that do not involve a change in labeling content.

To expedite the often-lengthy labeling review process, CDER officials began moving toward the electronic submission of the complete package insert during 2000. Ultimately, the center hopes to permit labeling submissions to be made, and related negotiations to be conducted, electronically. To this end, the FDA issued

December 2003 final regulation to require that companies submitting NDAs file a new section, called the "content of labeling" section, in electronic form (see Chapter 7). The agency is requiring this new section of the NDA, which comprises the package insert, including all text, tables and figures, to streamline the drug labeling review process and to expedite the approval of postapproval labeling changes.

Pursuing New Indications for Approved Drugs Despite the past and current level of regulatory activity regarding supplemental applications for postmarketing manufacturing supplements, sNDAs for new indications generally are more visible than most other types of supplements. Because these "efficacy supplements," as they are called, often propose therapeutically significant new uses for approved drugs, they are given a higher regulatory priority than other sNDAs. Under the user-fee program, for example, the FDA's review goals for priority efficacy supplements are identical to those for original NDAs.

Furthermore, FDAMA required the agency to publish standards for the prompt review of "supplemental applications submitted for approved articles," something that the statute's legislative history suggests means efficacy supplements. The agency decided to use the previously established user-fee review goals to fulfill this FDAMA requirement. FDAMA also called for the agency to issue a guidance to specify the types of efficacy supplements that would be eligible for priority review, a requirement that the agency met by releasing an industry guidance entitled, *Standards for the Prompt Review of Efficacy Supplements, Including Priority Efficacy Supplements* (May 1998). In this guidance, the agency establishes that sNDAs will be subject to the same priority review criteria applicable to NDAs—an sNDA will receive priority designation if the product "would be a significant improvement, compared to marketed products, including non-drug products/therapies in the treatment, diagnosis, or prevention of a disease."

Actually, FDAMA was only the latest of several developments that have affected regulatory requirements for sNDAs over the last decade. In the mid-1990s, the FDA's requirements for efficacy supplements had come under fire during the regulatory reform movement. Following months of efforts to find ways to encourage companies to develop and submit sNDAs for new uses of approved drugs, the FDA unveiled its so-called "New Use Initiative" in March 1997. This initiative was designed to give "industry clear guidance on whether the agency can determine that a drug is effective for a new use without requiring data from two new clinical trials. In some cases, for example, a drug's effectiveness can be extrapolated from existing efficacy data; it can be shown by evidence from a new single trial supported by already existing related clinical data; or it can be documented by adequate evidence from a single multi-center study."

The New Use Initiative comprised two guidelines—*Providing Clinical Evidence of Effectiveness for Human Drug and Biological Products* (May 1998) and FDA *Approval of New Cancer Treatment Uses for Marketed Drug and Biological Drugs* (December 1998). These guidelines provide what might be the most detailed discussion to date on the agency's efficacy standards for new and supplemental indications (for a further discussion of these guidelines, see Chapter 5). The December 1998 guidance provides the most direct, if brief, discussion of data requirements for supplemental indications:

"To add new use information to the labeling of a marketed product, a holder of an approved marketing application must submit a supplemental marketing application that provides data establishing the safety and effectiveness of the product for the proposed new indication... The application should include all relevant data available from pertinent clinical studies, including negative or ambiguous results as well as positive findings. Data can come from pharmaceutical company-sponsored clinical trials intended to test the safety and effectiveness of a new use of a product, or from a number of alternative sources... To support approval, the data submitted should be sufficient in quality and quantity to establish the safety and effectiveness of the produc with a high level of confidence, as required by law and scientific expectations."

In an October 2001 guidance entitled, *Cancer Drug and Biological Products-Clinical Data in Marketing Application* however, the FDA suggests that industry may be collecting more data in cancer trials than are necessary fc the approval of original or supplemental NDAs for cancer therapies. "Representatives of...noncommerci sponsors [such as cancer cooperative groups] have told FDA that commercial sponsors often encourage co lection of more data than the investigators would normally collect," says the guidance. "In fact, many of thes data may not be called for in a marketing application for cancer therapy. It is possible that industry repre sentatives are using data submission standards for marketing applications for less serious diseases c assuming standards that could be modified in many situations."

Approval Times for Efficacy Supplements In recent years, CDER's median total approval times for effic cy supplements have closely tracked the user-fee review goals for the applications. For priority efficacy sur plements cleared from 1998-2003, CDER's median review time was 6.0 months. For standard effica supplements cleared during 2002 and 2003, CDER's median review time was 10.0 months, down from 11. months in 2001 and 17.8 months in 1995.

CHAPTER 13

The FDA's Orphan Drug Development Program

Although orphan drugs represent only a minor percentage of the medicines prescribed in the United States, these products have gained an exceptionally high profile in recent decades. Early in the 1980s, for example, orphan drugs became not only the subject of major legislation, but the focus of an FDA office devoted solely to their development as well.

Regulatory, legal, and commercial controversies surrounding better-known orphan drugs, such as Genentech's human growth hormone and Amgen's erythropoietin, have done much to bring widespread attention to orphan products and industry efforts to develop and market these medicines. In part representing the government's response to these controversies, FDA regulations implementing the key elements of the orphan drug law were released in December 1992.

Despite various legislative and judicial challenges, the FDA's orphan drug development program has stood largely intact over its 21-year history. The program was one of relatively few of the agency's drug approval-related activities not earmarked for reform under several FDA reform bills debated in the mid-1990s.[1] In addition, the U.S. orphan drugs program has been the model for similar programs in both Europe and Japan.[2]

The special problems and issues facing orphan product development are well documented. Orphan products are unique because they are potentially useful drugs, biologics, and antibiotics that have limited commercial value. There are several reasons why they may lack profit potential—for example, a product may be used to treat a disease with a small patient population, it may be used only in minute doses, or it may have an unfavorable patent status.

In the past, few companies were willing to invest in an experimental drug whose potential sales did not justify, or whose actual sales might not even recover, these expenditures. Individuals suffering from such rare conditions as Turner's Syndrome, central precocious puberty, acute graft v. host disease (GVHD), and cystinosis were caught between the medical reality that few others shared their plight and the economic reality that a drug's development can cost several hundred million dollars.

Thanks to orphan drug legislation and the FDA's own efforts to shepherd these products through the development process, however, the last two decades brought no dearth of firms willing to invest in orphan products. According to FDA statistics, there were approximately 1,100 active orphan drug designations and 250 approved orphan drugs and biologics as of year-end 2003.

The FDA and Orphan Drugs: A Brief History

During the late 1970s, government leaders became increasingly concerned that the therapeutic abilities c many drugs went unexplored while millions of patients with one of an estimated 5,000 rare or orphan disease went untreated. A 1979 report by the FDA-organized Interagency Task Force on Significant Drugs of Limite Commercial Value stated that, "whenever a drug has been identified as potentially life-saving or otherwise c unique major benefit to some patient, it is the obligation of society, as represented by government, to see to make that drug available to that patient." The formal government response to the problem came sever years later in the form of the Orphan Drug Act of 1983, a law that provides incentives for manufacturers t develop and market orphan products, including drugs, antibiotics and biologics.

Responsibility for administering the law was given to the FDA's Office of Orphan Product Development (OPD which was founded in 1982. Today, the 24-person office continues to encourage orphan drug development b awarding financial incentives available under the law to sponsors of qualifying products, coordinating th efforts of investigators and drug companies, acting as a mediator between orphan sponsors and the FDA drug and biologic review divisions, administering a grant program, and performing other promotional an educational activities.

The Significance of Orphan Drug Designation

The incentives offered under the Orphan Drug Act are seen as the keys to orphan product development in th United States. The law provides major financial and marketing incentives to companies and investigators wil ing to research and develop qualified products. But before outlining the orphan product incentives them selves, it is worthwhile discussing orphan drug designation, a status that drugs must attain to become eligibl for the most valuable incentives.

Tax advantages and marketing exclusivity are perhaps the two most important incentives that the U. Congress made available to orphan product sponsors through the Orphan Drug Act of 1983. Since Congres did not want these incentives to be awarded indiscriminately, it wrote into law that only products meetin specific criteria would be eligible for the two principal benefits.

Today, there are at least five basic eligibility criteria for orphan drug designation. To be eligible, a product:

- Must be a drug, biologic, or antibiotic. Medical devices, medical foods, and other products do not qualify for designation.

- Must have a sponsor that is testing or is planning to test the product for use in a "rare disease or condition." According to the Orphan Drug Act, a rare disease or condition is one that: "A) affects less than 200,000 persons in the United States, or B) affects more than 200,000 persons in the United States but for which there is no reasonable expectation that the costs of developing and making available in the United States a drug for such disease or condition will be recovered from sales in the United States for such drug." The under-200,000 provision applies not only to diseases or conditions with a total patient prevalence of less than 200,000, but to subpopulations of more common diseases as well. The FDA insists that sponsors of orphan products for such indications be able to test the product in, and clearly label the product for, use in the relevant subpopulation. For prophylactic products such as vaccines and blood products, the figure of 200,000 applies to the number of patients receiving the product per year.

- Must not have been previously approved under a new drug application (NDA) or product license application/biological license application (BLA) for the disease or condition for which the sponsor is seeking orphan status. In other words, eligible products include both new molecular entities (NME)—substances never before approved as medicines in the United States—and products that have been approved for any indication other than the indication for which the sponsor is seeking orphan designation. When granted by the FDA, designation applies only to the subject product for use in the specific rare disease or condition.

- Must be shown to have an adequate pharmacologic rationale for use in the orphan indication. Historically, the FDA has not enforced this requirement rigidly. In a 1984 speech, Dr. Marion Finkel, former director of the FDA's Office of Orphan Products Development, stated that "a plausible hypothesis backed by some experimental evidence would be sufficient for orphan drug designation."

- Must not be the subject of a marketing application submitted prior to the filing of an orphan status request. This requirement was added in mid-1988 through the Orphan Drug Amendment Act of 1987. The amendment was an attempt by Congress to reserve marketing exclusivity and tax incentives for those firms whose initial intentions were to develop orphan drugs, and to withhold the incentives from companies that pursue designation simply as an afterthought to optimize the profitability of their products.

Obtaining Orphan Drug Designation Congress gave the FDA the authority to determine which drugs meet the criteria outlined above. To have its product designated, a firm must submit to the FDA an application called a Request for Designation of a Drug as an Orphan Drug.

The FDA's 1992 orphan drug regulations specify nine basic submission requirements for designation requests. According to these regulations, a sponsor must submit two copies of a completed, dated, and signed designation request that contains the following:

- A statement that the sponsor requests orphan-drug designation for a rare disease or condition, which must be identified with specificity.

- The name and address of the sponsor; the name and address of the sponsor's primary contact person and/or resident agent, including the person's title, address, and telephone number; the drug's generic and trade name (if any); and the name and address of the source of the drug if it is not manufactured by the sponsor.

- A description of the rare disease or condition for which the drug is being or will be investigated, the proposed indication or indications for the drug, and the reasons why such therapy is needed.

- A description of the drug, and a discussion of the scientific rationale for the use of the drug for the rare disease or condition, including all data from nonclinical laboratory studies, clinical investigations, and other relevant data that are available to the sponsor, whether positive, negative, or inconclusive. Copies of pertinent unpublished and published papers are also required.

- When the sponsor of a drug that is otherwise the same as an already-approved orphan drug seeks orphan-drug designation for the same rare disease or condition, an explanation of why the proposed variation may be "clinically superior" to the first drug (see discussion below).

- When a drug is under development only for a subset of persons with a particular disease or condition, a demonstration that this patient subset is medically plausible.

- A summary of the regulatory status and marketing history of the drug in the United States and in foreign countries (e.g., IND and marketing application status and dispositions; the specific uses under investigation in each country; the indication(s) for which the drug is approved in foreign countries; and any "adverse regulatory actions" that have been taken against the drug in any country).

- Documentation, with appended authoritative references, to demonstrate: (1) that the disease or condition for which the drug is intended affects fewer than 200,000 people in the United States or, if the drug is a vaccine, diagnostic drug, or preventive drug, that the persons to whom the drug will be administered in the United States are fewer than 200,000 per year as specified in federal regulations, or (2) for a drug intended for diseases or conditions affecting 200,000 or more people, or for a vaccine, diagnostic drug, or preventive drug to be administered to 200,000 or more persons per year in the United States, that there is no reasonable expectation that costs of research and development of the drug for the indication can be recovered by sales of the drug in the United States (e.g., cost data, a statement and justification of future development costs the sponsor expects to incur, and an estimate of, and justification for, the expected revenues from drug sales during its first seven years of marketing).

- A statement as to whether the sponsor submitting the request is the "real party in interest" in the development and the intended or actual production and sales of the product.

Drug sponsors may request orphan drug designation any time prior to the submission of a marketing appli cation for the product. Once a request for designation is submitted, the FDA's OPD attempts to issue a dec sion within 60 days. In most cases, the office handles the review itself, although it may refer certain technic; or scientific questions to one of the agency's drug or biological product review divisions. Within 14 month of a drug's designation, and annually thereafter, the sponsor must submit to OPD a brief progress report the includes a short account of the progress of drug development, the investigational plan for the coming yea and any changes that may affect the product's orphan-drug status.

When OPD denies these designation requests, the reasons range from poorly prepared designation reque: documents to the selection of invalid subpopulations. Before sponsors submit designation requests, OP officials recommend that companies educate themselves about designation request submission require ments, and have a defined rationale for the use of a drug for a selected indication, a reasonable strategy fi the product's development, and a highly specific indication and patient population that can be studied ar for which the drug can be labeled if ultimately approved.

The practical advantages of orphan drug designation essentially are limited to tax incentives and marketir exclusivity. Although some believe that designation makes FDA drug reviewers more aware of a specif orphan drug, there are probably no real advantages during the drug approval process (see discussion belov FDA staffers claim that many sponsors are surprised to learn that orphan drug designation itself affords r competitive advantages. For example, a drug's designation does not stop another firm from requesting (obtaining a designation for the same drug and indication.

It is also important to note that the seven-year marketing exclusivity is awarded to the first designated orpha drug to obtain marketing approval, not designation. Given this reality, there have been several intensely cor petitive and high-stakes races to gain FDA approval on the part of companies pursing approval for the same orphan drugs. One of the more recent was a race between Genzyme and Transkaryotic Therapies for the approval of agalsidase beta, an enzyme replacement therapy for Fabray's disease. Ultimately, Genzyme was the first to gain FDA approval for its product Fabrazyme in April 2003, thereby securing the marketing exclusivity award.

There seem to be few, if any, disadvantages to obtaining orphan drug designation. Having to prepare a designation request and having general information published about the drug upon designation are, in many cases, small inconveniences compared to the benefits designation offers.

Still, some drug firms do not pursue designation when developing a product that would qualify as an orphan drug. In some cases, these firms do not seek orphan designation because they view it as their corporate responsibility as health-care companies to develop these products. Others speculate that companies, knowing that orphan drugs may prove useful in additional, more profitable ways, do not want the possible public relations burden of profiting from a drug that was developed, in part, using public monies.

As measured by the number of designation requests, however, the FDA's orphan drug development program is as busy as it has ever been. The number of products for which industry and others sought orphan drug designations soared 45% in 2003, to what was easily a record high (see exhibit below). The FDA received 167 orphan designation applications in 2003, up from 115 in 2002 and virtually double the number received in 2000.

Orphan Drug Designation and Approval Statistics, 1990–2003

	1990	1991	1992	1993	1994	1995	1996	1997	1998	1999	2000	2001	2002	2003
Orphan Designation Applications Received*	131	84	77	72	81	73	78	72	123	94	88	129	115	167**
Orphan Designations Made*	89	80	56	65	58	56	60	55	67	79	68	78	63	89
Average NDA Approval Time (months) (all NDAs)	35.4	28.6	32.6	33.1	25.3	19.2[+]	17.8[+]	17.6	12.8	13.5	15.0	16.4[+]	17.8[+]	16.9[+]
Average Orphan NDA Approval Time (months)	24.4	20.2	17.6	12.8	25.1	14.3[+]	19.2[+]	17.5[+]	13.4[+]	12.0[+]	6.6[+]	7.3[+]	17.3[+]	15.2[+]
# of Orphan Drug Approvals	12	12	13*	13*	11*	11*	23*	19*	20*	20*	14*	6*	14*	11*
# of Active Orphan Designations	–	–	–	–	–	–	–	708*	752*	807*	858*	949*	1,002*	1,091*
Cumulative # of Orphan Product Approvals	–	–	–	–	–	–	–	167*	185*	197*	218*	228*	238*	250*

* drugs and biologics
[+] New Molecular Entities only
** record high

Source: PAREXEL's Pharmaceutical R&D Statistical Sourcebook 2004/2005

A Look at Orphan Drug Incentives

Currently, the Orphan Drug Act and the FDA offer orphan drug sponsors four primary incentives: marketing exclusivity, tax credits, protocol assistance, and grants and contracts. More recently, under the Food and Drug Administration Modernization Act of 1997, NDAs for orphan drugs were statutorily exempted from user fees unless "non-orphan" indications are sought in the application.

Marketing Exclusivity Marketing exclusivity may be the single most important incentive to orphan drug sponsors. Under the law, the first sponsor to obtain marketing approval for a designated orphan drug is awarded a seven-year period of marketing exclusivity for that product. During this period, no other sponsor can obtain FDA approval for the drug for the orphan indication. The agency can, however, approve identical versions of the drug for other indications.

The rewards of marketing exclusivity are linked directly to FDA approval. Although orphan designation make a drug eligible for exclusivity, that exclusivity is not awarded until a product's NDA is approved. Therefore, se eral identical products could be designated for the same orphan indication, but only the first company t receive approval will obtain marketing exclusivity rights.

Marketing exclusivity has at least two main advantages over traditional patent protection. First, designatic and product approval are virtually the only eligibility requirements for exclusivity. The product need not k new or unobvious, or meet any of the criteria used in determining a drug's patent eligibility. Because of thi natural substances and other products that are unable to receive any form of patent protection are eligib for marketing exclusivity.

The second significant advantage marketing exclusivity has over patent protection is that its life begins on tr date of a drug's approval. Although a patent award grants a 20-year monopoly, a drug's patent life begins c the date the patent is awarded, and many years of that patent life are generally lost during the drug testir and evaluation process. Since exclusivity is awarded upon approval, its seven-year life is not eroded durir product development.

While marketing exclusivity may be the most important orphan drug incentive, it is also the most complex. I the past, some critics have argued that the FDA's inability or unwillingness to deny marketing approval 1 drugs that are similar in structure to drugs that have already been awarded marketing exclusivity has unfai ly denied orphan product innovators the protection afforded to them under the Orphan Drug Act.

In fact, the FDA's criteria for determining when two orphan drugs designated for the same indication are co sidered identical have been tested at least four times, the last of which was ongoing as of this writing. Durir the late 1980s, the FDA faced a pair of widely publicized cases involving two human growth hormone prou ucts and two erythropoietin products. The issue, in both cases, involved the FDA's then-unpublished criter for differentiating between medical compounds, particularly biologics and biotechnology products, for tr purposes of marketing exclusivity.

Then, in December 1992, the FDA's orphan drug regulations first established the conditions under which tr agency would consider two drugs to be the same and, therefore, take action to block the approval of the se ond designated product:

> "(i) If it is a drug composed of small molecules, a drug that contains the same active moiety as a previously approved drug and is intended for the same use as the previously approved drug, even if the particular ester or salt (including a salt with hydrogen or coordination bonds) or other noncovalent derivative such as a complex, chelate or clathrate has not been previously approved, except that if the subsequent drug can be shown to be clinically superior to the first drug, it will not be considered to be the same drug.

> (ii) If it is a drug composed of large molecules (macromolecules), a drug that contains the same principal molecular structural features (but not necessarily all of the same structural features) and is intended for the same use as a previously approved drug, except that, if the subsequent drug can be shown to be clinically superior, it will not be considered the same drug. This criterion will be applied as follows to different kinds of macromolecules:

> > (A) Two protein drugs would be considered the same if the only differences in structure between them were due to post-translational events, or infidelity of translation or transcription, or were minor differences in amino acid sequence; other potentially impor-

tant differences, such as different glycosylation patterns or different tertiary structures, would not cause the drugs to be considered different unless the differences were shown to be clinically superior.

(B) Two polysaccharide drugs would be considered the same if they had identical saccharide repeating units, even if the number of units were to vary and even if there were post-polymerization modifications, unless the subsequent drug could be shown to be clinically superior.

(C) Two polynucleotide drugs consisting of two or more distinct nucleotides would be considered the same if they had an identical sequence of purine and pyrimidine bases (or their derivatives) bound to an identical sugar backbone (ribose, deoxyribose, or modifications of these sugars), unless the subsequent drug were shown to be clinically superior.

(D) Closely related, complex partly definable drugs with similar therapeutic intent, such as two live viral vaccines for the same indication, would be considered the same unless the subsequent drug were shown to be clinically superior."

These regulations established the concept of clinical superiority, and made it the criterion upon which the agency could base its approval of a second designated drug that is otherwise identical to, and is marketed for the same indication as, a previously approved designated orphan drug. To be considered clinically superior, a drug must offer a "significant therapeutic advantage" over the existing product. According to FDA regulations, this advantage can be based upon evidence of greater effectiveness, improved product safety in a significant segment of the target population, or, in exceptional cases, "a major contribution to patient care."

The FDA's application of these provisions was challenged in early 1996, when Berlex Laboratories filed suit to block the agency's approval of Biogen's Avonex (interferon beta), a competitor to Berlex' Betaseron (interferon beta), which was already marketed as a treatment for relapsing/remitting multiple sclerosis. Based on what is viewed as a safety advantage—fewer injection site reactions—the agency had approved Avonex, stating that "a small demonstrated improvement in efficacy or diminution in adverse reactions may be sufficient to allow a finding of clinical superiority." In late 1996, the U.S. District Court dismissed the Berlex suit.

A more recent challenge to the FDA's "sameness" provisions came in mid-1999, when Baker Norton, a generic drug company, challenged the agency's regulations for determining when two products are the same. The company sued the agency because it was seeking to market a generic version of Bristol-Myers Squibb's Taxol (paclitaxel), even though Taxol has orphan exclusivity for Karposi's sarcoma. Specifically, the company asked the court to establish that the orphan drug regulation's definition of the term "drug" is inconsistent with the provisions of the Orphan Drug Act. In arguments made before the court in May 1999, Baker Norton contended "that FDA's reliance on active moieties to distinguish one small molecule drug from another is not permissible under the statute." The company also argued that the concept of "clinical superiority," through which the agency can determine that two identical drugs are different, has no basis in the Orphan Drug Act. Baker Norton argued that the plain meaning of "drug" is the "drug product," rather than simply the active moiety. In other words, the company wanted to force the agency to consider factors other than the active moiety, including differences in formulation and labeling, in determining when two drugs are different. Ultimately, however, the Baker Norton arguments failed, as the court ruled in favor of the FDA and its interpretation of the Orphan Drug Act's provisions.

By approving Serono's Rebif (interferon beta-1a) on March 7, 2002, the FDA, for the first time ever, circumvented the orphan exclusivity awarded to one orphan product based on a subsequent product's superior efficacy. Serono successfully challenged the orphan exclusivity for Biogen's Avonex by showing, through comparative efficacy study, that Rebif is more effective in reducing MS exacerbations after 24 weeks.

Tax Credits Sponsors of designated orphan drugs are eligible for a 50 percent tax credit for funds spent o clinical development. Therefore, a firm can subtract directly from its annual tax bill one-half of the mone spent on the clinical testing of an orphan drug.

There are, however, several important limitations to the tax credit incentive:

- Sponsors can receive credits only for clinical testing conducted within the United States. The one principal exception to this is a situation in which the sponsor must go outside the United States to find the patients necessary to conduct the trial.

- The credits can be used only for clinical testing actually paid for and conducted by the sponsor. For example, a sponsor could not receive credits for another company's testing that is referenced in the sponsor's drug application.

- The credits are available only for products that are formally designated by the FDA.

- The credit can be applied only to testing conducted for the orphan indication for which a drug is designated.

- Tax credits do not apply to nonclinical testing. OPD staffers claim that this can be a problem, since basic animal toxicity and carcinogenicity testing alone can cost well over a million dollars.

Through the enactment of the Small Business Job Protection Act of 1996, Congress addressed what was, a least for many biotechnology and other fledgling companies, perhaps the most notable limitation to th Orphan Drug Act's tax incentives: Originally, tax credits were only beneficial to companies that were profitable Under previous law, orphan product tax credits could be applied against taxes on profits, but could not b used to increase a company's losses or be carried forward into a year in which the company would post pro its.

Tax code revisions made under the Small Business Job Protection Act permit companies to carry forward ta credits into a year in which they can be applied against profits. The law's provisions allow credits to be ca ried forward for 15 years, something that can impart immediate value on small, start-up firms interested i partnerships or other business arrangements (i.e., because a firm can pass along the tax credit to a larger fir that can use it immediately).

Because the orphan drug tax credit provisions traditionally had to be reauthorized periodically by Congres there was considerable uncertainty in this area. Ultimately, however, Congress passed legislation making th tax credit provisions permanent.

Protocol Assistance Protocol assistance is an incentive for which orphan designation is unnecessary. If sponsor can show the FDA that a drug will ultimately be used for a rare disease or condition, the agency pro vides written recommendations on the nonclinical and clinical studies needed for the product's approva With CDER and sponsors already working so closely on most drug development programs today, however, th value of this incentive is likely minimal.

To obtain protocol assistance, a sponsor must submit a formal request providing information on the dru including its intended use, available test data, regulatory and marketing status, and proposed testing plan

The FDA's 1992 orphan drug regulations specify 16 content requirements for such requests. OPD staffers warn that, unless sponsors ask specific questions in these requests, firms are likely to receive extremely vague recommendations. Protocol recommendations are made by product review divisions within CDER.

FDA Grants and Contracts The Orphan Drug Act authorizes the U.S. Congress to appropriate funds for grants and contracts to physicians, companies, and others who are developing orphan drugs. In recent fiscal years, the Office of Orphan Product Development was granted $11 to $11.5 million for such purposes.

More common than contracts, grants are awarded to university-based investigators and some smaller companies, particularly biotechnology firms, for the clinical testing of orphan drugs. Contract funds, on the other hand, are available to investigators and companies that agree to conduct testing for a drug or in a therapeutic area of particular interest to the FDA.

The FDA Approval Process: Advantages for Orphan Drugs?

Generally, orphan products receive no preferential treatment in terms of testing and submission requirements, and face the same safety and effectiveness criteria and review processes as undesignated products. FDA staffers do claim, however, that the agency will modify the drug testing and approval process for orphan products when appropriate. In the past, issues such as the availability of patients with orphan conditions and the lack of competitive therapies have forced the agency to consider alternative testing requirements and review criteria.

NDAs submitted for orphan products are reviewed within one of the FDA's drug review divisions. There, reviewers evaluate products strictly on the basis of safety, efficacy, and risk-benefit analyses. Although the product's status as an orphan drug may appear to be of little or no benefit, OPD staffers do work to make agency reviewers more sensitive to the special issues that orphan products present.

One advantage that many orphan drugs have over other products is that they often—although not always—receive priority reviews. This is related not to the fact that the products are designated orphan drugs, but that they are frequently the only treatments available for certain conditions. Because of this, the FDA often classifies them as high-priority drugs, and expedites their review. In fact, just over three-quarters of the new molecular entities that were also orphan drugs approved in the four-year period from 2000 to 2003 had been granted priority status. Still, the FDA has denied at least one petition requesting that all orphan drugs automatically receive the FDA's highest review priority.

Historically, approval times for orphan drugs have compared favorably with those of conventional drugs, according to FDA statistics (see exhibit below). In 2001, the agency approved NDAs for orphan drug NMEs in an average of 7.3 months, compared to 17.2 months for all other NME NDAs. In both 2002 and 2003, however, the review time gap narrowed considerably.

What is the OPD's role in the review of an orphan drug? The office actively monitors the progress of orphan reviews, but has no formal authority in product approvals or real influence in the decisions of FDA reviewers. OPD staffers do attend FDA-sponsor meetings, however, and act as mediators to help resolve special regulatory problems presented by orphan drugs.

Mirroring the decline in overall new drug approvals, orphan drug approvals have sagged in recent years. Over the most recent four-year period (2000-2003), the FDA approved 45 orphan drugs, compared to 82 in the preceding four-year period (1996-1999).

Mean Orphan Drug Approval Times vs. Approval Times of Other Drugs, 1993–2003

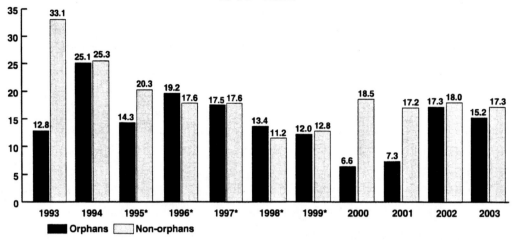

* 1995, 1996, 1997, 1998, 1999, 2000, 2001, 2002, and 2003 analyses include only New Molecular Entity (NME) drugs

What Other Recent Studies Reveal About Orphan Drug Trends

In a November 2003 study of 82 new chemical entities (NCE) approved in 1999, 2000, and 2001, the Tuft Center for the Study of Drug Development (Tufts CSDD) assessed the clinical and approval times for ne drugs in various categories, including orphan drugs and accelerated approval/fast track products. While th study found that drugs with orphan status had clinical and approval phases that "were similar to those for th full sample of 82 NCEs," it found that "the clinical and approval phases for combined accelerated and fa: track approvals were shorter than those for all NCEs by 30% and 50%, respectively."

The Tufts CSDD study found a slight FDA approval time advantage for orphan drugs compared to all oth NCEs (1.1 years to 1.4 years, respectively), although it found a substantially larger advantage for accelerate approval/fast track products (see exhibit below). Interestingly, the study also found that the clinical develo

Mean Clinical, Approval, and Total Phases in Years for NCEs Approved in 1999-2001 and Designated as Accelerated Approval, Fast Track Approval, or Both, Compared with Those for All Other NCEs and With Orphan Approvals

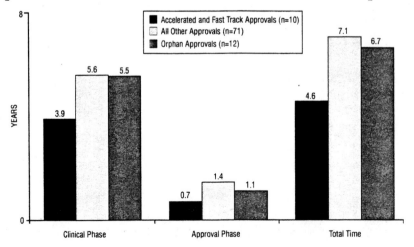

ment programs for orphan products were almost as lengthy as those for all other new drugs, a finding that runs counter to the perception that the smaller trial sizes for orphan products might result in a time advantage for the clinical trials of those drugs.

References

1. Shulman, S.R. and Manocchia, M. (Tufts Center for the Study of Drug Development), The U.S. Orphan Drug Program: 1983-1995.

2. Ibid.

CHAPTER 14

CDER's Bioresearch Monitoring Program

Given that its regulatory decisions are based directly on research data, CDER has a vested interest in the accuracy and validity of clinical and nonclinical study results submitted in NDAs and other applications. Under CDER's Bioresearch Monitoring Program (BIMO), agency investigators conduct on-site inspections of laboratories, clinics, and offices where scientific data are developed and stored to ensure the quality of the data submitted in such filings.

Specifically, CDER inspects clinical investigators, drug firms, IRBs, and nonclinical laboratories to ensure: (1) that data submitted in product applications are accurate and valid; and (2) that the rights and welfare of human subjects are protected in clinical studies. During these inspections, FDA investigators evaluate how well sponsors, monitors, contract research organizations, IRBs, and clinical and nonclinical investigational site staff have fulfilled their various responsibilities and commitments under good clinical practice (GCP), study protocols, and other standards and regulatory requirements.

Despite the FDA's adoption of the 1997 International Conference on Harmonization (ICH) guideline on GCP (see Chapter 6), CDER officials emphasize that, under the BIMO program, agency inspectors continue to assess sponsors, monitors, investigators, and others against FDA GCP standards exclusively. Since the ICH GCP provisions are generally seen as being consistent with—and in some cases being more specific than—the FDA's GCP regulations/guidelines, FDA inspectors, in theory, should not discover compliance problems when the ICH GCP standards are employed. Still, it is important to note that CDER's BIMO program is focused primarily on finding deviations from FDA GCP regulations, and *not* deviations from ICH or even FDA GCP-related guidelines.

CDER's BIMO program is still feeling the residual effects of a series of disclosures that, in the late 1990s, shook the center's confidence in the data collected by clinical investigators and in the pharmaceutical industry's ability to detect investigator noncompliance—and even fraud—through routine monitoring practices. Primary among these was the case of Southern California Research Institute President and Principal Investigator Robert Fiddes, M.D., who was sentenced in 1998 to 15 months in prison and was fined $800,000 for falsifying and fabricating clinical trial data used in NDAs for multiple drug products and for prescribing prohibited medications to manipulate clinical data. During 1998 and 1999, this case prompted a series of congressional inquiries into CDER's actions in the Fiddes case, FDA efforts to detect research fraud and the extent of fraud-related problems in clinical research, the agency's authorities to conduct oversight of and to discipline clinical investigators, and the general practices that clinical investigators employ to recruit patients for trials.

Although CDER since has released data indicating that the incidence of research fraud is small (i.e., well under 5% of studies), the disclosures in the Fiddes case and the congressional attention and widespread press coverage that they prompted helped to set in motion several agency initiatives and responses that continu to have fundamental effects on CDER's BIMO program. Sporadic, but high profile, reports of compliance prot lems in clinical trials have kept the public and political pressure on the U.S. government to continue to ste up its educational and compliance efforts with regard to clinical research.

In addition, CDER has looked in recent years to evaluate how it should modernize its BIMO program i response to emerging realities in the clinical research process, among them the commercialization of clinic research, the increasing use of computers to collect clinical data, the flood of new clinical investigators pa ticipating in trials, and the increasing use of pivotal trial data from foreign trial sites. In response to these an other developments, CDER has taken several steps under its GCP standards and BIMO program:

- As have other center programs, CDER's clinical trial compliance program has adopted more of a risk-based approach that focuses limited resources on high-risk and likely problem areas. In recent years, for example, CDER's Division of Scientific Investigations (DSI) has encouraged the voluntary submission of clinical trial-related complaints regarding regulatory noncompliance, fraud, and other issues. In FY2003, for example, voluntary complaints regarding clinical investigators, IRBs, sponsors, and other entities involved in the trial process rose 26%, while FDA inspections initiated to respond to such complaints rose even more. According to CDER data, almost a third of CDER's 33% increase in clinical investigator inspections during FY2003 was driven by the agency's response to voluntary complaints. During FY2003, CDER's "directed" inspections (i.e., non-routine inspections generally undertaken in response to a specific concern) of clinical study sites surged 70%, to an all-time high of 109 inspections. Overall, CDER claims that virtually a third of its clinical investigator inspectional assignments were triggered by voluntary complaints in FY2003, up from 23% in FY2002 and 8% in 1999. CDER continues to increase the visibility of its voluntary clinical trial complaint program, which it has identified as being "of vital strategic importance." In addition, during July 2004, FDA officials noted that the agency's inspectional focus will continue to shift toward studies in vulnerable populations and high-risk products and protocols.

- Since electronic data entry (EDC) has become an area of growing regulatory concern for the agency, CDER is developing a draft industry guidance on EDC standards. Of particular concern to the agency appear to be situations in which data (e.g., EKG) are collected from patients via an electronic device, which transmits the data directly to a so-called "trusted third party," or technology vendor, which collects and maintains the data. Because such situations cut the clinical investigator out of his/her traditional role (i.e., collecting/maintaining the data), it creates significant regulatory issues for the agency—for example, does the FDA have any authority over these technology vendors? Agency officials claim to have seen one "problematic" case involving EDC use already. To communicate its expectations for remote data entry systems and other computerized systems employed in the clinical development process, CDER originally released an April 1999 industry guidance entitled, *Computerized Systems Used in Clinical Trials*. The guidance, which center officials acknowledged at the time is vague due to the rapid evolution of computer systems and clinical settings, "addresses how data quality might be satisfied where computerized systems are being used to create, modify, maintain, archive, or transmit clinical data." In September 2004, CDER released a revised draft guidance entitled, *Computerized Systems Used in Clinical Trials* to reflect international harmonization efforts and changes in agency policy relevant to electronic records and electronic signatures (in August 2003, the agency issued guidance clarifying that it intended to interpret its Part 11 regulations for electronic records/signatures "narrowly" and to exercise enforcement discretion with regard to validation, audit trail, record retention, and record copying requirements while it re-examined the Part 11 requirements). The draft guidance, which will supersede the existing April 1999 guidance under the same title when it is finalized, states the following about systems used for direct entry of data: "We recommend that prompts, flags, or other help features be incorporated into the computerized system to encourage consistent use of clinical terminology and to alert the user to data that are out of acceptable range. We recommend against the use of features that automatically enter data into a field when the field is bypassed."

- CDER's DSI is continuing its efforts to provide greater input throughout the drug development process. Therefore, the division is attending more end-of-Phase 2 meetings between drug sponsors and the FDA in an effort to provide greater feedback on monitoring plans and other study conduct-related issues for pivotal Phase 3 trials.

- CDER's DSI is undertaking an internal assessment to closely examine CDER's GCP surveillance program and whether the agency is achieving ideal outcomes and interventions as a result of its human subject protection programs.

- Under a June 2004 proposed rule, the FDA established that it would no longer consider as support for an IND or NDA any clinical study that does not comply with the agency's GCP standards. In essence, the proposed rule would explicitly establish GCP as the standard for the agency's acceptance of data from foreign trials that are not conducted under an IND (GCP is already the standard for trials under an IND). Currently, non-IND foreign trials are not required to meet GCP standards, provided that such trials conform to the Declaration of Helsinki (DoH) or the national requirements of the country in which the study is conducted, whichever affords the greater protection for study subjects. GCP is now the better standard than the DoH, notes the agency, because it "provides more detail and enumeration of specific responsibilities of various parties, including monitoring the trial and reporting adverse events."

- In late 1999, what some FDA officials characterized as "grave and disturbing" clinical investigator noncompliance (e.g., non-reporting of adverse experiences to regulators) in several gene therapy studies, one of which resulted in the well-publicized death of a teenage study participant, galvanized government agencies to take action. In May 2000, the FDA and the Department of Health and Human Services (HHS) unveiled a "plan of action" in response to what then-FDA Commissioner Jane Henney, M.D., called the "failure of some researchers at prestigious institutions...to follow the most basic elements of what it takes to properly conduct clinical studies." As part of this plan, which seeks to heighten government oversight of clinical research and to reinforce to research institutions their responsibility to oversee their clinical researchers and IRBs, HHS was to pursue legislation authorizing the FDA to levy civil monetary penalties of up to $250,000 per clinical investigator and $1 million per research institution for violations of informed consent and "other important research practices." Although this legislative proposal was later dropped, the FDA/HHS action plan comprised several other moves focused largely on upgrading training and guidance for clinical investigators: (1) HHS will undertake an "aggressive effort" to improve the education and training of clinical investigators, IRB members, and associated IRB and institutional staff (FDA and NIH will work together to ensure that all clinical investigators, research administrators, IRB members and IRB staff receive "appropriate research bioethics training and human subjects research training"); (2) NIH and the FDA will issue specific guidance on informed consent, clarifying that "research institutions and sponsors are expected to audit records for evidence of compliance with informed consent requirements" (for risky or complex trials, IRBs will be expected to take additional measures, which might include requiring third-party observation of the informed consent process); (3) the FDA will issue guidelines for Data and Safety Monitoring Boards (DSMB)—something the agency did in November 2001 (see discussion below)—to define the relationship between DSMBs and IRBs and to establish when DSMBs are appropriate, that they should be independent, and what their responsibilities should be; and (4) the FDA and NIH will develop new conflict of interest policies for the biomedical community, including a requirement "that any researcher's financial interest in a clinical trial be disclosed to potential participants." Although the FDA has issued the guidance on DSMBs and HHS has issued a conflict-of-interest guidance, the FDA continued to work in other areas. The agency continues to develop an updated information sheet on informed consent to offer additional clarifications on the informed consent process and standards.

While clinical investigators are the focus of most CDER bioresearch inspections, there are several reasons wh the results of such inspections are of great importance to clinical trial sponsors. First, drug sponsors are ult mately responsible for the conduct of clinical studies, and FDA inspections are designed, today more tha ever, to determine how well sponsors perform in that role. Secondly, these inspections, should they uncov serious problems, can result in the agency's rejection of data essential to a drug's approval. Today, a sponsc will also likely face inspectional and compliance actions whenever it is found to have worked with noncon pliant clinical investigators and failed to address the noncompliance.

Like virtually all other CDER drug review and compliance efforts, the Bioresearch Monitoring Program ha been affected by the agency's prescription drug user fee program. Since the center faces mandated deadline for NDA reviews, preapproval bioresearch monitoring inspections must be conducted within short tim frames so that inspection results may be evaluated promptly. The compressed inspectional time frames hav presented challenges for FDA field investigators. This pressure likely increased further, given FDAMA prov sions establishing that review division actions cannot be delayed due to the unavailability of informatic from, or action by, field inspectors, unless the review division determines that a delay is necessary to assu a drug's safety or effectiveness.

Based on the numbers of NDA submissions and resource limitations, CDER reviewers and clinical investig tions staff carefully scrutinize the need for various inspectional assignments and the numbers of studies/site inspected. When the number of site inspections rose several years ago in response to the approval of mo NDAs, the number of studies and sites inspected per application were typically lower (e.g., two site inspe tions per NDA). Given that the agency has approved fewer NDAs in more recent years, CDER has been able increase the number of sites/investigators inspected per NDA (e.g., three or four sites per NDA).

A Brief History of the Bioresearch Monitoring Program

The origin of the FDA's authority to inspect research data and related records lies in the Food, Drug ar Cosmetic (FD&C) Act. The law states that every person required to maintain records must, upon the FD/ request, allow access to clinical data for review and copying. FDA regulations and Form FDA-1572-Statement Investigator, which clinical investigators sign before undertaking the study of an investigational drug, state th "...the investigator will make such records available for inspection and copying."

Because of physicians' importance in the development and collection of clinical safety and efficacy dat inspections of investigators represent the core of CDER's Bioresearch Monitoring Program. FDA inspectio of clinical investigators began in 1962, although only three inspections were conducted by 1965. The agency expanded its efforts in the years following, and established a four-person office to organize and conduct inspections. Since government authorities outside the FDA believed that only physicians should inspect other physicians, however, inspectional activities were limited (i.e., only seven or eight inspections were conducted annually).

By 1972, the U.S. government had gained a new respect for the importance and abilities of FDA inspectors. As a result, the FDA initiated a survey of 162 commercially sponsored clinical investigators, 70 noncommercial clinical investigators, and 15 manufacturers. The results of this multi-year study, and increased FDA staff and budget, led to the founding of the agency's Bioresearch Monitoring Program in June 1977.

Although this chapter focuses on clinical investigator and sponsor/monitor compliance activities, today's Bioresearch Monitoring Program consists of five separate compliance inspection programs, each designed to evaluate the activities of a key entity in the conduct of a scientific study:

- Clinical Investigator Compliance Program;

- Sponsor/Monitor Compliance Program;

- Institutional Review Board (IRB) Compliance Program;

- Nonclinical Laboratory Compliance Program (for information on the inspection of nonclinical laboratories, see Chapter 2); and

- In Vivo Bioequivalence Compliance Program.

These inspectional programs are managed by three branches within CDER's Division of Scientific Investigations (DSI): Good Clinical Practices Branch I, Good Clinical Practices Branch II, and the GLP and Bioequivalence Investigations Branch. DSI's former Human Subject Protection Team, which dealt with IRB issues, has been absorbed into the division's two GCP branches.

Due in part to rising government concerns about the abilities of IRBs to fulfill their responsibilities in the growing and increasingly complicated clinical research market, the FDA stepped up its inspections of the estimated 1,600 IRBs in the late 1990s. Although CDER inspections on IRBs have subsided somewhat (154 IRB inspections in 2003, compared to 223 in 1999), the FDA and other regulatory agencies are taking steps to upgrade their oversight of IRBs. To help it track, inspect, monitor, and communicate with IRBs, the agency proposed in July 2004 to require that IRBs register on a website maintained by the U.S. Department of Health and Human Services. In registering, IRBs would be required to provide contact information, the number of active protocols involving FDA-regulated products reviewed in the previous calendar year, an indication of whether the IRB is accredited, and a description of the types of FDA-regulated products involved in the protocols reviewed.

The Clinical Investigator Compliance Program

As noted, inspections of clinical investigators represent the core of CDER's Bioresearch Monitoring Program. CDER has three separate investigator inspection programs: _

- Study Oriented Inspection Program;

- Investigator Oriented Inspection Program; and

- Bioequivalency/Bioavailability Inspection Program.

Study Oriented Inspection Program Formerly called the Data Audit Program, the Study Oriented Inspectio Program is a routine surveillance effort that involves inspections of 300 to 400 clinical investigators per yea During these inspections, which are conducted during an NDA's review, an FDA field inspector looks at th conduct of the study and performs a data audit. In evaluating the investigator's conduct of a clinical study, th inspector considers several factors, including the following:

- what the investigator, each of his/her staffers, and others did during the study;
- the degree of delegation of authority;
- when and where specific aspects of the study were performed;
- how and where data were recorded;
- how the drug substance was stored and accounted for;
- the monitor's interaction with the physician;
- evidence that proper informed consent was obtained from subjects; and
- evidence that IRB approval was obtained for studies performed.

In the typical audit, data submitted in an NDA are compared with the on-site records that should support the validity. On-site records to which an FDA inspector must be given access include a physician's office record hospital records, and various laboratory reports. Records obtained prior to the initiation, and following th completion, of the study may be reviewed and copied.

Because of the inspectional program's nature, CDER's DSI does not publicize its criteria for selecting studie and sites for routine inspections. Obviously, however, a particular study's importance to the approval decisic will have a direct bearing on its likelihood of being inspected.

The division also uses a sampling method for determining the number of sites within a particular study t be inspected, although the number is often influenced by other factors, including a protocol's complexit CDER drug reviewers and DSI staff will also consider the number of patients at a site (i.e., sites with the mo patients), the number of adverse experiences reported (i.e., sites with far fewer or greater reports), and th number of dropouts at a site. Although CDER had been developing an internal policies and procedures ma ual to describe the study and site selection and assignment process, this project has been on hold sin mid-1999.

When CDER has targeted key clinical studies and sites for inspection, agency staffers send a field inspect an "assignment package," which includes copies of a representative case report form (CRF), case report for tabulations, the protocol, and other pertinent information. The assignment package will indicate the numb of subject records to be inspected at the site. If the field inspector discovers potential problems, he or she c then inspect other site records.

Due to the nature of physicians' work and schedules, study oriented inspections are made by appointmer Therefore, investigators are alerted as to which study is to be audited, and are given the opportunity to locat collect, and organize all relevant records.

After peaking in FY2000 (at 400 inspections), CDER's clinical site inspections declined by about 30% in FY20(and FY2002. In FY2003, however, CDER's site inspections rose again, to 368 inspections. About 12% of the FY2003 inspections involved foreign sites.

In a September 2004 industry guidance, the FDA outlined the types of investigator misconduct on which the agency could base a decision to suspend an investigator's participation in a clinical trial immediately through a clinical hold order. Data falsification, serious protocol violations, and any failure to obtain IRB reviews of protocol changes, acquire adequate patient informed consent, or report serious or life-threatening adverse events are among the reasons why the agency may seek to discontinue an investigator's participation in a trial, according to the guidance entitled, *The Use of Clinical Holds Following Clinical Investigator Misconduct*. The agency will consider using clinical hold orders (see Chapter 4) "where the investigator's misconduct appears to pose an ongoing threat to the safety and welfare of [clinical trial] subjects," the agency states. Although the agency notes that is has other options in responding to investigator misconduct, such as enforcement actions in federal court or investigator disqualification proceedings, it emphasizes that initiating such actions, which can take several months or years to complete, do not immediately halt an investigator's participation in ongoing or proposed clinical trials. After obtaining credible evidence of investigator misconduct, the agency states that it will consider two factors in determining the need for a clinical hold: (1) the nature of the violation and its significance for the safety, rights, and welfare of human subjects; and (2) the degree of certainty that there has been investigator misconduct that poses a significant risk to subjects.

"Investigator Oriented" Inspection Program The "investigator oriented" site inspection is, in most respects, similar to the study oriented, or routine, inspection. Investigator oriented inspections are not routine, however, and may be initiated for one or more of several reasons:

- the investigator is suspected of impropriety;
- the investigator is responsible for a large volume of work, particularly if that work involves different medical disciplines;
- the investigator has done work outside his or her specialty;
- the investigator reports drug effectiveness that appears to be too optimistic when compared to the reports of other physicians studying the same drug;
- the investigator reports no toxicity or few adverse reactions when other physicians report numerous reactions of a certain type;
- the investigator seems to have too many patients with a given disease for the locale or the setting in which he or she practices;
- the investigator reports laboratory results that are consistent beyond the usual biologic variation or that are inconsistent with results submitted by other investigators;
- representatives of the sponsor have reported to the FDA that they are having difficulty obtaining case reports from the investigator, or that they have found the investigator to be deficient in some other manner;
- a routine audit revealed problems too serious to be handled by correspondence; or
- the FDA receives letters or phone calls claiming violations of subject's rights, variations in protocol, or some other violation or noncompliance.

An investigator may also be selected for inspection as the result of questions raised regarding the effects of the investigator's financial interests or compensation on clinical data. Under regulations that went into effect in early 1999, NDA applicants are required to submit information regarding the financial interests of, and compensation paid to, clinical investigators who developed the data submitted in the application. Although

DSI will not review such disclosures in NDAs routinely, DSI will receive inspection requests whenever these financial disclosures raise questions regarding the validity of clinical data in the minds of review division medical officers, who will be responsible for evaluating these disclosures.

In mid-2000, CDER gave the first indications of how such financial disclosures were affecting NDA reviews and investigator inspections. When an NDA sponsor discloses financial ties with a clinical investigator, CDER reviewers will specifically look at the number of subjects the investigator recruited and if he or she had any reporting outliers in terms of adverse experiences, according to center officials. If such analyses turn up questionable findings, the reviewer will initiate data audits with DSI, which might ask that the data be analyzed further, request additional studies to confirm the study's results, or reject the study as a pivotal trial in the NDA. Of 129 marketing applications submitted between February 2, 1999, and April 30, 2000, 33 provided financial disclosure information on at least one investigator (i.e., rather than a certification that no financial arrangement was involved or a claim that the disclosure requirements were not relevant to the study). At that time, the agency had not rejected any study as a pivotal study because of a disclosed financial arrangement with a sponsor.

Investigator oriented inspections are usually conducted by a DSI reviewer and a field investigator. Although the procedures used parallel those of routine inspections, the inspection team probably reviews more data. For instance, the inspection team will probably evaluate more case reports—sometimes for the entire study—and may audit studies of more than one drug. Patient interviews may be conducted when there are questions as to whether a subject participated in a study, whether the subject had the condition being studied, or whether informed consent was obtained. In addition, investigator oriented inspections are more likely to focus on the particular aspect of a study in question (e.g., delegation of authority) rather than a general review of all aspects of a study.

Many investigator oriented inspections also differ from study oriented inspections in that they are unannounced inspections. In cases in which the agency suspects an investigator of study fraud, manipulation of records, or other misconduct, DSI will not contact the investigator prior to the inspection.

Despite the well-publicized cases of investigator misconduct in recent years, agency statistics indicate that few CDER site inspections are uncovering major regulatory violations. In FY2003, about 1% of investigator inspections in the United States were found to have objectionable conditions or practices representing significant departures from federal regulations (see exhibit below).

Bioequivalency/Bioavailability Inspection Program Bioequivalency/bioavailability inspections involve the inspection of both a clinical and an analytical facility. According to FDA staffers, these inspections are more important for the verification of biopharmaceutic data submitted for generic drugs than for new drugs. An FDA field inspector and an FDA laboratory scientist qualified in the evaluation of analytical techniques conduct this audit.

During the inspection of a biopharmaceutic facility, at which a drug is administered to, and blood samples are then taken from, human volunteers, the inspection team will verify that IRB approval was given for the study and that all regulatory requirements were met. The inspector might review such records and factors as drug accountability records, prescreening laboratory data, the presence of medical supervision, the handling of biologic samples, and the assessment of situations in which the health and safety of the subjects are placed at risk.

In the analytical audit, the inspection team reviews standard operating procedures for the technology utilized, the status of the samples to be analyzed, qualifications of the personnel performing the analyses, raw

CDER Clinical Site Inspection Results, FY1997-FY2003

According to new data, CDER's inspections of clinical trial sites/investigators surged to their third highest level in over a decade in fiscal year 2003. Although the number of clinical investigator inspections had fallen significantly in FY2001 and FY2002 tracking the overall decline in NDA submissions, inspections surged 33% in FY2003.

CDER Clinical Investigator Inspections, FY1992-FY2003

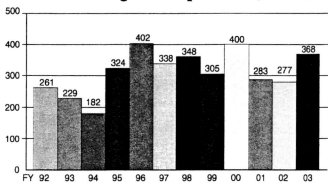

Source: PAREXEL's Pharmaceutical R&D Statistical Sourcebook 2004/2005

After falling nearly 50% in FY2001 and FY2002, CDER's inspections of foreign clinical investigators climbed as well during FY2003. Nearly half of the 44 inspections of foreign clinical investigators (45%) were at clinical sites based in Eastern Europe, while another 31% were at sites based in Western Europe.

CDER Inspections of Foreign Clinical Investigators, FY1991-FY2003

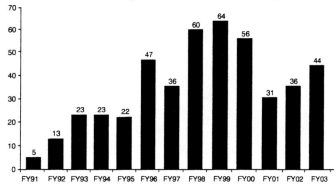

Source: PAREXEL's Pharmaceutical R&D Statistical Sourcebook 2004/2005

Complaints Trigger CDER Action

CDER continues to receive increasing numbers of, and to base more of its clinical site inspections upon, complaints regarding clinical investigators and clinical trials. After stabilizing over the previous four years, clinical trial-related complaints by study subjects, sponsors, site staff, and others surged 26%, to an all-time high of 139 complaints, in FY2003. In 2003, an all-time high of 30% of CDER's clinical investigator inspection assignments were triggered by complaints, compared to 23% in 2002 and 15% in 2000.

–continued–

Within CDER, these voluntary complaints are driving significant inspectional activities, according to *Good Clinical Practice: A Question & Answer Reference Guide* (www.barnettinternational.com). In fact, CDER's Division of Scientific Investigations (DSI) has made responding to voluntary clinical trial-related complaints a top priority in recent years and, as recently as March 2004, identified it as a continuing priority going forward and called complaint follow-up of "vital strategic importance." Unlike many GCP compliance inspections, complaint-related inspections often permit the agency to do real-time follow-up on issues while a clinical trial is ongoing.

Given that CDER hopes to continue to increase the visibility of its voluntary clinical trial complaint program, voluntary complaints are expected to have a significant effect on the center's GCP inspectional efforts going forward. CDER, for example, will include an on-line complaint form on a new DSI web site that it hopes to launch in 2004.

Although the voluntary complaints are confidential, officials from CDER's DSI have revealed that they are receiving complaints from trial sponsors, study subjects, IRBs, FDA staff, former employees, health professionals, informants, other government agencies, clinical investigators, private citizens, media, and clinical monitors. Some complaints are being made on an anonymous basis as well, agency officials note.

Although CDER has not released any recent data on the nature of the complaints received to date, earlier data had indicated that a full quarter of complaints received from 1998 to 2001 involved a failure to follow the protocol, 24% involved possible data falsification, 19% involved informed consent noncompliance, 14% involved poor adverse experience reporting, and 8% involved poor drug accountability. In March 2004, CDER officials disclosed that clinical investigators were easily the target of most complaints, although they noted that complaints have also targeted sponsors, IRBs, monitors/CROs, site management organizations, and hospitals as well. Also, in March 2004, the officials identified the range of issues underlying the complaints received to date:

- Informed consent issues
- Falsification
- Failure to report adverse events
- Failure to follow the protocol
- Inadequate records
- Qualifications of persons performing physicals
- Failure to get IRB approval, report changes in research
- Failure to follow FDA regulations
- Drug accountability

- Recruitment practices
- Poor supervision
- No active IND
- Violations of GLP regs
- Monitoring practices
- Blinding
- Charging for the test article
- Misleading advertisements
- IRB shopping

Domestic vs. Foreign Inspection Results

In FY2003 clinical site inspections overall, 36% of domestic sites were found to be in full compliance, compared to 22% of foreign clinical trial sites, according to CDER data (see exhibits below).

–continued–

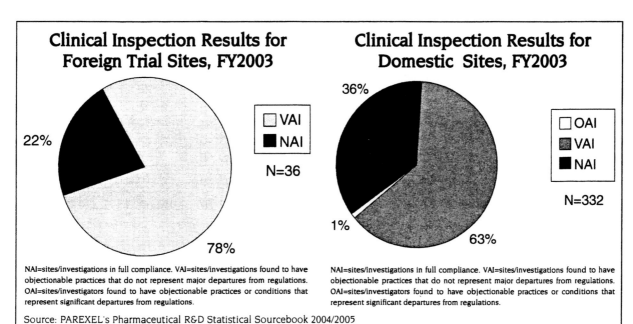

Clinical Inspection Results for Foreign Trial Sites, FY2003

22%

78%

VAI
NAI

N=36

NAI=sites/investigations in full compliance. VAI=sites/investigations found to have objectionable practices that do not represent major departures from regulations. OAI=sites/investigators found to have objectionable practices or conditions that represent significant departures from regulations.

Clinical Inspection Results for Domestic Sites, FY2003

36%

1%

63%

OAI
VAI
NAI

N=332

NAI=sites/investigations in full compliance. VAI=sites/investigations found to have objectionable practices that do not represent major departures from regulations. OAI=sites/investigators found to have objectionable practices or conditions that represent significant departures from regulations.

Source: PAREXEL's Pharmaceutical R&D Statistical Sourcebook 2004/2005

The Most Common Investigator Deficiency Categories

According to the FY2003 inspection results, problems with protocol compliance and patient records were the most common areas of noncompliance found by CDER inspectors.

Clinical Investigator Deficiency Categories, FY2003

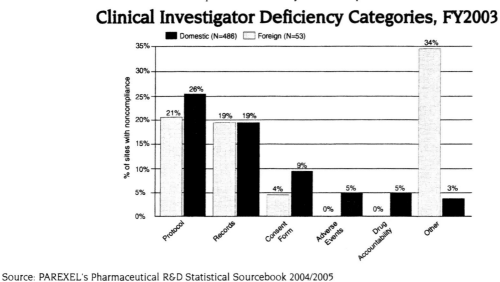

Domestic (N=486)   Foreign (N=53)

Protocol: 21%, 26%
Records: 19%, 19%
Consent Form: 4%, 9%
Adverse Events: 0%, 5%
Drug Accountability: 0%, 5%
Other: 34%, 3%

Source: PAREXEL's Pharmaceutical R&D Statistical Sourcebook 2004/2005

documentation of the reported results, and the presence of quality control techniques such as the use of standard curves.

Post-Inspectional FDA Actions

At the conclusion of all three types of inspections, the FDA inspector conducts what is called an "exit interview" with the clinical investigator. During this exchange, the two individuals discuss the inspector's findings, which will be reported to the FDA in the form of an Establishment Inspection Report (EIR).

In those cases in which an inspector observes possible violations of FDA regulations, he or she will leave wit the investigator a written statement of his/her observations on Form FDA-483, the *Inspectional Observation Forr* This statement identifies the relevant deviations from regulations, which may include protocol deviations, IR noncompliance, or inadequate informed consent. The inspection results are discussed in detail with the clir ical investigator, whose responses are recorded as part of the EIR. CDER provides a detailed discussion of th Clinical Investigator Compliance Program in its *Compliance Program Guidance Manual for Clinical Investigato* (7348.811).

When the agency determines that an investigator has repeatedly or deliberately failed to comply with regul tory standards or has submitted false information to the study's sponsor, it may disqualify that investigato from receiving investigational drugs, and thereby prevent the physician from participating in future clinical tr als. After regulatory violations are discovered, some investigators may agree to certain restrictions (e.g., pa ticipate in only a limited number of studies as a principal investigator at once, be personally involved i specified aspects of a study) in their activities regarding future studies. In rare instances in past years, th agency has agreed not to impose sanctions on certain noncompliant investigators because the investigato have given assurances for their performance in future studies (e.g., will use specific SOPs, will participate i single dose studies only).

The Sponsor/Monitor Compliance Program

Historically, CDER's Sponsor/Monitor Compliance Program has not been one of the center's most active mo itoring programs. In the past, FDA officials claimed that this has been due to several factors, including rel tively broad regulations on sponsor requirements and CDER's greater concerns about investigator activiti and compliance. Agency officials also maintained that, in comparing an NDA's data tabulations with si records during investigator inspections, CDER is also indirectly inspecting the sponsor's records and mon toring activities.

Not surprisingly given the increased focus on monitoring practices, however, CDER revised its approach sponsor/monitor inspections in the late 1990s. CDER's DSI was not only planning to conduct more spo sor/monitor inspections going forward, but also to evolve such inspections from the "information-gatherir investigations" (i.e., quick and focused reviews directed at specific records, such as randomization reports) more traditional compliance inspections, which are more comprehensive.

DSI's increased activity became obvious in FY2000 and FY2001. In each of the two years, the division co ducted 28 sponsor/monitor/CRO inspections, up from 4 in FY1998 and 10 in FY1999. CDER inspections sponsors/monitors/CROs declined markedly in FY2002 and FY2003, however, during which the center co ducted a combined 33 inspections. The downturn is likely due, at least in part, to a decline in drug applic tion submissions from industry.

"For cause" sponsor/monitor inspections, which have been less common in the past, are performed whe there are indications that a sponsor is not fulfilling its responsibilities. Due to CDER's continuing comm ment to increase its focus on voluntary complaints (see discussion above), DSI officials expect such inspe tions to rise in the future. Although the vast majority of complaints forwarded to CDER to date have focuse on clinical investigators, sponsors/monitors have been the subject of some voluntary complaints, center of cials note.

CDER initiates sponsor inspections to determine: (1) if a sponsor, a sponsor's employee, or a contract research organization (CRO) is monitoring a clinical investigation adequately; and (2) if the sponsor is fulfilling each of its requirements as outlined in existing federal regulations. The clinical sponsor and its research-related activities are the primary focus of inspections conducted under this program. It is worth mentioning, however, that the FDA may also investigate the activities of two other entities, essentially because they may assume some of the sponsor's responsibilities during a clinical study:

- Clinical Monitors. Monitors are those individuals selected by either a sponsor or contract research organization to oversee the progress of the clinical investigation. The monitor may be an employee of the sponsor, a contract research organization, or a consultant.

- Contract Research Organization (CRO). CROs are organizations or corporations that enter into contractual agreements with sponsors to perform one or more of the sponsor's duties in the clinical research process. Sponsors may delegate several of their responsibilities to a CRO, including the design of a protocol, the monitoring of clinical studies, the selection of investigators and study monitors, the evaluation of reports, and the preparation of materials to be submitted to the FDA.

Under its sponsor/monitor inspectional program, DSI continues to focus routine sponsor/monitor inspectional assignments on pending new molecular entities (NME), and to tie them to clinical investigator assignments. In other words, when DSI is called on to conduct a clinical site inspection regarding a pending NDA for an NME, it also considers conducting a sponsor/monitor inspection.

As noted, today's sponsor/monitor inspections are also more traditional compliance inspections. This means that the inspections are comprehensive investigations of the sponsor/monitor's practices, and that such inspections sometimes trigger formal regulatory communications, such as notices of adverse findings and warning letters.

The Inspection of Drug Sponsors Sponsor inspections take place at the company's headquarters, and generally involve the evaluation of records from recently conducted or active studies. According to the FDA's *Compliance Program Guidance Manual for Sponsors, Contract Research Organizations, and Monitors* (7348.810), the field inspector evaluates at least six elements of a clinical study: (1) the selection of, and directions to, a monitor; (2) test article accountability; (3) assurance of IRB approval; (4) the adequacy of facilities; (5) continuing evaluation of data; and (6) records retention.

Monitor Selection and Directions. In this aspect of the inspection, the FDA investigator determines whether the clinical monitor is adequately qualified, and whether the sponsor has given the monitor sufficient direction. Specifically, the inspector must determine:

- whether at least one individual has been charged with monitoring the progress of the investigation (if there are two or more monitors, the inspector must determine how the responsibilities are divided);

- what training, education, and experience qualify the monitor to oversee the progress of the clinical investigation;

- whether written procedures have been established for the monitoring of the clinical investigation; and

- whether the sponsor has assured that the monitor has met his or her obligations.

Test Article Accountability. The inspector must evaluate whether the sponsor maintained adequate dru accounting procedures before, during, and, if applicable, after a clinical investigation. The inspector i instructed to make six separate determinations:

- whether the sponsor maintained accounting procedures for the test article, including records showing: (1) the shipment dates, quantity, serial, batch lot or other identification number of units sent; (2) the receipt dates and the quantity of returned articles; and (3) the names of investigators;

- whether the records are sufficient to allow a comparison of the total amount of the drug shipped against the amounts used and returned by the investigator;

- whether all unused or reusable supplies of the test article were returned to the sponsor when either (1) the investigator discontinued or finished participating in the clinical investigation, or (2) the investigation was terminated;

- if all unused or reusable supplies of the test article were not returned to the sponsor, a determination of the alternate disposition of the test article and a description of how the sponsor determined the manner in which the investigator accounted for unused or reusable supplies of the test article dispensed to a subject and not returned to the investigator;

- whether the alternate disposition was adequate to ensure that humans or food-producing animals were not exposed to experimental risk; and

- whether records were maintained for alternate disposition of the test article.

Assurance of IRB Approval. For a clinical investigation subject to IRB approval, the FDA inspector must dete mine whether the sponsor maintains documentation showing that the clinical investigator obtained IR approval before any human subjects were allowed to participate in the investigation.

Ascertaining the Adequacy of Facilities. The FDA inspector must determine whether the monitor assessed th adequacy of all facilities used by the study investigator (e.g., office, clinic, hospital).

Continuing Evaluation of Data. The inspector must examine records to evaluate the clinical sponsor's eff ciency in reviewing data submitted by the investigator and in responding to reports of adverse reactions. I this aspect of the inspection, the investigator must make six determinations:

- whether the sponsor reviews all new case reports and other data received from the investigator regarding the safety of the test article within ten working days after receipt;

- whether all case reports and other data received from the investigator are periodically evaluated for effectiveness as portions of the study are completed (included in this determination are the practices of the monitor);

- what actions are taken in response to incomplete case report forms;

- whether there is a system for tabulating the frequency and character of adverse reactions;

- whether existing evidence indicates that the sponsor's present data receipt system is operating satisfactorily; and

- whether any deaths occurred among study subjects, and what actions were taken to determine whether the deaths were related to the use of the test article.

Record Retention. Finally, the inspector must determine the sponsor's compliance with whichever of the following two record retention requirements is applicable: (1) records must be retained for a period of two years after a drug's marketing application is approved; or (2) records must be retained for a period of two years following the date on which the sponsor discontinues the shipment and delivery of the drug for investigational use and so notifies the FDA.

Chapter 15

Accelerated Drug Approval/Expanded Access Programs

Over the past 25 years, various medical crises and political pressures have spurred the FDA to develop and implement several programs under which patients could gain access to desperately needed new drugs earlier than would otherwise be permitted under the conventional drug development and approval process. In creating such programs, the FDA has acknowledged that the traditional drug development process is a compromise in many respects, and that the system can be particularly costly to those in dire need of new therapeutic alternatives. After all, it is during this process that potentially valuable drugs may be withheld from patients who may need them while clinical testing and the NDA review move forward.

It is important to point out, however, that this process also protects such patients from unproven experimental drugs that may hurt them or that may keep them from using alternative and perhaps more appropriate therapies. And while critics have charged that some aspects of the drug approval process are unethical and even cruel, the FDA continues to hold that the randomized, placebo-controlled clinical trial remains the single best and most efficient vehicle for determining whether new drugs are safe and effective.

Under efforts that were sometimes called "compassionate drug use" or "emergency drug use," companies developing experimental therapies were permitted to provide the drugs to physicians not involved in the formal clinical trials in an attempt to help desperately ill patients. During the 1980s and early 1990s, however, the AIDS crisis thrust the FDA into a crucible of victim desperation and public and political pressure. Ultimately, the medical realities and politics of AIDS spurred the FDA to develop and implement several plans under which promising new therapies could reach desperately ill patients more quickly. From 1987 through 1992, the FDA developed and implemented four programs that were designed to expedite patients' access to emerging therapies, either by allowing patients access to unapproved therapies or by accelerating the drug development and review process: the treatment IND, a mechanism that provides patients with access to promising, but as-yet unapproved drugs for serious and immediately life-threatening diseases; parallel track, a plan that provides patients suffering from AIDS or AIDS-related diseases with early access to experimental-stage therapies; an accelerated drug development program for drugs designed to treat life-threatening and seriously debilitating diseases; and an accelerated drug approval program for therapies designed to treat serious or life-threatening illnesses.

For at least two reasons, the desperation and public pressure that prompted government action began to abate at least somewhat beginning in the early 1990s. First, victims of AIDS and AIDS-related conditions had a growing number of approved therapeutic options to treat their conditions. Secondly, increasing numbers of experts began to question the wisdom of providing early and expanded access to therapies whose risks ar benefits have not been characterized in traditional drug development processes. Since the early 1990s, f instance, some have questioned the relevance of the surrogate endpoints on which the approvals of the fir AIDS therapies were based.

Further, some agency advisors pointed to several patient deaths during a Phase 2 trial involving the hepatit B treatment fialuridine (FIAU) as both a warning about the dangers of expanded access plans and a confi mation of the value of traditional drug development schemes. Although FIAU was not used in an expande access program, members of the FDA's Antiviral Drugs Advisory Committee pointed out that, if the drug ha shown early activity against AIDS, it might have been used in such a scheme. Five trial-related deaths mig have become dozens or even hundreds under an expanded access program, they speculated during a 199 meeting. One member of the committee, which reviewed AIDS treatments as well, suggested that the pend lum had begun to swing away from early drug access and expedited development plans and back toward co ventional drug development programs.

During the mid-1990s, the very patient advocacy groups that had most aggressively sought earlier access unproven therapies seemed to seek what a traditional drug development process could offer: Better labelir and a more thorough assessment of a drug's safety and effectiveness. At FDA advisory committee meetin and in communications with agency officials, it was the AIDS community itself that had begun to question t use of surrogate markers, which could speed drug development but which would require validation followir a therapy's approval.

More recently, other factors seemed to undermine the appeal of at least some of these programs. For exar ple, with CDER approving high-priority new drugs in an average of 12 months or less (less than half the tin required in the early 1990s), and AIDS treatments in an average of about 6 months, some companies may r longer consider participation in these programs necessary to ensure rapid approvals and rapid patient acce to new therapies.

Despite this, the FDA's four initial expanded access and accelerated development/approval programs star largely as they did when introduced, although they are now, in some cases, less active than they once wer Further, during the mid-1990s, a pair of programs designed to expedite drug approvals took their places alon side the programs mentioned above.

In March 1996, the FDA unveiled a formal program designed to expedite the development and approval of ne cancer treatments. In response to mounting criticism over the imbalance of resources targeted to AIDS dr reviews versus those targeted to other life-threatening illnesses, the FDA established what it called t Oncology Initiative. This program brought several reforms that some analysts estimated would reduce canc drug development times by at least a year and cut average oncology drug review times from 12.4 to 6 mont (see discussion below).

A more recent evolution in the FDA's expanded access/accelerated development programs came in the for of a program authorized under the FDA Modernization Act of 1997 (FDAMA). Through this law, Congre added a program designed to facilitate the development and expedite the review of new drugs for unmet me ical needs associated with serious or life-threatening conditions. Under the "fast track" program, which inc porates and, therefore, mirrors the accelerated approval program and similar programs in many respec Congress introduced certain new provisions, including the submission of "rolling"—or incomplete—NDAs f agency review (see discussion below).

Congress also used FDAMA to codify, in the Food, Drug and Cosmetic Act, some of the FDA's existing expanded access programs for which federal regulations already provided:

Access to Experimental Drugs in Emergency Situations. FDAMA added to the FD&C Act a new section specifically allowing the FDA to authorize the shipment of investigational drugs designed to diagnose, monitor, or treat a serious disorder or condition in so-called "emergency situations." This element of the law essentially codified existing FDA regulations, which permit the agency to authorize the shipment of a drug for a specified emergency use in advance of an IND submission (see Chapter 3). In its discussions of experimental drug access programs, the agency has also mentioned "special exemptions," or "compassionate exemptions," which can be used when a particular patient cannot meet the eligibility criteria of a certain study protocol. If a sponsor and investigator agree to treat a patient under a special exemption, a request that includes the rationale for the request and a brief patient history must be submitted to the agency.

"Individual Patient Access" to Investigational Drugs. FDAMA also adds to the FD&C Act provisions that permit a patient, through a licensed physician, to request from a manufacturer or distributor access to an investigational drug intended to diagnose, monitor, or treat a serious disease or condition. A manufacturer or distributor may provide such a drug to a physician under the following circumstances: (1) the physician determines that the patient has no comparable or satisfactory alternative therapy and that the probable risk from the investigational drug does not surpass the probable risk from the disease or condition; (2) the FDA determines that there is sufficient evidence of the drug's safety and effectiveness to support its use in this situation; (3) the FDA determines that permitting the use of the drug in this instance will not interfere with the initiation, conduct, or completion of the clinical investigations designed to support marketing approval; and (4) the drug's sponsor or clinical investigator submits a clinical protocol consistent with the regulations associated with treatment use in a single patient or a small group of patients (see discussion on treatment INDs below).

Treatment INDs. FDAMA essentially codified in law the FDA's existing treatment IND regulations (see discussion below). Upon the submission of what FDAMA terms an "expanded access protocol," which is equivalent to a treatment IND or treatment protocol, by a sponsor or clinical investigator, the FDA will permit an investigational drug to be made available for widespread patient access under a treatment IND, provided that specific conditions are met, including that the drug is for the diagnosis or treatment of a serious or life-threatening disease or condition. FDAMA also authorizes the agency to inform national, state, and local medical associations, health organizations, and other appropriate groups about the availability of investigational drugs under expanded access protocols.

Today, the FDA is busily working to tweak its various accelerated approval and expanded access programs on several fronts:

- In August 2004, FDA officials promised to move ahead on a proposed rule to liberalize the "treatment use" of investigational drugs by early 2005. Specifically, the agency will issue a proposed rule that will provide patients suffering from serious or life-threatening conditions with greater access to developmental-stage drugs. According to the federal government's June 2004 Unified Agenda, the proposed rule will make the treatment use of investigational drugs available to: (1) individual patients, including in emergencies; (2) intermediate size patient populations; and (3) larger populations under a treatment protocol or IND. For the last several years, agency officials have talked about developing a proposed regulation on treatment use that would outline the agency's criteria for a variety of drug access options under which patients not enrolled in formal clinical trials can gain access to experimental therapies. At June 2001 congressional hearings prompted by the increased attention that

FDA policies regarding patient access to experimental therapies have received due in part to the promise of developmental-stage cancer treatments, FDA officials emphasized that they "actively support" wider access to drugs prior to approval.

- In 2003 and 2004, the FDA worked to revise its interpretation of the eligibility criteria for its accelerated approval (Subpart H) and fast track programs to eliminate what it saw as a barrier to the development of products under these plans. Because an accelerated approval or fast track designation could be granted only for drugs that met an "unmet medical need," the FDA held that the approval of a first drug for this unmet indication was, in effect, a grant of market exclusivity (i.e., because other drugs for the same indication could not then meet the "unmet medical need" criterion). At a May 2003 oncology meeting, then-FDA Commissioner Mark McClellan, M.D., Ph.D., noted that the agency had modified its accelerated drug approval policies to permit the agency to clear multiple cancer drugs for a single indication. McClellan noted that the agency took this step "so that for cancer drugs that have met accelerated approval, other products will also be able to get accelerated approval status for that indication until one of these therapies actually demonstrates in its Phase 4 study commitments a confirmatory clinical benefit in patients." In July 2004, the agency then revised its September 1998 fast track guidance to "make it clear that a drug can be said to address an unmet medical need if the only available treatments for the condition are approved under the accelerated approval regulations (21 CFR 314.500 and 601.40), either on the basis of an effect on a surrogate endpoint or with restrictions on distribution." Therefore, the agency noted, "if the only therapies that exist for a condition are approved under the accelerated approval regulations on the basis of a surrogate endpoint or are approved with restrictions on distribution necessary to ensure the safe use of the drug, FDA may designate a product as fast track notwithstanding the availability of other therapies approved under the accelerated approval regulations."

- Through a July 2004 final guidance, the FDA established a new regulatory definition to address uncertainty regarding the interpretation of terms associated with virtually all of the agency's accelerated approval/development and expanded access programs. In the guidance entitled, *Available Therapy*, the agency attempts to put to rest uncertainty regarding the term "available therapy" and related terms such as "existing treatments" and "existing therapy," all of which are important elements in determining a drug's eligibility for treatment INDs, accelerated development (Subpart E), accelerated approval (Subpart H), fast track, and priority review. Each of these programs incorporates the concept that the FDA can regulate a particular product in a certain manner because of a lack of available therapy or because of the product's advantage over available therapy. Confusion, the agency notes, persists over whether "available therapy refers only to products approved by FDA for the use in question, or whether the term could also refer to products used off-label or to treatments not regulated by FDA, such as surgery." Because the regulations and policies for the above-mentioned programs do not explicitly define the term, CDER states that: "*available therapy* (and the terms *existing treatments* and *existing therapy*) should be interpreted as therapy that is specified in the approved labeling of regulated products, with only rare exceptions." About its definition, the FDA notes that "most of the Agency programs that use the term *available therapy* are intended to encourage the development and expedite the review of innovative drug products. By defining *available therapy* to focus on approved products with labeling for use in the disease or condition at issue, FDA (1) emphasizes the importance of the approval process for establishing that a drug is safe and effective for a particular use and (2) provides the greatest opportunity for development and approval of appropriately labeled drugs. For these programs, products that are used off-label for the indication at issue and products that have not had formal FDA review are rarely considered *available therapy*; the definition of *available therapy* in this guidance provides only a limited exception for particularly well-documented therapies."

- To expedite global access to HIV/AIDS therapies, the FDA announced an expedited review process to ensure that the U.S. is providing safe, effective drugs to developing countries under the Bush Administration's $15 billion Emergency Plan for AIDS Relief. In May 2004, the FDA and HHS announced an "expedited pathway" for the FDA to review low-cost, safe and effective fixed dose combination, co-packaged, and single-ingredient HIV/AIDS therapies so these products can be provided to developing countries. The pathway, under which the FDA hopes to review and approve products in six weeks, will apply to new products that combine already approved individual HIV/AIDS therapies into a single dose, as well as to new co-packaging of existing therapies. The agency issued a May 2004 draft guidance for the expedited pathway, under which the FDA had approved two new fixed-dose combinations by August 2004.

Further, under PDUFA III, the FDA is formally studying the costs and benefits of two of the cornerstones of many of its existing accelerated approval and expanded access plans—close sponsor/agency interactions during the development process and the presubmission of elements of an NDA. Under continuous marketing application (CMA) Pilot 1, the agency will accept the presubmission of so-called "reviewable units" in advance of an NDA's submission, and will formally assess whether this approach leads to a more efficient review. Under CMA Pilot 2, the agency will enter into agreements to engage NDA sponsors in "frequent scientific feedback and interactions" during the clinical development process and will assess whether such "enhanced interaction" improves the efficiency and effectiveness of development programs. In part, these assessments are designed to provide the first empirical evidence necessary to determine whether the agency and industry should continue to invest in such efforts.

The following discussions highlight the principal expanded access/accelerated approval programs mentioned above.

The Treatment IND

Although the FDA had been pressured to reform clinical testing methodologies in the past, the unique issues posed by AIDS highlighted the drawbacks of the drug development process perhaps as never before. As Burroughs Wellcome's AZT, or Retrovir, emerged as the first therapy to show promise in treating AIDS, victims of the disease not fortunate enough to be enrolled in clinical trials refused to die silently in the name of science. While the intense public debate that followed was often bitter, it was not unproductive. After early clinical studies of AZT showed promising results, the FDA quickly reviewed what it called a treatment IND, under which more than 4,000 patients were allowed access to AZT while the drug underwent final FDA review.

The realities of AIDS first brought formal changes to FDA regulations on May 22, 1987, when the agency published a final rule allowing the treatment use and sale of investigational drugs intended to treat desperately ill patients. Specifically, the regulations were "intended to facilitate the availability of promising new drugs as early in the drug development process as possible...to patients with serious and life-threatening diseases for which no comparable or satisfactory alternative drug or other therapies exist."

In many respects, the treatment IND was a compromise that attempted to satisfy those who believed that the desperately ill should have unlimited access to an emerging therapy, and those who believed that a developmental-stage drug should be withheld from patients outside the clinical trial setting until such testing is com pleted and is judged to have demonstrated the drug's safety and effectiveness. Under a treatment IND, des perately ill patients gain access to a promising drug while the all-important clinical development and FD review of a drug continue.

Although it was the AIDS crisis that eventually brought the FDA to formalize the treatment IND as it is no known, agency officials point out that the treatment IND has its roots in the 1960s and 1970s. At that time applications commonly referred to as "compassionate INDs" were used to make unapproved antiarrhythmic calcium channel blockers, and beta blockers accessible to patients intolerant to other therapies. In the earl 1980s, FDA regulations formally recognized the treatment IND, allowing its use in cases in which: (1) ther was sufficient evidence of safety and effectiveness; (2) the potential benefits outweighed the risks; and (3) th medical condition under study was a serious disease with no satisfactory therapies.

The 1987 regulations took a relatively loose concept and, for the first time, defined the treatment IND's pu pose, established more specific criteria for the treatment IND/treatment protocol submission, and describe how and when the treatment IND could be used. The regulations specify the point in a product's developmer at which treatment use may begin, a key factor since preapproval accessibility was the primary goal of th treatment IND.

To qualify for treatment use under the FDA's treatment IND regulations, a drug must meet four principal cr teria. According to federal regulations, "FDA shall permit an investigational drug to be used for a treatmer use under a treatment protocol or treatment IND if: (i) The drug is intended to treat a serious or immediate ly life-threatening disease; (ii) There is no comparable or satisfactory alternative drug or other therapy avai able to treat that stage of the disease in the intended patient population; (iii) The drug is under investigatio in a controlled clinical trial under an IND in effect for the trial, or all clinical trials have been completed; an (iv) The sponsor of the controlled trial is actively pursuing approval of the investigational drug with due dil gence." In FDAMA's codification of the FDA's treatment IND regulations, the law reiterates the four criteri above and specifies one additional criterion: For drugs being tested in a controlled clinical trial, the avai ability of an investigational drug under a treatment use must not interfere with the enrollment of patients i the ongoing investigation.

The second criterion noted above deserves a brief discussion, primarily because the entire treatment IND cor cept is designed for desperately ill individuals with no therapeutic alternatives. Responding to concern abou its interpretation of the "no comparable or satisfactory alternative drug or other therapy available" requir ment for treatment IND eligibility, the FDA clarified that this standard is met "when there are patients who a not adequately treated by available therapies, even if the particular disease does respond in some cases t available therapy. This criterion would be met, for example, if the intended population is for patients who hav failed on an existing therapy (i.e., the existing therapy did not provide its intended therapeutic benefit or di not fully treat the condition); for patients who could not tolerate the existing therapy (i.e., it caused una ceptable adverse effects); or for patients who had other complicating diseases that made the existing ther py unacceptable (e.g., concomitant disease making available therapy contraindicated) for the patiel population."

In reality, FDA regulations provide for two different treatment IND vehicles—one for drugs designed to tre immediately life-threatening illnesses, and the other for drugs intended to treat serious diseases. The timir of, and FDA criteria for granting, treatment INDs for the two types of indications differ considerably.

Treatment Use for Immediately Life-Threatening Conditions Under the May 1987 regulations, the FDA defined "immediately life-threatening disease" as a stage of a disease in which there is a reasonable likelihood that death will occur within a matter of months or in which premature death is likely without early treatment. The agency claimed that it would apply a common sense definition so that death within more than a year would not normally be considered immediately life threatening, but that death within several days or even several weeks would fall under the definition.

For illustrative purposes, the FDA identified in the regulations nine diseases that would "normally" be considered immediately life threatening: advanced cases of AIDS, advanced congestive heart failure (New York Heart Association Class IV), recurrent sustained ventricular tachycardia or ventricular fibrillation, herpes simplex encephalitis, most advanced metastatic refractory cancers, far advanced emphysema, severe combined immunodeficiency syndrome, bacterial endocarditis, and subarachnoid hemorrhage (see listing below of treatment INDs approved).

Provided that a drug meets the four principal criteria outlined above, the FDA may only deny a treatment IND "if the available scientific evidence, taken as a whole, fails to provide a reasonable basis for concluding that the drug: (A) May be effective for its intended use in its intended patient population; or (B) Would not expose the patients to whom the drug is to be administered to an unreasonable and significant additional risk of illness or injury." The rather vague efficacy standard was discussed just briefly in the regulation's preamble, which stated that, "...the level of evidence needed is well short of that needed for a new drug approval—and may be less than what would be needed to support treatment use in diseases that are serious but not immediately life-threatening."

One of the more hotly debated aspects of the treatment IND regulations was the timing of treatment programs for drugs used against immediately life-threatening conditions. Some regarded the FDA's criteria as too liberal, and claimed that these criteria allow general accessibility before a drug development program can be expected to provide sufficient evidence of safety and/or effectiveness. The FDA, however, held to the provisions of its early proposals, and allowed drugs for immediately life-threatening conditions to be "made available for treatment use...earlier than Phase 3, but ordinarily not earlier than Phase 2."

The FDA emphasized, however, that available scientific evidence, rather than simply the phase of development, is more important to its decision-making process: "FDA expects that data from controlled clinical trials will ordinarily be available at the time a treatment IND is requested. However, FDA is committed to reviewing and considering all available evidence, including results of domestic and foreign clinical trials, animal data, and, where pertinent, in vitro data. FDA will also consider clinical experience from outside a controlled trial, where the circumstances surrounding an experience provide sufficient indication of scientific value."

Treatment Use for Serious Conditions The FDA's criteria for granting treatment INDs for serious conditions were considerably less controversial than those for immediately life-threatening illnesses. Interestingly, however, the FDA provided no specific definition of "serious" in either the treatment IND proposal or final rule. The agency did give examples of serious conditions: Alzheimer's disease, advanced multiple sclerosis, advanced Parkinson's disease, transient ischemic attacks, progressive ankylosing spondylitis, active advanced lupus erythematosus, certain forms of epilepsy, nonacidotic or hyperosmolar diabetes, and paroxysmal supraventricular tachycardia.

To qualify for treatment use, drugs intended to treat serious illnesses must meet a tougher, if more vague, safety and effectiveness standard than that described above for life-threatening conditions. The FDA "may deny a request for treatment use...if there is insufficient evidence of safety and effectiveness to suppo such use."

Considering this requirement, it is not surprising that treatment INDs for serious illnesses are more likely t be granted later in the clinical development process than are therapies for immediately life-threatening cor ditions: "In the case of serious diseases, a drug ordinarily may be made available for treatment use...durin Phase 3 investigations or after all clinical trials have been completed; however, in appropriate circumstance a drug may be made available for treatment use during Phase 2."

Obtaining FDA Permission for Treatment Use Both drug sponsors and practicing physicians may pursu FDA approval for a treatment use. The sponsor of a drug's IND may do so through a treatment protocol, whil "licensed practitioners" must submit a treatment IND.

According to FDA regulations, a sponsor-submitted treatment protocol must provide:

- the intended use of the drug;
- an explanation of the rationale for use of the drug, including, as appropriate, either a list of what available regimens ordinarily should be tried before using the investigational drug, or an explanation of why the use of the investigational drug is preferable to the use of avail- able marketed treatments;
- a brief description of the criteria for patient selection;
- the method of administration and the dosages of the drug; and
- a description of clinical procedures, laboratory tests, or other measures designed to moni- tor the effects of the drug and to minimize risk.

Additionally, a treatment protocol must "be supported" by an informational brochure for each treating phys cian, technical information relevant to the safety and effectiveness of the drug for the intended treatment pu pose, and a commitment by the sponsor to ensure the compliance of all participating investigators wit informed consent requirements.

Like a traditional IND submission, a treatment protocol becomes active 30 days after the FDA receives th protocol, or on earlier notification by the FDA that the treatment use may begin. Of course, treatment prot cols are also subject to clinical holds any time after submission.

If a practicing physician wants to obtain for treatment use a drug whose sponsor will not establish a trea ment protocol for this purpose, the practitioner must submit his or her own treatment IND. Such application must contain:

- a cover sheet (Form FDA 1571);
- information on the drug's chemistry, manufacturing, and controls, and prior clinical and nonclinical experience with the drug (when not provided by the sponsor either directly or through the incorporation-by-reference of information in the existing IND);
- a statement of the steps taken by the practitioner to obtain the drug from the sponsor under a treatment protocol;
- a treatment protocol containing all the information required for such a submission (see dis- cussion above);

- a statement of the practitioner's qualifications to use the investigational drug for the intended treatment use;

- the practitioner's statement of familiarity with information on the drug's safety and effectiveness derived from previous clinical and nonclinical experience with the drug; and

- the practitioner's commitment to report to the FDA safety information in accordance with current regulations.

The licensed practitioner who submits a treatment IND is the "sponsor-investigator" for such an IND, and is responsible for meeting all applicable sponsor and investigator responsibilities. Like standard INDs and treatment protocols, treatment INDs may be initiated 30 days after their submission or upon earlier notification by the FDA.

The Sale of Investigational Drugs The FDA's treatment IND regulations also feature provisions that allow sponsors to sell investigational drugs under some conditions. Drug sponsors may not "commercialize an investigational drug by charging a price larger than that necessary to recover costs of manufacture, research, development, and handling of the investigational drug," however.

According to federal regulations, a sponsor may charge for an investigational drug under a treatment protocol or treatment IND, provided that: "(i) There is adequate enrollment in the ongoing clinical investigations under the authorized IND; (ii) charging does not constitute commercial marketing of a new drug for which a marketing application has not been approved; (iii) the drug is not being commercially promoted or advertised; and (iv) the sponsor of the drug is actively pursuing marketing approval with due diligence."

At least 30 days prior to selling an investigational drug for treatment use, a sponsor must notify the FDA in writing and, with this notification, include a certified statement that the requested price is not greater than the amount necessary to recover costs associated with the drug's manufacture, research, development, and handling. If the FDA does not contact the sponsor within the 30-day review period, the sponsor is free to begin selling the drug.

A sponsor may also sell a drug in any clinical trial, provided the sponsor can gain the FDA's prior permission. To obtain this permission, the sponsor must provide an adequate explanation of why sale of the drug is necessary to either begin or continue a trial. In late 2004, the FDA was developing a proposed rule to expand the conditions under which it would permit charging for investigational drugs.

Unfortunately, the final regulations give few details on how a company can show that the sale of a drug is necessary or how this necessity should be determined. The regulation's preamble states that "charging for investigational drugs during a clinical trial would normally not be allowed... FDA believes that cost recovery is justified in clinical trials only when necessary to further the study and development of a promising drug that might otherwise be lost to the medical armamentarium. The agency believes that this situation is most likely to arise in the context of new products derived through biotechnology which are produced by small, medium and large firms alike."

The FDA has approved the sale of at least 14 of the 44 investigational products tested under the treatment IND program from June 1987 through February 2002. Among the more recent products that the agency has permitted to be sold under the treatment IND program are Orphan Medical's narcolepsy treatment Xyrem (sodium oxybate) and Chi Rho Clin's synthetic porcine secretin for the evaluation of exocrine pancreatic function and the diagnosis of gastrinoma.

Although the FDA granted 44 treatment INDs from June 1987 though February 2002, the submission an approval of treatment INDs have diminished considerably since the early 1990s (see listing below). Fror January 1996 through February 2002, for example, the agency granted just seven treatment INDs (one in eac year). The reasons, many believe, are related partly to continuing industry ambivalence toward the IND pr gram, perhaps because of issues related to the potential costs, complexities and liabilities associated wit expanded access. And while the agency still recommends treatment INDs to some sponsors, it is also obv ous that the FDA has never been as aggressive in recruiting treatment INDs as it once was under Frank Youn M.D., who was the FDA commissioner when the program was introduced and who left the agency in 1989.

In addition to granting treatment INDs for HIV/AIDS therapies, the agency has granted treatment INDs fc severe sepsis, the diagnosis of gastrinoma, the treatment of subfoveal choroidal neovascularization se ondary to age-related macular degeneration, narcolepsy, in vitro fertilization, and the management of sever chronic pain.

It is worth noting that another expanded access program, called the Group C program, is considered to be subset of the larger treatment IND program. Established under an agreement between the FDA and Nation Cancer Institute (NCI), the Group C treatment IND provides a mechanism for distributing investigational car cer agents to oncologists outside a controlled clinical trial. Group C drugs, which are typically in Phase 3 tr als and have shown evidence of relative and reproducible efficacy in a specific tumor type, are distributed on by the NCI under an NCI protocol.

The FDA's Accelerated Drug Development Program (Subpart E)

By mid-1988, the FDA had successfully implemented several initiatives designed to make drugs more acce sible through both preapproval availability plans and speedier reviews. At that time, the treatment IND regi lations were in effect, and seven experimental therapies had been made available to patients with AID: cancer, Parkinson's disease, and other life-threatening conditions. In addition, the agency had established new level of review priority for all AIDS products, and had created a new drug review division to focus on eva uating these therapies. The FDA credited such initiatives with the rapid availability and review of AZT, whic the agency approved only 107 days after the submission of Burroughs Wellcome's NDA.

In August 1988, then-Vice President George Bush, in his capacity as the chairman of the Presidential Ta: Force on Regulatory Relief, asked the FDA to build on these "successes" by developing procedures for exp diting the marketing of new therapies intended to treat AIDS and other life-threatening illnesses. In the tw months that followed, FDA officials met with representatives from other government agencies, AIDS group and consumer, health, and academic organizations to obtain input on developing this program.

The FDA released such a plan on October 21, 1988: its *Interim Rules on Procedures for Drugs Intended to Treat Lij Threatening and Severely Debilitating Illnesses*, or Subpart E procedures. The interim rule, which the FDA claime was based on its experience with AZT, was described by the agency as an attempt "to speed the availability new therapies to desperately ill patients, while preserving appropriate guarantees for safety and effectivenes These procedures are intended to facilitate the development, evaluation, and marketing of such product especially where no satisfactory therapies exist. These procedures reflect the recognition that physicians ar patients are generally willing to accept greater risks or side effects from products that treat life-threatenir and severely debilitating illnesses than they would accept from products that treat less serious illnesse These procedures also reflect the recognition that the benefits of the drug need to be evaluated in light of tl

Designated Treatment INDs: June 1987-February 2002

(drugs and biologics)

Generic (Trade Name)	Sponsor	Indication	Designation Date
Cytomegalovirus immunoglobulin[b,o]	Mass. Dept. of Public Health	Prevention of cytomegalo-virus infections in certain renal transplant patients	10/19/87
Ifosfamide[c,e,o] (Ifex)	NCI/BMS	Testicular cancer (in conjunction w/mesna)	12/24/87
Mesna[c,o] (Mesnex)	NCI/Asta	Hemorrhagic cystitis (in conjunction w/ifosfamide)	12/24/87
Trimetrexate[e,o] (Neutrexin)	NIAID/Warner-Lambert (licensed to U.S. Bioscience)	PCP	2/12/88
Clomipramine (Anafranil)	Ciba Geigy	Severe OCD	6/3/88
Selegiline[o] (Eldepryl)	Somerset	Parkinson's	6/16/88
Pentostatin[c,e,o] (Nipent)	NCI/Warner-Lambert	Hairy cell leukemia	7/28/88
Teniposide[c,o] (Vumon)	NCI/BMS	Refractory acute lymphoblastic leukemia	10/7/88
Gancyclovir[e] (Cytovene)	NIAID/Syntex	Cytomegalovirus retinitis	11/28/88
Aerosolized Pentamadine Isethionate[e,o] (Nebupent)	Lyphomed/Fujisawa	PCP (AIDS) [new formulation]	2/3/89
Levamisole HCL[c] (Ergamisol)	NCI/Janssen	Colon cancer (in conjunction w/ 5-flurouracil)	5/4/89
Erythropoietin[b,o] (Eprex)	Ortho	AIDS-associated anemia [new indication]	6/27/89
Colfosceril Palmitate[e,o] (Exosurf neonatal)	Burr. Wellcome	Neonatal respiratory distress syndrome	7/26/89
Didanosine/ddl[a] (Videx)	NIAID/BMS	AZT-intolerant AIDS-related Complex	9/28/89
Beractant[b,e,o] (Survanta)	Abbott	Neonatal respiratory distress syndrome	9/29/89
Zidovudine/AZT[a] (Retrovir syrup)	Burr. Wellcome	AIDS in children [new indication]	10/26/89
Alglucerase[b,e,o] (Ceredase)	NINDS/Genzyme	Gaucher's disease	11/7/89
Fludarabine Phosphate[c,e,o] (Fludara)	NCI/Triton Biosciences*	Chronic lymphocytic leukemia	11/24/89
Baclofen Intrathecal[d,o] (Lioresal)	Medtronic	Spasticity in oral baclofen-intolerant MS/SCI patients [new formulation]	3/7/90
Sargramostim/ GM-CSF[b,o] (Leukine)	Immunex	Neutropenia due to bone marrow transplant	9/24/90
Zalcitabine/ddC[a,o] (Hivid)	Hoffmann La Roche	AZT-intolerant ARC/AIDS patients	5/30/91
Perfosfamide/4-HC[o] (Pergamid)	Scios-Nova	Ex vivo treatment of bone marrow	6/14/91
Oxandrolone[o] (Oxandrin)	Gynex**	Boys with constitutional delay of puberty [new indication]	10/17/91

—continued—

Designated Treatment INDs: June 1987-February 2002 (continued)

Generic (Trade Name)	Sponsor	Indication	Designation Date
Atovaquone[e,o] (Mepron)	Burr. Wellcome	PCP	11/8/91
Tacrine (Cognex)	Warner-Lambert	Alzheimer's disease	12/02/91
Rifabutin[e,o] (Mycobutin)	Adria	Prophylaxis of myco-bacterium avium complex	3/6/92
Cladribine/2-CDA[c,o] (Leustatin)	Ortho	Hairy cell leukemia	3/6/92
Paclitaxel[c] (Taxol)	BMS	Ovarian cancer	7/15/92
Oxandrolone[o] (Oxandrin)	Gynex**	Girls with Turner's Syndrome [new indication]	10/21/92
Copolymer-1[o] (Copaxone)	Teva Marion Partners	Multiple sclerosis	1/5/93
Metformin (Glucophage)	Lipha	Non-insulin dependent diabetes mellitus	9/10/93
Vinorelbine (Navelbine)	Burr. Wellcome	Non-small cell lung cancer	4/14/94
Human Growth Hormone[b,e,o] (Serostim)	Serono	AIDS-associated wasting/weight loss	12/20/94
Gemcitalbine HCl (Gemzar)	Lilly	Locally advanced or metastatic pancreatic cancer	1/27/95
Atorvastatin (Lipitor)	Warner-Lambert	Homozygous familial hypercholesterolemia or severe refractory hypercholesterolemia	2/9/95
Riluzole[o] (Rilutek)	RPR	Amyotrophic lateral sclerosis (ALS)	6/20/95
Cell Therapy[b,o] Autologous Peripheral Blood Lymphocytes	Cellcor	Treatment of metastatic (Stage IV) renal cell carcinoma	9/15/95
Cidofovir[b] (Vistide)	Gilead	Relapsing cytomegalovirus retinitis	9/1/95
Carmustine Wafer[o] (Gliadel)	Guilford/RPR	Recurrent malignant glioma-intracranial therapy	10/27/95
Insulin-like Growth Factor IGF[o] (Myotrophin)	Cephalon/Chiron	Protein-based therapeutic treatment of amyotrophic lateral sclerosis	6/24/96
Nelfinavir mesylate (Viracept)	Agouron	Protease inhibitor for use by patients for whom other treatments have failed	9/12/96
Progestereone Vaginal Gel (Crinone)	Columbia Research Labs	In vitro fertilization	2/7/97
Xyrem (sodium oxybate)	Orphan Medical	Narcolepsy	12/16/98
Verteporfin (Visudyne)	QLT Photo Therapeutics	Subfoveal choroidal neovascularization secondary to age-related macular degeneration	7/8/99
Synthetic Porcine Secretin	Chin Rho Clin	Evaluation of exocrine pancreatic function/ diagnosis of gastrinoma	11/1/00
Human, Recombinant, Human Kidney Cells (Activated Protein C)	Lilly	Severe sepsis	1/8/01
Ziconotide	Elan	Management of severe, chronic pain	1/18/02

a=accelerated approval; b=biological; c=group C cancer drug; d=device; e=Subpart E designation; o=orphan drug designation. * Berlex acquired Triton Biosciences in 1990; ** Gynex merged with Bio-Technology General in 1993.

Source: Shulman, SR, Tufts Center for the Study of Drug Development, June 1997; FDA

severity of the disease being treated. The procedures apply to products intended to treat acquired immunod-eficiency syndrome (AIDS), some cancers, and other life-threatening and severely debilitating illnesses."

Like the treatment IND program, the FDA's accelerated development plan was announced with considerable fanfare and, in turn, was met by some degree of skepticism. Even officials within the FDA review units responsible for the approval of AIDS and cancer therapies claimed that the plan's primary elements—close sponsor consultation and an accelerated clinical testing scheme—were already common practice.

But because it provides for a drug's approval before its sale, the accelerated development program had three key advantages over the treatment IND, according to the FDA: (1) no limitations were put on the pricing or profitability of FDA-approved drugs; (2) consumers who bought FDA-approved drugs were eligible for third-party reimbursement, for which patients under treatment INDs could not qualify; and (3) FDA approval conferred some liability protection to manufacturers.

Essentially, there were four key components to the FDA's expedited development plan: (1) early and increased FDA and sponsor consultation aimed at formulating agreements on the design of preclinical and clinical studies needed for marketing approval; (2) the "compression" of Phase 3 clinical trials into Phase 2 testing; (3) the FDA's adoption of a modified medical risk-benefit analysis when assessing the safety and effectiveness of qualifying drugs; and (4) the use of Phase 4 postmarketing studies to obtain additional information about drug risks, benefits, and optimal use.

Eligibility for Accelerated Development Eligibility was perhaps the most fascinating aspect of the interim regulation when it was first released. Recognizing the great opportunities that expedited approval could offer, the drug industry quickly turned to the agency for guidance on which products might qualify for the plan.

In general terms, the expedited development program applies to new drugs, antibiotics, and biologics under study for treating life-threatening or severely debilitating diseases. As was true for every other regulation, the scope of this interim rule was subject to FDA interpretation, which the agency based on two primary definitions:

- *Life-Threatening Conditions.* For the purposes of the plan, "life-threatening" illnesses include: "(1) Diseases or conditions where the likelihood of death is high unless the course of the disease is interrupted; and (2) Diseases or conditions with potentially fatal outcomes, where the end point of clinical trial analysis is survival." Any disease whose progression is likely to lead to death, particularly in a short period (e.g. six months to one year), would also fall under this definition, as would any "condition on which a study is to be carried out to determine whether the treatment has a beneficial effect on survival (e.g., increased survival after a stroke or heart attack)."

- *Severely Debilitating Conditions.* The FDA has defined "severely debilitating" illnesses as "diseases or conditions that cause major irreversible morbidity," such as severe function deficits in multiple sclerosis, Alzheimer's disease, or progressive ankylosing spondylitis, and blindness due to cytomegalovirus infection in AIDS patients." The agency cautioned that accelerated development would be relevant only for studies that "will examine the treatment's capacity to prevent or reverse what would otherwise be irreversible damage such as putting ankylosing spondylitis into remission and stopping joint damage and deformity, or preventing blindness."

Despite these definitions, eligibility remained a widely discussed issue in the months following the interim rule's publication. To help educate industry as well as its own staff, the FDA completed a retrospective review of approximately 200 new molecular entities (NME) approved during the 1980s to determine which of thes would have been eligible under the new rules. The agency also reviewed its existing inventory of approx mately 10,000 drug INDs, and reportedly contacted the sponsors of qualifying drugs.

The Cornerstone of Accelerated Development: Early FDA-Sponsor Consultation Despite serious ques tions about whether the agency should involve itself in the research process, FDA officials maintained tha early consultation was the single most critical element of this program. The FDA believes that the insights has gained in reviewing both acceptable and unacceptable drug applications could prove invaluable to spor sors, and that close consultation would allow the agency to share its expertise in the planning and design c both preclinical and clinical development programs.

According to the FDA's interim rule, FDA-sponsor consultations would take two forms:

- Pre-Investigational New Drug Application (IND) Meetings. Prior to an IND submission, the sponsor may request a meeting "to review and reach agreement on the design of animal studies needed to initiate human testing. The meeting may also provide an opportunity for discussing the scope and design of Phase 1 testing, and the best approach for presentation and formatting of data in the IND."

- End-of-Phase 1 Meetings. In the FDA's ideal accelerated drug development program, Phase 3 clinical trials are "compressed" into Phase 2 studies, which then provide the data on which the drug is to be approved. Therefore, after Phase 1 data are available, the sponsor may again request a meeting to "review and reach agreement on the design of Phase 2 controlled clinical trials, with the goal that such testing will be adequate to provide sufficient data on the drug's safety and effectiveness to support a decision on its approvability for marketing."

Restructuring Clinical Trials In attempting to use data derived from Phase 2 trials as the basis for the fin approval of a new drug, the FDA brought about, in theory at least, a reasonably significant departure from tr traditional drug development and approval path. Interestingly, however, the FDA drug review divisior responsible for evaluating AIDS and cancer therapies claimed to have approved desperately needed ne drugs based upon Phase 2 clinical data well before the plan's introduction.

Under the accelerated development scheme, Phase 3 trials are "compressed" into Phase 2 studies, with Phas 1 trials taking on the significance of conventional Phase 2 studies. According to the interim rule, "to increas the likelihood that phase 2 testing can provide sufficient results, sponsors could need to plan phase 2 stu ies that are somewhat larger and more extensive than is currently the norm, including a mode for replicatic of key findings. Moreover, to avoid missing an effect by using too little drug, or to avoid studying a dose th proves toxic, it may be necessary to study several doses in the first formal trials, an approach that may requi a larger study but can plainly save time, thereby enabling physicians to treat patients with life-threatening il nesses more rapidly. However, it should be appreciated that if a drug has only minor or inconsistent ther peutic benefits, its positive effects may be missed in this stage of clinical testing, even if the drug ultimate proves to be beneficial following more extensive phase 3 trials."

On the issue of the quantity of data needed for approval, the FDA stated that, in most cases, two pivotal Phas 2 studies would be necessary: "...the agency cautions that persuasively dramatic results are rare and that tw entirely independent studies will generally be required." The approvals of the first AIDS drugs under the acce erated program, however, indicated that the FDA was willing to base the approval of desperately needed dru on a single pivotal study.

Other Provisions of the Interim Rule The FDA's interim rule contained key provisions in several other areas, including the following:

- Treatment IND. The accelerated development plan was not meant to eliminate the need for treatment INDs. In fact, when the preliminary analyses of Phase 2 results appear promising, the FDA may ask the sponsor to submit a treatment IND, under which the test drug could be made available while the sponsor prepares, and the FDA reviews, the NDA.

- FDA Risk-Benefit Analysis. According to the interim rule, the "FDA will consider the serious-ness of the disease being treated in balancing risks and benefits... Clearly, for a life-threat-ening illness, a relatively high level of known risks and some uncertainty about potential risk from the drug can be acceptable in exchange for the improved survival provided by effective drug treatment for a condition that, if left untreated, would result in death. Similarly, for the same life-threatening illnesses, evidence of effectiveness must be weighed against risks of the drug and the knowledge that death would result in the absence of treatment."

- Phase 4 Testing. Although FDA officials state that approvals granted under the accelerated plan are in no way conditional on sponsor willingness to conduct postmarketing testing, the agency says that it "...may seek agreement from the sponsor to conduct certain postmarketing (phase 4) studies to delineate additional information about the drug's risks, benefits, and opti-mal use. These studies could include, but would not be limited to, studying different doses or schedules of administration than were used in phase 2 studies, use of the drug in other patient populations or other stages of the disease, or use of the drug over a longer period of time."

The limited data that are available suggest that the Subpart E program may have become less relevant given the availability of other options for industry. According to research by the Tufts Center for the Study of Drug Development, the FDA had approved 48 drugs under the Subpart E regulations from October 1988 through December 1999. The study also indicates, however, that only 2 of these 48 drugs were approved from 1997 through 1999. The program appeared to have reached its peak of approval activity in 1991, when the FDA approved 12 drugs under the Subpart E program.

Recent FDA data suggest that the Subpart E program has remained at least somewhat active for biological products. CDER, for example, recently listed those therapeutic biological products (inherited by CDER as part of CDER/CBER consolidation) that have been approved under the Subpart E program. These included Erbitux (approved in February 2004), Fabrazyme (April 2003), Zevalin (February 2002), and Campath (May 2001). From January 1998 through February 2004, the FDA had approved seven biological products under the Subpart E program.

By most accounts, however, the Subpart E program has become less relevant given the agency's successes under the prescription drug user fee program and given the availability of the fast track program and related provisions under FDAMA. In addition, the agency now routinely works with sponsors of all drugs so early in the development process that the accelerated development program's focus on early sponsor-FDA interaction likely is no longer viewed as a worthwhile incentive to participate.

Accelerated Drug Approval Program (Subpart H)

With its 1988 accelerated drug development program in place, the FDA wanted to take "additional steps...to facilitate the approval of significant new drugs...to treat serious or life-threatening diseases." The agency did so under a final regulation (Subpart H) published in December 1992.

Today, the Subpart H program remains perhaps the most active and relevant of the accelerated developmen and early/expanded access programs that the FDA introduced in the late 1980s and early 1990s. In part reflec ing this fact, the Food and Drug Administration Modernization Act codified, in law, the key concepts of th accelerated drug approval program by creating the fast track program (see discussion below).

Unlike the FDA's accelerated development program, which focused largely on expediting the drug testin process, the Subpart H regulations focused on accelerating the agency's review and approval of promisin therapies. The regulations attempted to do so by modifying the criteria on which the agency can base ma keting approval for desperately needed new drugs, and by giving the agency greater authority regarding th study and use of the drugs following approval.

Specifically, the accelerated approval program allows the agency to base marketing approval on a drug's effec on a surrogate endpoint or on a clinical endpoint other than survival or irreversible morbidity. According t the regulation, "FDA may grant marketing approval for a new drug product on the basis of adequate and wel controlled clinical trials establishing that the drug product has an effect on a surrogate endpoint that is rea sonably likely, based on epidemiologic, therapeutic, pathophysiologic, or other evidence, to predict clinica benefit or on the basis of an effect on a clinical endpoint other than survival or irreversible morbidit Approval under this section will be subject to the requirement that the applicant study the drug further, t verify and describe its clinical benefit, where there is uncertainty as to the relation of the surrogate endpoir to clinical benefit, or of the observed clinical benefit to ultimate outcome. Postmarketing studies would usu ally be studies already underway. When required to be conducted, such studies must also be adequate an well controlled."

In recent years, however, the dearth of postmarketing trials confirming the clinical benefit of drugs approve under the accelerated approval program has caused some to question the wisdom of the program. During March 2003 meeting, members of CDER's Oncologic Drugs Advisory Committee indicated that they might b more reluctant to recommend that cancer drugs receive accelerated approval based on limited clinical ev dence, given the fact that only four of the 15 oncology drugs approved under Subpart H at that time had bee shown to have clinical benefits in confirmatory trials. The committee agreed that the FDA needs a mechanis to ensure that companies marketing cancer drugs under accelerated approval complete confirmatory tria demonstrating clinical benefit. Division of Oncology Drug Products Director Richard Pazdur, M.D., noted du ing the meeting that such companies should, as a rule, initiate their confirmatory studies earlier in the deve opment process.

In its April 1992 regulatory proposal for the accelerated approval plan, the FDA discussed the benefits of n requiring companies to study the effects of desperately needed new drugs on primary endpoints (i.e., morta ity or morbidity). "Approval of a drug on the basis of a well-documented effect on a surrogate endpoint ca allow a drug to be marketed earlier, sometimes much earlier, than it could if a demonstrated clinical bene were required... Approval could be granted where there is some uncertainty as to the relation of that endpoi to clinical benefit, with the requirement that the sponsor conduct or complete studies after approval to esta lish and define the drug's clinical benefit."

Ironically, it was controversy over the use of surrogate endpoints that led FDA officials to begin considerir possible improvements in the accelerated approval program in the mid-1990s.[1] At FDA advisory committe meetings and in communications to the agency, it was the AIDS community itself that had begun to questic the wisdom of basing approval on largely unvalidated surrogate endpoints.

Despite such concerns, the FDA's accelerated approval program has been perhaps the most active of the agency's expedited development and review initiatives in recent years (with the exception of the fast track program). According to CDER data, 46 NDAs for 43 drugs were approved under its Subpart H program from its inception through August 2004 (see listing below). It is interesting to note that more than a third of these NDAs gained approval from January 2000 to July 2004. CDER approved five Subpart H drugs in 2003 and three in 2002.

According to a 2003 Tufts Center for the Study of Drug Development analysis, 37% of the drugs approved under Subpart H from June 1992 to June 2003 were HIV/AIDS therapies, while another 33% were for cancer (see exhibit below).

Eligibility for Accelerated Approval Under the FDA's regulations, the accelerated approval program "applies to certain new drug and antibiotic products that have been studied for their safety and effectiveness in treating serious and life-threatening illnesses and that provide meaningful therapeutic benefit to patients over existing treatments (e.g., the ability to treat patients unresponsive to, or intolerant of, available therapy, or improved patient response over available therapy)."

Although the agency stated in its April 1992 proposal that it would apply the terms "serious" and "life-threatening" as it had in its treatment IND program and other programs, the FDA did discuss their application once again in the context of the accelerated approval plan. "The seriousness of a disease is a matter of judgment, but generally is based on its impact on such factors as survival, day-to-day functioning, or the likelihood that the disease, if left untreated, will progress from a less severe condition to a more serious one. Thus, acquired immunodeficiency syndrome (HIV) infection, Alzheimer's dementia, angina pectoris, heart failure, cancer, and many other diseases are clearly serious in their full manifestations. Further, many chronic illnesses that are generally well managed by available therapy can have serious outcomes. For example, inflammatory bowel disease, asthma, rheumatoid arthritis, diabetes mellitus, systemic lupus erythematosus, depression, psychoses, and many other diseases can be serious for certain populations or in some or all of their phases."

As noted above, the FDA has attempted recently to revise or clarify its interpretation of the eligibility criteria for its accelerated approval (Subpart H) and fast track programs to eliminate what it saw as a barrier to the development of products under these plans. Because an accelerated approval or fast track designation could be granted only for a drug that essentially meets an unmet medical need, the FDA held that the approval of a first drug for this unmet indication was, in effect, a grant of market exclusivity (i.e., because other drugs for the same indication could not then meet the unmet medical need criterion). At a May 2003 oncology meeting, then-FDA Commissioner Mark McClellan, M.D., Ph.D., noted that the agency had modified its accelerated drug approval policies to permit the agency to clear multiple cancer drugs for a single indication. McClellan noted that the agency took this step "so that for cancer drugs that have met accelerated approval, other products will also be able to get accelerated approval status for that indication until one of these therapies actually demonstrates in its Phase 4 study commitments a confirmatory clinical benefit in patients." [Editor's note: In reality, the FDA's eligibility criteria for Subpart H do not use the term "unmet medical need," but instead refer to treatments that are for "treating serious and life-threatening illnesses and that provide meaningful therapeutic benefit over existing treatments."]

Typically, when a Phase 4 study confirms the clinical benefit of a drug approved under Subpart H, the sponsor will submit the Phase 4 study data in an NDA supplement. If the agency decides to approve the NDA supplement, it will issue an approval letter, which in effect converts the accelerated approval to a traditional approval.

NDAs Approved Under CDER's Accelerated
Approval Program (Subpart H), 1992-August 2004

Drug	Indication	Approval Time (months)
Hivid	Combination w/ zidovudine in advanced HIV	7.6
Biaxin (suspension)	Disseminated mycobacterial infections	13.7
Zerit	Advanced HIV in adults	5.9
Zinecard	Reduce incidence/severity of cardiomyopathy assoc. w/ doxorubicin administration in certain breast cancer patients	9.7*
Casodex	Combination w/ LHRH analogue for treating advanced prostate cancer	12.7
Epivir	HIV infection	4.4
Doxil	AIDS-related Kaposi's sarcoma in unresponsive patients	14.3
Invirase	Advanced HIV in combination w/ nucleoside analogues	3.2
Norvir (2 NDAs)	HIV infection as monotherapy or in combination w/ nucleoside analogues	2.3
Crixivan	HIV infection in adults	1.4
Taxotere	Patients with locally advanced or metastatic breast cancer who have relapsed or progressed during anthracycline-based therapy	21.6
Camptosar	Refractory colorectal cancer	5.6
Viramune	Combination w/ nucleoside analogues for HIV-1-infected adults experiencing clinical or immunologic deterioration	3.9
Serostim	AIDS wasting assoc. w/ catabolism loss or cachexia	11.4
ProAmatine	Symptomatic orthostatic hypotension	11.4**
Viracept (2 NDAs)	HIV infection	2.6
Rescriptor	Treatment of HIV infection in combination w/ antiretroviral agents	8.7
Xeloda	Treatment of patients w/ metastatic breast cancer who are resistant to both paclitaxel and an anthracyline-containing chemotherapy regimen or resistant to paclitaxel and for whom further anthracycline therapy may be contraindicated	6
Sulfamylon	Adjunctive topical antimicrobial agent to control bacterial infection of excised burn wounds	14.2***
Priftin	Pulmonary tuberculosis	6
Thalidomide	Cutaneous manifestations of erythema nodosum leprosum	18.8
Sustiva	Use in combination w/ other antiretroviral agents for HIV-1	3.2
Actiq	Breakthrough cancer pain	23.7
Ziagen	Treatment of HIV-1 in combination w/ other antiretroviral agents	5.8
DepoCyt	Intrathecal treatment of lymphomatous meningitis	5.9
Temodar	Adults w/ refractory anaplastic astrocytoma	5.9
Synercid	Vancomycin resistant Enterococcus faecium	7.8****
Mylotarg	Treatment for patients 60 or older with CD33 positive acute myeloid leukemia in first relapse	6.6
Kaletra (2 NDAs)	Treatment of HIV in combination w/ other antiretroviral agents	3.5
Mifeprex	Termination of pregnancy through 49 days of pregnancy	18.0†
Trizivir	Alone or in combination w/ other antiretroviral agents in treating HIV	10.9
Gleevec	Treatment of chronic myeloid leukemia	2.4
Viread	In combination w/ other antiretrovirals to treat HIV	5.9
Tracleer	Primary pulmonary arterial hypertension	12.1
Remodulin	Primary pulmonary hypertension	19.1
Xyrem	Cataplexy associated w/ narcolepsy	21.5
Eloxatin	Metastatic carcinoma of colon or rectum	1.5
Fuzeon	HIV-1	5.9
Gleevec	Chronic myeloid leukemia	4.0
Iressa	Non-small cell lung cancer	9.0
Velcade	Multiple myeloma	3.7
Plenaxis	Palliative treatment of advanced symptomatic prostate cancer	35.4
Truvada	HIV-1	4.7

* Review time based on date of submission of significant new clinical data. ** Review time based on date of submission of significant new clinical data *** Review time based on date of submission of significant new clinical data supporting a new indication. **** Total approval time adjusted because o negative plant inspection. †Time adjusted due to manufacturing issues, submission of final study report late in review.

Source: CDER

The Parallel Track Program

In mid-1989, National Institute of Allergy and Infectious Diseases (NIAID) Director Anthony Fauci, M.D., publicly proposed a new experimental drug accessibility plan called "parallel track." As proposed, the plan would allow the availability of experimental AIDS therapies earlier than ever during the clinical development process.

The federal government officially unveiled the parallel track program in April 1992 as a plan "intended to make promising new investigational drugs for AIDS and other HIV-related diseases more widely available as early as possible in the drug development process." The approach called for AIDS drugs to be made available after the completion of Phase 1 studies to subjects who are unable to enroll in the controlled trials or are unable to benefit from current therapies. Although similar to the treatment IND concept, parallel track was a more liberal mechanism in that it could provide for expanded drug access when the evidence of a drug's effectiveness could not meet the threshold necessary to qualify for a treatment IND.

There were other, if more subtle, differences between the two experimental access programs. While the treatment IND required approval at the commissioner's office level, parallel track was technically a protocol amendment, which needed the approval of review division directors. Also, sponsors could submit their parallel track proposals for review by the AIDS Research Advisory Committee of the National Institute of Allergy and Infectious Diseases in addition to the FDA.

In October 1992, Bristol-Myers Squibb's AIDS drug Zerit (stavudine) became the first drug made available under parallel track. The company established the parallel track arm during Phase 2/3 trials, and at a time when the controlled trials were enrolling rapidly. Just six weeks into the parallel track program, the company's controlled trials were fully enrolled, while the parallel access arm had enrolled several hundred patients. Ultimately, more than 13,000 patients received the drug under the parallel track program. Two earlier expanded drug access programs—for Hoffmann-La Roche's Hivid (zalcitabine or ddC) and Bristol-Myers Squibb's Videx (didanosine or ddI)—were said to be the models for the parallel track program.

Since this time, however, the parallel track program has failed to attract willing industry participants. Although some companies had discussed parallel track programs with the FDA, Zerit remains the only drug made available in the program's history.

While it is generally acknowledged that AIDS patients have many more therapeutic options than they did in the early 1990s, FDA officials are uncertain why the program has not been more active. Like the treatment IND program and any other expanded access plan, however, parallel track access can be extremely expensive. Some point out that other drug access mechanisms, such as large, open-label safety studies, are easier for industry to implement. In addition, since parallel track drugs would be made available even earlier in drug development than they would under other expanded access mechanisms, it is likely that many sponsors and AIDS patients were reluctant to participate in this program.

The Oncology Initiative

Unveiled in March 1996, CDER's Oncology Initiative was, at least in part, a response to public criticism and congressional inquiries regarding why there was such an imbalance of agency resources dedicated to the review of therapies for AIDS compared to the review of drugs for illnesses that kill far more Americans each year, including cancer and heart disease. Responding to such inquiries, then-FDA Commissioner David Kessler, M.D., agreed to evaluate the perceived imbalances in resource allocations and to evaluate methods for expediting cancer drug reviews.

Over the past several years, the focus on the Oncology Initiative as a distinct program or initiative has fade to some degree. During this time, however, the Division of Oncologic Drug Products has assimilated th Oncology Initiative's goals and provisions into standard divisional practices and policies.

Introduced as "a uniform policy" rather than as a regulation, CDER's Oncology Initiative (formally calle "Reinventing the Regulation of Cancer Drugs") was designed to reduce cancer drug development times by ẹ least a year and to cut FDA oncology drug review times from an average of 12.4 months to 6 months. The in tiative itself comprised four separate elements, each of which the FDA claimed to have the authority to imple ment immediately:

- Accelerated Approval for Cancer Drugs. "To speed the availability of cancer drugs, FDA may now rely on partial response (such as measurable but incomplete shrinkage of a tumor) to a therapy, in addition to the current criteria such as a patient's survival and improved quality of life," the agency stated in the policy document. "While the predictive value of partial responses may still be a matter of discussion and study for all types of cancer patients, FDA has concluded that for patients with refractory malignant disease or for those who have no adequate alternative, clear evidence of anti-tumor activity is a reasonable basis for approving the drug. In these cases, studies confirming a clinical benefit may appropriately be completed after approval. By basing accelerated approval on surrogate markers such as tumor shrinkage for patients who have no satisfactory alternative therapy, and by allowing more definitive data on survival or other criteria to be developed after marketing approval, FDA believes that many cancer therapies will reach patients sooner." Under the policy, the agency also applied the accelerated approval provisions to certain products intended to remove a serious or life-threatening toxicity associated with a particular cancer treatment.

  In effect, this aspect of the Oncology Initiative simply extended the accelerated approval process (Subpart H) to cancer drugs. While the FDA pointed out that the accelerated approval program has been applicable to promising drugs for cancer patients who do not benefit from or cannot tolerate available therapy, the agency stressed that, in the past, "this approval mechanism has not been frequently utilized, largely because general agreement on reasonable surrogate endpoints has been lacking." Post-approval studies would be required for most drugs approved on the basis of tumor shrinkage and for all products that remove treatment-associated toxicities.

- Expanded Access for Drugs Approved in Other Countries. Under this aspect of the Oncology Initiative, the FDA was to contact the U.S. sponsor and encourage the company to pursue an expanded access protocol "whenever a cancer therapy for patients who are not curable or well-treated by currently available therapies is approved by a recognized foreign regulatory authority." To qualify, a drug must be in a controlled clinical trial in the United States and be approved by "an identified regulatory agency in a foreign country." Although the FDA did not specifically identify any "recognized" regulatory authorities, it did state that the authorities must have "review practices, review standards, and access to specialized expertise in the evaluation of agents for use in cancer treatment that are sufficient to allow FDA to conclude that a marketing approval action by that authority is likely to provide an adequate basis for proper consideration of an expanded access protocol for U.S. patients."

  In considering such expanded access protocols, the agency was willing to accept an English-language version of the data submitted to the foreign regulatory authority. The expanded access protocols should be directed at the "same general type of patient condition and similar dosage and schedule" as approved by the foreign regulatory authority.

In following up on the expanded access component of the Oncology Initiative, the FDA's Office of International Affairs originally wrote to regulatory authorities in 25 "major" countries to request a list of all cancer or cancer-related therapies approved in each country during the previous ten years. According to the agency, "no further action is indicated for a number of these drugs, which are not needed for patients in the U.S. due to the availability of other similar or superior drugs." At the time of this original assessment in 1999, the other drugs that were approved in these countries were either approved in the United States or were actively being reviewed for approval in this country.

- Cancer Patient Representation at FDA Advisory Committee Meetings. The FDA agreed to expand the "consumer member" concept in the context of its advisory committees, each of which typically includes a consumer member. "Because cancer is not one disease but many, FDA will now include a person who has experienced the specific cancer on each cancer-therapy advisory committee... FDA will now ensure that an individual who has personal experience with the specific cancer being studied be included as an ad hoc member of each cancer therapy committee."

- Clarification of the FDA's Policy for Studies of Marketed Cancer Products. To reduce the number of unnecessary INDs submitted by clinical investigators, the agency clarified its policy on INDs for studies of marketed drugs and announced that it would now refuse to accept INDs for exempt studies of marketed drugs (see Chapter 3). The agency states that it will not accept an IND for a study of a lawfully marketed drug if: (1) the study is not intended to support approval of a new indication or a significant change in product labeling or advertising; (2) the study does not involve a route of administration or dosage level or use in a patient population or other factor that significantly increases the risks (or decreases the acceptability of the risks) associated with the use of the product; and (3) the study meets the requirements for IRB approval and informed consent and does not commercialize the investigational product. The agency also clarified that it will not view a drug company's act of providing a marketed drug free of charge for an investigator-initiated study as constituting a promotional activity.

Fast Track Initiative

The so-called "fast track" initiative is not only the newest of CDER's formal accelerated drug development/approval programs, it is also the only one that was implemented directly by statute. Under the FDA Modernization Act of 1997, Congress established the fast track process to facilitate the development, and expedite the review, of products that demonstrate the potential to address unmet medical needs in the treatment of serious or life-threatening conditions.

Through its fast track provisions, FDAMA authorizes CDER to:

- Approve a new drug that qualifies for fast track status "upon a determination that the product has an effect on a clinical endpoint or on a surrogate endpoint that is reasonably likely to predict clinical benefit." The agency has pointed out that this element of FDAMA in effect codified in law the Subpart H program, which permits the agency to approve a new drug product on the basis of the product's effect "on a surrogate endpoint that is reasonably likely, based on epidemiologic, therapeutic, pathophysiologic, or other evidence, to predict clinical benefit or on the basis of an effect on a clinical endpoint other than survival or irreversible morbidity."

355

- Accept for review portions of a marketing application prior to the receipt of the complete application. Sponsors of designated fast track products can request, by submitting clinical data indicating that the product may be effective, that the agency accept for formal review completed portions of an NDA before the other sections of the application are submitted. If the agency permits this submission—sometimes called a rolling submission—the sponsor is required to provide a schedule for submitting the information necessary to make the NDA complete. Although the agency's emerging good review management principles (GRMP) strongly advocate the submission of a complete NDA, the agency is also running, under PDUFA III, a pilot program under which it is accepting so-called "reviewable units" in advance of a full NDA submission (see Chapter 7). The agency then plans to conduct a "comprehensive assessment of the added value, costs, and impact of...early reviews of parts of marketing applications," what will comprise the first formal evaluation of whether rolling NDAs actually promote efficient application reviews.

Although industry encouraged Congress to include the fast track program in FDAMA, it was unclear to mar at the time what real advantages the program offered aside from those that were already available under othe programs. The agency itself conceded that, with the exception of the "rolling NDA" provisions, other element of the fast track program had been available under regulations authorizing the other accelerated develop ment/approval programs. In many ways, FDA officials noted, the fast track program is an amalgamation of th provisions of these various other programs.

Still, industry had sought over 400 fast track designations (275 for drugs) as of June 2004, and companie appeared to be fairly aggressive in seeking such designations. While many industry officials did not see th benefits offered under the fast track program as intrinsically valuable, they had begun to view a fast track de: ignation as a valuable "staging mechanism" for what they increasingly saw as the real gateway to rapid dru approval—priority review status. With priority NMEs being approved, on average, over 7 months faster tha their standard counterparts (i.e., for drugs approved in 2003 and 2002), companies are attempting to get wha ever edge they can in obtaining the prized priority status for their products.

Although priority review status is not necessarily automatic once a firm obtains a fast track designatio industry officials note that such a designation does seem to help a company set the expectation at the agenc that the drug will be a significant new therapy—an expectation that the company can use to its advantag CDER's guidance entitled, *Fast Track Drug Development Programs-Designation, Development, and Application Revi* (September 1998, updated in July 2004) specifically notes that "a fast track development program ordinari will be eligible for priority review." In its July 2003 draft good review management principles (GRMP) guidanc however, the agency noted that it will not automatically bestow priority review status on fast track product "The [review priority] decision should be based on the merits of the product and the application data ar should not be contingent on internal FDA considerations such as competing workload or currently availab resources in the review division or on whether the subject product was designated fast track during the deve opment phase," the guidance states.

Qualifying for Fast Track Status To become eligible for the benefits offered under the fast track program, drug sponsor must first apply for, and obtain, a fast track designation for its drug product. In its fast track guic ance, the agency establishes the specific eligibility criteria that sponsors, drugs, and product developme programs must meet to qualify for designation.

In outlining the fast track eligibility criteria, which industry has applauded as being fairly liberal, the agen emphasizes that a fast track classification applies not to a product alone, but to a combination of the produ and specific indication for which it is being studied. "The indication, for the purposes of [the fast track guidance], includes both the condition for which the drug is intended (e.g., heart failure) and the anticipated or established benefits of use (e.g., improved exercise tolerance, decreased hospitalization, increased survival)," the agency states. "It is therefore the development program for a specific drug for a specific indication that will receive fast track designation. Such a program is referred to...as a fast track drug development program."

Although the fast track program applies to drugs that are designed to treat, diagnose, or prevent serious or life-threatening conditions and that demonstrate the potential to address unmet medical needs, the agency chooses not to distinguish between serious or life-threatening conditions in its guidance. Rather, the agency points out that all life-threatening conditions, as defined under the accelerated drug development (Subpart E) program (see discussion above), automatically qualify as serious conditions, which the guidance document focuses on defining.

To qualify for a fast track development program, a drug must "not only be used in patients with a serious condition, it must be intended to treat a serious aspect of that condition" (i.e., either a serious manifestation or serious symptom), the agency emphasizes. "A product intended to ameliorate or prevent a side effect of therapy of a condition would be considered to treat a serious condition if the side effect were serious (e.g., serious infections in patients receiving immunosuppressive therapy)."

The agency notes that a preventive product will be considered to treat a serious condition if it is being evaluated for its ability to prevent a serious manifestation of the condition, or if it is being studied for its ability to prevent the condition and it is scientifically reasonable to assume that prevention of the condition would prevent its serious consequences.

"A product intended and being studied for its ability to treat a condition while avoiding the side effects of currently accepted treatments of the condition might be considered to treat a serious condition if such side effects were serious (e.g., a less myelosuppressive treatment for a tumor or an anti-inflammatory drug that does not cause gastrointestinal bleeding)," the guidance states. "The potential for a new drug to avoid the serious sequelae of existing drugs would qualify that drug development program for fast track designation only in limited circumstances. Many therapies, even those intended to treat non-serious conditions, are associated with rare, serious, adverse reactions, and new therapies, despite initial hopes, often are associated with their own set of serious reactions. Nonetheless, some adverse reactions are significant public health problems, and the development of therapies that do not cause such serious reactions would merit close attention."

In addition to being intended for a serious or life-threatening condition, a drug must also meet a second critical criterion—it must demonstrate the potential to address an unmet medical need—to qualify for fast track status. While an unmet medical need is obvious when no therapy exists for a qualifying condition, it is not as apparent when alternative therapies exist. In such cases, the agency's guidance indicates that programs for new agents would qualify if they evaluate any of the following:

- improved effect(s) on serious outcomes of the condition that are affected by alternate therapies;
- effect(s) on serious outcomes of the condition not known to be affected by the alternatives;
- the ability to provide benefit(s) in patients who are unable to tolerate or are unresponsive to alternative agents;

- the ability to provide benefits similar to those of alternatives while avoiding serious toxicity present in existing therapies, or avoiding less serious toxicity that is common and causes discontinuation of treatment of a serious disease; or

- the ability to provide benefit(s) similar to those of alternatives but with improvement in some factor, such as compliance or convenience, that is shown to lead to an improved effect on serious outcomes.

As noted above, however, the FDA revised its September 1998 guidance in July 2004 specifically to clarify it interpretation of the "unmet medical need" eligibility criterion and thereby eliminate what it saw as a barrie to the development of products under the program. Because a fast track designation could be granted onl for drugs that met an "unmet medical need," the FDA held that the approval of a first drug for this unmet indication was, in effect, a grant of market exclusivity (i.e., because other drugs for the same indication could no then meet the "unmet medical need" criterion). In the July 2004 revised fast track guidance, the agency sough to "make it clear that a drug can be said to address an unmet medical need if the only available treatment for the condition are approved under the accelerated approval regulations (21 CFR 314.500 and 601.40), eithe on the basis of an effect on a surrogate endpoint or with restrictions on distribution." In the revised guidance the agency emphasized the desirability of having multiple treatment options available under the fast track an accelerated approval programs:

"FDA recognizes that, as a general matter, it is preferable to have more than one treatment approved unde the accelerated approval provisions because of the uncertainty inherent in an approval under these prov sions. For example, post-approval studies of a drug product may fail to establish a relationship of the surro gate endpoint to clinical benefit, or of the observed clinical benefit to ultimate outcome. In thes circumstances, it is important to continue to expedite the development and review of important new thera pies for serious and life-threatening illnesses under the accelerated approval provisions. Therefore, if the on therapies that exist for a condition are approved under the accelerated approval regulations on the basis of surrogate endpoint or are approved with restrictions on distribution necessary to ensure the safe use of th drug, FDA may designate a product as fast track notwithstanding the availability of other therapies approve under the accelerated approval regulations."

Seeking a Fast Track Designation As noted, a firm must apply for and obtain a formal fast track designatio before its drug becomes eligible for the program's benefits. According to the FDA's fast track guidance, desig nation requests can be made as early as the IND submission stage, but generally should not be made late than the pre-NDA meeting. The request must be submitted either with the IND or as an IND amendment.

Regarding the content of the designation request, the agency states that the sponsor should "identify the ser ous condition and the unmet medical needs, provide a plausible basis for the assertion that the drug has th potential to address such unmet medical needs, and include in the development plan (at a level of deta appropriate to the stage of development) trials designed to evaluate this potential." Although the agenc claims that the submission "should not be voluminous," it should contain the discussion and supporting do umentation necessary to allow a reviewer to assess whether the criteria for fast track designation are met wit out having to refer to information located elsewhere.

The nature and quantity of data submitted in a designation request will depend on several factors, includir whether the drug is designed to treat a fatal or non-fatal condition (i.e., less discussion/data if for a fatal co dition), the availability of alternative therapies (i.e., less discussion/data if no alternatives available), and th stage of a drug's development (i.e., only animal and pharmacology data may be available). The evidentiary standard for obtaining a fast track designation was modest by design so that firms would be able to seek designation as early as the IND submission (i.e., because many of the benefits of designation are more valuable early in the development process).

The FDA will respond to a designation request within 60 calendar days of receiving the request. If the agency determines that the sponsor and drug/development program have met the criteria for fast track designation, it will forward a "designation letter" to inform the sponsor that designation has been granted and that the sponsor must design and perform studies that can show whether the product fulfills unmet medical needs, and to emphasize that the development program must continue to meet the fast track designation criteria. Alternatively, the agency may issue a "non-designation letter" informing the sponsor that the request was incomplete or that the development program failed to meet the criteria for fast track designation. Sponsors can re-apply for designation after receiving non-designation letters.

FDA performance data released in mid-2004 showed that CDER had taken action on 92.6% of fast track designations within the 60-day goal. At the time, CDER had taken action on the requests in a median time of 50 days.

Fast Track and the Rolling NDA As noted above, the right to submit rolling NDAs was the only element of the fast track program that was not already available under previous accelerated drug development and approval regulations. The theory behind the rolling NDA, which some CDER review divisions have accepted in the past, is that the review process may be expedited if the agency can begin its review of parts of an NDA while the final elements of the application are being completed. Although the rolling NDA was addressed under FDAMA's fast track provisions, CDER officials have maintained that FDAMA permits the rolling NDA's use under existing programs, including the priority review and accelerated approval programs.

It is important to note that FDAMA establishes only that the FDA "may consider" a sponsor's request that the agency accept and begin the review of portions of a marketing application before the complete NDA is submitted. According to the fast track guidance, "after the sponsor submits to the IND a preliminary evaluation of data from the clinical trials, the Agency may consider accepting portions of the application if (1) the clinical trials that would form the basis for the Agency's determination of the safety and effectiveness of the product and that would support drug labeling are nearing completion or have been completed, (2) the Agency agrees that the product continues to meet the criteria for fast track designation, and (3) the Agency agrees that preliminary evaluation of the clinical data supports a determination that the product may be effective." Typically, the sponsor's request to submit a rolling NDA should be included in the company's information package submitted in advance of the pre-NDA meeting (i.e., so that the firm and review division can discuss relevant issues during the meeting).

Applicants seeking to submit a rolling NDA must first provide a schedule for the submission of portions of the NDA and obtain the agency's agreement to accept portions of the application as well as its agreement to the submission schedule. About the standards that partial NDA submissions must meet, the agency states that, "it is expected that a section submitted for review will be in a form adequate to have been included in a complete...NDA submission. Drafts should not be included in a submission... Occasionally, the Agency may, in its discretion, accept less than a complete section (e.g., a CMC section lacking final consistency lot data and long term stability data; an acute toxicology section lacking chronic toxicology data or final study reports for some or all of the principal controlled trials without integrated summaries) if it determines that such a

subsection would constitute a reviewable unit and would be useful in making the review process more eff
cient overall." The agency also emphasizes that its acceptance of a rolling NDA does not necessarily guarar
tee that its review will begin prior to the complete dossier's submission, and that review assignments ar
based on several factors, including staffing and workload.

A sponsor must submit the full user fee associated with an NDA when it submits the initial portion of th
application for review. In addition, the review clock applicable to the NDA (i.e., likely the six-month timefram
for priority products) will not begin until the complete application is submitted, the agency notes.

The agency establishes in its July 2004 guidance that applicants with fast track drug programs can seek trad
tional approval based on data demonstrating an effect on clinically meaningful endpoints or well-establishe
surrogate endpoints, or under the existing accelerated approval regulations based on evidence of a drug
effect on a less than well-established surrogate endpoint. Generally, approval based on clinical endpoini
other than survival or irreversible morbidity would be granted under traditional procedures rather than unde
the accelerated approval process. Approval based on clinical endpoints other than survival or irreversibl
morbidity would "be considered under the accelerated approval regulations only when it is essential to dete
mine effects on survival and irreversible morbidity in order to confirm the favorable risk/benefit judgment tha
led to approval," the agency notes.

Assessing the Activity and Success of the Fast Track Program Although it seemed that industry was some
what slow to embrace the fast track program, perhaps due to poorly defined benefits and the lack of a form;
guidance document initially, there has been considerable effort to seek designations in the seven-year-ol
program. According to CDER statistics, drug companies had submitted 275 fast track designation requests ;
of June 30, 2004. Industry sought another 115 designations for biological products.

Based on the 244 designation requests acted on as of June 2004, industry is enjoying a roughly 74% succe:
rate in obtaining fast track designations for their drugs. At that point, CDER had approved 180 of the desi;
nation requests and denied only 64 of them.

Although a 2000 study found that just over half of all designation requests were submitted to either th
Division of Antiviral Drug Products or the Division of Oncologic Drug Products, more recent studies are shov
ing that other indications are accounting for a growing number of fast track designations. In a 2003 study, th
Tufts Center for the Study of Drug Development found that fast track designations for products aimed at trea
ing diseases other than cancer and HIV/AIDS grew from more than 30 in 2001 to more than 50 in 2003 (se
exhibit below). Further, more than 10% of fast track designations in 2003 were for diabetes and obesity, 21
were for rare inherited conditions affecting children, and 21% were for infectious diseases, the study found

With the growing number of approvals for drugs with fast track designations (17 alone from January 20(
through August 2004), the first studies on the impact of the program on development and approval times a
becoming available. According to the Tufts Center for the Study of Drug Development study, the clinical deve
opment times of fast track drugs approved between 1998 and 2003 were, on average, 2 to 2.5 years short
than those for non-fast track drugs. Mean FDA approval times for fast track drugs were about a third of tho:
of standard drugs (non-fast track) and about half of those of priority drugs (non-fast track).

The FDA's Fast Track Initiative and Its Impact on Drug Development Time

Tufts Center for the Study of Drug Development (CSDD)
December 2003

In November 1997, Congress passed the FDA Modernization Act, which codified existing FDA regulations permitting accelerated approval of new drugs and biological products under certain circumstances. The new law also expanded current regulations and created a fast track program to expedite development and approval of products that address unmet medical needs for serious or life-threatening conditions. Whereas, by 1997, the five-year-old accelerated approval regulations had resulted in about 20 approvals, mostly for AIDS and cancer treatments, within its first five years the fast track program led to 200 fast track product development designations and another two dozen approvals.

The agency's fast track program is rapidly evolving. The flexibility of fast track designation criteria has allowed the FDA to expand eligibility to include development programs that meet emerging public health needs (e.g., diabetes and obesity).

Fast Track and Development Time

The Tufts CSDD study found that the FDA's fast track program has cut nearly three years off the time necessary to develop and obtain agency approval for a new drug. Average clinical development time for fast track drugs was about 2 to 2.5 years shorter than that for non-fast track standard and priority drugs, respectively. Average approval time for fast track drugs was about a third that of standard drugs and half that of priority drugs.

Mean Drug Development Times for Standard, Priority, and Fast Track Drugs, 1998 to Mid-2003

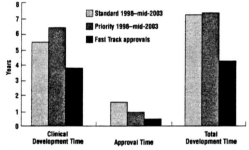

Note: Chart includes data for 9 of 13 fast track drugs.

Source: *Tufts Center for the Study of Drug Development*

Although mean FDA review time for fast track biologicals was shorter than that for priority or standard biologicals, longer average clinical development time resulted in a slightly longer total development time for fast track biological products. Compared to 66% of fast track drugs, only 40% of the fast track biologicals evaluated for this analysis benefited from the FDA's accelerated approval regulations, which provide mechanisms for speeding clinical development. This, in part, explains the apparent lack of a positive impact of fast track designation on clinical development time for biologicals.

Mean Biological Product Development Times: Standard, Priority, and Fast Track Approvals, 1998 to Mid-2003

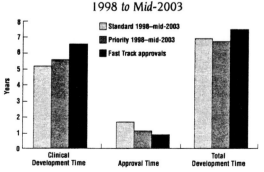

Note: Analysis based on data for six of nine fast track biologicals; chart excludes one product with an exceptionally long development time.

Source: *Tufts Center for the Study of Drug Development*

As of mid-2003, CDER granted nearly 70% of the 201 fast track designation requests it had received. During the same period, CBER received 110 designation requests and granted 56%. Although the number of designations tracked rose from 65 in 2001 to 142 in 2003, the percentage of products in various stages of development remained about the same.

Cumulative Distribution of Fast Track Designations, 1998-01 vs. 1998-03

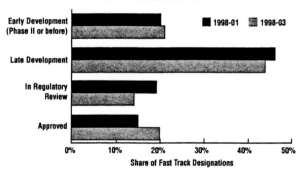

Note: Chart excludes two products with unknown development stages.

Source: *Tufts Center for the Study of Drug Development*

The Effects of Various Expedited Development and Approval Programs

Earlier programs to expedite drug development—Subpart E and Accelerated Approval—had the greatest impact in shortening clinical development times, but they addressed a limited spectrum of diseases. Priority review, which includes a specific FDA performance goal of six months to first action on new drug applications, primarily affected approval time and had little or no impact on development time. Fast track is a critically important initiative because it addresses both development and approval times and broadens the range of disease treatments beyond cancer and HIV/AIDS.

FDA's Expedited Development and Approval Programs: Share by Disease Indication

Program	Cancer	HIV/AIDS	Other
Subpart E Approvals (12/88-2/99)	25%	50%	25%
Accelerated Approvals (6/92-6/03)	33%	37%	30%
Priority Review Approvals (1/97-9/03)	20%	9%	71%
Fast Track Approvals (9/98-6/03)	39%	21%	39%

—continued—

—*continued*—

As more treatment regimens for AIDS and AIDS-related diseases became available during the late 1990s, the share of AIDS fast track designations fell by more than half between 2001 and 2003. At the same time, cancer fast track designations, which encompass dozens of neoplastic diseases, pre-cancerous conditions, and cancer-associated complications, increased substantially. Whereas the share of non-AIDS or cancer products receiving fast track designation held steady between 2001 and 2003, the number of products in this category more than doubled to 65.

Fast track designations for products aimed at treating diseases other than cancer and HIV/AIDS grew from more than 30 in 2001 to more than 50 in 2003. Almost a quarter (24%) of the designations were for rare inherited conditions affecting children (many also had orphan disease designations from the FDA). More than 10% were for diseases of the elderly. Among the 21% aimed at infections are several for treating resistant bacteria and countering anthrax.

Nearly 10% of fast track designations in 2003 were for diabetes and obesity, reflecting the FDA's recent emphasis on conditions that contribute significantly to health care costs and that would benefit from innovative treatments.

Fast Track Designations by Type of Disease, 2001 vs. 2003

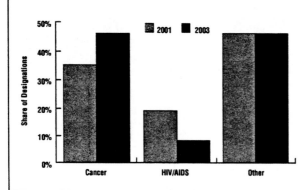

Fast Track Designations for Disease Treatments Other than Cancer and AIDS/HIV, 2003

	Percentage
Autoimmune	9%
Diabetes and Obesity	9%
Age-related	11%
Surgery, Transplant, and Critical Care	15%
Infection	21%
Pediatrics/orphan	24%
Miscellaneous	11%

Source: "FDA's fast track initiative cut total drug development time by 3 years," Impact Report, Vol. 5, No. 6, November/December 2003

References

1. Shulman, S.R. and Brown, J.S. (Tufts Center for the Study of Drug Development), The Food and Drug Administration's Early Access and Fast-Track Approval Initiatives: How Have They Worked? *Food and Drug Law Journal*, 1995, pp. 503-531.

2. Ibid.

3. Hewitt, P. (Tufts Center for the Study of Drug Development). Data from Tufts Center for the Study of Drug Development Marketed Drug and Expedited/Accelerated Datasets, March 1997.

CHAPTER 16

The Pediatric Studies Initiative

by Christopher-Paul Milne
Assistant Director
Tufts Center for the Study of Drug Development

By breaking new ground in both law and science, the so-called pediatric studies initiative in the United States truly embodies the meaning of the word "initiative"—a fresh start or new departure. From the beginning, the initiative faced numerous hurdles, and it continues to face challenges today. The concept was simple, and a mainstay of regulatory diplomacy—the carrot and the stick. Industry would be rewarded for doing the right thing (i.e., correcting an inequity: two-thirds of the drugs used in children had not been studied in children) with the carrot of market protection, referred to as "pediatric exclusivity." Meanwhile, industry would be encouraged to keep doing the right thing (i.e., making pediatric studies a routine part of new drug development) by means of a stick: an FDA regulation (the "pediatric rule") mandating pediatric assessments for new drug and biological products.

The pediatric rule has had a brief, but stormy tenure, having been promulgated, harmonized, enjoined, and codified all within just a little over five years. The FDA first finalized the pediatric rule in December 1998, having been rendered "complementary and supplementary" (in the words of then-FDA Commissioner Jane Henney) with the pediatric exclusivity provision that Congress had passed a year earlier through a harmonization clause. Instead, the rule was soon challenged and later invalidated by an October 2002 federal court ruling under which the FDA was found to have exceeded its authority by promulgating a mandatory pediatric testing requirement incompatible with the voluntary pediatric exclusivity program. Acting quickly, the advocates of mandatory pediatric assessments were able to resurrect the pediatric rule by having Congress codify the regulation as the Pediatric Research Equity Act (PREA), which was signed in December 2003. PREA was "re-harmonized" with pediatric exclusivity when it was made clear that, whenever circumstances allow, voluntary measures must be tried before mandatory ones are invoked.

For its own part, pediatric exclusivity has had its own difficult history. It took seven years from the time that the incentive was first proposed to the concept's incorporation into law. Initially, the concept was met with disdain by regulators, who thought that it was a distraction from the pediatric rule, and by industry, which thought that the concept would not work. After a slow start, however, industry became an active participant in the program, and the FDA ultimately embraced the concept once it began to produce results. In reality, despite the pediatric exclusivity incentive's reauthorization in January 2002 and even the addition of incentives for off-patent drugs and its integration with mandatory requirements, such developments have not made up entirely for the momentum that was lost during the period in which the pediatric rule was dormant and the new incentive law's passage was in doubt.

Today, the FDA's pediatric studies initiative faces new challenges. The drug industry's recent economic woe in general along with allegations that pediatric exclusivity program deadlines may have contributed to the col lection of flawed data regarding the safety and effectiveness of SSRI depressants are among the factors tha could influence the future of the pediatric studies initiative, particularly as Congress prepares to debate th initiative's 2007 renewal.

Historical Development

Although most of the early legislation regulating drugs and biologics in the United States was influenced b poisoning tragedies that largely involved children, neither the Public Health Service Act nor the Food, Drug & Cosmetic Act (FFDCA) were particularly concerned with children. In fact, the 1962 amendments to th FFDCA Act actually made children "therapeutic orphans" (a term coined by Dr. Harry Shirkey) by establishin that, if a drug is not tested in children, then the label should discourage its use in such patients.

A few years later, an article in a pediatrics journal noted that 78% of all medications listed in the 197 Physician's Desk Reference (PDR) either included a disclaimer or lacked adequate dosing information for ped atric patients. In recognition of this problem, the American Academy of Pediatrics (AAP) Committee on Drug issued guidelines on the evaluation of drugs for pediatric use in 1974. Three years later, the organizatio released guidelines to encourage ethical conduct in studies evaluating drugs in pediatric populations. Th FDA responded in 1979 by publishing regulations requiring sponsors to conduct pediatric clinical trials befor including pediatric information on the label.

In 1990, a resurgence of concern about the lack of labeling for pediatric use drugs prompted the Institute o Medicine (IOM) to convene a workshop on the topic. The emergence of AIDS as a pediatric disease ha resulted in a renewed sense of urgency regarding the need for new drugs in pediatric medicine. At the IOM workshop, speakers highlighted the long delay in the pediatric availability of AZT, and the fact that 70% o the drugs used to treat infants in hospitals lacked pediatric labeling. Although the FDA noted an increase i pediatric studies at the time, that meeting can be viewed as the seminal event for the current pediatric stud ies initiative.

The early FDA response was to initiate the so-called "Pediatric Page" and "Pediatric Plan," which were intenc ed to encourage industry to focus attention voluntarily on pediatric patients throughout the new drug deve opment process. The real impetus for manufacturers "to think pediatric," however, was the FDA's 199 pediatric labeling regulation, which required manufacturers to decide if existing data warranted a change t the label for pediatric use and to submit supplemental new drug applications accordingly. The 1994 regula tion was considered "voluntary" because it did not impose a general requirement for manufacturers to cor duct pediatric studies. The FDA later noted, in fact, that industry's response to the regulation did no substantially address the need for more information. Labeling supplements were submitted for only a sma fraction of the prescription drugs and biologicals on the market, and 75% of the supplements that were file did not significantly improve the pediatric use information.

In response, the FDA began crafting what would become the 1998 pediatric rule, which shape-shifted the reg ulatory nature of the pediatric initiative from voluntary to mandatory. Chris Jennings, the Clinto Administration's deputy assistant for health policy development, trumpeted the arrival of the proposed ru by declaring that the government had tried it industry's way (i.e., through voluntary programs) and that th approach had failed. In recognition of both the public health needs and the difficulties inherent in conduc ing pediatric studies, Congress viewed the Clinton Administration's efforts as a clarion call to add pediatric research incentives to ongoing legislative efforts aimed at reforming the FDA. Congress grafted an earlier version of the pediatric research incentive legislation—The Better Pharmaceuticals for Children Act—onto the FDA Modernization Act of 1997 (FDAMA), which became law on November 21, 1997. FDAMA's pediatric provision offered an incentive—six months of market exclusivity—to manufacturers that would, in response to an FDA request, conduct pediatric studies for drugs that seemed to have the potential for use in children. To render the statute and pediatric regulations mutually re-enforcing, the provision contained a harmonization clause that allowed studies conducted for the purpose of applying for FDAMA exclusivity to potentially do "double-duty" by also fulfilling FDA regulatory requirements for pediatric studies. This coupling of a temporary legislative "carrot" under FDAMA (it was scheduled to sunset in January 2002) with the regulatory "stick" of the FDA's 1998 regulation requiring the assessment of pediatric safety and effectiveness engendered the pediatric studies initiative.

The Carrot: FDAMA Pediatric Exclusivity as Reauthorized Under the Best Pharmaceuticals for Children Act (BPCA)

After considering the FDA's January 2001 status report on the pediatric exclusivity provision and the testimony of several hearings in May 2001, Congress reauthorized FDAMA's pediatric exclusivity provision and, in January 2002, President Bush signed the Best Pharmaceuticals for Children Act (BPCA). The BPCA left the basic incentive program in place: In exchange for a sponsor undertaking FDA-requested studies, a six-month period of market exclusivity would be added to whatever patent life or market exclusivity period remained on the products containing the particular active moiety. During this so-called "pediatric exclusivity" period, the agency cannot approve another company's abbreviated new drug application (ANDA) that is submitted for the same drug or biological and that relies on the safety and effectiveness data in the original company's full new drug application (NDA).

Only drugs that are indicated for conditions that occur in children are eligible for this incentive. However, eligible drugs may currently be approved only in adults, or they may be drugs that are indicated only for use in children. Both new drugs and already-marketed drugs are eligible for this incentive. Over-the-counter drugs that are the subject of approved NDAs are eligible, as are a small number of biological products that are subject to section 505 of the FFDCA. Biological products approved under the Public Health Service Act (PHSA) are not eligible, even if they have orphan exclusivity or patent protection. Antibiotics that were the subject of any marketing application received before November 21, 1997, are not eligible for the pediatric exclusivity program, unless such antibiotics also received orphan drug exclusivity (see Chapter 13).

In addition to the unique eligibility requirements, pediatric exclusivity differs from other forms of exclusivity in several ways. Pediatric exclusivity is not a patent extension per se, but is a period of market exclusivity that attaches to the end of the existing patent or exclusivity period listed in the *Orange Book* (a compendium of patent and market exclusivity and other information published by CDER, formally entitled, *Approved Drug Products With Therapeutic Equivalence Evaluations*) instead of running concurrently. It accrues not only to the drug product that was investigated in the pediatric study, but also to any drug product containing the same active moiety (including all dosage forms and indications) for which the sponsor of the pediatric study holds the approved NDA. Finally, the awarding of pediatric exclusivity is not conditional upon the FDA's approval of the labeling information that may result from the study reports submitted in support of the pediatric exclusivity application, but may be granted merely upon acceptance of the study reports themselves.

As an added incentive "to think pediatric," a sponsor can earn an additional six-month period of pediatri exclusivity if it submits a supplement for a new use (i.e., one not already covered in the approved labeling) i response to a written request. If approved, the supplement qualifies for three-year Hatch-Waxman exclusivi ty, to which the six-month pediatric exclusivity extension would attach. In the case of a second award, how ever, the supplement (including the labeling) must be approved before the pediatric exclusivity would hav anything to which it could attach. The FDA has pointed out that this approach could also provide a way fc sponsors to take advantage of pediatric exclusivity, even if they do not have any remaining patent or exclu sivity protection remaining. Although the circumstances under which the FDA will grant a second period c pediatric exclusivity are limited (as is the reward itself because it applies only to the label change for whic the three-year exclusivity was awarded), the FDA now lists Lamivudine as well as Metformin and Ibuprofe (both in combination with a second drug) as having received second periods of exclusivity.

The *quid pro quo* for the enviable reward of pediatric exclusivity under the program involves four basic steps (1) the sponsor's submission of a proposed pediatric study request justifying the need for additional pediatri research for a particular active moiety; (2) an FDA determination on whether the active moiety qualifies, an if so, the agency's issuance of a written request specifying what the sponsor will be required to do; (3) th sponsor's conduct of the studies; and (4) the sponsor's submission of the pediatric study reports and subse quent acceptance or rejection by FDA.

Step 1-Proposed Pediatric Study Request (PPSR) Unless the FDA issues a written request to a sponsor o its own initiative (about 20% of written requests are generated in this manner), the process begins with th sponsor submitting a proposed pediatric study request (PPSR) to the appropriate FDA reviewing division. A a minimum, the PPSR should address the following 15 issues: study objective; the indications to be studiec types of studies; study design; number of patients; age groups; inclusion/exclusion criteria; clinical endpoint: study evaluation; safety concerns; statistical analysis; potential label changes; report format; timeframes; an dosage form, regimen, route of administration, and formulation information on the drug. Within approx mately 120 days (an FDA-suggested timeframe), the agency will decide if the PPSR is acceptable and issu either an inadequacy letter or a written request.

Step 2-The Written Request (WR) In developing its written request, the agency may use the sponsor's PPS or other information. The FDA "written request" is a detailed legal and scientific document that specifies number of study elements, such as the indication, population, type of studies, safety parameters, longer teri follow-up, the timeframe for response (typically no longer than two to three years, although extensions ma be requested), and provisions for amending the written request (e.g., for deviations from the study protoco before the data are submitted. This last item may be of particular interest to sponsors, since the FDA stron; ly urges companies to document changes to the written request as formal amendments. There have been 27 amendments for the 295 written requests issued as of October 2004.

Written request criteria are based on the FDA's evaluation of three questions:

- Is there substantial use in the pediatric age group (i.e., 50,000 pediatric patients in the United States with the disease or condition)?

- Is there a meaningful therapeutic benefit (i.e., significant improvement in the treatment, diagnosis, or prevention of disease compared to already approved drugs)?

- Is there adequate safety data to move into the pediatric population?

The agency will determine what studies must be conducted by asking the following question: "What information do health care providers or parents need to use this active moiety appropriately in the pediatric population?" The FDA will first examine what pediatric labeling exists for the drug products, any additional pediatric information submitted for labeling, and pediatric information contained in NDAs for other products with the same active moiety. The agency will evaluate the need for studies in all pediatric subpopulations and for all indications (approved and pending indications, as well as unapproved uses) for which the active moiety is being used in the pediatric population.

Pediatric studies were defined in the FDAMA statute as "at least one clinical investigation (that at the Secretary's discretion may include pharmacokinetic studies) in pediatric age groups in which the drug is anticipated to be used." In practice, an average of two to three studies will be requested. Both safety and pharmacokinetic studies are commonly required. Efficacy studies have also been frequently requested, especially when the course of the disease and the drug's effects in pediatric patients are not known to be similar to those in adults (see exhibits below).

A general sample written request template as well as templates for particular categories of drugs are available on the agency's Pediatric Drug Development website (see Information Sources Checklist below). Since this program is voluntary, a sponsor is not required to respond to a written request.

Step 3–Conducting the Studies Studies must be conducted according to the written request and commonly accepted scientific principles and protocols. The sponsor can request a voluntary protocol review. Pediatric protocols relevant to pediatric exclusivity are considered special protocols, and the FDA should respond to requests for protocol reviews within 45 days of receiving them. In particular, the FDA recommends that the following documents be consulted: FDA regulations at 21 CFR 312.23 (describing protocol contents) and 314.126 (describing adequate and well-controlled studies); the ICH guidelines E3 (Structure and Content of Clinical Study Reports), E4 (Dose-Response Information to Support Drug Registration), E5 (Ethnic Factors), E6 (Good Clinical Practices: Consolidated Guideline), E8 (General Considerations for Clinical Trials), and E11 (Clinical Investigation of Medicinal Products in the Pediatric Population); and FDA guidances regarding the format and content of pediatric use supplements, the clinical and statistical sections of the NDA, pediatric pharmacokinetic studies, pediatric oncology studies, and others listed on the agency's Pediatric Drug Development website (see Information Sources Checklist).

The types of studies that the FDA will accept include new studies conducted by the sponsor or new studies performed by third parties either before or after the agency issues a written request. However, studies conducted prior to the FDA's issuance of the written request generally will not be acceptable when it is already apparent that the studies provide no additional information that might support a labeling change. Generally, data submitted to an NDA in advance of the written request may not be used to respond to the written request, although data submitted to an IND may be used to prepare a proposed pediatric study request.

Step 4–Submitting the Study Reports In general, the FDA will not accept pediatric study reports unless they are submitted in response to a formal agency written request. The study reports must be submitted according to the FDA's filing requirements (i.e., accompanied by an NDA, supplement, or NDA amendment). Although the NDA or supplement need not be approved for the pediatric studies to qualify for pediatric exclusivity, the completed study reports must be filed before the product's existing patent or exclusivity protection expires. As specified in FDAMA, the FDA will notify a sponsor within 60 days (through written agreements, which are now rarely used) or 90 days (without a written agreement) of its decision as to whether pediatric exclusivity will be granted or denied. The FDA's Pediatric Exclusivity Board decides whether study reports wi be accepted, and does so while offering the sponsor little opportunity to intercede on its own behalf if a dis pute regarding either the nature of the process or the timeframe for the decision arises. The recent imple mentation history indicates that the FDA has required that firms remain in strict compliance with the term of a written request, and that studies be conducted consistent with the specifications defined in writte agreements or commonly accepted scientific principles. If this process moves forward as planned, all of th sponsor's products that have the same active moiety as the one studied will have six months of pediatri exclusivity added to their patents and exclusivity periods listed in the *Orange Book*. If the studies were cor ducted for an unapproved indication, then the additional period of exclusivity will accrue upon approval.

Modifications of the FDAMA Pediatric Exclusivity Scheme Under the BPCA

The BPCA was developed to address certain gaps in the FDAMA pediatric exclusivity program. Most signif cantly, the changes implemented under the BPCA focused on the lack of incentives for off-patent drugs (an certain "uneconomical" on-patent drugs), the need for better dissemination of information (especially expe dited labeling changes), and an improved prioritization of studies (necessitating NIH and FDA collaboration It should be noted, however, that studies conducted under the BPCA are still voluntary, and that the time frame of the law was adjusted to sunset simultaneously with the current iteration of the Prescription Dru User Fee Act (October 1, 2007).

Expanded Incentive Program The BPCA provides that the FDA may issue a written request for pediatric studies t sponsors who are holders of the approved applications for drugs that: (1) lack any remaining patent life c market exclusivity (i.e., off-patent drugs); and (2) have been identified by the NIH in conjunction with the FD and other pediatric experts on a priority list of drugs for which pediatric studies are needed (see exhib below). Because there is no existing patent period or exclusivity to extend for such products, the sponsor car not receive the additional six-month "reward." The sponsor may elect to conduct the requested pediatric stuc ies, file a supplemental application for a new pediatric indication, and receive three years of marketin exclusivity plus the pediatric exclusivity award for the pediatric use.

Alternatively, the sponsor may decide not to respond to the written request. If the sponsor chooses not t respond, the Secretary of the Department of Health and Human Services (HHS) must publish, after 30 day a request for contract proposals (RFCs) for the conduct of the studies. The sponsor is not allowed to respon to this RFC, which is directed to third-party contractors with pediatric trial expertise, such as "qualified un versities, hospitals, laboratories, contract research organizations, federally funded programs such as pediatr pharmacology research units (PPRUs) and other public or private institutions." These studies are to be fund ed through an NIH-administered research fund that has an initial appropriation of $200,000,000 (reportedl the funds have been somewhat slow in coming, with $25 million made available in FY 2003, and $50 millic in FY 2004) and such sums as are necessary for each of the five years of the BPCA's current statutory perioc

Drugs with existing patent life or market exclusivity (i.e., on-patent drugs) may also be identified as priori drugs. If the sponsor declines to pursue a written request within 180 days of its receipt, then the Secreta may refer the drug to the NIH Foundation. The Foundation, which is authorized to collect gifts, grants ar other donations to fund pediatric studies, will propose the awarding of a grant for the conduct of the stud unless it certifies that it lacks sufficient funds. In the absence of sufficient funds, the drug is referred back t the priority list for consideration under the third-party contract process that is funded by appropriations.

Process for the Study of On-Patent Drugs

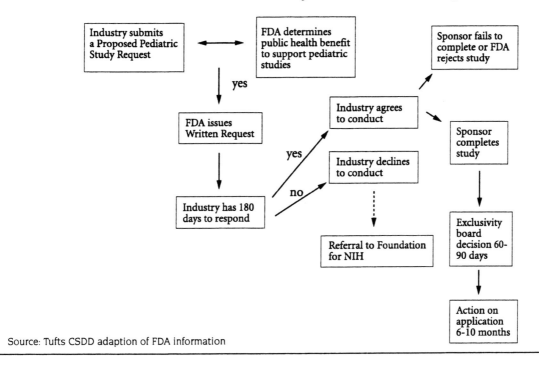

Source: Tufts CSDD adaption of FDA information

Process for the Study of Off-Patent Drugs

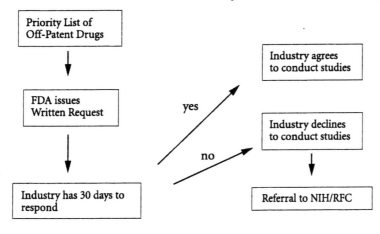

Source: FDA

Dissemination of Information The BPCA includes several provisions that will assist in the dissemination of the information collected by pediatric studies, either through labeling or posting of important data in the public domain. Under the law, the FDA is required to make summaries of the medical and clinical pharmacology reviews of pediatric studies available to the public, which the agency is accomplishing through postings on its website (see listing in Information Sources). The BPCA also provides for the enhanced collection of adverse event data through a toll-free number listed on a product's label and for the review of the data and recommendations for remedial action. In addition, recipients of third-party contracts and NIH grants are required to provide a report that describes the results of their studies and other relevant data, which will be posted in the public domain.

Finally, the BPCA features strong labeling provisions. The FDA has 180 days to review the pediatric stud
results and to determine what labeling changes are appropriate (both the study results and the FDA's prc
posed labeling changes must be published in the *Federal Register*). If the sponsor does not agree to the label
ing changes within the 180-day period, the FDA will refer the matter to the Pediatric Advisory Committe
(formerly the Pediatric Advisory Subcommittee of the Anti-Infective Drugs Advisory Committee), which wa
established as a full committee under PREA and which will review the labeling within 90 days and make rec
ommendations to the agency. If the sponsor does not respond within 30 days of receiving the FDA's fina
request for labeling changes, the agency may deem the drug to be misbranded and bring an enforcemen
action, most likely in the form of a court injunction requiring the sponsor to label the drug.

Prioritization of Studies The BPCA eliminated FDAMA's original priority testing list, in part because the list wa
too extensive to serve the goal of prioritization (i.e., the list contained 400 to 500 drugs at any one time) an
because updating the list on an annual basis was deemed a waste of resources. The BPCA charged the FD,
and NIH with developing a list of drugs for which pediatric studies are needed and that were generics (or otr
erwise off-patent) or for which written requests had been passed over by sponsors. The law provided that th
following criteria be used for a drug's inclusion on the list: the availability of information on the drug's use
whether additional information is needed; whether new studies would produce health benefits for the ped
atric population; and whether reformulation of the drug is necessary.

The FDA has stated that prioritization was a lengthy, iterative process involving the Pediatric Advisor
Committee, the FDA and NIH, the American Academy of Pediatrics (AAP), the United States Pharmacopei
(USP) and other experts. The agency started with a list of over 400 drugs, which was essentially halved fo
lowing consideration of the drugs' regulatory status and remaining patent or market exclusivity life. The lis
was then whittled down to about 100 drugs after consultation with pediatric disease specialists. Currently, th
priority list comprises 20 drugs and will be updated annually (see exhibit below).

List Of Drugs For Which Pediatric Studies Are Needed

Ampicillin/Sulbactam	Lindane
Azithromycin	Lithium
Baclofen	Lorazepam
Bumetanide	Meropenem
Diazoxide	Metoclopramide
Dobutamine	Nitroprusside
Dopamine	Piperacillin/Tazobactam
Furosemide	Promethazine
Heparin	Rifampin
Isoflurane	Spironolactone

Source: *Federal Register*, Feb.13, 2004

The Stick: The FDA's 1998 Rule as Codified under the Pediatric Research Equity Act (PREA)

In August 1997, the FDA made a controversial proposal to counteract the widespread practice of using adu
drugs in children on an off-label basis. The proposal called for companies submitting applications for ne
medicines considered "therapeutically important and/or likely to be used in children" to provide pediatric clir

ical study data to support pediatric use at the time of, or soon after, marketing approval. Subsequently in December 1998, the agency published a final rule for the "assessment of pediatric safety and effectiveness," which created a presumption that all new drugs and biological products would be studied in pediatric patients, but that allowed manufacturers to obtain a waiver or deferral from the requirement under certain circumstances.

The pediatric rule, however, was declared invalid on October 17, 2002, by the Federal Court for the District of Columbia (*Association of American Physicians and Surgeons, Inc. v. FDA*), which held that the rule exceeded the FDA's existing statutory authority. Recognizing the void created by the court's decision, Congress worked quickly to draft new legislation to more clearly establish the FDA's authority to require pediatric studies in specific cases. Upon its implementation on December 3, 2003, the Pediatric Research Equity Act (PREA) largely resurrected the pediatric rule just over a year after it was struck down.

PREA essentially reinstated the FDA's 1998 pediatric rule, even so far as to be retroactive to the rule's original effective date of April 1, 1999. Basically, PREA requires that each new drug or biological product application (filed under section 505 of the FD&C Act or section 351 of the PHSA, respectively) for a new active ingredient, new indication, new dosage form, new dosing regimen, or new route of administration contain data adequate to assess the safety and effectiveness of the drug or biological product for its claimed indications, and to support dosing and administration for each pediatric subpopulation (i.e., age group) for which the product is safe and effective, using appropriate formulations for each age group. If a product sponsor can submit evidence that the drug or biological product is likely to be ineffective or unsafe in children, or does not confer a significant therapeutic benefit for pediatric patients, then a sponsor can request a waiver or partial waiver (typically for certain pediatric age groups, such as infants and neonates).

For already-marketed drugs and biological products, no pediatric assessment is required unless the FDA has issued a written request for the voluntary conduct of the pediatric assessment and the sponsor refuses to agree or does not respond to the request. PREA allows the FDA, in compelling circumstances, to require that all holders of approved applications for a product submit data on safety and effectiveness as well as dosing and administration. Compelling circumstances are triggered when: (1) a product is used (or is likely to be used) in a "substantial number of pediatric patients;" or (2) the product provides a "meaningful therapeutic benefit" for pediatric use over existing treatments, and inadequate labeling could pose significant risks.

The "substantial number of pediatric patients" threshold is met when there are 50,000 pediatric patients with the disease or condition for which the drug or biological product is indicated. Currently, such assessments are predicated on physician-mention data from the National Disease and Therapeutic Index (a database maintained by IMS America Ltd.), which tracks the use of drugs by measuring the number of times physicians mention drugs during outpatient visits. The FDA has pointed out, however, that this numerical threshold is not set in stone and that it may be modified after consultation with pediatric experts.

The term "meaningful therapeutic benefit," which was derived, in part, from CDER's definition of a priority drug, attaches to a drug when it provides an improvement over existing products labeled for pediatric use. The term may be applied, for example, when there is evidence supporting any of the following: (1) increased effectiveness in the treatment, prevention, or diagnosis of disease; (2) elimination or substantial reduction of a treatment-limiting reaction; (3) documented enhancement of patient compliance; or (4) safety and effectiveness in a new subpopulation. In addition, a product can be considered to provide "meaningful therapeutic benefit" if it is in a class of products or has an intended indication for which there is a need for additional

therapeutic options, even if it is not necessarily considered a priority drug. This second criterion was devel
oped to address instances in which a drug might not be the first product in its class labeled for pediatric us
and, therefore, would not be considered a priority drug. Depending upon the severity of the disease and th
adverse reaction profile of existing treatments, however, such a product may still be necessary to ensure tha
a range of products is available for pediatric patients.

When the FDA decides that the use of a marketed product in children crosses the compelling circumstance
threshold, the agency will consult with the manufacturer on the types of pediatric studies needed and th
applicable time frame for such studies. By letter, the FDA will then notify the manufacturer of its tentative cor
clusion regarding the need for a pediatric study. In the penultimate step, the agency will provide the manu
facturer with an opportunity to provide a written response and to participate in a meeting, perhaps even a
advisory committee meeting. Ultimately, if the FDA determines that there is still a need for a study afte
reviewing the manufacturer's response, it will order the manufacturer (in a letter) to submit a pediatric assess
ment within a specified time. A failure to comply with this order can result in a drug being considered mis
branded. In this case, the agency may seek an injunction to enforce the requirement that a firm conduct
pediatric assessment. Only in a worst-case scenario will a company's failure to complete a pediatric assess
ment be considered misbranding. Such circumstances might arise when a product's predominant use is i
pediatric patients rather than adults, and when there are life-threatening risks associated with the drug's us
in the absence of pediatric dosing and safety information on the label. The FDA has indicated that it intend
to use seizure as a remedy only in rare cases, if at all.

The FDA will track the progress of pediatric assessments by having meetings with sponsors at appropriat
times before and during the product development process. During such meetings, the FDA will discuss th
sponsor's plans and timelines for pediatric studies, or its plans to submit a request for deferral or waiver o
pediatric studies. In their postmarketing annual reports, sponsors must submit information on the status o
their postmarketing commitments or other studies relevant to possible pediatric labeling changes.

PREA contains a number of "bailout" provisions (i.e., from the requirement that sponsors submit pediatr
safety/efficacy assessments), some of which are temporary or limited. The first bailout is an exemption fo
any drug or biological product with an orphan designation. Second, PREA generally does not apply to gene
ics because they are not products with a new active ingredient, new indication, new dosage form, new dos
ing regimen, or new route of administration. Generic manufacturers, however, must refer to the FDA Office o
Generic Drugs' requirements (MAPP 5230.2) regarding the pediatric use information that must or must no
appear on product labeling (see Information Sources Checklist below). Third, the FDA could conclude tha
in the case of a similar course of disease or effect, a product's pediatric effectiveness may be extrapolate
from adequate and well-controlled studies in adults (e.g., ibuprofen for pain; ondansetron for nausea or von
iting from cancer chemotherapy; AZT for AIDS; and imitinab mesylate for chronic myelocytic leukemia) whe
supplemented with other information (e.g., safety, PK/PD studies) or from one age group to another. Fourth
the submission of pediatric studies may be deferred until after a drug product is approved for use in adult
Such deferrals can be granted if two requirements are met. The threshold requirement is that the drug mu
be ready for approval in adults before studies in pediatric patients are complete, or that pediatric studie
need to be delayed until additional safety and effectiveness data have been collected or for another appro
priate reason. Pediatric assessments for "me-too drugs" may be deferred, for example, until adequate safe
and efficacy profiles have been established through extensive marketing in the adult population. In contras
for drugs intended to treat life-threatening illnesses that lack adequate treatment, pediatric studies ma
begin as early as preliminary safety data become available in adults (i.e., after Phase 1). The second requir

ment is that the applicant must submit a certification of the grounds for deferral, a description of the planned or ongoing studies, and evidence that the studies are being conducted or will be conducted with due diligence.

A decision regarding the amount of additional time allowed, like the decision to grant a deferral itself, will be made on a case-by-case basis. These decisions will depend on several factors, such as the need for the drug, when sufficient safety data become available, the nature and extent of the pediatric data that will be required to support pediatric labeling, and substantiated difficulties encountered in enrolling patients and in developing pediatric formulations. Deferral decisions will provide a specific date by which data submissions are required. In past public discussions, the FDA has said it expects that deferred pediatric studies will be initiated prior to a drug's approval for an adult indication, and that the results will be submitted no more than two years after the initial approval. If the applicant fails to conduct the assessment within the specified time, the FDA reviewing division will first notify and meet with the applicant to discuss the reasons for this failure. When an applicant cannot provide a reasonable explanation for the delay and obtain a further deferral from the division, the division may pursue regulatory actions in consultation with the FDA's Office of the General Counsel. If the study submitted with the application is not adequate, a further study will be necessary unless the review division waives or defers the requirement based on its desire to approve the application for adults.

The fifth and sixth bailout provisions involve waivers and partial waivers. A full waiver may be granted if the drug product has no therapeutic advantage or anticipated use in pediatric patients, if the studies are impossible or impractical, if the drug product is ineffective or unsafe for the pediatric population, or if the condition does not occur in children. A partial waiver can be granted for similar reasons, but would be related to the drug's use in specific age groups of the pediatric population. Partial waivers are also available when the applicant can demonstrate that reasonable attempts to produce a pediatric formulation for that specific age group have failed. When a full or partial waiver is granted, however, that information must be included in the labeling. Any planned request by the sponsor for waiver or deferral or sponsor plans and timelines for pediatric studies will be discussed at meetings held before and during a new drug or biological product's development process.

The FDA reviewing division responsible for a drug will make the waiver decision. To request a waiver from the appropriate reviewing division, the applicant must certify that one or more of the grounds for a waiver exist and supply supporting information and documentation. In other words, the burden is on the manufacturer to justify a waiver. The agency has emphasized that cost ordinarily will not be a factor in the waiver decision, that unsupported assertions will be rejected, that methods are available to conduct adequate studies in small populations, and that studies in small populations may have to be at least attempted before a waiver will be granted.

Waiver discussions with the FDA should take place at the end-of-Phase 2 or pre-NDA/BLA meeting, or at least 60 days prior to an application's submission. A manufacturer's first step in preparing a waiver request should be to check the FDA's list of diseases and conditions for which waivers are likely to be granted (see exhibit below). The FDA has noted, however, that changes are expected as more pediatric indications of drugs previously thought to treat only adult diseases are explored.

Finally, it is worth noting that the FDA has committed to adopt policies consistent with the spirit of the law—that is, all the voluntary options should be exhausted before the FDA invokes its pediatric research authori-

---

Diseases for Which Pediatric Waivers Are Likely

Alzheimer's disease	Age-related macular degeneration
Prostate cancer	Breast cancer
Non-germ cell ovarian cancer	Renal cell cancer
Hairy cell leukemia	Uterine cancer
Squamous cell cancers of the oropharynx	Pancreatic cancer
Basal cell and squamous cell cancer	Endometrial cancer
Osteoarthritis	Parkinson's disease
Amyotrophic lateral sclerosis	Arteriosclerosis
Infertility	Symptoms of menopause
Small cell and non-small cell lung cancer	

Source: FDA

---

ty (PRA) to mandate studies. By not making PRA a permanent regulatory tool, Congress demonstrated that wanted the mandatory and voluntary options to go hand in hand. In contrast to the former 1998 pediatric rule PREA will sunset on the same day as the BPCA (October 1, 2007) unless it is reauthorized.

Incorporating Pediatric Studies into Drug Development Planning

The agency frequently notes that the focus and scope of the BPCA and PREA are different. The BPCA progran for example, is focused mainly on marketed products, while PREA is primarily concerned with ensuring tha new drugs and biological products provide adequate pediatric labeling for the approved indications at th time of, or soon following, approval. The scope of PREA is broader than the BPCA in some respects and na rower in others. PREA is broader because it covers biological products as well as subsequent indications an multiple pediatric subpopulations for drug products that may not get addressed under the BPCA's third-part contracting or NIH Foundation grant processes. In some respects, however, the scope of coverage under PRE is narrower because it requires an assessment only for the product and indications contained in the applica tion submitted for review (or for marketed drugs specified by the FDA), while the BPCA covers an entire activ moiety, possibly with multiple indications and product forms. Moreover, PREA applies to products used in substantial number of children or products that would provide a meaningful therapeutic benefit for pediatr patients, while the BPCA has a broader compass related to drugs for which additional information may pro duce health benefits in the pediatric population.

Even though a pediatric study could be rejected under PREA and still meet the terms of a written reque: under the BPCA (or vice versa), Congress provided a harmonization provision in the enabling legislation fo pediatric exclusivity (i.e., FDAMA). Under this provision, when the two laws overlap in scope, pediatric stud ies mandated under PREA could also be used to meet the requirements of a written request. The FDA ana lyzed how often this occurs in the preamble to PREA. During the first three years that both the regulato requirement and pediatric exclusivity incentive were operational (April 1, 1999, to March 31, 2002), there we 404 NDAs and efficacy supplements that fell within the scope of the FDA's mandatory authority to requi pediatric assessments. Sponsors of approximately two-thirds of the NDAs would have been required to actu ally conduct studies in one or more pediatric age groups, while the other third received waivers because safety concerns or because the indications were not relevant to childhood diseases. Overall, one-third of th applications contained complete or partial pediatric use information (with another one-third presumably receiving deferrals), and only one-sixth of the total number of applications included pediatric use information due to the pediatric rule (now PREA) alone.

Planning Considerations I: What Types of Studies Will Be Needed?

As previously discussed, although the BPCA's scope differs from that of PREA, the types of studies and methodological issues involved will be similar. Further, because the FDA has committed under FDAMA to work toward the global harmonization of regulatory requirements, the agency's recommendations often refer to the guidelines developed by the International Conference on Harmonization (ICH), a joint regulatory/industry initiative designed to harmonize the regulatory requirements for developing and registering new medicinal products in Europe, Japan, and the United States. For both the BPCA and PREA, a company's determination of the types of studies that will be needed for a particular indication in a particular pediatric age group should begin with an evaluation of animal toxicology, relevant prior human data from adults or other pediatric age groups, and FDA and ICH guidelines.

Preclinical Studies Since the FDA has no standard requirements for the number or type of preclinical studies that must accompany an application for a pediatric indication (but see the FDA's draft industry guidance *Nonclinical Safety Evaluation of Pediatric Drugs*, February 2003), the agency may need to have the applicant conduct animal studies to provide adequate data. To support pediatric exclusivity under the BPCA, toxicology studies in immature animals may be necessary even before determining if a written request should be issued and before conducting pediatric clinical studies. For example, if the pediatric indication being explored involves short-term drug exposure but a chronic condition (e.g., asthma), then nonclinical studies must be conducted before the NDA is approved. If, however, the pediatric exposure is thought to be long-term, then the nonclinical trials should be conducted before any trials are undertaken in children.

The FDA believes that juvenile animal studies should be considered when the drug or biological product is for chronic use, when the product presents specific health concerns that require investigation (e.g., neurotoxicity), when problems are associated with the drug class (e.g., bone/joint toxicity in the adult—human or animal), and when little or no other safety data exist from preclinical or clinical toxicity studies. However, each drug will be considered on a case-by-case basis because this area is still very much evolving, especially regarding the applicability of juvenile animal data. Some experts have stated that prospective validation of the predictive power of standard toxicity testing, adult human experience, and nonclinical juvenile toxicity testing is needed before the appropriate role of extrapolation and preclinical testing can be determined for pediatric studies.

For the FDA, the starting point is that juvenile rats and dogs are not smaller versions of the adult animal models, just as children are not little adults. The most significant differences across species are in the earliest age groups, especially with regard to specific organs, physical and neurological developmental endpoints, and maturation of renal and hepatic clearance pathways. The next level of consideration is choosing the appropriate animal model in terms of age, species, effects of typical diet, handling and restraint logistics, among other factors.

Clinical Studies When pediatric clinical studies are required, researchers must consider the unique aspects of such studies. Alternative endpoints are often necessary in pediatric clinical trials—it may be impractical, for example, to measure the same clinical endpoints that are used in adult trials in some cases (e.g., because it would require cooperation, verbal skills, or comprehension beyond the ken of the typical pediatric study participant). Suggested approaches for tailoring trial design to children involve modifying adult efficacy measures, devising new ones, or identifying and validating surrogate endpoints. Pediatric clinical studies will also have to accommodate school and caregiver schedules and employ sampling schemes that will vary, in some cases from those used in adult studies. The availability of appropriate facilities and specially trained staff are othe considerations that the FDA has suggested should become a routine part of a sponsor's planning process fc pediatric clinical studies.

The agency has noted that the type and amount of data required in any particular case will depend upon man factors (see exhibits below). As for the number of pivotal clinical trials required, the FDA has further state that two adequate and well-controlled clinical trials are not necessarily required to establish adequate evi dence of a drug's pediatric safety and effectiveness. For example, the FDA may approve a pediatric use for drug on the basis of extrapolations from adult efficacy data that are supplemented with supporting pediatri data, such as pharmacokinetic, dosing, and safety information. If additional controlled trial data are neede to support a drug's effectiveness in a pediatric population, a single controlled trial generally should suffice Safety studies are typically required when the drug has a narrow therapeutic index or when major safety prot lems have been identified in adult studies.

Types of Pediatric Studies for FDAMA and the 1998 Rule, by Percent

	Efficacy	PK	Safety	PK/PD	Other[t]
Rule*	23%	16%	21%	14%	26%
	Eff/Safety	PK/Safety	Safety	PK/PD	Other[tt]
FDAMA ** (1999)	38%	28%	23%	9%	3%
FDAMA** (2001)	32%	31%	19%	9%	9%
BPCA** (2004)	35%	30%	15%	9%	11%

Other[t]—Dosing and extrapolation studies

Other[tt]—Prophylaxis, OTC use, and combination efficacy, safety and PK studies

*Source: Tufts Center for the Study of Drug Development
**Source: Food and Drug Administration

The ICH guidelines point out that a pharmacokinetic (PK) approach may not be sufficient for medicinal proc ucts for which blood levels are not known to correspond with efficacy, or for which there is concern that th concentration-response relationship may differ between adult and pediatric patients. When the compatibil ty of the disease course and/or outcome of therapy in the pediatric patient is expected to be similar but th appropriate blood levels are not clear, it may be possible to utilize measurements of a pharmacodynamic (PL effect to confirm the expectations of effectiveness and to define the dose and concentration needed to attai that PD effect. Such studies would provide additional assurance that achieving a given pediatric exposure likely to result in the desired therapeutic outcomes. This could circumvent the need for clinical efficacy stuc ies. Aside from adult data, the necessary safety information would comprise repeat dose toxicology (may nc be applicable for some biotechnology products) and reproductive toxicology and genotoxicology data.

The FDA has described three basic methods for providing clinical evidence to support the safe and effectiv use of drugs in children: (1) using evidence from adequate and well-controlled investigations of a specif pediatric indication different from the indication approved for adults; (2) using evidence from adequate and well-controlled investigations in children to support the same indication approved for adults; and (3) evidence from adequate and well-controlled adult studies in which the course of the disease and the effects of the drug (both beneficial and adverse) are sufficiently similar in the pediatric and adult populations to permit extrapolation of the adult efficacy data to pediatric patients. This last approach would likely involve the need for pharmacokinetic studies to permit appropriate dosing. There are two basic approaches for conducting pharmacokinetic studies: the standard pharmacokinetic approach and the population pharmacokinetic approach. The standard approach is, as the name implies, the approach typically employed, and involves the administration of either single or multiple doses of a drug to a relatively small (e.g., 6-12) group of subjects with relatively frequent blood and sometimes urine sample collection. The population PK approach is generally used in patients being given the drug therapeutically, and relies on infrequent (sparse) sampling from a larger population.

As the pediatric studies initiative has evolved, the FDA has refined its approach to the interaction of adult and pediatric clinical data away from a yes/no decision based on extrapolation to a pediatric study decision tree (see exhibit below). Regarding extrapolation, the FDA cites HIV (antiretrovirals) as an example of a case in which the adult and juvenile forms are considered sufficiently similar, despite differences in disease stage, the etiologic agent, the disease mechanism, and viral load and immune suppression. The FDA cites antihistamines as an example of a case in which the pathophysiology and manifestations between the adult and juvenile forms are sufficiently similar such that only pharmacokinetic and safety trials are needed.

The Pediatric Study Decision Tree approach has its origin in the FDA's *Guidance on Exposure-Response Relationships* (i.e., determined by dose-response or concentration-response). Briefly, this method is based on bridging studies involving exposure-response data that compare PK/PD response curves in two populations with confidence intervals used to measure "similarity" in the two populations. The FDA defines a bridging study in this context as a study performed in a new scenario that will provide pharmacodynamic or clinical data on effica-

Pediatric Study Decision Tree

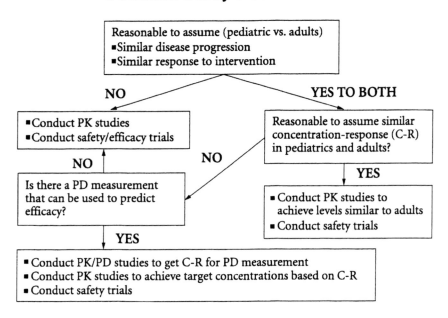

Source: FDA

cy, safety, dosage, and dosage regimen and that will allow for the extrapolation of the efficacy and safety dat from original studies to the new scenario (derived from ICH E5, Ethnic Factor Studies).

Age Group Considerations In most cases, the FDA believes that pharmacokinetic (PK) data will be necessar in each age group to allow dosing adjustments, and that studies in more than one age group may be neces sary, depending on the expected therapeutic benefit and use in each age group and on the degree to whic data from one age group can be extrapolated to other age groups. When PK parameters have not been we correlated with activity in adults (e.g., topicals), a clinical study will most likely be necessary. Specific require ments for each study will be determined on a case-by-case basis, however. In general, the FDA states that spe cific drug studies in the relevant age category should be conducted whenever major differences exist, such a in the formation of different metabolites. The agency indicates that neonates, in particular, are likely t require age-specific studies.

Although the FDA and the American Academy of Pediatrics (AAP) maintain that the standard FDA age group (neonates: birth-1 month; infants: 1 month-2 years; children: 2-12 years; and adolescents: 12-16 years) pro vide acceptable guidelines, both organizations concede that the ranges should not be followed rigidly whe it is reasonable to define subgroups by some other method, such as stage of development. If a sponsor con ducts a study based on characteristics other than age, the company should support its categories with scien tific, developmental, compliance, or ethical considerations. Most recently, the FDA has stated that age group should be defined in a flexible manner, depending on the drug or biologic's pharmacology, the disease's mar ifestations in various age groups, and the ability to measure the response to therapy.

With regard to pre-term infants, neonates, and infants, the AAP emphasizes that the difficulties involved i studying drug effects in these groups do not outweigh the importance of studying them. The FDA acknow edges that studies in these groups may be waived, or at least deferred, until additional experience with th drug or biological product has been gained. There will be cases, however, in which the drug or biologic is a important advance and is expected to be used in these age groups. In such cases, studies will be required unless the applicant obtains a partial waiver.

The ICH guidelines state that pre-term and term newborn infants may have unique manifestations of disease that preclude the extrapolation of efficacy from older pediatric patients. Rarely is it possible to extrapolat efficacy from studies in adults or even older pediatric patients to the pre-term infant. Oral absorption of mec icinal products may be less predictable in term newborn infants than in older pediatric patients. In childrer it may be necessary to define age by Tanner stages. The extrapolation of efficacy data from older children t younger children may be necessary, especially when the assessment of outcome variables is particularly di ficult in younger patients (e.g., forced expiratory volume (FEV1) below the age of 6 years).

Long-Term Studies Long-term follow up (i.e., more than six months) covers a wide spectrum of studies, rang ing from studies that evaluate neurodevelopment, behavior, or bone and joint growth over several years t studies that monitor psychosocial, hormonal, or physical and endocrinologic maturation for as long as te years. Such studies may be required when drugs could affect growth and development (e.g., steroids), CN development (e.g., drugs affecting neurotransmitters, drugs given chronically during CNS/brain developmen drugs with CNS toxicity), or the musculoskeletal system (e.g., quinolones). Other diseases and conditior that the FDA has suggested are likely to require long-term studies include chronic lung disease, asthma inflammatory diseases, attention deficit disorder, depression, and psychoses. The FDA, however, also ha emphasized that, if early studies do not indicate a problem, then long-term studies will not be an impedimer

---

Diseases and Conditions for which Efficacy Trials were Requested by the FDA for Pediatric Exclusivity Studies Under FDAMA

- Hypertension
- Depression
- Anesthesia/Sedation
- Pain
- Hepatitis C
- Complicated UTI
- Obesity
- Transplant rejection
- End stage renal disease
- Malaria

- GAD
- Allergic conjunctivitis
- Eye allergies
- Hepatitis B
- Asthma
- OCD
- HIV
- Influenza
- Seizures
- Atopic dermatitis

- Intraocular pressure
- Allergic rhinitis
- Cholesterol lowering
- Antibiotics
- Smoking cessation
- Migraines
- JRA
- Diabetes
- Anti-fungal
- Acne

Source: FDA

---

to marketing the product, and that the postapproval study approach may be a way to accomplish the twin goals of making needed products available while investigating long-term effects.

Planning Considerations II: How Often Will New Formulations be Needed?

It is becoming increasingly clear that one of the FDA's main goals in the pediatric studies initiative is to promote the development of pediatric formulations. The development of age-appropriate formulations is technically challenging and time-consuming, and requires a number of steps, including the identification of problem drugs, the application of specialized formulation technology (e.g., tastemasking and transdermal enhancement), and the completion of dosing and pharmacokinetic studies. Taste is crucial for compliance, especially in children—a survey of 500 parents conducted by Ascent Pediatrics indicated that approximately 50% of children refuse to take their medication at some time and that, for 75% of the noncompliers, the reason is related to a drug's taste.

Dosage form is another complicating factor in pediatric formulation, and significant variation occurs even between pediatric age groups. According to the Physician Drug & Diagnosis Audit conducted by Scott Levin in 1997, four times as many 16-year olds took their medications as oral solids than did six-year-olds. In addition, the selection of inert ingredients requires greater care, since children can have adverse reactions to preservatives, colorings, and flavoring agents routinely used in adult formulations.

The AAP emphasizes that the FDA must require appropriate formulations for each age group in which a drug will be used, taking into account the ease of administration and the ability to dose accurately. The agency believes that, for drugs and biologicals that offer a meaningful therapeutic benefit, it is essential to ensure a drug's bioavailability and accurate dosing. The agency may require that an applicant develop a new formulation when one is needed for the targeted pediatric population.

The FDA recognizes that it may be necessary for a manufacturer to begin developing a pediatric formulation before initiating clinical trials—in some cases, before Phase 1 studies are completed. In general, the agency believes that 25% of all new dosage forms developed would be initiated at the start of Phase 2 trials and 75% by the start of Phase 3 trials. By the FDA's own estimates, the financial impact of new formulation development is considerable: The agency has projected that, for about 40% of drugs and biologicals studied each year under the original 1998 rule, manufacturers would have to develop new dosage forms at an average cost of $1 million per formulation.

Under PREA, if formulation difficulties are to provide the basis for the waiver request, the burden is on the applicant to provide evidence that "experts" in formulation chemistry had encountered unusually difficult technical problems. In evaluating formulation issues, the FDA will also consider the potential importance of the product to pediatric patients. The agency can, at its discretion, subject the waiver request to the scrutiny of an advisory committee, which will consider whether reasonable attempts were made in a particular case. Although the FDA recognizes that the difficulty and cost of producing a formulation can vary "greatly" based on such factors as the compound's solubility and taste, the agency will have to rely on the manufacturer to supply "informative cost information." Under the BPCA, the FDA believes that greater costs can be incurred when a product has "significant" patent or exclusivity life remaining. Even if a stable commercial formulation cannot be developed, the agency will consider, on a case-by-case basis, whether to accept labeling direction for producing extemporaneous pediatric formulations as an alternative. In a recent JAMA article that examined the results of the pediatric exclusivity program, the authors found that new formulations were developed for 15% of the drugs that had completed labeling. For another 6% of the drugs, companies had developed labeling instructions for compounding extemporaneous formulations (e.g., ranging from simple instruction for mixing with apple sauce to more complex formulas for preparing pediatric liquid preparations utilizing commercially available electrolyte and suspension agents).

The ICH guidelines regard pediatric formulation needs as potentially expansive, despite the FDA's belief that a liquid formulation may serve all age groups in many cases. The ICH suggests that several formulations, such as liquids, suspensions, and chewable tablets, may be needed or desirable for pediatric patients in different age groups. Different concentrations may be necessary, as well as alternative approaches, such as patches or suppositories. For injectables, the concentration must be appropriate for the doses administered, including doses for small premature infants or when fluid restrictions are relevant for extremely small patients. Since the development of pediatric formulations can be difficult and time consuming, it is important that this process be considered early in medicinal product development.

Planning Considerations III: What Resources Are Available?

Pediatric Research Organizations and Outsourcing Some pediatric research organizations predated the FDA's pediatric initiative. One such organization is the network of Pediatric Pharmacology Research Units (PPRUs), which currently comprises 13 academic medical centers and children's hospitals in the United States. Collectively, these PPRUs, which are organized under the auspices of the NIH and have been operational since 1994, serve a population of 160,000 pediatric inpatients and nearly three million pediatric outpatients. Similarly, some additional children's hospitals and academic medical centers that were previously conducting pediatric research on an individual basis have established their own networks or other collaborations. Moreover, the NIH and its Division of AIDS have created the Pediatric AIDS Clinical Trials Group to design and conduct pediatric HIV drug trials. In addition, a Pediatric Oncology Group has been established under the auspices of the National Cancer Institute.

There has also been an impressive marshalling of resources within the outsourcing sector in response to the FDAMA incentive and the perception that many pharmaceutical companies would find value in external pediatric research capacities and expertise. Some organizations reshaped themselves in response to what the perceived as new industry needs and market opportunities. One form was the makeover of academic medical centers into academic research organizations (AROs). Another was the formation of site management organizations (SMOs) dedicated exclusively to pediatric research. The PPRU network mentioned above is an example of a nonprofit SMO. Other outsourcing entities, including several CROs, supplemented existing resources and established discrete pediatric research units.

In late 2000, the Tufts Center for the Study of Drug Development (CSDD) conducted a survey of sponsors that had received the first 40 written requests. The sponsors reported that the personnel responsible for conducting the pediatric studies were assembled by diverting existing in-house resources in some cases. More than half the sponsors, however, relied on outsourcing service providers.

In addition, the Tufts CSDD surveys of outsourcing entities have chronicled changes in the resources available for conducting pediatric studies since 1998. At the beginning of the pediatric studies initiative in 1998, 60% of CROs sampled stated that they had experience in conducting pediatric studies, although only 15% had conducted ten or more studies. By 2000, although the same percentage of CROs said that they had pediatric trial expertise, 73% reported an increase in demand for pediatric trial services, and 30% reported adding new staff and even starting pediatric trial-specific units within their organizations. By 2002, the frenetic pediatric services build up was beginning to plateau, as surveys indicated that the increase in the number of special-population studies requested for pediatrics came in third out of five areas, behind fast track and orphan diseases. During these years, CROs experienced significant consolidation overall, and the trend toward developing specialized pediatric service units seemingly had declined. Among SMOs surveyed in 1998, about 60% reported having pediatric research expertise, and 50% stated that they had performed ten or more pediatric studies. While SMOs have experienced consolidation similar to the CROs, the trend toward pediatric service specialization still appears to be on the rise within this group.

Ethical Guidance Given the need for large numbers of pediatric patients within a relatively brief timeframe, ensuring the ethics of patient recruitment, informed consent procedures, trial design and conduct, and the use of appropriate facilities and adequately trained personnel has become especially challenging. This is one of the reasons that, although FDAMA mentioned consultation with pediatric experts only in passing and the 1998 rule referred to it even more obliquely, the FDA decided early on in the initiative to convene a panel with expertise in pediatric health. In April 1999, the FDA held the first meeting of what is now called the Pediatric Advisory Committee. The committee comprises 12 voting members who are selected by the FDA commissioner or the commissioner's designee from among experts in pediatric research, pediatric subspecialties, statistics, and/or biomedical ethics and who include a member from a patient advocacy organization and a consumer rights organization. There are also provisions that allow the committee to incorporate non-voting members and to borrow scientific and technical experts from other FDA advisory committees or consultants. The committee advises the FDA commissioner on a range of issues, including pediatric research conducted under the BPCA and PREA, the assessment of research priorities, pediatric labeling disputes, adverse event reports engendered by the BPCA, and ethical questions and concerns. Ethical issues are addressed by the Pediatric Ethics Subcommittee (formerly the Pediatric Ethics Working Group), which held the first of its several meetings in November 1999. Among the issues that the Pediatric Ethics Subcommittee has considered include the role of pediatric volunteers and assent (11/15/99), placebo-controlled trials (9/11/00), and vulnerable pediatric populations and formulations appropriate for pediatric use (4/24/01). Consensus statements on ethical issues and other information generated by the Pediatric Advisory Committee meetings are available online (see Information Sources Checklist below).

The FDA's basic position statement on the ethical conduct of pediatric studies notes that pediatric clinica studies should adhere to the principles set forth by the Department of Health and Human Services (DHHS in Subpart D-Additional Protections for Children Involved as Subjects in Research (45 CFR Subtitle A: 46.401 46.409). Under an April 2001 interim rule, the FDA adopted the DHHS regulations for the conduct of clinica studies in children. The AAP's Committee on Drugs has also issued a document entitled, *Guidelines for the Ethica Conduct of Studies to Evaluate Drugs in Pediatric Populations* (see Information Sources Checklist below). In additior the Institute of Medicine's report on the ethical conduct of pediatric trials, which was chartered in the BPCA is now available from the National Academies Press (visit <http://national-academies.org>).

The ICH guidelines advise minimizing the distress experienced by pediatric study patients by recommending (1) the use of protocols and investigations specifically designed for the pediatric population (i.e., no reworked adult protocols); (2) oversight by competent and experienced IRB/IECs (independent ethics com mittee); (3) the involvement of personnel knowledgeable and skilled in dealing with the pediatric populatio and its age-appropriate needs, including skills in performing pediatric procedures; (4) a physical setting witl age-appropriate furniture, play equipment, activities, and food; and (5) a familiar environment for conductin the trials, such as hospitals or clinics at which pediatric patients normally receive care.

Information Sources

Since the pediatric studies initiative is constantly evolving and because many FDA decisions are bein reached on a case-by-case basis after consultation with outside experts, access to up-to-date information i especially crucial. In addition, it is essential that sponsors communicate directly with the FDA or the EME, when they have questions that are not addressed sufficiently in currently available information sources (se Information Sources Checklist below).

Information Sources Checklist

Contacting EMEA directly- Dr. Agnes Saint Raymond: Agnes.Saint-Raymond@emea.eu.int or Dr. Nathalie Seigneuret: Nathalie.Seigneuret@emea.eu.int

Contacting FDA directly- PEDS Line: 301-594-PEDS (7337); Office of Pediatric Therapeutics: 301-827-1996, 301-827-1017 (fax), opt@fda.gov; Office of Counterterrorism and Pediatrics: 301-827-7777; E-mail questions to CDER: pdit@cder.fda.gov; Human Subject Protection, CDER: 301-594-1026; Human Subject Protection, CBER: 301-827-6221

Websites:

FDA Pediatric Drug Development Page- http://www.fda.gov/cder/pediatric/index.htm

NIH Information Sheet on Research in Children- <http://helix.hih.gov:8001/ohsr/info/jinfo_10.phtml>

European Commission Pharma Unit- <http://pharmacos.eudra/F2/>

International Conference on Harmonization [ICH] Guidelines- http://www.eudra.org/emea.html

Guidelines for the Ethical Conduct of Studies to Evaluate Drugs in Pediatric Populations-
    <http://www.aap.org/policy/00655.html>

Ethics Working Group Consensus Statements- http://www.fda.gov/cder/pediatric/index.htm#advisory

-continued-

–continued–

Pediatric Study Information (generally available from FDA Pediatric Drug Development website**):**

The Pediatric Exclusivity Provision of FDAMA as codified: 21 U.S.C. 355a.

The 1998 FDA Pediatric Rule: 63 Fed. Reg. 66632 (December 2, 1998)

Guidance for Industry: Qualifying for Pediatric Exclusivity, CDER and CBER, September 1999

Guidance for Industry: General Considerations for Pediatric Pharmacokinetic Studies for Drugs and Biological Products, CDER and CBER, November 1998

Guidance for Industry: Pediatric Oncology Studies in Response to a Written Request, CDER and CBER, June 2000

Guidance for Industry: Providing Evidence of Clinical Effectiveness for Human Drug and Biological Products, CDER and CBER, May 1998

Guidance for Industry: The Content and Format for Pediatric Use Supplements, CDER and CBER, May 1996

Guidance for Industry: Format and Content of Clinical and Statistical Sections of New Drug Applications, CDER, July 1998

Office of Counter-Terrorism and Pediatric Drug Development/Organization Chart

Sample Letter for General Written Request for Pediatric Studies (basic template), August 1999

Sample Written Request for specific drug classes (oral hypertensives, antidepressants, HIV drugs, obsessive-compulsive disorder and oncology drugs), Aug/1999-May/2000

Guidance on Clinical Investigation of Medicinal Products in the Pediatric Population, 4/20/2000 (FDA publication of ICH Topic E-11: Clinical Investigation of Medicinal Products in the Pediatric Population, October 1999)

Review of Generic Drug Product Labeling Requiring Input From Multiple FDA Components, CDER Manual of Policies and Procedures 5230.2

The Present

In reflecting upon how the knowledge gap occurred for pediatric studies, the FDA has proffered the following possible reasons: ethical concerns; limited populations for certain diseases; difficulties in conducting trials in pediatrics (from logistical to technical); the belief that dosing could be determined by weight-based calculations ("little adults" fallacy); the lack of accepted endpoints and validated pediatric assessment tools; and limited marketing potential compared to adults. Examining the pediatric studies initiative's progress in closing the gap may be instructive in assessing whether the carrot and stick was the right approach. In 2000, Dianne Murphy, M.D., currently the director of CDER's Office of Counter Terrorism and Pediatric Drug Development, was reported as predicting that the number of unlabeled medicines for children would decrease from 75% to 50% over the subsequent five years. While that prediction remains an optimistic one, there is no doubt that this approach has motivated the industry "to think pediatric." Already, firms have completed pediatric studies for close to 200 drugs, and the FDA has posted close to 100 labeling changes (including results from both the pediatric exclusivity program (n=80) and the pediatric rule (n=12)) in a number of therapeutic areas critical to pediatric practice (see exhibit below).

Fully 12% of the products featuring new pediatric use labeling are for HIV/AIDS, influenza, and hepatitis B and C, for example. These are diseases of major public health concern both in the United States and abroad. The lack of labeled medicines for hospital use in pediatric AIDS patients was an early impetus for the pediatri studies initiative. Further, 16% of the new labels reflect information on pediatric use for dermatological and ocular conditions, which are prevalent in children but which are not studied widely in pharmaceutical research programs. Another 8% of the products now labeled for pediatric use are several drugs used for anesthesia, anal gesia, and other conditions related to surgery, which has been a much needed but difficult area for clinica investigations in children. Thus, the sparse evidence base for pediatric medicine is growing, especially in ther apeutic areas that were poorly studied before the pediatric initiative. If these percentages are compared to th proportions of the prescription market for children (i.e., approximately 25% vaccines; 23% allergy/respiratory 21% anti-infectives; and 32% for all other disease categories), the need for follow-on pediatric indications from adult drugs is easy to appreciate, since the range of indications supported by pediatric use alone is limited.

New Labeling Information for Pediatric Use by Therapeutic Area

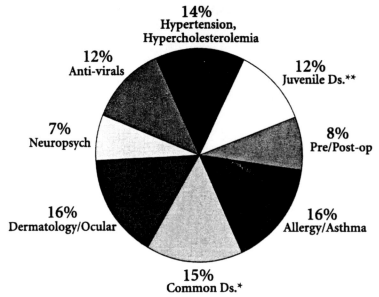

*Some with adult and pediatric forms, e.g., cancer, GERD, etc.
**JRA, enuresis, Diabetes Type I

Source: FDA

With written requests having been issued to nearly 70 companies for 125 different pediatric diseases and cor ditions, several hundred more drugs are currently under study. The FDA expects that 80% of the writte requests will result in pediatric studies being undertaken by the private sector. Tufts CSDD survey results ind cate that, during the FDAMA period, 95% of companies at least attempted to respond to written requests. Thi will also help to increase activity in poorly studied therapeutic areas. According to a recent article in a lead ing medical journal, for example, the most under-funded areas of pediatric research in the United States ar obesity, diabetes and cardiology, while a recent U.S. Surgeon General report revealed that fewer than 20% of children with severe mental illness receive treatment. Interestingly, however, the top three categories of spor sor PPSR submissions for the study of adult drugs for pediatric indications were for metabolic and endocrine neuropharmacology, and cardio-renal indications. Under the BPCA program enhancements, safety informa tion is now available earlier for newly studied drugs, and outcomes are monitored over longer periods for ce tain pediatric indications for which the FDA has concerns about long-term drug effects.

Tufts CSDD survey results indicate that one-third of pediatric exclusivity projects resulted in the development and validation of new clinical assessment tools and sampling and analytical techniques. Congressional testimony on the reauthorization of the pediatric exclusivity provision indicated that 20% of the initial 200 studies were conducted in neonates and infants, 30% in children aged 2 to 12, and 50% in adolescents. Other testimony by the FDA and the AAP showed that a third of the drugs studied had label information that was either inaccurate (e.g., dosing ranges that were too high or too low) or incomplete (e.g., no information on the drug's toxic properties for certain pediatric age groups).

Coincident with the pediatric studies initiative, overall interest in pediatric research grew. While the number of drugs being studied for pediatric indications (typically along with adult indications) grew by 28% from 1990 to 1997, for example, it increased by 49% from 1997 to 2000, or twice the increase in half the time. In fact, the pediatric R&D paradigm became a harbinger of the evolving paradigm for mainstream drug development, in which collaboration on development projects has grown significantly. In 1990, large pharmaceutical companies were the primary collaborators in 75% of projects; in the 2000s, they have been the primary collaborators in only 16% of projects, with biotechnology companies and government assuming the primary collaborator role in the majority of projects. In summary, the pediatric studies initiative had, within a few years, launched a pediatric infrastructure that was comparable to what it took 40 years to achieve for adults.

Such a dramatic reapportionment of resources, however, takes its toll and is often difficult to sustain. Although the pharmaceutical industry has been able to marshal resources to meet the pediatric study-related demands so far, the FDA struggled under the workload. Agency officials conceded that the demands of the resource-intensive and deadline-driven pediatric studies initiative may have affected its capacity to deal with its traditional regulatory activities, such as reviewing standard NDAs. The impact of the initiative on FDA personnel can be appreciated by considering the fact that, throughout most of the FDAMA implementation period, the FDA had 65 staffers spread over 12 pediatric oversight activities.

While the FDA remains resource-challenged, the pediatric studies program was one of only four agency programs to actually receive increased funding in FY2004 (along with food safety, generic drugs, and bioterrorism programs). The BPCA has provided some assistance by withdrawing the previous user-fee exemption for pediatric supplements, a change that will help provide additional funding that the FDA plans to use to hire 36 full-time equivalents.

Industry also invested considerable resources into the pediatric exclusivity program because, as one industry spokesperson pointed out during the reauthorization hearings, the pediatric exclusivity incentive was sufficiently attractive to raise "the priority of pediatric studies among competing programs within a company." According to a Tufts CSDD study on the early years of the pediatric initiative, a project took about three years from protocol development to labeling, cost $20,000 per patient (plus another $750,000 for the 20% developing new formulations), and required 20 to 25 staffers. Companies spent an estimated $300 million a year on such studies, and just slightly more than half of the firms gained pediatric exclusivity. Although the written requests have been issued to a variety of companies, the firms gaining the exclusivity awards seem to be narrowly clustered within big pharma. While large pharmaceutical firms comprise just under a quarter of the companies issued written requests, for example, they comprise over half of the companies receiving pediatric exclusivity awards. Perhaps this is not surprising, since many of these companies are among the top firms based on annual number of pediatric prescriptions and, thus, would have both the interest and resources to pursue such studies (see exhibit below)

Number of Written Requests (WR) and Pediatric Exclusivities (PEs) for Top 10 Companies Ranked by Number of Pediatric Prescriptions (as of 2004)

(# in parentheses is millions of Rx in 2002)

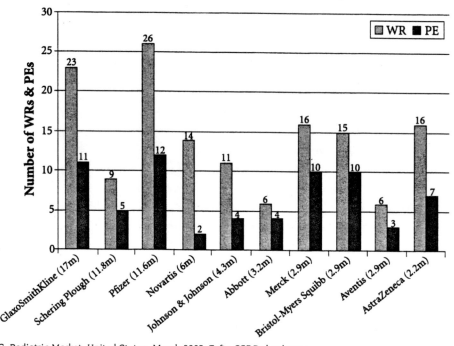

Source: Durrant, C. Pediatric Market, United States, March 2003; Tufts CSDD databases

As we move forward under the new regime of PREA and the BPCA, however, these results make one wonde if pediatric studies will, in fact, become a routine part of product development among various segments of th clinical trials industry or if the pediatric research infrastructure will only last as long as big pharma is active ly engaged. Admittedly, the growth curves for the basic measures characterizing the pace of the pediatric stud ies initiative have all flattened somewhat since the end of the FDAMA period in January 2002 (see exhibi below).

Based on extrapolations from various government reports published during the BPCA reauthorization hear ings, an estimated 300 to 400 pediatric drug studies will be undertaken on a voluntary and mandatory basi from 2003 to 2007, roughly equaling the number undertaken from 1998 to 2002. The relative contribution c the voluntary and mandatory programs to the study total will change, however. While the number of studie conducted under the voluntary program may diminish somewhat from 2003 to 2007, this decline will be coun terbalanced by an increase in the number of mandatory studies initiated during this period.

The Future

Therapeutic needs, global demographics, and trends in market forces all favor a robust future for pediatri drug and biological product research and development. The therapeutic needs of children in the United State are increasing perhaps more than those of any other age-related sub-population. This is due not only to a bet ter recognition of the need to treat disease in childhood, but also, unfortunately, to a greater prevalence c diseases. While only 2% of adults manifest food allergies, 6% to 8% of children have such allergies. Meanwhile asthma is reaching epidemic proportions—with 5 to 7 million pediatric patients, asthma is the leading caus

Pediatric Studies Initiative Update

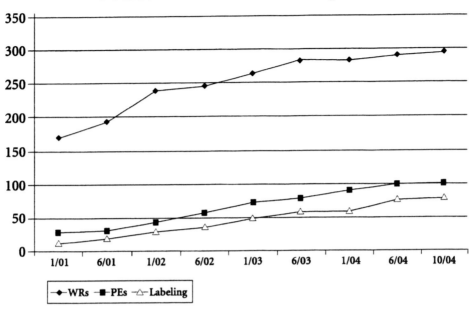

Source: FDA

---

of school absences and hospitalization (costing $2 billion per year). Type 2 diabetes and obesity are on the rise among children, and a million teenagers may have metabolic syndrome (considered to be present when a patient has three of the five following signs: high blood pressure; excess weight around abdomen; high triglycerides; low HDL; and high blood sugar). Although seasonal allergic rhinitis (SAR) is often overlooked as a health problem, it affects 10% of school children and results in missed school days, lower school performance, and impaired functioning on standardized testing.

The costs of the undertreatment of children are highlighted by the fact that 33% of adult absenteeism is believed to be caused not by adult illness but by family issues, often involving sick children. Because of this, the availability of a treatment for respiratory syncytial virus (RSV), which the CDC estimates resulted in 73,000 to 126,000 pediatric hospitalizations in 1999, is being hailed as an extremely cost-effective medicine, despite its $5,000-per-patient treatment costs. Europe and other developed countries are plagued by some of these same problems, while children in developing countries suffer a myriad of respiratory and gastrointestinal infections as well as parasitic infestations.

Worldwide population projections indicate that the future of pediatric clinical trials is global. Why go global? For one reason, because a global approach may be necessary to gain access to potential research participants in the short-term. Shortages of pediatric patients are likely to arise in the United States, especially in certain therapeutic areas (perhaps already a problem with cancer, AIDS and hypertension studies) and possibly in terms of healthy pediatric study participants as well. Another reason is that off-label use of medicines in children is reportedly high in Europe, the United Kingdom, Japan, Australia, Israel, and likely the rest of the world.

Europe is particularly concerned because the accession of a number of Eastern European countries to the European Union will raise its pediatric population from 75 million to 100 million. Pediatric public health advocates in Europe also hope to address the inequity evidenced by the fact that, although 20% of prescrip-

---

It's A Small World After All

- Netherlands – only 34% of Rxs written for children in hospital were label-approved uses (2000)

- England – only 35% of Rxs for neonates "were licensed drugs used in a licensed way" (2000)

- Israel – 42% of Rxs for children in ambulatory hospital units were off-label/unlicensed (2000)

- Australia – 70-80% of drugs lack adequate pediatric labeling (1997)

- Japan – only 16% of package inserts had sufficient dose and usage description (2002)

Source: Roberts, R et al. 2003. Pediatric drug labeling: Improving the safety and efficacy of pediatric therapies. JAMA 290(7): 905-11

---

tions are for children, only 7% of clinical trials involve children. For this reason, there is a growing interest in the pediatric initiative overseas, with Europe pursuing a "carrot and stick" approach similar to the U.S. model

Within Japan, which also recognizes that it must address the issue of pediatric off-label use, two such programs already exist: (1) Japan's notification on "Medicinal Drug Use with Off-label Indications" states that, if there is substantial evidence and experience with a drug approved outside of Japan and the drug is recommended by the relevant physicians' association, the drug may be approved without domestic trials (1999); and (2) the "MHLW Ordinance on Postmarketing Surveillance" provides that, when a company conducts clinical trials for a pediatric indication, the drug will have its reexamination period extended for up to ten years (a form of protection from generic drug competition). Flexibility in accepting bridging studies and the creation of the National Center for Child Health & Development in March 2002 should help Japan overcome a lack of specialists and pediatric studies activity, although incentives such as the easing of price controls (for political reasons) or priority review (for practical reasons) are unlikely. Overall, the current status is changing for the better, although many obstacles remain.

The growing movement toward regulatory harmonization and the internationalization of clinical research together with the growth of multinational CROs, should facilitate the conduct of pediatric trials in multi country settings, and should lay the groundwork for a global pediatric research infrastructure.

Another reason for the pharmaceutical industry to "think pediatric" relates to market forces in the long-term In the United States, recent reports assert that the under-19 patient population is the fastest growing segment of the prescription drug market, now valued at somewhere between $7 to 14 billion and perhaps as high as $18 billion. Some have estimated that the dollar volume has increased 85% in the last five years, and that children are using medicines 34% longer than they did just five years ago. Nonetheless, it remains a small market overall within the United States. In addition, product liability concerns are increasing rather than diminishing due to allegations of thimerosal-induced autism associated with vaccines and the increased risk of suicidal ideation in teenagers using the SSRI class of anti-depressants.

In contrast, long-term market dynamics may favor a sustainable pediatric market overseas, especially in developing countries. The demographics of such countries may support the development of a viable market for pediatric drugs in the near future based on volume alone. The under-19 population, which is about 26% of the total population in the United States and which is likely to decrease, is approaching 50% in the developing world and is unlikely to decrease anytime soon. At the same time, while the current market for prescription drugs outside of the three major markets is only equal to that of Japan, its growth potential is considered to be ten-fold that of Japan. Additionally, the proportion of chronic diseases, such as depression and cardiovas cular illness (generally requiring more cost-intensive therapeutic intervention), throughout the world is expected to rise from 55% in 1990 to 73% in 2020, with the most rapid increase expected in the developing world.

In the final analysis, statutory and regulatory incentives in the United States may help to build a global pediatric research infrastructure with a sufficient economy of scale and performance to permit pediatric medicine development to come into its own as a sustainable sector of the drug and biological products industry. In this respect, it may be a harbinger of the direction in which research and development is heading as a whole. Pharmacogenomics, consumer empowerment, public policy pressures for price controls, formulary requirements, regulatory incentive programs and competitive forces may compel the industry to subdivide research and development, marketing, and manufacturing units along subpopulation lines as well as by therapeutic areas or market sectors. Some European-based members of big pharma (Roche, Novartis, and GlaxoSmithKline) are already moving in such countercurrent directions by taking actions such as: embracing the concept of personalized medicines (and thus the concept of smaller patient markets); investing heavily in pharmacogenomics, early-stage biotechnology projects, and unmet medical needs; moving away from the primary care market to the specialty care market; and targeting future growth from sales in the developing world. The pediatric clinical trials industry should benefit from these trends and soon emerge from the periphery and become part of the mainstream of drug and biological product development.

References

Cooper, K. Pediatric Marketing Exclusivity - As Altered by the Best Pharmaceuticals for Children Act of 2002, *Food & Drug L J*,2002; 57(3):519-544.

Durrant, C., *Pediatric Market: United States*. Presentation at Pharmaceutical Education Associates conference on Pediatric Drug Development, Washington, DC, Feb. 23-24, 2004.

European Commission, *Commission consultation on a draft proposal for a European Parliament and Council Regulation (EC) on medicinal products for paeditric use*, European Commission 8 March 2004.

European Commission, *Proposal for a Regulation of the European Parliament and of the Council on medicinal products for paediatric use and amending Council Regulation (EEC) no. 1786/92, Directive 2001/83/EC and Regulation (EC) No 726/2004*.

Labson M.L., A legal and regulatory update on pediatric exclusivity and the pediatric rule. Presented at Barnett International workshop, "Pediatric Clinical Trials," Philadelphia, December 5-6, 2001.

Milne, C-P. Pediatric research: coming of age in the new millennium, *Am J Therapeutics*, 1999; 6: 263-282.

Milne, C-P., *The Pediatric Studies Incentive: Equal Medicines For All*, Tufts Center for the Study of Drug Development [White Paper], April 2001.

Milne, C-P., Exploring the frontiers of law and science: FDAMA's pediatric studies incentive, *Food & Drug L.J.*, 2002;57(3):491-517.

Roberts, R., et al., Pediatric Drug Labeling: Improving the Safety and Efficacy of Pediatric Therapies, JAMA, 2003; 290(7): 905-911.

Schreiner, M. Paediatric Clinical Trials: Redressing the Imbalance, *Nature Reviews Drug Discovery*, December 2003; 2:949-961.

Turner J., A regulatory perspective from the pharmaceutical industry for pediatric trials. Presented at Barnett International workshop, "Pediatric Clinical Trials," Philadelphia, December 5-6, 2001.